INTRODUCTION TO POLYMER CHEMISTRY

McGraw-Hill Book Company
New York
St. Louis
San Francisco
Düsseldorf
London
Mexico
Panama
Rio de Janeiro
Singapore
Sydney
Toronto

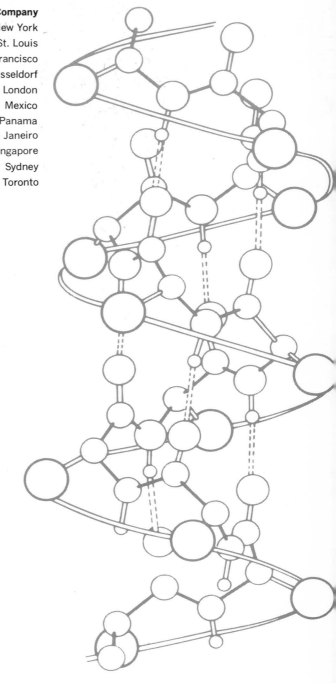

Introduction to Polymer Chemistry

RAYMOND B. SEYMOUR
Professor of Chemistry
and Coordinator of Polymer Science
University of Houston

Introduction to Polymer Chemistry

Library of Congress Catalog Card Number 75-118802

56353

1 2 3 4 5 6 7 8 9 0   M A M M   7 9 8 7 6 5 4 3 2 1 0

This book was set in Laurel by Graphic Services, Inc., and printed on permanent paper and bound by The Maple Press Company. The designer was Merrill Haber; the drawings were done by John Cordes, J. & R. Technical Services, Inc. The editors were James L. Smith and Anne Marie Horowitz. Sally Ellyson supervised production.

Preface

This treatise was written for use as a two-semester undergraduate textbook for senior students majoring in chemistry or chemical engineering. A prior knowledge of organic chemistry is a prerequisite but no previous knowledge of polymer science is required for an understanding of this textbook. In manuscript form, this book was classroom-tested in undergraduate courses for four successive years. It has also been used for an equivalent period for leveling work in graduate courses in polymer science.

Over one hundred industrial scientists and technologists from over a score of different companies have taken courses in which this manuscript served as the textbook. A larger number of industrial chemists who had had no formal training in polymer science have also found the manuscript to be a valuable reference. It is hoped that the book will also be helpful to those who have not had the opportunity of taking a formal course as well as to students in polymer chemistry.

The subject matter has been arranged so that the book may also be used in a one-quarter or one-semester course. Some chapters, such as those on natural products, inorganic polymers, processing, testing, and technology, may be omitted if sufficient time is not available. The last chapter and sections of "Modern Plastics Encyclopedia" may be assigned as outside reading. When time is available, it is also advisable to assign some of the reference material following sections of this book and to direct the students' attention to current literature in the polymer field.

A course in polymer science is essential for the many students who will find employment in this field. Because polymer science is interdisciplinary in nature, those students who may go into other fields will find

that polymer science is a valuable senior course.   Polymer science is a requirement for the B.A. degree in chemistry at the University of Houston
and many other institutions of higher learning.

Dr. R. A. V. Raff has made many valuable suggestions on the contents
and the arrangement of chapters in this book.   Many other chemists have
graciously spent time in reviewing sections related to their specialties.   I am
grateful to the following for their valued comments: Amel Anderson,
J. S. Ham, Ernest J. Henley, Jerry G. Higgins, Burnett H. Johnson,
Theodore O. K. Kresser, Eby N. McElrath, John C. Moore, Loren B. Odell,
Malcolm M. Renfrew, R. B. Roennaw, Thomas H. Rogers, M. Herbert
Roth, Jose M. Sosa, and Hing-Shya Tsang.

The typing was done under the direction of Miss Julie Norris.   The
work of her assistants, Miss Linda Anderson, Miss Pat Summerville, Mrs.
Jean Seymour, Mrs. Sharon Simmons, and Mrs. Sally Nolen, is also greatly
appreciated.

RAYMOND B. SEYMOUR

Contents

Introduction
History of Polymers

The ancient classification of matter as animal, vegetable, and mineral placed appropriate emphasis on nonmineral or organic substances. Yet, presumably because of the quest for precious metals, the alchemists reversed this order. Hence, early chemical developments were related primarily to minerals, i.e., inorganic chemistry.

The "vital-force" concept discouraged experimentation in organic chemistry prior to the nineteenth century. In spite of Wöhler's synthesis of urea in 1828, progress in this field during the first half of that century was much slower than that of noncarbon chemistry.

The elucidation of the structure of organic compounds by Kekulé in the 1850s aided the development of organic chemistry. However, in spite of the prevalence of large organic molecules in the animal and vegetable kingdom, little attention was devoted to these polymeric materials. Polymeric materials such as wood, skins, fibers, horn, and bitumens were used by early man for transportation, tools, and shelter. His foodstuffs consisting of proteins and carbohydrates were also polymeric. Considerable information on the constitution of minerals, metals, and ceramics was developed in the nineteenth century but little was known about polymeric materials until the 1930s.

Some of the delay is attributable to the relative difficulty of working with products that could not be purified by classic distillation and crystallization techniques. However, the principal deterrent was associated with misconceptions which retarded the understanding of polymer chemistry.

1

These misconceptions were analogous to the phlogiston and vital-force concepts which delayed the advancement of inorganic and organic chemistry in previous centuries.

Primitive man used animal furs for clothing and as a covering for the floor in his cave. Both animal (wool and silk) and vegetable fibers (cotton, flax, and ramie) were used at least 5,000 years ago. Cotton was used for making cloth in the Indus Valley and in Mexico before 2500 B.C. Cotton bolls found in Mexico are believed to be over 7,000 years old. Silk cloth was used in China over 5,000 years ago, and linen (flax) was the preferred wrapping material for mummies in ancient Egypt.

Bitumen under the name *slime* is mentioned in the books of *Genesis* and *Exodus*. Shellac was used as a protective and decorative coating at least 3,000 years before it was patented as a molding resin in 1868. Pliny the Elder described amber and recognized its ability to attract dust in the early part of the first century.

Columbus and other early explorers observed the use of rubber (*Hevea braziliensis*) as elastic balls, containers, and waterproof footwear. Gutta-percha, a plastic product obtainable from trees in Malaya, has been used successfully for submarine cables as a result of a recommendation made by Faraday in the early part of the nineteenth century.

Goodyear reacted natural rubber with sulfur to obtain vulcanized rubber in 1839. The vulcanization process for the production of soft rubber was patented by Hancock in England in 1843 and by Goodyear in the United States in 1844. Charles Goodyear's brother, Nelson, used larger amounts of sulfur to produce hard rubber (ebonite). He patented this process in 1851.

It was not recognized until the twentieth century that both natural rubber and cellulose are polymers and that ebonite is actually a plastic. Hence, the plastics industry has used the date of Hyatt's Celluloid patent (1868) rather than that of Goodyear's ebonite (1851) as the date for its genesis.

Cellulose nitrate as produced by Schönbein in 1846 was more important as an explosive (guncotton) than as a plastic because of difficulties and hazards associated with the processing of this polymer. However, Menard succeeded in dissolving cellulose nitrate in a mixture of ethanol and ethyl ether later in 1846. This solution (collodion), which is still used as a liquid court plaster, paved the way for the development of Celluloid by Hyatt and artificial silk by Chardonnet. Parkes in England and Hyatt in the United States observed that a useful plastic could be produced by the addition of camphor to collodion. Chardonnet extruded this solution through spinnerets and obtained regenerated cellulose by denitrification of the resulting filaments.

It is of historical interest to note that poly(vinyl chloride) and cellulose nitrate had been prepared before ebonite. However, the technology essential for the use of these products as plastics was not developed until many years later. It is of technical interest to note that the pioneer techniques used to produce ebonite are similar to those in use today.

Polymeric materials had also been produced prior to 1900 by the reaction of phenol or urea with formaldehyde, by the acetylation of cellulose, and by the polymerization of isobutylene, isoprene, 2,3-dimethylbutadiene, coumarone, or indene. However, the only plastics available commercially in 1900 were amber, bitumens, shellac, gutta-percha, ebonite, and Celluloid which are actually naturally occurring polymers or their derivatives.

The first truly synthetic polymer resulted from Baekeland's controlled condensation of phenol and formaldehyde in the very early part of the twentieth century. It should be noted that glyceryl phthalate resins, poly(2,3-dimethylbutadiene), ethyl cellulose, and urea-formaldehyde resins had also been prepared in the first two decades of this century but the only synthetic polymer available commercially in 1925 was Bakelite.

Few advances in polymer technology were recorded prior to the pioneering efforts of Staudinger, Carothers, Mark, and many other modern polymer scientists who recognized the true structure of macromolecules. One of the first textbooks to present these modern concepts was written by Powers in 1943. These ideas were expanded and brought up to date in books by Flory in 1953, by Billmeyer in 1957, and by Winding and Hiatt in 1961.

In spite of the abundance of naturally occurring polymers and their biological and economic importance, few scientists recognized the true structure of polymers prior to Staudinger's monumental treatise. He was awarded the Nobel Prize in 1955 in recognition of his outstanding contributions to polymer science.

The term *colloid* was coined by Graham in 1861 to differentiate gluelike substances from crystalline materials (crystalloids). Later, Ostwald advanced the colloidal-state-of-matter concept which was related to particle size or colloidal dimensions. Graham was concerned with proteins, such as albumin or gelatin, and vegetable gums, such as gum arabic. These met the dimension criterion of the colloidal state (10 to 1000 Å or 10^{-7} to 10^{-5} cm) but they differed greatly from many colloids, such as stable suspensions of Prussian blue or sulfur and gold prepared previously by Selmi and Faraday.

Subsequently, Raoult, van't Hoff, and Brown and Morris used cryoscopic techniques to obtain large molecular-weight values for polymer molecules such as amylodextrin. However, they and other leading chemists of that era were unable to comprehend the significance of these values and explained the anomaly by concluding that Raoult's solution laws did not apply to these materials. The alternative and correct conclusion that polymers were high-molecular-weight materials was not generally accepted until the 1930s.

Most early-twentieth-century chemists erroneously considered polymers as physical aggregates of low-molecular-weight cyclic molecules. However, in spite of these incorrect concepts and the reluctance of leading chemists to study goos, gunks, and messes, considerable progress in rubber, plastics, and fiber technology occurred.

Today, all organic polymers, regardless of origin or final form, are known to consist of long chains of atoms held together by the same types of bonds (covalent bonds) as simpler low-molecular-weight organic molecules. Because of their high molecular weight, these macromolecules have less effect on colligative properties than smaller molecules. Contrary to the opinion of the nineteenth-century chemists, they do obey Raoult's law. Also contrary to concepts expressed by early chemists, these long molecules do have end groups which are detectable by techniques now available in most organic chemical laboratories.

Intermolecular forces or secondary bond forces which affect the physical properties of small molecules have a multitudinous effect on macromolecules since these forces are essentially a summation of the forces of the smaller units which are joined together in the long molecular chain. Fortunately, these concepts, which are essential for the understanding of polymer science, are in accordance with modern organic and physical chemistry.

REFERENCES

Brydson, J. A.: "Plastics Materials," chap. 1, D. Van Nostrand Company, Inc., Princeton, N.J., 1966.

Flory, P. J.: "Principles of Polymer Chemistry," chap. 1, Cornell University Press, Ithaca, N.Y. 1953.

Garvey, B. S.: chap. 1, in M. Morton (ed.), "History and Summary of Rubber Technology," Reinhold Publishing Corporation, New York, 1959.

Golding, B.: "Polymers and Resins," D. Van Nostrand Company, Inc., Princeton, N.J., 1959.

Kaufman, M.: "The First Century of Plastics—Celluloid and Its Sequel," The Plastics Institute, London, 1963.

Morrell, R. S.: "Synthetic Resins and Allied Plastics," 3d ed., chap. 1, Oxford University Press, London, 1951.

Ott, E., H. M. Spurlin, and M. W. Graffin: "Cellulose and Its Derivatives," Pt. I, Interscience Publishers, Inc., New York, 1954.

Paist, W. D.: "Cellulosics," chap. 1, Reinhold Publishing Corporation, New York, 1958.

Powers, P. O.: "Synthetic Resins and Rubbers," chap. 1, John Wiley & Sons, Inc., New York, 1943.

Ravve, A.: "Organic Chemistry of Macromolecules," chap. 1, Marcel Dekker, Inc., New York, 1967.

Staudinger, H.: "Die Hochmolekularen Verbindungen," Springer-Verlag OHG, Berlin, 1932.

Vold, M. J., and R. D. Vold: "Colloid Chemistry," Reinhold Publishing Corporation, New York, 1964.

1

Polymer Structure

1-1 STEREOCHEMISTRY OF POLYMERS

In spite of objections raised by many respected chemists during the early part of the twentieth century, the modern polymer chemist accepts the principles proposed by Staudinger. It is now recognized that the principal difference between ordinary organic molecules, like ethane, and macro-molecules, like linear polyethylene, is their size. Thus the student who has already learned the fundamentals of organic chemistry needs merely to recall this knowledge in order to understand this phase of polymer chemistry.

The covalent bonds in all natural and synthetic macromolecules have the same bond lengths and bond angles as those present in simple organic molecules. The principal difference is that the polymer molecule has multi-tudinous repeating chemical units (mers) held together by covalent bonds. The name is derived from the Greek "poly," or many, and "meros" or parts. The number of *mers*, i.e., the number of repeating units, present in a polymer chain is called the *degree of polymerization* (DP).

From this definition, one might consider the dimer ethane, the trimer propane, and the tetramer butane as polymers of methylene with DP's of 2, 3, and 4. However, the polymer scientist or technologist is interested primarily in high polymers or giant molecules, i.e., those with a DP of at least 100. This lower limit for the DP of high polymers has been established because the physical properties required for useful fibers, elastomers, plastics, and coatings are not characteristic of low-molecular-weight polymers (*oligomers*). However, there is no upper limit. The average molecular-weight range for most synthetic polymers is 10,000 to 100,000 but molecular weights of over 100 million have been observed.

These large polymers are not visible to the naked eye but their full contour lengths are at least 100 times the length of the building units (mers). The size of these molecules becomes more obvious when one writes their semiempirical formulas such as that for polyethylene as $(C_2H_4)_n$. In this case, n is equivalent to the degree of polymerization. Hence, the molecular weight of this polymer is equal to n times the molecular weight of the monomer, that is, $28n$. Thus, if $n = 100$, the molecular weight is 2,800.

As shown in Table 1-1, covalent-bond lengths vary from less than 1 angstrom (Å) in the O—H bonds in the pendant groups on poly (vinyl alcohol) to almost 2 Å for the C—Br bonds in poly(vinyl bromide). The dissociation energies of these covalent bonds vary from less than 65 kcal/mole for C—S to more than 200 kcal/mole for C≡N. The bond angles may vary as much as $\pm 5°$ from the normal tetrahedral angle of $109°28'$.

Polymers, like other organic compounds, may have different structures, and, as has been observed for simple compounds, these different *configurations* have different physical properties. The term *normal* is used to designate low-molecular-weight straight-chain organic compounds but the term *linear polymer* is preferred for polymers in which the carbon atoms are joined together as a continuous sequence in a chain. Of course, the carbon chains are not represented correctly by convenient projections. They exist as

Table 1-1   Approximate Bond Lengths and Dissociation Energies for Typical Covalent Bonds

BOND	LENGTH, Å	DISSOCIATION ENERGY, kcal/mole
C—H	1.07	98
N—H	1.00	93
O—H	0.96	111
S—H	1.34	81
C—C	1.54	83
C—N	1.47	70
C—O	1.43	84
C—S	1.81	62
C—F	1.33	105
C—Cl	1.76	79
C—Br	1.94	66
C=C	1.35	145
C=O	1.22	179
C≡N	1.16	213

crumpled zigzag-shaped chains in accordance with the characteristic valence bond angles for C—C bonds, viz., 109°28′.

The Fischer projections for *n*-butane and isobutane are as follows:

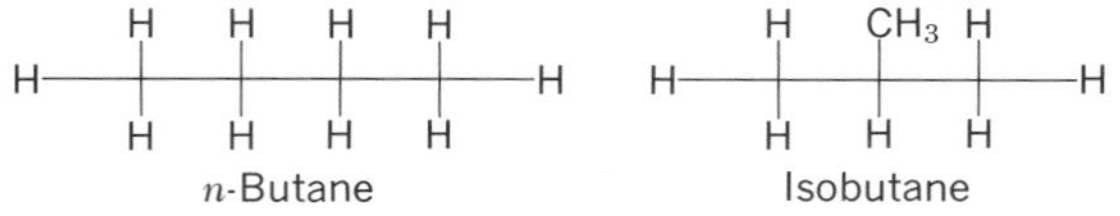

$$ (1\text{-}1) $$

n-Butane   Isobutane

Fischer projections for model compounds

In organic chemistry isobutane is described as a branched structure. This term is used differently in polymer chemistry. The term *branched polymer* is not usually applied to polymer structures with groups which are part of the monomer structure (i.e., functional groups). As shown in the Fischer projections for chain segments [formula (1–2)], these groups appear at regular intervals on the polymer backbone and are called *pendant groups* rather than branches. The methyl groups in polyethylidene and the acetyl groups in poly(vinyl acetate) are representative pendant groups.

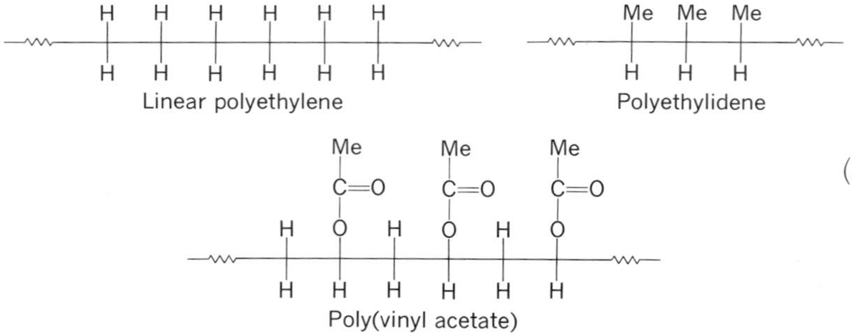

Linear polyethylene   Polyethylidene

$$ (1\text{-}2) $$

Poly(vinyl acetate)

Fischer projections of typical polymer chain segments

Polymers with bulky pendant groups such as those present in poly(vinyl stearate) are also considered linear polymers provided all carbon atoms from the vinyl groups are joined together in a continuous chain called the *polymer backbone*. However, since linear and branched polymers may be softened by heat, both types are called *thermoplastics*.

In accordance with recommendations of the International Union of Pure and Applied Chemistry (IUPAC), parentheses are used when more than one word follows poly, as in poly(vinyl acetate). Parentheses are not used with polystyrene or polyethylene since these words are unambiguous. However, in the absence of parentheses, polychlorobutadiene could mean a mono-meric butadiene molecule containing chlorine atoms.

In contrast to linear polyethylene, all carbon atoms in branched poly-ethylene are not chain-extending; i.e., this macromolecule does not consist solely of a continuous chain of catenated carbon atoms. Instead, other car-bon atoms are attached to the polymer backbone at irregularly spaced *branch points.* The branches in low-density polyethylene are mostly short chains consisting of three or four carbon atoms. The number of branches on nonlinear polyethylene may vary from one on a polymer backbone with 100 methylene groups to one branch on a backbone with 20 methylene groups.

Polymers may also have crosslinked or *space network structures.* These infusible and insoluble polymers are also called *three-dimensional systems.* This term describes only the three-dimensional arrangement of the carbon-carbon bonds since in reality the simplest linear molecule is three-dimen-sional.

The change of natural rubber from a viscoelastic sticky solid to a useful elastomer is the result of the introduction of sulfur crosslinks. Hard rubber (ebonite) is obtained when the maximum number of sulfur crosslinks are introduced. When a difunctional carboxylic acid such as terephthalic acid is condensed with a difunctional alcohol such as ethylene glycol, a linear polyester and water are produced. If part of the ethylene glycol is replaced by a trifunctional alcohol such as glycerol, a network polymer is produced. The number of crosslinks is related to the relative amount of glycerol present in the reactants. Network polymers are also called *thermosetting polymers.* Simulated linear, branched, and network polymer structures are shown below:

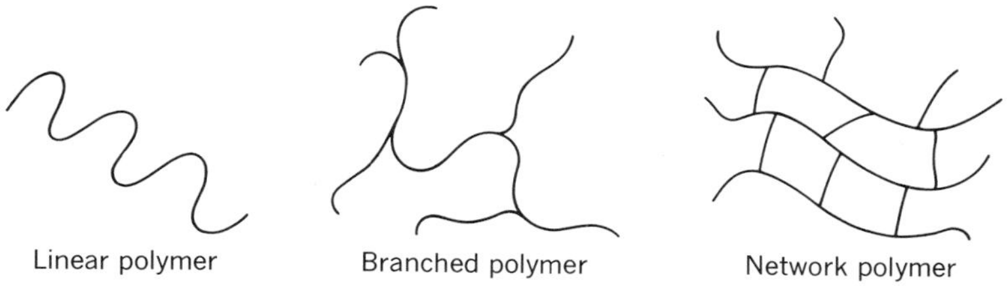

| Linear polymer | Branched polymer | Network polymer |

Simulated polymer structures

When double bonds are present, as in polydienes, rotation about these bonds cannot take place unless energy of the order of 50 kcal is supplied to break the π bonds. Thus cis isomers in which the groups are on the same side of the double bond and trans isomers in which the groups are on opposite sides exist as stable configurations in polymer molecules. The differences in properties are much more evident in *geometric polymer isomers* than in small molecules. For example, *cis*-polyisoprene (natural rubber) is an elastomer whereas the trans form (gutta-percha) is a plastic. Isomers such as these which cannot be readily converted from one to the other except by cleavage and re-formation of covalent bonds are said to differ in *configuration*.

Different arrangements of mers in a chain and different arrangements of functional groups around an asymmetric carbon atom in a vinyl polymer are also termed differences in configuration. The usual arrangement of mers in a polymer chain is as a *head-to-tail* configuration in which the functional groups are not present on adjacent carbon atoms, as illustrated by the simple model compound 1,3-dichlorobutane. In contrast, *head-to-head* configurations occur, as illustrated by the model compound 2,3-dichlorobutane. The possibility of a random arrangement also exists in which both head-to-tail and head-to-head configurations occur in the same chain, as illustrated by the model compound 2,3,5-trichlorohexane. These structures are shown below:

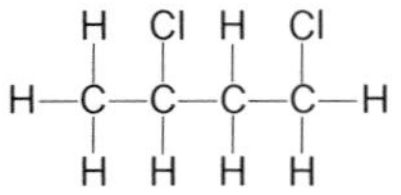

Head-to-tail configuration 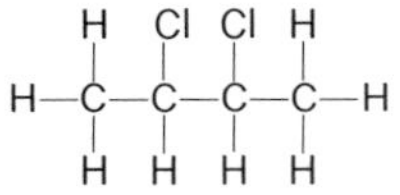   Head-to-head configuration

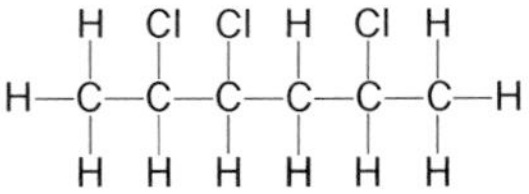

(1-3)

Random configuration

Configurations of model compounds

Polymer isomers with configurations similar to those found in low-molecular-weight optical isomers, such as *d*- and *l*-lactic acid, are present in polymers. It should be remembered that in the original terminology the prefixes *d* and *l* were abbreviations for *dextro* and *levo*. They now describe different arrangements of the four different groups or atoms around the carbon atom. The *d* and *l* enantiomers are mirror images and are nonsuperimposable. X-ray data have confirmed the assumed configurations for $d(+)$ and $l(-)$ glyceraldehydes.

All *d* and *l* enantiomers have configurations related to the glyceraldehyde isomers but all *d* enantiomers do not rotate the plane of polarized light clockwise and vice versa. However, the specific rotations of *d* and *l* isomers are equal and opposite and, of course, all + enantiomers rotate the plane of polarized light clockwise. It should be noted that asymmetry usually has little effect on the optical activity of polymers but that differences in this type of configuration (*tacticity*) do affect their physical properties.

The nomenclature developed by Natta uses the term *isotactic* to describe a head-to-tail configuration in which the functional groups are all on the same side of the polymer chain, that is, -*dd,dd,dd*- or -*ll,ll,ll,ll*-. IUPAC has accepted a nomenclature system suggested by Huggins. Accordingly, isotactic polyethylidene, represented by the Fischer projection in formula (1-4), is called isotactic poly(methyl methamer) or *it*[CH(CH3)]$_n$.

$$\begin{array}{ccccccc}
\text{Me} & \text{Me} & \text{Me} & \text{Me} & \text{Me} & \text{Me} & \text{Me} \\
| & | & | & | & | & | & | \\
\hline
| & | & | & | & | & | & | \\
\text{H} & \text{H} & \text{H} & \text{H} & \text{H} & \text{H} & \text{H}
\end{array}$$

$$\text{Isotactic polyethylidene}$$

(1-4)

It is now known that poly(vinyl isobutyl ether) prepared by Schildknecht prior to Natta's monumental work has an isotactic structure. However, most synthetic head-to-tail polymers prepared prior to the investigations of Ziegler and Natta in the 1950s had a random arrangement, that is, -*dlldld*-, or, if the Fischer projection for polyethylidene is used, they would be shown as

$$\begin{array}{cccccc}
\text{Me} & \text{H} & \text{H} & \text{Me} & \text{H} & \text{Me} \\
| & | & | & | & | & | \\
\hline
| & | & | & | & | & | \\
\text{H} & \text{Me} & \text{Me} & \text{H} & \text{Me} & \text{H}
\end{array}$$

$$\text{Atactic polyethylidene}$$

(1-5)

The alternating configuration -*dldldl*- was also synthesized by Natta, using stereospecific catalysts. This configuration was termed *syndiotactic*. A syndiotactic polyethylidene, that is, *st*[CH(CH$_3$)]$_n$ could be represented by the following Fischer projection:

$$\begin{array}{cccccc}
\text{Me} & \text{H} & \text{Me} & \text{H} & \text{Me} & \text{H} \\
| & | & | & | & | & | \\
\hline
| & | & | & | & | & | \\
\text{H} & \text{Me} & \text{H} & \text{Me} & \text{H} & \text{Me}
\end{array}$$

$$\text{Syndiotactic polyethylidene}$$

(1-6)

It is now known that the structure of poly(methyl methacrylate) prepared at moderate temperatures is predominantly syndiotactic and that the structure becomes more random as the polymerization temperature is increased.

Randomness, or lack of order of mers, in a polymer chain prevents the orderly packing that is essential for crystalline structures. Provided the substituents are not bulky, the degree of regularity is also reflected in the density, melting point, and stiffness of polymer chains. Thus, tactic polypropylene prepared by the use of stereospecific catalysts is much denser and stiffer and has a higher melting point than the amorphous atactic polymer. Controlled propagation has also made possible the synthesis of stereospecific elastomers such as ethylene-propylene copolymers [poly(ethylene-co-propylene)] and polybutadiene *homopolymers.*

The nomenclature becomes more complicated when more than one asymmetric carbon is present in each mer, as in poly((1-ethyl)(2-methyl) ethamer). The nomenclature is analogous to that used for erythrose and threose in carbohydrate chemistry. Thus, poly((1-ethyl)(2-methyl) ethamer) [$(CHC_2H_5CHCH_3)_n$] could have erythrodiisotactic (*eit*), threodiisotactic (*tit*), erythrosyndiotactic (*est*), and threosyndiotactic (*tst*) arrangements, as shown below:

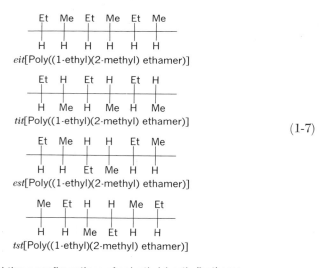

eit[Poly((1-ethyl)(2-methyl) ethamer)]

tit[Poly((1-ethyl)(2-methyl) ethamer)]

(1-7)

est[Poly((1-ethyl)(2-methyl) ethamer)]

tst[Poly((1-ethyl)(2-methyl) ethamer)]

Erythro and threo configurations of polyethyl (methyl) ethamers

In the absence of intra- or intermolecular hindrance, the energy barrier preventing free rotation about a carbon-carbon single bond is less than 3 kcal. Thus many different arrangements or *conformations* may occur at room temperature. However, the staggered conformation which has a lower potential energy will be favored. These concepts which may have appeared to be unimportant for small organic molecules are of utmost importance in polymer chemistry. The magnitude of the potential barrier for such rotations is reflected in the physical properties of the polymer and determine whether a polymer chain is rigid, as in polystyrene, or flexible, as in natural rubber.

The planar projections customarily used in organic chemistry represent a big improvement over formulas used in the prekekulean era but they are inadequate for conformation studies. This important concept can be more readily demonstrated by using Newman projections. Fortunately, the Newman projection for ethane can be used to explain the possible conformations resulting from rotation about the carbon-carbon bond. These projections are simply the view one gets when looking at a ball-and-stick model along the carbon-carbon axis.

In general, the *staggered conformation* in which the hydrogens are as far apart as possible is most stable. Energy must be supplied to rotate the bond so that the hydrogens are as close together as possible in the *eclipsed conformation*. Newman projections of these conformers are shown below:

$$(1\text{-}8)$$

Newman projections of staggered and eclipsed conformations

In a polymer such as polyethylene, the staggered form is also energetically favored over the eclipsed conformation. Two types of staggered conformation are possible with polymers, such as polyethylene, viz., *trans* (T) and *gauche* (G), as shown below:

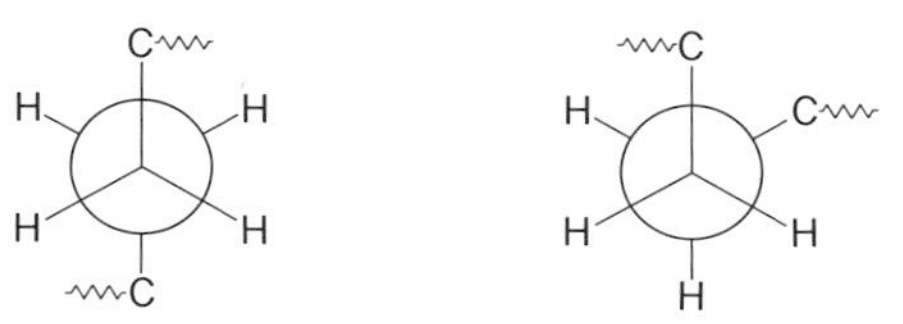

$$(1\text{-}9)$$

Newman projections of trans and gauche conformations

The trans form is energetically favored to a small degree for polyethylene since it allows the two portions of the polymer chain to have maximum separation. Thus, in its most stable conformation, polyethylene would be represented as -*TTTT*-.

In contrast, the energy barriers between the trans and the gauche form in polyisobutylene are small; hence this solid polymer behaves somewhat as a liquid, i.e., it is viscoelastic whereas polyethylene is more rigid.   However, it must be remembered that continuous rotation occurs in polymers such as polyethylene but that this motion is negligible in rigid polymers at ordinary temperatures.   Nevertheless, all possible conformations are assumed for both rigid and flexible polymers but the times required for rotation are vastly different.

The difference in chain flexibility between polyisobutylene and a polymer such as poly(methyl methacrylate) may be predicted from their Newman projections shown below:

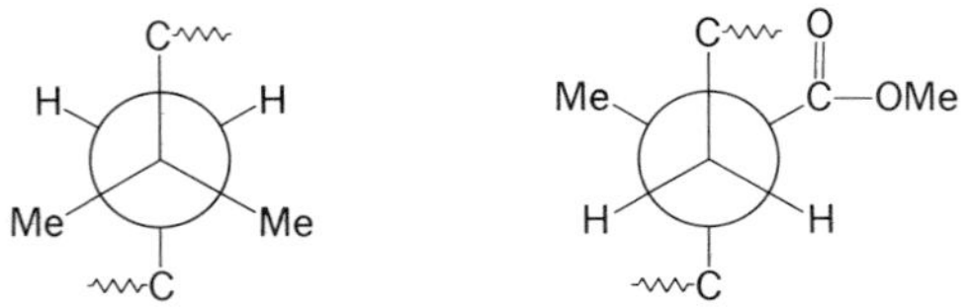

(1-10)

Newman projections of polyisobutylene and poly(methyl methacrylate)

In contrast to polyisobutylene in which the energy barrier between conformations is low, the rotation of the polar ester group in poly(methyl methacrylate) is restricted because of interactions with other groups.   Thus, this polymer is stiffer than polyisobutylene and polyethylene.   Viscoelasticity can be attained by heating poly(methyl methacrylate) to over $100°C$ so that rotation about the C—C bond may occur.

REFERENCES

Alfrey, T., and E. F. Gurnee: "Organic Polymers," Prentice-Hall, Inc., Englewood Cliffs, N.J., 1967.

Bawn, C. E. H., and A. Ledwith: Stereoregular Addition Polymers, *Quart. Rev. (London)*, **16**(4):361 (1962).

Billmeyer, F. W.: "Textbook of Polymer Science," Interscience Publishers, a division of John Wiley & Sons, Inc., New York, 1964.

Cram, D. J., and G. S. Hammond: "Organic Chemistry," 2d ed., chap. 9, McGraw-Hill Book Company, New York, 1964.

Frith, E. M., and R. M. Tuckett: "Linear Polymers," Longmans, Green & Co., Ltd., London, 1951.

Goodman, M., and J. S. Schulman: Stereochemistry of Polymers, *J. Polymer Sci.*, Pt. C, **12**:23 (1966).

Lenz, R.: "Organic Chemistry of High Polymers," Interscience Publishers, Inc., New York, 1967.

Margerison, D., and G. C. East: "An Introduction to Polymer Chemistry," chap. 1, Pergamon Press, New York, 1967.

Mark, H. F.: Giant Molecules, *Sci. Am.*, **197**:80 (1957).

Marvel, C. S.: "An Introduction to the Organic Chemistry of High Polymers," John Wiley & Sons, Inc., New York, 1959.

McGraw, F. C.: Structure of Synthetic High Polymers, *J. Chem. Educ.*, **35**:178 (1958).

Meares, P.: "Polymers—Structure and Properties," chap. 2, D. Van Nostrand Company, Inc., Princeton, N.J., 1965.

Natta, G.: How Giant Molecules Are Made, *Sci. Am.*, **197**:98 (1957).

———: Stereospecific Macromolecules, *J. Polymer Sci.*, **16**:143 (1955).

Noller, C. R.: "Chemistry of Organic Compounds," chap. 2, W. B. Saunders Company, Philadelphia, 1965.

O'Driscoll, K. F.: "The Nature and Chemistry of High Polymers," chap. 5, Reinhold Publishing Corporation, New York, 1964.

Ravve, A.: "Organic Chemistry of Macromolecules," chap. 2, Marcel Dekker, Inc., New York, 1967.

Robb, J. C., and F. W. Peaker: "Progress in High Polymers," vol. I, p. 279, Academic Press, Inc., New York, 1967.

Schmidt, A. X., and C. A. Marlies: "Principles of High-polymer Theory and Practice," McGraw-Hill Book Company, New York, 1948.

Stille, J. K.: "Introduction to Polymer Chemistry," chap. 3, John Wiley & Sons, Inc., New York, 1962.

Winding, C. C., and G. D. Hiatt: "Polymeric Materials," McGraw-Hill Book Company, New York, 1961.

1-2 MOLECULAR INTERACTIONS

The difference in stiffness of amorphous polymers is related to the strength of the stiffening groups present in the polymer backbone and to the energy of the intermolecular secondary valence bonds. The latter cohesive forces are only about 1 or 2 percent as strong as the primary valence bonds, and they operate at a distance as great as 3 Å or more. However, there are many opportunities for interactions along the polymer chain; hence the total effect is the summation of these forces.

These interactions, which are sometimes grouped under the heading of van der Waals' forces, may be subclassified as London forces (transient polarization forces), permanent dipole-dipole forces, induction or induced dipole forces, and hydrogen bonding. The constant $\mathscr{A}$ in the van der Waals equation of state

$$\left(P + \frac{\mathscr{A}N^2}{V^2}\right)(V - Nb) = NRT \tag{1-11}$$

Van der Waals'
equation

includes all these forces.

The process of liquefaction of methane is dependent on fluctuations in the symmetry of the electron clouds in molecules which produce temporary dipoles or micromagnets having temporary attractions for each other. These London forces are the most important intermolecular attractive forces in methane as well as in uncharged polymer molecules such as polyethylene. London demonstrated that the attractive forces are inversely proportional to the sixth power of the distance between the centers of charge of the dipoles (r^{-6}). These forces are independent of temperature.

Dipole-dipole attractions occur when the electron cloud around the molecule is unsymmetrical, as in methyl chloride or in a polymer such as poly(vinyl chloride). Methyl chloride has a dipole moment (μ) of 1.02 debye units (D). The dipole moment is a measure of polarity. It is equal to the product of the distance between centers of charge of the dipoles and the electronic charge q, that is, $\mu = qD$. Dipole-dipole attractions are inversely related to temperature.

Polar molecules also cause displacement of electrons of nonpolar molecules by induction. The term *polarizability* is used to describe the relative ease of displacement of electrons by polar molecules. These weak induction forces are proportional to r^{-6} and are independent of temperature.

The hydrogen bond which is responsible for the principal attractive force between methanol molecules is important in polymers containing OH, NH_2, $CONH_2$, and COOH groups. Many of the characteristic properties of cellulose and proteins are the result of hydrogen bonding.

Amorphous plastics are transparent and brittle, or glasslike, because of restricted molecular motion. This motion of the polymer backbone in the glassy state is limited to bond distortions and molecular vibrations. In contrast, a wriggling type of segmental movement occurs in the polymer chains of elastomers.

Flow is the result of cooperative movement of the segments in the polymer chain. This flow is decreased by chain entanglements; by reinforcing agents, like carbon black; and by crosslinks, like sulfur linkages in vulcanized rubber. Crosslinks restrict the rotational motion of the polymer chains.

The flexibility of plastics or fibers is reduced when stiffening groups like phenylene groups are present in the polymer backbone. For example, the melting point (T_m) of poly(ethylene terephthalate)

$$(1\text{-}12)$$

Poly(ethylene terephthalate)

is 215° higher than that of poly(ethylene adipate)

$$\left(\begin{array}{c} \overset{H}{\underset{|}{C}} \overset{H}{\underset{|}{C}} -O-C-\overset{H}{\underset{|}{C}}-\overset{H}{\underset{|}{C}}-\overset{H}{\underset{|}{C}}-\overset{H}{\underset{|}{C}}-C-O- \\ \overset{|}{H}\ \overset{|}{H}\quad \overset{||}{O}\ \overset{|}{H}\ \overset{|}{H}\ \overset{|}{H}\ \overset{|}{H}\ \overset{||}{O} \end{array}\right)_n \qquad (1\text{-}13)$$

Poly(ethylene adipate)

In contrast, the flexibility of polymer chains is increased by the presence of many C—C or C—O—C bonds in the polymer backbone. Thus the melting point of aliphatic polyesters

$$\left(-(CH_2)_n-O-\overset{}{\underset{\overset{||}{O}}{C}}-(CH_2)_n-\overset{}{\underset{\overset{||}{O}}{C}}-O-\right)_n \qquad (1\text{-}14)$$

Aliphatic polyester

and polyamides

$$\left(-\overset{}{\underset{\overset{||}{O}}{C}}-(CH_2)_n-\overset{}{\underset{\overset{||}{O}}{C}}-\overset{}{\underset{\overset{|}{H}}{N}}-(CH_2)_n-\overset{}{\underset{\overset{|}{H}}{N}}-\right)_n \qquad (1\text{-}15)$$

Aliphatic polyamide

is decreased as the number of methylene groups in either of the bifunctional reactants is increased. The melting point is also reduced when mixtures of different difunctional homologous reactants are used.

The stiffness of amorphous polymers is also related to the strength of the van der Waals' forces which hinder segmental rotation. The relative stiffness or flexibility of polymer molecules at a specified temperature may be estimated qualitatively by comparing their *glass transition temperatures* (T_g). These values are sometimes referred to as the second-order transition temperatures. However, T_g is usually considered to be a kinetic rather than a thermodynamic property. The glass transition temperature is the characteristic temperature at which a rubberlike amorphous polymer becomes glasslike and vice versa.

At temperatures immediately above T_g, considerable unrestricted localized segmental (microbrownian) motion occurs and the polymer which was brittle or glasslike below T_g becomes ductile. In addition to an abrupt change of a polymer from a plastic to a viscoelastic liquidlike solid at T_g, changes in specific volume, refractive index, density, heat content, thermal conductivity, and electrical properties also occur.

A convenient technique for measuring T_g of polymers consists in plotting

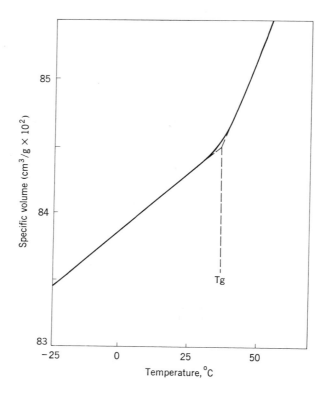

Fig. 1-1   Determination of glass transition temperature.

specific volume vs. temperature and observing the temperature at which a change in slope of the volume-temperature curve occurs. Glass transition temperatures for several polymers are shown in Table 1-2.

Natta and Dannis observed that the glass transition temperatures of esters of poly(acrylic acid) and poly(methacrylic acid) decreased as the size of the ester groups increased. Wurstlin showed a similar depression in T_g when equal mole fractions of normal alcohols were added to several different polymers.

Both T_g and T_m may be used as qualitative measurements of the segmental motion in the polymer backbone. According to Beaman, the ratio of these values, T_g/T_m, is in the range of 0.49 to 0.75. Independent movement of pendant groups may occur below T_g. Hence, this dominant value is sometimes designated as alpha to differentiate it from the less significant lower temperature transitions, which are designated as beta, gamma, etc.

It should be pointed out that, in spite of their utility, T_g values are de-

Table 1-2   Approximate Glass Transition Temperatures (T_g) for Typical Polymers

POLYMER	T_g, °C
Poly(methyl methacrylate)	+105
Polyacrylonitrile	+105
Polystyrene	+100
Poly(vinyl alcohol)	+85
Poly(vinyl chloride)	+81
Poly(ethylene terephthalate)	+69
Nylon 6,6	+57
Poly(vinyl acetate)	+28
Poly(methyl acrylate)	+6
Poly(*trans*-1,3-butadiene)	−18
Polyisobutylene	−73
Poly(*cis*-1,3-butadiene)	−108
Polyethylene	−125

pendent to some extent on the time of the test and the method.   It must also be remembered that numerous conformations are possible in linear and branched polymers.   Since these arrangements affect the shape of the macromolecule, a statistical approach is used to determine the root-mean-square end-to-end distance $(\bar{r}^2)^{1/2}$.   Because hindered conformations are less probable, the average end-to-end distance $\bar{r}$ is greater than that of an ideal volumeless unhindered chain.   The distance between chain ends for branched chains is usually expressed as the radius of gyration $(\bar{S}^2)^{1/2}$, that is, the root-mean-square distance of a chain end from the center of gravity of the chain.   The relationship of these distances in linear polymers is $\bar{r}^2 = 6\bar{S}^2$.

The most probable dimension may be approximated by assuming an equivalent free jointed volumeless model chain consisting of n links of length l.   Thus the fully extended chain length or contour length would be nl but the actual displacement length would be the vector distance between chain ends,

Fig. 1-2   End-to-end distance (r).

that is, r. This problem may be solved by *random flight methods* suggested by Raleigh at the beginning of the twentieth century and used by Flory in the 1950s to approximate the root-mean-square distance $(\bar{r}^2)^{1/2}$.

When an equal probability of steps or movement in any direction is assumed, as would be possible in the random walk of a blindfolded person, the distance from start to finish is equal to $ln^{1/2}$, where l is the length of each step and n is the number of steps. Actually, the approximated $(\bar{r}^2)^{1/2}$ is less than the real value even when corrections are made to provide for fixed bond angles and hindered rotations in a polymer chain. Thus, because of *excluded volume*, the length is greater than that calculated.

An analytical solution to this problem has been obtained by using a computer programmed to reject forbidden chain crossings, providing for excluded volume, and including a large number of steps or links. The value for $(\bar{r}^2)^{1/2}$ obtained by this sophisticated method was $l(1.4n^{1.18})^{1/2}$ instead of the gaussian distribution-based value of $ln^{1/2}$ for a freely oriented volumeless chain.

Since it is assumed that there is no segmental motion in the backbone of an amorphous polymer below T_g, what is commonly termed a plastic is actually a brittle glasslike material. However, polymers at temperatures above T_g are viscoelastic macromolecules which may assume a random coiled conformation. This coil may be stretched to its full contour length (nl) if it is completely uncoiled by careful stretching. This unimolecular process involves rotations about the C—C bonds and is potentially reversible when the stress is removed.

The orientation time τ_m is a rate constant which is a measure of the relative ease of uncoiling. This time is temperature-dependent. Whether a polymer is a plastic or an elastomer may be determined by determining the relationship of the orientation time τ_m and the time t elapsed after the application of stress.

If t is much less than τ_m, as is true for polystyrene at 25°C, the polymer is a plastic. In contrast, if τ_m is much less than t, as is true for natural rubber at 25°C, the polymer is an elastomer. As indicated by the Arrhenius type of expression shown below,

$$\tau_m = Ae^{-E/RT} \tag{1-16}$$

Arrhenius equation

an elastomer will change to a plastic when the temperature is lowered sufficiently and vice versa. The transition temperature is, of course, T_g.

Anisotropic physical and optical properties may be observed if an amorphous polymer such as polystyrene is stretched at a temperature above T_g and cooled while stressed. This orientation of the polymer chains in the direction of stress will be destroyed when this plastic is heated above T_g.

Sheetlike crystals consisting of parallel fully extended chains are typical when there are primary bonds between these chains, as in some silicate minerals (mica), or when there is strong intermolecular bonding, such as hydrogen bonds in polyamides. Pauling and Corey postulated that β-keratin existed as a pleated sheet. It is now known that hydrogen bonds may form between the amide hydrogen atoms and the carbonyl groups in other polyamides, such as nylon 6,6, to produce extended sheetlike structures.

Polymer chains with bulky groups may exist in stable conformations resulting from a close packing of these groups which provides a minimum distortion of the bond angles. Such helical structures were also postulated for α-keratin by Pauling and Corey in 1944.

Spiraling of polymer chains is very common. Cellulose chains are hydrogen-bonded and may be packed in several different ways based on geometric arrangements. These chains are only mildly spiraled because the rotation of the beta acetal oxygen atoms is restricted by intramolecular hydrogen bonding. More extensive spiraling occurs when there is less restriction to rotation of the atoms in the chain. Thus the polymer chains of amylose coil through their alpha acetal linkages to produce helices.

The size of the helix is related to the size of the pendant groups. Thus polyisobutylene, which has two small methyl groups on every other carbon atom in the chain, has 1.6 mers per turn. Poly(methyl methacrylate), which has a methyl and a larger carboxymethyl group on every other carbon atom, has 2.5 mers per turn. It is now known that there are 3.67 α-amino acid residues in each turn of the spiral in α-keratin. This right-handed helical arrangement, in which the amide groups assume a trans arrangement, exists both in solid proteins and in solutions.

A convenient model of α-keratin may be constructed around a cylinder with an outside diameter of 7.5 cm, using Dreiding[1] tetrahedral models with flattened nitrogen bonds. When a right-hand helix is constructed around this cylinder from the top down, there will be 3.67 amino acid residues in each turn. The pitch will be 1.5 Å per residue, and the height of each turn will be 5.4 Å. The hydrogen bonds will be 2.8 Å in length and parallel with the vertical axis of the cylinder.

Proteins may also have beta conformations or pleated sheets in which there is considerable intermolecular hydrogen bonding. Silk has this conformation; hence its elongation (25 percent) is much less than that of wool which may exist in both the alpha and beta forms.

---

[1] Schaar and Co., Chicago, Ill.

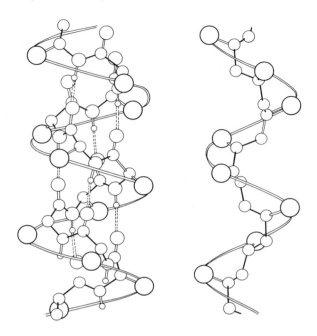

Fig. 1-3   Helical conformations.

It has been postulated that the elasticity of hair and muscle is dependent on the transformation from a pleated sheet to a helical conformation. In 1953 Watson and Crick proposed a hydrogen-bonded *double-stranded helix* with 10 residues per turn for deoxyribonucleic acid (DNA).

REFERENCES

Boyer, R. F.: Multiple Transitions in Polymers, *ACS Div. Polymer Chem., Polymer Preprints,* **6**(2):503 (1965).

Bunn, C. W.: in R. Hill (ed.), "Fibers from Synthetic Polymers," chap. 11, American Elsevier Publishing Company, Inc., New York, 1953.

Chargaff, E., and J. N. Davidson: "The Nucleic Acids," vols. I–III, Academic Press, Inc., New York, 1955 –1960.

Dannis, M. L.: T_g for Methacrylates, *J. Appl. Polymer Sci.,* **1**:121 (1959).

De Winter, W.: *Rev. Macromol. Chem.,* **1**(2):329 (1966).

Di Benedetto, A. T.: "The Structure and Properties of Materials," chap. 8, McGraw-Hill Book Company, New York, 1967.

Faith, E. M., and R. F. Tuckett: "Linear Polymers," Longmans, Green & Co., Ltd., London, 1951.

Flory, P. J.: "Principles of Polymer Chemistry," chap. 10, Cornell University Press, Ithaca, N.Y., 1954.

Goodman, M., and J. S. Schulman: Protein Helix Structures, *J. Polymer Sci.*, Pt. C, **12**:23 (1966).

Ketelaar, J. A. A.: "Chemical Constitution," 2d ed., American Elsevier Publishing Company, Inc., New York, 1958.

Lee, W. A., and G. J. Knight: Glass Transition Temperature of Polymers, in J. Brandrup and E. H. Immergut (eds.), "Polymer Handbook," Interscience Publishers, a division of John Wiley & Sons, Inc., New York, 1965.

Mears, P.: "Polymers—Structure and Bulk Properties," chap. 7, D. Van Nostrand Company, Inc., Princeton, N.J., 1965.

Miller, M. L.: "The Structure of Polymers," chap. 6, Reinhold Publishing Corporation, New York, 1966.

Natta, G., F. Danusso, and G. Moraglio: T_g for Acrylates, *J. Polymer Sci.*, **24**:119 (1957).

Peterlin, A.: Conformational Statistics, *ACS Div. Polymer Chem.*, *Polymer Preprints*, **9**(1):323 (1968).

Rayleigh, Lord: Random Flight Problem, *Phil. Mag.*, (6)**37**:321 (1919).

Reding, F. P., and E. R. Walter: in E. Baer (ed.), "Engineering Design for Plastics," chap. 2, Reinhold Publishing Corporation, New York, 1964.

Tanford, C.: "Physical Chemistry of Macromolecules," John Wiley & Sons, Inc., New York, 1961.

Wall, F. T., and J. J. Erpenbeck: Computer Calculations of Root Mean Square Distance, *J. Chem. Phys.*, **30**:634 (1959).

Watson, J. D., and F. H. C. Crick: DNA Double Helix Structure, *Nature*, **171**:737 (1953).

Wurstlin, F., and H. Klein: Plasticizers vs. T_g, *Kunststoffe*, **47**:527 (1957).

1-3   POLYMER CRYSTALS

The crystalline nature of naturally occurring fibers, such as cellulose, and naturally occurring elastomers, such as *Hevea braziliensis* rubber, has been recognized since the 1920s.   The strength of high-tenacity rayon is associated with the increase in crystallinity which takes place when the filaments are stretched.   Considerable information on the arrangement of polymer chains in cellulose was provided by Haworth.   By use of x-ray diffraction techniques, he showed that the length of the longest axis in the unit cell is 10.3 Å, which is equal to the length of the cellobiose [4-0-(β-D-glucopyranosyl)-D-glucopyranose] segment of cellulose.

The development of crystallinity during the stretching of natural rubber can be observed qualitatively by its increase in opacity.   In 1925 Katz showed that, in addition to the diffuse amorphous rings in the x-rays diffraction pattern observed for unstretched rubber, interference spots were also present in stretched samples.   He attributed these interference spots to *crystallites* which developed during the stretching process. It is now known that very highly stretched rubber is devoid of characteristic elasticity because of its high degree of crystallinity. This so-called "racked rubber" retracts instantly when heated above the melting point of the crystallites.

That some degree of crystallinity is present in polyethylene films is evident from their translucency. Transparent polyethylene can be obtained by heating polyethylene film above 100°C and rapidly cooling this amorphous material. Crystallites of polyethylene obtained by stretching fibers of this polymer were studied by Bunn in 1939. However, there was little emphasis on the crystallinity of polyolefins and other plastic materials until the development of stereospecific catalysts in the 1950s.

Most pure low-molecular-weight organic compounds have sharp characteristic thermodynamic melting points (T_m). The glass transition temperature (T_g) which is characteristic of organic polymers is seldom observed for low-molecular-weight compounds. However, Bueche showed that diethyl phthalate undergoes a transition to a glasslike liquid of very low thermal energy when cooled to $-65°C$.

This change from a very viscous liquid to a glass is comparable to the glass transition noted for amorphous organic polymers. This phenomenon is not characteristic of the structure of diethyl phthalate and is time-dependent. When liquid diethyl phthalate is held at $-53°C$ for several hours, needlelike crystals form which melt sharply at $-8°C$.

Little change in the properties of noncrystallizable polymers is noted at T_m; hence T_g, the temperature at which they become glasslike, is a more significant constant. However, molten crystallizable polymers like polyethylene become partly crystalline at T_m and glasslike at T_g. Hence, both these constants are significant for polymers with regular geometric structures. The study of structure on a macroscale is termed *morphology*.

Since all polymers are not crystalline and the degree of crystallinity of crystalline polymers is dependent on the thermal history of crystal formation, early investigators considered crystallinity in polymers to be different from that of low-molecular-weight organic compounds. This led to the development of the *fringed-micelle model* which served as a useful tool in the development of this phase of polymer science. Although this concept may still be valid at low orders of crystallinity, it is not required to explain the structure of single polymer crystals which were produced by several investigators in the 1950s.

The fringed-micelle concept stated that crystallites consisting of a bundle of parallel polymer chain segments were embedded in an amorphous phase. Most modern polymer chemists consider highly crystalline polymers to be one-phase systems containing crystals with some defects. These imperfect crystallites, which were proposed by Hosemann, are called *paracrystals*.

Since imperfection could move along the chain when the polymer is heated, the one-phase system could be used advantageously to explain changes that occur in the annealing process. However, this concept has not been universally accepted. Some polymer scientists maintain that polymers with a low order of crystallinity consist of both crystalline and amorphous phases.

According to Krigbaum, the crystalline regions are the result of chain straightening in the amorphous region. Thus the distribution may be described better by inverse Langevin statistics than as the gaussian distribution characteristic of the amorphous state.

Regardless of differences in interpretation, the degrees of crystallinity or amorphism in macromolecules are important. An atactic structure is essential for amorphism for polymers with asymmetric carbon atoms. However, polymers with isotactic or syndiotactic structures are not necessarily crystalline since kinetic as well as geometric factors are also important criteria for crystal formation.

According to Mark, the requirements for crystallinity are complete regularity of chemical and geometric structures, free rotational and vibrational motion, periodic arrangement of potential van der Waals' forces, and absence of irregularly spaced bulky groups. Crystalline polymers are characterized by the arrangement of atoms in unit cells, the degree of crystallinity, T_m, and the size, shape, and orientation and aggregation of the crystallites.

According to an equivalence postulate derived by Natta, there are only four possible arrangements of monomer units in the polymer chain. When the requirements of this postulate are met, the energy of the crystalline structure is at a minimum. In this concept, the polymer is considered a theoretical isolated catenated carbon chain in which energy contributions of neighboring chains are negligible. This concept is a useful tool for the investigation of crystalline structures.

X-ray diffraction may be used to classify stereoregular (*eutactic*) polymers as isotactic or syndiotactic but has limited utility in the determination of the degree of tacticity. More sophisticated techniques such as spin decoupling, infrared dichroism, and density-gradient sedimentation are applicable for estimating the order of microtacticity but considerable information can be obtained from density and thermal measurements.

Before crystallization of a eutactic polymer can occur, polymer chains must be disentangled to permit the attainment of a greater degree of order. Thus the degree of crystallinity is dependent both on the time available for this disentanglement and the stereoregularity of the polymer chains. The tightness of the packing attained is reflected in the density of the polymer.

From a practical viewpoint, the difference in density may be used to differentiate stereoregular polymers (high density d_c) from amorphous polymers (low density d_a) and to estimate the degree of crystallinity when the density is between the two extremes. The weight percent crystallinity (C) can be calculated from the density of the test sample (d) by use of the following equation:

$$C = \frac{d_c}{d} \frac{d - d_a}{d_c - d_a} 100 \qquad (1\text{-}17)$$

Degree-of-crystallinity equation

The degree of crystallinity may also be calculated from the ratio of the heat of fusion of the test sample to that of the completely crystalline material. The use of this calorimetric technique has been somewhat limited because it lacks the simplicity of density-gradient tube measurements and is dependent on the assumption that the regions are either crystalline or amorphous.

Aggregates of crystallites called *spherulites* contribute to the opacity of polyolefin films. The size of these spherulites is related to the rate of cooling and to the presence of nucleating agents. When polymer melts are cooled slowly, large spherulites are formed and the polymer is brittle and susceptible to stress cracking. Rapid cooling and the addition of nucleating agents, such as benzoic acid, promote the formation of smaller spherulites.

Spherulites may be observed as Maltese-like extinction crosses or as ringed structures when viewed through a polarizing microscope. It should be noted that polymers do not form spherulites under all conditions and that low-molecular-weight organic compounds like sucrose may also form spherulites from viscous solutions. Spherulites may be considered as highly organized polycrystalline clusters or networks of lamellar (platelike) crystals oriented radially and curled with a screwlike twist.

Early studies of polymer crystals were made on spherulites obtained from melts. The fringed-micelle model and accepted concepts of chain entanglement were compatible with spherulites but were not compatible with single polymer crystals. Polymer crystals had been reported by Sauter in 1932 and Schlesinger in 1953. However, the present concept of the structure of polymer crystals was not accepted until Fischer, Keller, and Tell working independently prepared single polymer crystals by the slow cooling of dilute solutions of polyethylene. Single polymer crystals have also been obtained from polymer melts.

The rate of crystal growth is dependent on disentanglement of chains, primary crystal nucleation, and a growth stage in which imperfections are decreased, as in the annealing process. The growth rate may be approximated by use of the Avrami equation which was derived for the study of the crystallization of metals. As shown in this equation, the ratio of change in specific volume (V_o, V_t, and V_f) which are the specific volumes initially, at time t, and the limiting value, respectively, may be related to time t. K is a kinetic constant related to the rates of nucleation and growth, and n is an integer related to the geometry of nucleation and growth. The value of n may be 1, 2, 3, or 4 and is equal to 4 for homogeneous three-dimensional crystal growth.

$$\frac{V_t - V_f}{V_o - V_f} = e^{-Kt^n} \tag{1-18}$$

Avrami equation

Single polymer crystals are essentially flat plates about 100 Å thick in which the polymer chains about 20,000 Å long are folded at intervals equal to the thickness of the lamellar crystal. Presumably this structure is produced by displacing three carbon atoms from the planar zigzag chain at each fold. It is assumed that additional growth and defects may be reduced during an annealing process by internal mobility of the chain folds. This results in thickening, i.e., changing the length of the interval between folds, and reduction of irregularities such as kinks by movement to the folds. Crystals with thicknesses as great as 1000 Å may be obtained by proper temperature control. Wunderlich obtained more nearly perfect single crystals by the use of pressures of the order of 5,000 atm.

It has been suggested that the chain folds are specific sites for attack on the polymer by oxidizing agents, such as nitric acid or chlorine. For example, Bassett showed that the chlorination of poly(4-methyl-pentene-1) takes place preferentially at the folds.

Synthetic polydienes with irregular sequences of cis and trans configurations are not crystalline. However, stereospecific polydienes with cis or trans configurations may crystallize when stressed, as evident from x-ray diffraction patterns. Bunn showed that natural-rubber crystallites have repeat distances of 8.1 Å which corresponds to two isoprene units in the chain.

The effectiveness of hydrogen bonding in nylons depends on the relative positions of the $C=O$ on one chain and the NH group on the neighboring chain. Thus maximum bonding and strength are observed for nylon 6,6 and 6,10 in a centrally symmetrical structure. However, a different arrangement must be assumed for nylon 6 to achieve maximum hydrogen bonding. That these structures are approached in cold-drawn or stretched filaments is demonstrated by x-ray diffraction patterns of these fibers.

Bunn used x-ray diffraction data of drawn polyethylene fibers to show the dimensions of the unit cell of this polymer. The length along the fiber

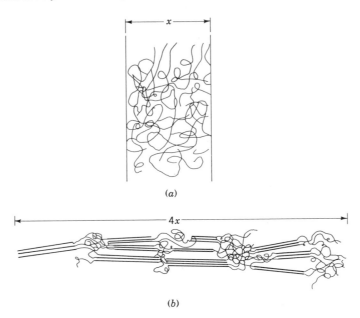

Fig. 1-4   (a) Amorphous polymer. (b) Oriented crystallites.

axis (2.53 Å) corresponds to the repeat distance along the polymer backbone with normal bond distances and bond angles. The other values of 7.40 and 4.93 are characteristic of the side-by-side packing of the polymer chains. Similar information has been obtained for poly(vinyl alcohol) and many isotactic vinyl polymers. The bond angles for poly(vinyl alcohol) and polyethylene are similar since CHOH and CH_2 are similar in size. However, distortion of the normal angle is essential when larger substituents like chlorine are present.

Natta showed that the repeat distance for syndiotactic poly(1,2-butadiene) is twice that found for polyethylene since two mers are required for symmetry in poly(1,2-butadiene). Bunn showed a repeat distance of 16.8 Å for polytetrafluoroethylene. He concluded that the bond angles were increased to 116° to provide room for the fluorine atoms. The out-of-plane twist results in half a complete turn of the chain for every 13 carbon atoms.

According to Fuller, the structure of the crystallites in linear polyesters

$$-(CH_2)_n-O-\underset{\underset{O}{\|}}{C}-(CH_2)_n-\underset{\underset{O}{\|}}{C}-O- \qquad (1\text{-}19)$$

Linear polyester

depends on whether n is even or odd. If n for the dibasic acid methylenes is odd, the unit cell is rectangular and the ester groups are arranged in planes perpendicular to the axis of the polymer backbone. However, when this n is even, the ester groups are arranged in planes which are oblique to the backbone. A trans zigzag arrangement exists when an even number of methylene groups are present in the glycol used to form the polyester.

REFERENCES

Bassett, D. C.: Preferential Attack on Folds, *Polymer*, **5**:457 (1964).

Blackadder, D. A.: Single Crystals, *J. Macromol. Sci. Rev., Macromol. Chem.*, **1**(2):297 (1967).

Bueche, F.: "Physical Properties of Polymers," chap. 13, Interscience Publishers, a division of John Wiley & Sons, Inc., New York, 1962.

Bunn, C. W.: "Chemical Crystallography," Clarendon Press, Oxford, 1946.

Doremus, R. H., B. W. Roberts, and D. Trumbell: "Growth and Perfection of Crystals," Chapman & Hall, Ltd., London, 1958.

Faucher, J. A., and F. P. Reding: in R. A. V. Raff and K. W. Doak (eds.), "Crystalline Olefin Polymers," Pt. I, Interscience Publishers, a division of John Wiley & Sons, Inc., New York, 1965.

Geil, P. H.: "Polymer Single Crystals," Interscience Publishers, a division of John Wiley & Sons, Inc., New York, 1964.

Hermans, P. H.: "Physics and Chemistry of Cellulose Fibers," Elsevier Publishing Company, Amsterdam, 1959.

Katz, J. R.: Crystalline Structure of Rubber, *Kolloid*, (2)**36**:300 (1925).

Keith, H. D.: in M. M. Labes and A. Weissberger (eds.), "Physics and Chemistry of the Organic Solid State," vol. 1, chap. 1, Interscience Publishers, a division of John Wiley & Sons, Inc., New York, 1962.

Keller, A.: "Growth and Perfection of Crystals," John Wiley & Sons, Inc., New York, 1958.

———: Polymer Single Crystals, *Polymer*, **3**(3):393 (1962).

Krigbaum, W. R.: New Methods of Polymer Characterization, in B. Ke (ed.), "Studies in Microtacticity," chap. 1, Interscience Publishers, a division of John Wiley & Sons, Inc., New York, 1964.

Lindenmeyer, P. H.: Single Crystals, *J. Polymer Sci.*, Pt. C **1**, 5 (1963).

Magel, B.: Synthetic Fibers, *J. Polymer Sci.*, Pt. C, **12**:119 (1966).

Mandelkern, L.: "Crystallization of Polymers," McGraw-Hill Book Company, New York, 1964.

Meares, P.: "Polymers—Structure and Bulk Properties," chap. 4, D. Van Nostrand Company, Inc., Princeton, N.J., 1964.

Miller, R. L.: Crystallographic Data, in J. Brandrup and E. H. Immergut (eds.), "Polymer Handbook," Interscience Publishers, a division of John Wiley & Sons, Inc., New York, 1965.

——— and J. Powers: Rate of Crystallization, in J. Brandrup and E. H. Immergut (eds.),

"Polymer Handbook," chap. 3, Interscience Publishers, a division of John Wiley & Sons, Inc., New York, 1965.

Natta, G., and P. Corradini: Poly 1,2-butadiene; Crystallization Principles, *J. Polymer Sci.*, **20**:251 (1956); **39**:29 (1959).

Peiser, H. S., H. P. Rooksby, and A. J. C. Wilson: "X-ray Diffraction by Poly Crystalline Materials," Chapman & Hall, Ltd., London, 1955.

Peterson, J. M., and P. H. Lindenmeyer: Polymer Crystallization, ACS *Div. Polymer Chem., Polymer Preprints*, **9**(1):547 (1968).

Reding, F. P., and E. R. Walter: Crystal Structure and Morphology, in E. Baer (ed.), "Engineering Design for Plastics," chap. 2, Reinhold Publishing Corporation, New York, 1964.

Rochow, T. G.: "Morphology of Polymers," Interscience Publishers, a division of John Wiley & Sons, Inc. New York, 1963.

Sharples, A.: "Introduction to Polymer Crystallization," St. Martin's Press, Inc., New York, 1966.

Statton, W. O.: Small Angle X-ray Studies of Polymers, in B. Ke (ed.), "Newer Methods of Polymer Characterizations," chap. 6. Interscience Publishers, a division of John Wiley & Sons, Inc., New York, 1964.

Wunderlich, B.: Crystalline Polyethylene, in G. L. Clark and G. G. Hawley (eds.), "Encyclopedia of Chemistry," p. 301, Reinhold Publishing Corporation, New York, 1966.

2

Rheology and Solubility

2-1 RHEOLOGY

The term *rheology*, like other English words with the prefix "rheo," was derived from the Greek word meaning current or flow. This word was coined by Bingham who is considered to be the father of modern rheology. This subject includes the interrelated fields of fluid mechanics, viscosity, plasticity, and elasticity. Rheology is the study of the deformation and flow of matter and is concerned with stress-strain-time relationships and the effect of variables, such as temperature, on these relationships. Notable contributions to modern rheology were made by Hooke in 1676, Newton in 1687, and Poiseuille in 1842.

A substance is said to be *Hookean* or an ideal elastic body when the instantaneous deformation or *strain* (γ) is proportional to the applied *stress* (s). The ratio of unit stress to unit strain is termed the *elastic modulus*. When the strain in simple tension is measured as the change in length of the test specimen, this stress-strain ratio is called *Young's modulus of elasticity* (E).

$$s = E\gamma \tag{2-1}$$

Stress applied tangentially to an object is called *shear*. The *shear modulus of elasticity* (G) is the ratio of shear stress (s) to shear strain (γ);

that is, $G = s/\gamma$. The ratio of applied hydrostatic pressure to the change in volume (volume strain) of a test sample is called the *bulk modulus (K)*. The reciprocal of K is the *coefficient of compressibility* of a material.

Polymers have the characteristics of both elastic solids and viscous liquids and hence are termed *viscoelastic*. At temperatures below T_g, polymers are glassy solids with high moduli. Deformation below the glass transition temperature is extremely slow and related essentially to the distortion of primary valence bonds. Deformation above T_g is time-dependent and in addition to bond distortion includes chain disentanglement, segmental or microbrownian motion, and slippage of chains.

The flow of a liquid through a tube is related to its viscosity (η) or resistance to flow. One may use Poiseuille's equation to determine the viscosity of a liquid provided the flow is streamline or laminar. According to this equation, the viscosity η for a liquid with a volume V flowing through a tube of length L for time t is proportional to the pressure P and the radius r of the tube to the fourth power; i.e.

$$\eta = \frac{\pi r^4 \, \Delta P}{8VL} \tag{2-2}$$

Poiseuille's equation

The liquid is said to be ideal or *newtonian* when the shear stress (s) is proportional to the rate of flow $\left(\dfrac{d\gamma}{dt}\right)$ or shear-strain rate. The proportionality factor η is the coefficient of viscosity or resistance to flow, i.e.,

$$s = \eta \frac{d\gamma}{dt} \tag{2-3}$$

Newton's equation for flow

There is no recovery of the deformation (flow) of an ideal liquid. The unit of measurement for viscosity is the *poise*.

The viscosity of polymers may be interpreted as a measure of the rate at which the polymer chains can move relative to each other. This movement is related to the ease of disentanglement of chains, the strength of intermolecular forces, and the degree of segmental motion. As shown by the following Arrhenius-type equation, in which A is a constant related to molecular motion and E is the activation energy for viscous flow, the viscosity η decreases as the temperature increases; i.e.,

$$\eta \cong Ae^{-E/RT} \qquad (2\text{-}4)$$

Arrhenius' equation for viscosity

Convenient models have been developed to aid in the interpretation of rheological properties.   An ideal elastic spring with a modulus of G is used as a model for *Hookean solids*.   A dash pot consisting of a piston and a cylinder containing an ideal liquid with viscosity η serves as a model for *newtonian fluids*.   A block with zero inertia resting on a plane surface may also be used to represent some properties of polymers.   When stress is applied to this *St. Venant body*, it may move at any required rate between zero and infinity.

Since polymers are viscoelastic, i.e., have characteristics of elastic liquids and solids, some of their behavior may be interpreted by the use of appropriate combinations of these models or bodies.   The Voigt or Kelvin model shown in Fig. 2-1, which represents a viscoelastic solid, is constructed by connecting the spring and dash pot in parallel.   The Maxwell model, which represents a fluid under applied load, is constructed by connecting these

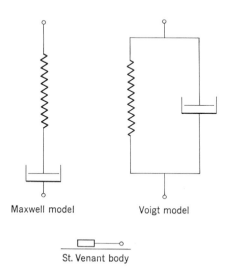

Maxwell model   Voigt model

St. Venant body

Fig. 2-1

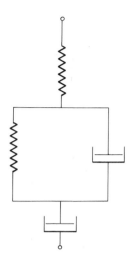

Fig. 2-2   General purpose viscoelastic model.

two models in series. As shown in Fig. 2-2, the Voigt and Maxwell models may be joined to obtain a general-purpose model representing an approximation of a combination of elasticity, flow, and viscoelasticity for linear viscoelastic materials.

When an amorphous polymer is stretched at a temperature above T_g, some of the segments are uncoiled instantaneously like a Hookean spring; some of this deformation is recovered when the force is removed. However, there is also a retarded newtonian dash-pot-like response as well as some permanent deformation or cold flow. The latter is related to the impedance of pendant groups which retard the rate of recovery and to irreversible slippage between chains. Occasional crosslinks, such as those present in vulcanized rubber, hinder this irreversible slippage.

The retarded elastic response may be expressed by combining the equations for shear stress s in the Hookean and newtonian relationships, i.e.,

$$s = G\gamma + \eta \frac{d\gamma}{dt} \tag{2-5}$$

Equation for viscoelastic shear

The shear strain γ obtained by rearranging and integrating this equation is as follows:

$$\gamma = \frac{s}{G}(1 - e^{-G/\eta t}) \tag{2-6}$$

Equation for deformation of viscoelastic substances

This equation may be simplified by substituting the *retardation time* τ for η/G, as follows:

$$\gamma = \frac{s}{G}(1 - e^{-t/\tau}) \tag{2-7}$$

Equation for retardation time

The retardation time τ is the time required for the shear strain γ to be reduced to $1/e$ of the maximum value after the stress has been released.

The total deformation $d\gamma/dt$ may be expressed as a combination of newtonian flow s/η and Hookean elastic deformation $(1/G)(ds/dt)$. These values may be equated at a fixed value for deformation since $d\gamma/dt = 0$ under these conditions. Thus,

$$-\frac{s}{\eta} = \frac{1}{G}\frac{ds}{dt} \tag{2-8}$$

Relationship of flow to deformation

Since the modulus G and viscosity η are constants, the value for shear stress s may be obtained by integration, i.e.,

$$s = s_0 e^{-G/\eta t} \tag{2-9}$$

Relationship of shear stress to modulus and viscosity

This equation may be simplified by substituting the *relaxation time* τ for η/G, as follows:

$$s = s_0 e^{-t/\tau} \tag{2-10}$$

Equation for relaxation time

The relaxation time is the time required for the original stress (s_0) to decrease to $1/e$ of its original value.

Materials which require a threshold stress before flow occurs are termed ideal plastic materials or *Bingham plastics*. These materials behave initially as elastic bodies and then undergo plastic deformation. They differ from newtonian fluids by the yield value (s_0). These and less common types of flow, i.e., shear thinning (pseudoplasticity) and shear thickening (dilatancy) are also shown in Fig. 2-3. Another type of liquid which undergoes a decrease in viscosity when stirred under fixed conditions is termed *thixotropic* (false-bodied). Liquids which increase in viscosity with time (shear thickening) are called *rheopectic*.

The Herschel and Bulkley equation, in which ϕ is a function of η, may be used to approximate many types of flow, as follows:

$$(s - s_0)^n = \phi \frac{d\gamma}{dt} \tag{2-11}$$

Herschel and Bulkley equation

This becomes the equation for ideal or Bingham plastics when $n = 1$ and $\phi = \eta$. When $s_0 = 0$, it is identical to Newton's equation.

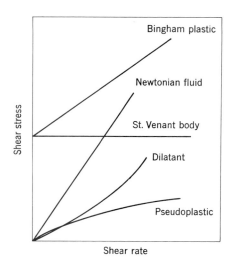

Fig. 2-3   Types of flow.

Viscous flow may be explained by using an oversimplified but convenient random-hole-filling model. According to Eyring, the liquid may be considered as a lattice with some unoccupied sites or holes. These holes are assumed to be comparable in size to small molecules and to be protected by an energy barrier. The number of holes increases as the temperature is raised and vice versa. Pressure coefficient values indicate that about 15 percent of the space in ordinary liquids is empty at room temperature.

When sufficient pressure is applied to a liquid to overcome the energy barrier, molecules may jump to unoccupied sites and thus create new holes. The activation energy required for hole jumping for small molecules is about one-third of the heat of evaporation.

The energy values for linear high polymers are less than those for related model compounds because hole filling takes place by successive correlated jumps of chain segments along the polymer chain. The jump frequency ϕ is governed by the segmental friction factor f_0, and both are related to polymer structure and temperature.

The mechanical properties of polymers are related to the viscosity raised to an appropriate power which is a function of intermolecular attractions and the extent of entanglement. The latter is negligible for very short chains but increases with branching and lengthening of the chain. Since high viscosity makes processing and fabrication more difficult, the chain length of elastomers and plastics is often reduced by mastication or processing at elevated temperatures.

A typical power-law equation is the Ostwald-de Waele-Nutting model shown below. In this equation, m is a consistency factor and n is an index of flow.

$$s = m \left(\frac{d\gamma}{dt} \right)^{n-1} \tag{2-12}$$

Power-law equation

Thus, when the shear rate (flow) $d\gamma/dt$ is plotted against the logarithm of the shear stress s, the slope of the line is $n-1$ and the intercept is log m. This equation becomes that for a newtonian liquid when $m = \eta$ and $n = 2$.

When flow processes of molten polymers, such as extrusion, are not controlled, irregularities related to elastic stresses may be noted on the surfaces of the extrudate. One type of defect, called *melt fracture*, has been attributed to turbulent flow which causes buckling of the material as it recovers from strain at the orifice. Another defect investigated by Herzog and Weissenberg is characterized by an expansion at the orifice which results in rough or distorted surfaces. This defect has been attributed to relaxation of oriented chain molecules which in turn is related to the length of the polymer chain.

The time-temperature dependence of polymers may also be related to polymer structure. The rate of flow may be increased by raising the temperature since this increases the segmental motion of the polymer chain. However, the length of flow at the original temperature may correspond to that at the elevated temperature provided sufficient time is available.

The relationship of the *shift factor* ($\mathcal{A}_t$) to temperatures (T_g and T) may be approximated by the Arrhenius equation:

$$\log \mathcal{A}_t = -\frac{b}{2.302 T T_g}(T - T_g) \tag{2-13}$$

Arrhenius equation for shift factor

Williams, Landel, and Ferry developed a modified empirical equation (WLF) which may be used to predict creep at temperatures up to 100°C above T_g. According to the WLF equation shown below, all polymers should have similar viscoelastic behavior at comparable temperature intervals above their glass-transition-temperature values. The constants C_1 and C_2 in the WLF equation are related to holes or free volume.

$$\log \mathcal{A}_t = \frac{-C_1(T - T_g)}{C_2 + T - T_g} \tag{2-14}$$

WLF equation for shift factor

REFERENCES

Alfrey, T.: "Mechanical Behavior of High Polymers," Interscience Publishers, Inc., New York, 1948.

—— and E. F. Gurnee: "Organic Polymers," chap. 2, Prentice-Hall, Inc., Englewood Cliffs, N.J., 1967.

Baer, E.: "Engineering Design for Plastics," Reinhold Publishing Corporation, New York, 1964.

Bartenev, G. M., and Y. V. Zelenev: Viscoelasticity, *Mater. Sci. Eng.*, **2**(3):136 (1967).

Bernhardt, E. C.: "Processing of Thermoplastic Materials," Reinhold Publishing Corporation, New York, 1959.

Bingham, E. C.: "Fluidity and Plasticity," McGraw-Hill Book Company, New York, 1922.

———— and H. Green: Paint Flow, *Proc. ASTM,* **19:**640 (1919).

Bueche, F.: "Physical Properties of Polymers," Interscience Publishers, Inc., New York, 1959.

Eirich, F. R.: "Rheology," vols. 1–4, Academic Press, Inc., New York, 1956–1967.

Ferry, J. D.: "Viscoelastic Properties of Polymers," John Wiley & Sons, Inc., New York, 1961.

Fox, D., M. M. Labes, and A. Weissberger: "Physics and Chemistry of the Solid State," Interscience Publishers, a division of John Wiley & Sons, Inc., New York, 1963.

Frederickson, A. G.: "Principles and Applications of Rheology," Prentice-Hall, Inc., Englewood Cliffs, N.J., 1964.

Godfrey, D. E. R.: "Theoretical Elasticity and Plasticity for Engineers," Thames and Hudson, London, 1950.

Hermans, J. J.: "Flow Properties of Disperse Systems," Interscience Publishers, Inc., New York, 1953.

Leaderman, H.: "Elastic and Creep Properties of Filamentous Materials and Other Polymers," The Textile Foundation, Washington, D.C., 1943.

McKelvey, J. M.: "Polymer Processing," John Wiley & Sons, Inc., New York, 1962.

Mill, O. C.: "Rheology of Disperse Systems," Pergamon Press, New York, 1959.

Nielson, L. E.: "Mechanical Properties of Polymers," Reinhold Publishing Corporation, New York, 1962.

Passaglia, E., and J. R. Know: Viscoelastic Behavior and Time-Temperature Relationships, in E. Baer (ed.), "Engineering Design for Plastics," chap. 3, Reinhold Publishing Corporation, New York, 1964.

Schmidt, A. X., and C. A. Marlies: "Principles of High-polymer Theory and Practice," McGraw-Hill Book Company, New York, 1948.

Scott-Blair, G. W.: "A Survey of General and Applied Rheology," 2d ed., Sir Isaac Pitman & Sons, Ltd., 1949.

Severs, E. T.: "Rheology of Polymers," Reinhold Publishing Corporation, New York, 1962.

Sokolnikoff, I. S.: "Mathematical Theory of Elasticity," 2d ed., McGraw-Hill Book Company, New York, 1956.

Timoshenko, S. P., and J. N. Goodier: "Theory of Elasticity," 2d ed., McGraw-Hill Book Company, New York, 1951.

Tobolsky, A. V.: "Properties and Structure of Polymers," John Wiley & Sons, Inc., New York, 1962.

Treloar, L. K. G.: "The Physics of Rubber Elasticity," 2d ed., Clarendon Press, Oxford, 1958.

Van Wazer, J. R.: in D. E. Kirk and D. Othmer (eds.), "Encyclopedia of Chemical Technology," Interscience Publishers, Inc., New York, 1953.

Wilkinson, W. L.: "Non-Newtonian Fluids," Pergamon Press, New York, 1960.

Williams, M. L., R. R. Landel, and J. D. Ferry: *J. Am. Chem. Soc.,* **77:**3701 (1955).

2-2 SOLUBILITY OF POLYMERS

When a polymer is added to a solvent, the solution process takes place in two steps. The first step is a slow swelling process called *solvation* in which solvent molecules are absorbed on the surface of the polymer molecule, causing a change in its average dimensions. In this step the polymer molecule expands by a factor (δ) which is dependent on an entropy parameter related to the degree of solvency. This factor δ, which is proportional to the temperature, is related to the thermodynamic intramolecular action between chain segments.

When a polymer is swollen by a good solvent, it may be gradually dispersed in a second step to yield a polymer solution. No primary valence bonds are cleaved in this process; hence network polymers which swell in good solvents do not dissolve in the second step.

By the application of information obtained from osmotic pressure-concentration studies, Flory developed a universal parameter theta (Θ) to represent the lowest temperature at which a polymer with infinite molecular weight would be *completely miscible* with a specific solvent. Thus, Θ is the critical miscibility temperature at which the molecule assumes an unperturbed conformation; i.e., there are no long-range or short-range interactions and $\delta = 1$. Hence, free rotation about the bonds occurs, and the solution is said to be *pseudoideal.*

The theta temperature corresponds to the Boyle point in an imperfect gas and is the range in which the virial coefficient (B) in the expanded gas law becomes zero. This same concept applies to the osmotic-pressure modification of this fundamental equation, i.e.,

$$\pi = \frac{RT}{\bar{M}} C + BC^2 + \cdots \tag{2-15}$$

Relationship of osmotic pressure to average molecular weight

A polymer solution is characterized by a high viscosity which is related to the chain length and the solvent power or solvency of the solvent for the dissolved polymer. At temperatures below the theta temperature, the polymer molecule appears as a ball or tight coil. When the temperature is raised to the theta temperature, the polymer behaves as an *ideal statistical coil.* Under these conditions, the solvent is called a *theta solvent* and the polymer is said to be in a theta state; i.e., typical intramolecular interactions between groups in the same molecule are nonexistent.

There is little change in chain dimensions, i.e., the virial constant is essentially zero, when the system is heated above the theta temperature in a poor solvent. However, the polymer expands when heated in a good or active solvent, because the chain tends to uncoil to its full contour length. Theta temperatures for typical polymer-solvent systems are given in Table 2-1.

Table 2-1   Theta Temperatures for Typical Polymer-Solvent Systems

POLYMER	SOLVENT	THETA TEMPERATURE, °C
Amylose	Dimethyl sulfoxide 25/ 0.5 M KCL (75)	25
Poly(acrylic acid)	Dioxane	30
Polyisobutylene	Benzene	24
Polyethylene	Diphenyl ether	161
Poly(hexamethylene adipamide)	0.3 M KCL in 90% formic acid	25
Poly(methyl methacrylate)	Acetone	−50
Polypropylene	Isoamyl acetate	34
Polystyrene	Decalin	31
Poly(vinyl acetate)	3-Heptanone	29
Poly(vinyl chloride)	Benzyl alcohol	155

For solution to take place, it is necessary that the *free energy* (G) which is related to the driving force for the solution process decrease. The thermodynamics of this process may be demonstrated by referring to the free-energy equation,

$$\Delta G = \Delta H - T \Delta S \tag{2-16}$$

Gibbs' free-energy equation

in which $\Delta H = -\Delta Q$, the heat of mixing, and ΔS, the change in entropy, are related to the increase in freedom of movement or disorder in the solution. Systems with low theta-temperature values have high values for $-\Delta G$, and the tendency for solution to occur is increased as the temperature is raised.

The solubility of a polymer decreases as the chain length increases; thus polymer chains of different lengths may be separated (*fractionated*) by proper choice of solvents. Branched polymers are more soluble than linear polymers but crosslinked polymers are insoluble. From a practical viewpoint, solutions may be prepared readily by dispersing a finely divided polymer in a good solvent at a temperature below the theta temperature and gradually warming the stirred system. The viscosity of a polymer solution, like a polymer melt, decreases as the temperature is increased since

$$\eta = Ae^{-E/RT} \tag{2-17}$$

Arrhenius equation

Thus the relationship of log η of a solution and T^{-1} is linear over a limited temperature range.

The ratio of the viscosity of the polymer solution (η) and that of the solvent (η_0) is called the *relative viscosity* (η_{rel}). The increase in relative viscosity, that is, $\eta_{rel} - 1$, is called the *specific viscosity* (η_{sp}). The *reduced viscosity* or *viscosity number* is obtained by dividing the specific viscosity (η_{sp}) by the concentration (C). The limiting value of the reduced viscosity, or of the viscosity number, is called the *intrinsic viscosity* [η].

According to Flory, the limiting viscosity number [η] is related to the root-mean-square end-to-end distance $(\bar{r}^2)^{1/2}$ and the proportionality constant ϕ. This constant is independent of solvent, molecular weight, and temperature and has a value of (2.5×10^{23})/mole. The Flory equation

$$[\eta] = \phi(\bar{r}^2)^{3/2}\overline{M}^{-1} \qquad (2\text{-}18)$$

Flory equation

has been replaced by the related semiempirical Mark-Houwink equation in which the constants K and $\mathcal{A}$ must be obtained from absolute or direct molecular-weight measurement.

$$[\eta] = K\overline{M}^{\mathcal{A}} \qquad (2\text{-}19)$$

Mark-Houwink equation

The intrinsic viscosity or limiting viscosity number is a measure of the effective hydrodynamic volume. As shown in Fig. 2-4, the intrinsic viscosity [η] is the intercept when the reduced viscosity-concentration curve is extrapolated to zero concentration.

The values for $\mathcal{A}$ range from 0.5 for tightly coiled molecules to 2.0 for rigid rod-shaped molecules present in good solutions. Values for both $\mathcal{A}$ and K may be obtained from the slope and intercept of the lines obtained when known values of log $\overline{M}$ are plotted against log [η]. Values for the average molecular weight $\overline{M}$ may be obtained directly from absolute methods based on colligative properties, light scattering, sedimentation, or end-group analysis which are discussed in Chap. 3. The values for $\mathcal{A}$ may also be predicted from the solubility-parameter values. Typical values for K and $\mathcal{A}$ are given in Table 2-2.

Solvency may be evaluated by the Flory-Huggins value (μ) which is derived from the lattice-hole concept. This value is related to the slope of the line when the ratio of the osmotic pressure π and the polymer concen-

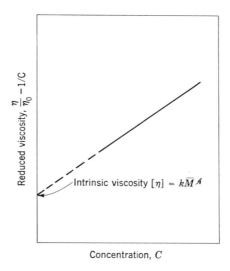

Fig. 2-4   The relationship between reduced viscosity and concentration.

tration C is plotted against the polymer concentration C. The slope μ is a measure of polymer-solvent interaction and hence increases as the solvent activity increases. The solvency may also be estimated by observing the temperature of the *cloud point* (T_c) for solutions of equal concentration in different solvents.

Solvency may also be evaluated by application of the Gibbs free-energy equation. The work function ΔG in this equation is a measure of the spon-

Table 2-2   Relationship of K (and Exponent A in Polymer Solutions
([η] $= K\overline{M}^A$ Mark-Houwink equation)

POLYMER	SOLVENT	TEMPERATURE, °C	$K \times 10^5$	A
Amylose	Dimethyl sulfoxide	20	3.97	0.82
Poly(acrylic acid)	Dioxane	30	76	0.50
Polyisobutylene	Benzene	40	43	0.60
Polyethylene	Decalin	135	62	0.70
Poly(hexamethylene adipamide) in 90% formic acid	90% Formic acid	25	110	0.72
Poly(methyl methacrylate)	Acetone	25	6.2	0.72
Polypropylene	Isoamyl acetate	34	168.5	0.50
Polystyrene	Decalin	18	77	0.50
Poly(vinyl acetate)	3-Heptanone	26.8	82	0.50
Poly(vinyl chloride)	Benzyl alcohol	155.8	156	0.50

taneity of the solution process and is related to the entropy ΔS and the enthalpy of mixing ΔH in the expression

$$\Delta G = \Delta H - T \, \Delta S \qquad (2\text{-}20)$$

Gibbs free-energy equation

If one assumes a relatively small value for enthalpy ΔH, the magnitude of the negative value of the work function (free energy ΔG) increases as the temperature increases. Thus a negative value for ΔG, which is a requirement for spontaneity, is assured if the enthalpy value ΔH is small or negligible. This requirement is met when the intermolecular interactions between solvent-solvent and polymer-polymer molecules are similar.

These forces, which have been called internal pressure $(\Delta E/\Delta V)$ or *cohesive energy density* (CED) by Hildebrand, are related to the energy of vaporization (ΔE) per cubic centimeter (ΔV). According to Hildebrand, the enthalpy of mixing (ΔH) is related to the total molar volume of solution (V) and the volume fraction of each component (ϕ). The value of the square root of the internal pressure $(\Delta E/\Delta V)^{1/2}$, called the *solubility parameter* (δ), may be obtained from the following semiempirical equation developed by Scatchard and Hildebrand:

$$\Delta H = V(\delta_1 - \delta_2)^2 \phi_1 \phi_2 \qquad (2\text{-}21)$$

Scatchard-Hildebrand equation

Since the enthalpy of mixing ΔH approaches zero when the solubility parameters δ are similar, these constants, which are sometimes expressed as "Hildebrand units," may be used to predict solubility. The term *regular solutions* was proposed for systems that could be described by the Scatchard-Hildebrand equation.

Provided the solvents are not too dissimilar in molecular structure, the solubility parameter for a solvent mixture is usually equal to the sum of the products of the mole fractions multiplied by the solubility parameters of each component. Thus the solubility of cellulose nitrate in a 50:50 mixture of ethyl alcohol and ethyl ether can be explained by the solubility parameter of the mixture in spite of the insolubility of the resinous solute in the individual solvents.

It is of interest to note that methylcellosolve $(CH_3OCH_2CH_2OH)$, which was synthesized as a replacement for the solvent mixture, has a similar solubility parameter (10.8). The pioneer development of collodion preceded the use of the Hildebrand equation but the latter is now used widely to predict solubility or lack of it in solvent mixtures and for the selection of more economical and more effective solvent systems.

Solubility parameters of volatile substances may be calculated from the latent heat of vaporization (ΔH) but this technique is not applicable for estimating solubility parameters of resinous products. The solubility parameter δ of a volatile liquid may be calculated from the following formula which includes the gas constant R and molar volume V. The latter is obtained from values for molecular weight M and density D.

$$\delta = \left(\frac{\Delta H - RT}{M/D}\right)^{1/2} \tag{2-22}$$

Solubility-parameter equation

The use of this technique is illustrated in the calculation of the solubility parameter of n-heptane [$CH_3(CH_2)_5CH_3$], as follows:

$$\delta = \left(\frac{\Delta H - RT}{M/D}\right)^{1/2} = \left(\frac{87(100) - 2(298)}{100/0.68}\right)^{1/2} = 7.4$$

The solubility parameter of any substance may also be estimated from Small's *molar attraction constants* (G) by using the following formula:

$$\delta = \frac{D\Sigma G}{M} \tag{2-23}$$

Small's formula for solubility parameters

Typical G values in Small's formula are $CH_3 = 214$, $CH_2 = 133$, and $CH = 28$. The use of this formula in the calculation of solubility-parameter values of resinous products may be illustrated by using polypropylene in which the segmer [$-CH(CH_3)CH_2-$] has a formula weight of 42. Thus,

$$\delta = \frac{D\Sigma G}{M} = \frac{(0.905)(28 + 214 + 133)}{42} = 8.1$$

Solubility parameters of resinous products may also be estimated by comparing the relative effect of solvents with known values on soluble resinous

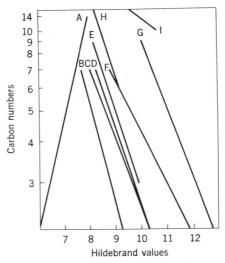

A = Normal alkanes, B = Normal chloroalkanes, C = Methyl esters, D = Other alkyl formates and acetates, E = Methyl ketones, F = Alkyl nitriles, G = Normal alkanols, H = Alkyl benzenes, I = Dialkyl phthalates.

Fig. 2-5   Relationship of solubility parameters and carbon numbers of solvents.

products or their swelling effect on crosslinked (insoluble) resinous products. The relationship of solubility-parameter values (Hildebrand value) to the carbon number of various solvents is shown in Fig. 2-5.

Hayes related the cohesive energy density to the glass transition temperature T_g and a chain stiffness constant M. As shown below, this equation may be modified to show the effect of chain stiffness and glass transition temperature on the solubility parameter δ.

$$\delta = [M(T_g - 25)]^{1/2} \tag{2-24}$$

Relationship of solubility parameter and glass transition temperature

Prior to the use of Hildebrand solubility parameters for the characterization of the solubility of resinous products in solvent systems, paint technicians used other more empirical methods such as Kauri-Butanol values, aniline points, and solubility indices. In the American Society for Testing Materials (ASTM) D1133-54T method, the Kauri-Butanol value is related to the volume of test solvent required to cause turbidity of a standard solution of Kauri-Copal resin in normal butanol. As described by ASTM D1012-51, the aniline point is the lowest temperature at which equal volumes of aniline and the test solvent are completely miscible. Both techniques are a measure of the aromaticity of the test solvent, and the values obtained may be converted to Hildebrand solubility-parameter values.

In spite of the difficulties associated with the study of the solution of resinous products, good agreement is observed between calculated and experimental parameters for hydrocarbon resins dissolved in hydrocarbon solvents. However, anomalies are observed as the polarity of either component increases.

In order to account for some of these anomalies with *irregular solutions,* Lieberman proposed a *hydrogen-bonding index* (γ) and classified solvents in the order of increasing hydrogen-bonding indices, as follows: class I, 2.5γ; class II, 5.5γ; and class III, 8.5γ. Lieberman established zones of solubility by plotting these indices (γ) against Hildebrand's parameters (δ). This technique may be used to predict solubility of a resinous material in a solvent system when both γ and δ values are within the area or zone of solubility.

Three-dimensional zones of solubility were proposed by Crowley who applied corrections for all types of intermolecular interaction. Tests on cellulose nitrate have indicated that this method is more reliable than simpler techniques for predicting zones of solubility.

Much of the early success with Kauri-Butanol values and aniline points was observed with hydrocarbons which produced regular solutions. Since the Hildebrand solubility-parameter values for aliphatic hydrocarbons decrease with molecular weight, a spectrum of regular solvents ($\delta = 6.0$ to 8.9) may be established with these solvents, as shown in Table 2-3.

Additional solvents may be added to this spectrum of solvents by using aliphatic fluorohydrocarbons for values of 5.5 to 6.2 and adding the solvents listed in Table 2-4 for values greater than 8.9. These values are also shown in Table 2-4.

Table 2-3   Spectrum of Solubility-parameter Values for Regular Solvents

	δ
Ethane	6.0
Propane	6.4
n-Pentane	7.1
n-Octane	7.6
n-Hexadecane	8.0
n-Propylbenzene	8.6
Toluene	8.9

Table 2-4 Spectrum of Solubility-parameter Values for Solvents ($\delta = 9.5$ to 15.4)

Chlorobenzene	9.5
o-Dichlorobenzene	10.0
Butyronitrile	10.5
Nitroethane	11.1
Acetonitrile	11.9
Nitromethane	12.7
N,N-diformylpiperazine	15.4

Solvents with higher values, such as glycerol (16.5), formamide (19.2), and water (23.4), are available but these are strongly hydrogen-bonded and hence do not yield regular solutions. Solubility parameters for typical solvents are listed in Table 2-6.

A spectrum of solvents may be used to estimate the solubility parameter of a resinous product from solubility data. Likewise, a spectrum of resinous products may be used to study affects of various solvents, as shown in Table 2-5.

The approximate solubility-parameter values for typical polymers are shown in Table 2-7.

Plasticizers are nonvolatile solvents which have solubility parameters similar to those of the polymer. The use of camphor as a plasticizer for cellulose nitrate and tricresyl phosphate for poly(vinyl chloride) was the result of empirical discoveries which are in agreement with modern solubility-parameter data. The importance of plasticizers is demonstrated by an annual production of over 1 billion pounds in the United States. The subject of plasticizers will be discussed in detail in a later chapter.

Table 2-5 Spectrum of Solubility-parameter Values for Polymers ($\delta = 6.2$ to 15.4)

Polytetrafluoroethylene	6.2
Poly(dimethyl silicone)	7.3
Polystyrene	9.1
Natural rubber	8.3
Poly(vinyl chloride)	9.7
Poly(vinyl chloride (87)– co-vinyl acetate(13))	10.4
Cellulose nitrate	11.5
Poly(vinylidene chloride)	12.2
Nylon 6,6	13.6
Polyacrylonitrile	15.4

Table 2-6 Solubility Parameters (δ) for Typical Solvents

POORLY HYDROGEN-BONDED SOLVENTS	δ_p	MODERATELY HYDROGEN-BONDED SOLVENTS	δ_m
Hydrogen	3.0	Diisopropyl ether	6.9
Dimethyl siloxane	5.5	Diethyl ether	7.4
Difluorodichloromethane	5.5	Isoamyl acetate	7.8
Ethane	6.0	Diisobutyl ketone	7.8
Neopentane	6.3	Di-n-propyl ether	7.8
Amylene	6.9	sec-Butyl acetate	8.2
Nitro-n-octane	7.0	Isopropyl acetate	8.4
n-Pentane	7.0	Methyl amyl ketone	8.5
n-Octane	7.6	Butyraldehyde	9.0
Turpentine	8.1	Ethyl acetate	9.0
Cyclohexane	8.2	Methyl ethyl ketone	9.3
Cymene	8.2	Butyl cellosolve	9.5
Monofluorodichloromethane	8.3	Methyl acetate	9.6
Dipentene	8.5	Dichloroethyl ether	9.8
Carbon tetrachloride	8.6	Acetone	9.9
n-Propylbenzene	8.6	Dioxane	10.0
p-Chlorotoluene	8.8	Cyclopentanone	10.4
Decalin	8.8	Cellosolve	10.5
Xylene	8.8	N,N-dimethylacetamide	10.8
Benzene	9.2	Furfural	11.2
Styrene	9.3	N,N-dimethyl formamide	12.1
Tetralin	9.4	1,2-Propylene carbonate	13.3
Chlorobenzene	9.5	Ethylene carbonate	14.7
Ethylene dichloride	9.8		
o-Dichlorobenzene	10		
Propionitrile	10.8	STRONGLY HYDROGEN-BONDED SOLVENTS	δ_s
Nitroethane	11.1	Diethyl amine	8.0
Acetonitrile	11.9	n-Amyl amine	8.7
Nitroethane	12.7	2-Ethylhexanol	9.5
		Isoamyl alcohol	10.0
		Acetic acid	10.1
		Meta-cresol	10.2
		Aniline	10.3
		n-Octyl alcohol	10.3
		tert-Butyl alcohol	10.6
		n-Amyl alcohol	10.9
		n-Butyl alcohol	11.4
		Isopropyl alcohol	11.5
		Diethylene glycol	12.1
		Furfuryl alcohol	12.5
		Ethyl alcohol	12.7
		N-ethyl formamide	13.9
		Methanol	14.5
		Ethylene glycol	14.6
		Glycerol	16.5
		Water	23.4

Table 2-7 Approximate Solubility-parameter Values for Polymers

POLYMER	δ_p	δ_m	δ_s
Polytetrafluorocarbons	5.8–6.4		
Ester gum	7.0–10.6	7.4–10.8	9.5–10.9
Alkyd 45% soy oil	7.0–11.1	7.4–10.8	9.5–11.8
Silicone DC-1107	7.0–9.5	9.3–10.8	9.5–11.5
Poly(vinyl ethyl ether)	7.0–11.0	7.4–10.8	9.5–14.0
Poly(butyl acrylate)	7.0–12.5	7.4–11.5	
Poly(butyl methacrylate)	7.4–11.0	7.4–10.0	9.5–11.2
Silicone DC-23	7.5–8.5	7.5–8.0	9.5–10.0
Polyisobutylene	7.5–8.0	. . .	
Polyethylene	7.7–8.2	. . .	
Gilsonite	7.9–9.5	7.8–8.5	
Poly(vinyl butyl ether)	7.8–10.6	7.5–10.0	9.5–11.2
Natural rubber	8.1–8.5	. . .	
Hypalon 20	8.1–9.8	8.4–8.8	
Ethyl cellulose N-22	8.1–11.1	7.4–10.8	9.5–14.5
Chlorinated rubber	8.5–10.6	7.8–10.8	
Dammar gum	8.5–10.6	7.8–10.0	9.5–10.9
Versamid 100	8.5–10.6	8.5–8.9	9.5–11.4
Polystyrene	8.5–10.6	9.1–9.4	
Poly(vinyl acetate)	8.5–9.5	. . .	
Poly(vinyl chloride)	8.5–11.0	7.8–10.5	
Phenolic resins	8.5–11.5	7.8–13.2	9.5–13.6
Buna N (butadiene-acrylonitrile copolymer)	8.7–9.3	. . .	
Poly(methyl methacrylate)	8.9–12.7	8.5–13.3	
Carbowax 4000 [poly(ethylene oxide)]	8.9–12.7	8.5–14.5	9.5–14.5
Thiokol [poly(ethylene sulfide)]	9.0–10.0	. . .	
Polycarbonate	9.5–10.6	9.5–10.0	
Pliolite P-1230	9.5–10.6	. . .	
Mylar [poly(ethylene phthalate)]	9.5–10.8	9.3–9.9	
Vinyl chloride–acetate copolymer	9.5–11.0	7.8–13.0	
Polyurethane	9.8–10.3	. . .	
Styrene acrylonitrile copolymer	10.6–11.1	9.4–9.8	
Vinsol (rosin derivative)	10.6–11.8	7.8–13.0	9.5–12.5
Epon 1001 (epoxy)	10.6–11.1	8.5–13.3	
Shellac	. . .	10.0–11.0	9.5–14.0
Polymethacrylonitrile	. . .	10.6–11.0	
Cellulose acetate	11.1–12.5	10.0–14.5	
Nitrocellulose	11.1–12.5	8.0–14.5	12.5–14.5
Polyacrylonitrile	. . .	12.0–14.0	
Poly(vinyl alcohol)	. . .	. . .	12.0–13.0
Nylon, 6,6 [poly(hexamethylene adipamide)]	. . .	. . .	13.5–15.0
Cellulose	. . .	. . .	14.5–16.5

REFERENCES

Burrell, H.: Solubility Parameter Concept, *ACS Div. Org. Coatings and Plastics Chem., Preprints*, **28**(1):682 (1968).

———: Solubility Parameter Values, in J. Brandrup and E. H. Immergut (eds.), "Polymer Handbook," Interscience Publishers, a division of John Wiley & Sons, Inc., New York, 1966.

Crowley, J. D., and D. S. Teague: *J. Paint Technol.*, **38**(496):269 (1966).

Doolittle, A. K.: "The Technology of Solvents and Plasticizers," John Wiley & Sons, Inc., New York, 1954.

Elias, H. G., G. Adank, et al.: Theta Solvents, in J. Brandrup and E. H. Immergut (eds.), "Polymer Handbook," Interscience Publishers, a division of John Wiley & Sons, Inc., New York, 1966.

Flory, P. J.: "Principles of Polymer Chemistry," chap. 14, Cornell University Press, Ithaca, N.Y., 1953.

Hayes, R. A.: Relationship of Cohesive Energy Density to Glass Transition Temperatures, *J. Appl. Polymer Sci.*, **5**:318 (1961).

Hildebrand, J. H., and R. L. Scott: "Regular Solutions," Prentice-Hall, Inc., Englewood Cliffs, N.J., 1962.

Huggins, M. L.: Evaluation of Important Parameters, *ACS Div. Polymer Chem., Polymer Preprints*, **9**(1):558 (1968).

Kurata, M., M. Iwama, and K. Kamada: Viscosity–Molecular Weight Relationships, in J. Brandrup and E. H. Immergut (eds.), "Polymer Handbook," Interscience Publishers, a division of John Wiley & Sons, Inc., New York, 1966.

Lieberman, E. P.: *Offic. Dig., Fed. Soc. Paint Technol.*, **34**:30 (1962).

Meyersen, K.: Solvents and Non-solvents for Polymers, in J. Brandrup and E. H. Immergut (eds.), "Polymer Handbook," Interscience Publishers, a division of John Wiley & Sons, Inc., New York, 1966.

Severs, E. T.: "Rheology of Polymers," chap. 6, Reinhold Publishing Corporation, New York, 1962.

Seymour, R. B.: Solubility Parameters, *Australian Paint J.*, **13**(10):18 (1968).

Sheehan, C. J., and A. L. Bisio: *Rubber Chem. Technol.*, **39**(1): 149 (1966).

Small, P. A.: *J. Appl. Chem.*, (3)**71**: (1953).

Tompa, H: "Polymer Solutions," Academic Press, Inc., New York, 1956.

3

Molecular Weights of Polymers

Pure low-molecular-weight organic compounds, such as sucrose, and some polymers, such as proteins, are *monodisperse;* i.e., all the molecules in any sample of pure material have identical molecular weight (M). In contrast, *polydispersity* is a characteristic of most macromolecules. The range of different molecular weights of the molecules in a sample may be narrowed by fractionation but monodisperse systems are seldom encountered in synthetic polymer systems. Hence, the polymer scientist is usually concerned with an average molecular weight $(\overline{M})$.

In general, properties such as density, refractive index, and hardness of high polymers are essentially independent of molecular weight. However, properties of amorphous polymers, such as melt viscosity, softening temperature, tensile and impact strengths, and heat resistance, are related to the length of the polymer chain.

As shown in Fig. 3-1, tensile- and impact-strength properties increase rapidly as the chain length increases and then level off. Thus a range of usefulness or commercial range has been established in which the polymer chain is of sufficient length, i.e., above the *threshold value,* to provide minimum useful properties. The melt viscosity continues to increase rapidly as the molecular weight increases above the threshold value. Since polymers with very high molecular weights are difficult to process and fabricate, an appropriate compromise is usually made between maximum physical properties and processibility. It should be noted that physical properties are also related to the degree of polydispersity.

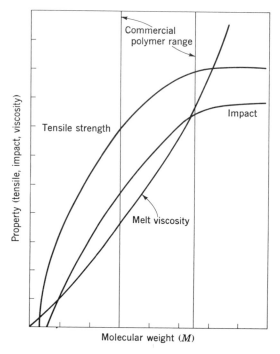

Fig. 3-1   Relationship of polymer properties to molecular weight.

A threshold molecular weight is essential for attainment of the unique properties that characterize high polymers. As indicated in Fig. 3-2, the softening temperature of low-molecular-weight polyethylene is a function of the degree of polymerization (DP). Thus, dimers and trimers of ethylene are gases. Oligomers with a DP of 4 or more are liquid.

The viscosities of these liquids increase as the chain lengths increase. Polyethylenes with $\overline{DP}$'s of about 30 are greaselike. Those polymers with $\overline{DP}$'s around 50 resemble paraffin wax and become harder as the $\overline{DP}$ increases. Polyethylenes with DP's greater than 400 are hard resins with softening points above 100°C. The number of carbon atoms in the polymer backbone and intermolecular forces must also be considered when polymers with similar $\overline{DP}$'s are compared. Thus poly(hexamethylene adipamide) (nylon 6,6) with a $\overline{DP}$ in the 50 to 100 range is more rigid than the polyethylene with a comparable $\overline{DP}$ because of the increased strength associated with the higher intermolecular attractive forces. Polymers with $\overline{DP}$'s in the 500 to 1,000 range are more useful for commercial fibers. The $\overline{DP}$ values for most amorphous plastics and elastomers are usually above 1,000.

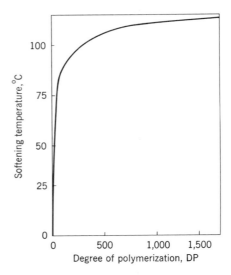

Fig. 3-2   Relationship of softening temperature and degree of polymerization for polyethylene.

The pioneering discoveries of Raoult and van't Hoff provided techniques which are extremely useful for the determination of the molecular weights of small molecules, such as sucrose. Unprecedented high values were obtained when early investigators used techniques such as osmometry for measuring the molecular weights of natural products. However, the significance of the data was not recognized. Hence, the early experiments proposed aggregates of molecules rather than long polymeric chains.

In spite of a clearer understanding of polymer structure demonstrated later by Staudinger, Meyer, Mark, Carothers, Guth, and Kuhn, erroneous interpretations of polymer structure and chain length were prevalent in the early 1930s. The study of polymer structure by the more enlightened pioneers was complicated by polydispersity and intermolecular attractions between polymer molecules in solution. Progress was made by Staudinger in the determination of molecular weights from viscosity measurements. Unfortunately, the effect of solvents on the shape of the dissolved polymer molecules was not recognized at that time.

Staudinger's values were based on the erroneous assumption that the intrinsic viscosity $[\eta]$ was directly proportional to the molecular weight. Thus, although his molecular-weight values were higher than the unextrapolated values obtained by measurement of colligative properties, they were considerably smaller than those now accepted as correct. The viscosity method and the many other indirect and direct techniques for the determination of molecular weights will be discussed in this chapter.

3-1   VISCOSITY

As explained under the subject of rheology in Sec. 2-1, the intrinsic viscosity is the intercept obtained by extrapolating the straight line obtained when η_{sp}/C is plotted against C. The specific viscosity η_{sp} may be obtained from simple measurements of the time of flow of the solvent (t') and of the solution (t) in a capillary viscometer such as an Ubbelohde viscometer. Thus

$$\eta_{sp} = \frac{t}{t'} - 1 \qquad (3\text{-}1)$$

Viscosity–flow-time equation

The time of flow for a liquid between a fixed mark in a capillary viscometer at constant temperature is related to Poiseuille's equation for streamline flow. Provided values for the constants are known and the relationships are linear, the average molecular weight may be calculated from the Mark-Houwink equation.

3-2   NUMBER AVERAGE MOLECULAR WEIGHT

The average-molecular-weight values $(\overline{M}_v)$ obtained by viscosity techniques are between the number average $\overline{M}_n$ and weight average $\overline{M}_w$ and closer to the latter. When the values for the exponent A in the Mark-Houwink equation are less than 0.7, $\overline{M}_w$ and $\overline{M}_v$ are similar.

The number average $\overline{M}_n$ or arithmetic mean may be obtained by actually counting the molecules. The molecules may be counted by end-group analysis, tagged atoms, or chromophoric groups. Similar values are obtained by indirect counting, i.e., measuring the effect of the molecules on colligative properties, viz., osmometry, cryoscopy, and ebullioscopy.

The number average molecular weight $\overline{M}_n$ assumes that each molecule makes an equal contribution to polymer properties regardless of size or weight. Facetiously, this is equivalent to saying that hash made from one horse and four chickens is 80 percent chicken hash. However, the number average values $\overline{M}_n$ are obtained by similar reasoning.

Thus the number average $\overline{M}_n$ for three macromolecules with individual molecular-weight values of 150,000; 200,000; and 250,000 is $(600 \times 10^3)/3 = 200 \times 10^3$. The number average is a good index of physical properties such as impact and tensile strength but is not a good index of other properties such as flow. In the kinetics of polymerization, which will be discussed subsequently, one must know the number of molecules present; hence $\overline{M}_n$ is essential for kinetic studies.

3-3 WEIGHT AVERAGE MOLECULAR WEIGHT

Light scattering and sedimentation equilibrium (ultracentrifugation) techniques, which measure molecular size, yield weight average molecular weight $(\overline{M}_w)$ data. These values, in which each molecule contributes in accordance with its weight, are obtained by dividing the summation of the square of the molecular-weight values by the summation of the molecular weights of all the molecules present.

Thus the hash that was called 80 percent by the number-average approach would be shown to be essentially horse hash with a trace of chicken by the weight-average approach. The weight average $\overline{M}_w$ for the three macromolecules with molecular weights of 150,000; 200,000; and 250,000 would be equal to $[(150)^2 + (200)^2 + (250)^2] \times 10^6/(600 \times 10^3) = 208 \times 10^3$.

The weight average $\overline{M}_w$ is always greater than the number average $\overline{M}_n$ for polydisperse systems. Since $\overline{M}_w = \overline{M}_n$ in monodisperse systems, the ratio $\overline{M}_w/\overline{M}_n$ or $(\overline{M}_w/\overline{M}_n) - 1$ may be used as a measure of the molecular-weight distribution or as an index of polydispersity.

The z-average molecular weight $\overline{M}_z$ obtainable from measurements of the radial distribution of the refractive-index gradient in sedimentation equilibrium is greater than the weight average $\overline{M}_w$. Thus, as shown in Fig. 3-3, the distribution of molecular weights for typical nonhomogeneous polydisperse systems is as follows: $\overline{M}_z > \overline{M}_w > \overline{M}_v > \overline{M}_n$.

3-4 FRACTIONATION OF POLYMER SYSTEMS

A polydisperse system may be separated into fractions with narrower distribution ranges of molecular weight by cooling, diffusion, solvent volatilization, precipitation, elution or extraction, centrifugation, ultrafiltration through graded sieves, zone melting, and exclusion chromatographic adsorption. The discrete fractions obtained are characterized by appropriate molecular-weight determinations.

Since solubility of members of a homologous series in a specific solvent decreases as the molecular weight increases, the change in solubility parameter of a solvent system may be used for fractionation of discrete molecular-

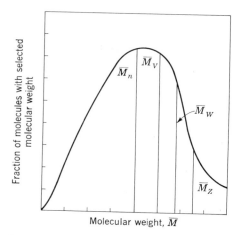

Fig. 3-3   Molecular-weight distribution in a typical polymer.

weight ranges. In this technique, the higher molecular-weight fractions are precipitated preferentially by the addition of a small amount of miscible solvents with different solubility parameters.

This preferred method may be illustrated by the addition of sufficient isopropanol to cause turbidity in a benzene solution of polystyrene at constant temperature. Attainment of equilibrium may be assured by heating the heterogeneous mixture and cooling to the specified temperature. This process is repeated on the filtrate after the precipitate has been removed. Better separations are possible with *refractionation*.

This process may be simplified by the use of precipitation chromatography based on an automatic continuous precipitation and dissolution in a column equipped with an automatic fraction collector. In elution fractionation, the lowest molecular polymers are preferentially extracted from solid polymers which have been distributed on the surface of glass beads in a column.

3-5   OSMOMETRY

Osmometers are available commercially for the determination of molecular weights $(\overline{M}_n)$ of polymers. The Fuoss-Mead osmometer consists of a semipermeable cellulosic membrane held between two grooved circular metal blocks equipped with glass capillaries and supply standpipes. Solvent and solution are added to separate standpipes. Thus the solvent passes through the semipermeable membrane until a specific hydrostatic head is established in the capillary tube. The difference in liquid heights in the two capillaries (Δh) at equilibrium is related to *osmotic pressure* or activity.

The difference in height Δh may be converted to osmotic pressure π by multiplying by gravity g and solution density ρ in the following equation: $\pi = \Delta h \rho g$. The preparation of membranes is extremely important. Useful membranes include cellophane, denitrated cellulose nitrate film, and bacterial cellulose. Some of the modern dynamic osmometers have a servo-mechanism to detect the initial flow of solvent through the membrane and then provide a measurable hydrostatic head to prevent this flow.

Since the unrestricted capillary rise in a dilute solution is a function of concentration, one may employ a modified van't Hoff equation

$$\pi = \frac{RT}{\overline{M}_n} C + BC^2 \qquad (3\text{-}2)$$

Modified van't Hoff equation for osmotic pressure

to determine the molecular weight $\overline{M}_n$. When $1/RT$ multiplied by the reduced osmotic pressure π/C is plotted against C, the intercept is $1/\overline{M}_n$.

The slope of this line is the virial constant B which is related to the difference in solubility parameters and intermolecular forces of the solvent and polymer, tacticity, temperature, and molecular weight. The slope would be 0 at the theta temperature, i.e., when the polymer chain is coiled and the solution obeys van't Hoff's law. The slope increases as the solvency increases. Hence it is desirable to use a dilute solution of a poor solvent and to make the determination at a temperature near the theta temperature.

Another type of osmometer depends on *nonequilibrium vapor-pressure-lowering* techniques. This type of instrument measures the temperature difference when a pure solvent and a polymer solution evaporate in an atmosphere saturated with solvent vapor. This technique overcomes a major disadvantage of osmometric determinations of molecular weight, i.e., the diffusion of a low-molecular-weight polymer through the semipermeable membranes.

3-6 EBULLIOSCOPY AND CRYOSCOPY

The colligative effect on osmotic pressure (22.4 atm/mole) is much greater than its effect on the increase of boiling point or of the freezing-point depression. However, ebullioscopic and cryoscopic methods may be used to determine the average molecular weight of macromolecules; these tech-

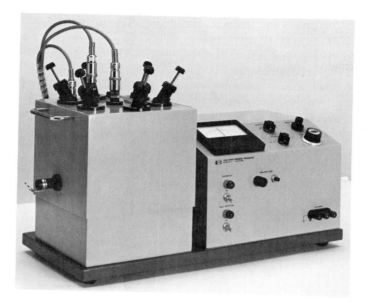

(*a*)

(*b*)

Fig. 3-4   (*a*)   Vapor-pressure osmometer (*Hewlett-Packard*).
            (*b*)   Membrane osmometer (*Hewlett-Packard*).

niques will become more popular as more sensitive instrumentation, such as differential transistors, is developed.

Even with unsophisticated measuring devices, these techniques are useful for the determination of molecular weights $\overline{M}_n$ below 50,000. Since relatively small macromolecules may pass through semipermeable membranes in osmometry, these other colligative measurements are often important supplements for osmotic-pressure measurements.

The limitations of ebullioscopic methods are readily understood by an examination of Raoult's law in which ρ is the density of the solvent and ΔH_b is the latent heat of evaporation of a gram of solvent. The thermodynamic relationships are as follows:

$$\left(\frac{\Delta T_b}{C}\right)_{C \to 0} = \frac{RT^2}{\rho \, \Delta H_b \overline{M}_n} \tag{3-3}$$

Relationship of boiling-point elevation to molecular weight

Thus the boiling-point elevation of a 1 percent solution of a polymer with an average molecular weight of 50,000 would be about $1 \times 10^{-3}\,°C$. Additional difficulties in this high-precision method are associated with the foaming tendencies of boiling solutions of polymers. Of course, all colligative measurements must be extrapolated to infinite dilution.

The limitations of cryoscopic measurements are similar but are somewhat less severe. The following thermodynamic relationships are comparable to those used for the ebullioscopic method but the magnitude of the measurements are larger and more readily obtained:

$$\left(\frac{\Delta T_F}{C}\right)_{C \to 0} = \frac{RT^2}{\rho \, \Delta H_f \overline{M}_n} \tag{3-4}$$

Relationship of freezing-point depression to molecular weight

3-7 END-GROUP ANALYSIS

Since the end groups of macromolecules are usually different from the other groups in the chain, the analysis of sensitive end groups may be used to measure the average molecular weight $\overline{M}_n$. The predominant end groups in condensation polymers are carboxyl, hydroxyl, methyl, aldehyde, ester, and amino. The end groups in addition (chain-reaction) polymers consist of unsaturated groups, fragments, of the initiators, or telogens.

End groups are readily detected when atoms such as halogen or deuterium are present. For example, when p-bromobenzoyl peroxide is used as an initiator for chain-reaction polymerization, the bromine content is related to the molecular weight $\overline{M}_n$. End-group analysis is routinely applied to the detection of amino end groups in solution of nylon in m-cresol by titration with methanolic solutions of perchloric acid. The $\overline{M}_n$ values from end-group analysis may be compared with those obtained from osmometry to evaluate the extent of branching.

3-8 LIGHT-SCATTERING MEASUREMENTS

Raleigh's investigations of the optical heterogeneity of gases were extended to liquids by Einstein and Smoluchowski in 1908. This heterogeneity is increased when dissimilar molecules are present in solution or as colloidal suspensions. Hence, light-scattering techniques were developed by Debye in 1944 for the determination of the molecular weight $(\overline{M}_w)$ of uncharged polymers.

Light passing through a solution produces an induced oscillatory dipole between the electrons in the polymer and those in the solvent. The resultant oscillation reradiates the energy as *scattered light*. This scattering, which is readily observable as turbidity (τ), or the Tyndall effect, is related to the size of the molecules and the difference between the index of refraction of the polymer and the solvent.

According to Debye, the turbidity τ or scattered flux, i.e., the energy scattered per second, is related to the heterogeneity of the system and the molecular dimensions, such as the root-mean-square end-to-end distance $[(\bar{r}^2)^{1/2}]$ as well as the average molecular weight $\overline{M}_w$. The turbidity τ is equal to the logarithm of the ratio of the intensities of the incident (I_0) and emergent (I) beams observed at right angles to the direction of the incident beam; that is, $\tau = \ln I_0/I$. The proportionality constant H in the following equation is related to the wavelength (λ^{-4}) of the incident light, the index of refraction, and the rate of change of this index with the square of the concentration (C^2). Thus the reciprocal of the molecular weight ($\overline{M}_w^{-1}$) is the intercept when Hc/τ is plotted against C at low concentrations. The constant B is similar to the virial constant described under osmometry:

$$\frac{Hc}{\tau} = \frac{1}{\overline{M}_w}(1 + 2Bc + \cdots) \tag{3-5}$$

Relationship of turbidity to molecular weight

When the molecular weight of a random coiled polymer is greater than 100,000, it is also necessary to extrapolate to zero angle of scattering (θ). This is accomplished by use of a *Zimm plot* in which extrapolations to zero concentration and zero angle are made independently when Hc/τ is plotted against $\sin^2\theta/2 + Kc$. Provided background scattering in a dust-free solution is reduced to a minimum, $\overline{M}_w$ may be measured on commercial turbidimeters by observing the turbidity τ and the specific refractive increment dn/dC.

3-9 ULTRACENTRIFUGATION

Polymer molecules remain suspended in solution under ordinary conditions because the kinetic energy of the solvent molecules (brownian motion) is very much greater than the sedimentation force of gravity. However, by use of appropriate centrifugal velocities, the gravitational field may be increased so

Fig. 3-5   Light-scattering photometer (*Hewlett-Packard*).

that the macromolecules are distributed in accordance with their molecular weights M_w.

The relative position of the solvent and solution phase is dependent on the centrifugal forces. The interface or boundary between the solvent and solution may be observed by *schlieren optics* which permit the determination of the ratio of the change of index of refraction and the change in concentration. In spite of high cost and complicated procedures, ultracentrifugation provides extremely useful information on the molecular weight M_w of monodisperse systems and on the molecular-weight distribution of polydisperse systems.

Sedimentation velocity experiments must be carried out in dilute solutions under high centrifugal forces ($250 \times 10^3 g$), at constant temperature, and the results must be extrapolated to infinite dilution. The sedimentation constant at zero concentration (S_0^{-1}) is the intercept and K is the slope when the reciprocal of the sedimentation constant (S^{-1}) is plotted against concentration C in accordance with the following equation:

$$\frac{1}{S} = \frac{1}{S_0} + \frac{K}{S_0} C \qquad (3\text{-}6)$$

Relationship of sedimentation constant to concentration

These data are obtained by observing the change in the boundary in the early stages of centrifugation. The constant K is related to solvency and shape of the macromolecules. The *diffusion constant D* is inversely proportional to the *frictional constant f* which may be calculated from the Stokes equation by assuming spherically shaped particles.

As shown in the following equation, the diffusion constant at infinite dilution (D_0) is the intercept when the diffusion constant D is plotted against C: $D = D_0(1 + Kc)$. The molecular weight may be calculated from a modified Svedborg equation in which ρ = density of the solvent and V = partial molar volume of the polymer, i.e.,

$$\overline{M}_w = \frac{S_0 R T}{D_0(1 - V\rho)} \qquad (3\text{-}7)$$

Relationship of molecular weight to diffusion constant

The sedimentation equilibrium method requires several days or weeks of continuous operation for the attainment of thermodynamic equilibrium under moderate centrifugal forces $(50 \times 10^3 g)$. Diffusion and sedimentation occur simultaneously, and a concentration gradient may be observed under these conditions. This technique may be used to characterize polymers with molecular weights in the 5,000 to 500,000 range.

Osmometry and ultracentrifugation yield similar values for molecular weight. However, when there is an unusually wide distribution range, the latter technique yields high values.

3-10 ELECTRON MICROSCOPY AND GEL PERMEATION CHROMATOGRAPHY

Magnifications of 40,000 diameters by direct *electron microscopy* and up to 200,000 diameters by photographic enlargement permit the characterization of many monodisperse macromolecules. The principal use of this technique for the study of polymers has been in the protein field. The combination of specific reactants, such as thiosemicarbazide and background staining by osmium tetroxide, has provided important biological information on protein molecules. Electron microscopy has been used to examine polydispersed macromolecules but other techniques are usually preferred for their characterization.

Naturally occurring macromolecules have been fractionated for many years by use of columns packed with aqueous dextran gels. This separation is based on the selective separation of the polymer molecules which penetrate the rigid gel structure constituting the stationary phase in these columns.

Moore used crosslinked polystyrene swollen by appropriate solvents in order to utilize this technique for the separation of a large number of synthetic polymers. It is essential that the swollen gels neither retain nor reject the penetrant molecules on the basis of polarity. Thus, by matching the solvent with the gel structure, it is possible to elute larger molecules while retaining the smaller ones. Silica gels (Porasil) may be used for the fractionation of nonpolar polymers, such as polystyrene, but they are not suitable for many more polar polymers.

This technique, called *gel-permeation chromatography* (GPC), has been adapted to automated commercial equipment. By the use of appropriate liquid-solid elution columns, it is now possible to characterize molecules as small as helium and as large as macromolecules with an average molecular weight of 100 million.

The use of the commercial GPC units is based on the constancy of the change in index of refraction with concentration (dn/dC) for specific polymers in dilute solution. The efficiency of these columns may be calculated as the number of theoretical plates (n) which is proportional to the square of the ratio of the elution volume (V_e) from the injection of the sample to the apex of the peak and the width (w) of the base, in milliliters of an idealized peak. The idealized chromatographic peak is obtained by drawing lines tangent to the sides of the actual peak obtained from a chromatogram of a single pure substance.

$$n = \left(\frac{4V_e}{w}\right)^2$$

(3-8)

GPC equation for calculating the number of theoretical plates

Sigmoidal curves are obtained when the elution volume is plotted against the logarithm of molecular weight. However, a linear relationship may be approximated in regions which are sufficiently large to make the technique extremely useful. Thus, when bulkiness, branching, hydrogen bonding, and size are considered, GPC techniques may be used to characterize a wide variety of natural and synthetic polymers.

The elution volume is related to flow rate, sample size, type of solvent, and temperature. Hence it is advisable to calibrate each column, using samples of known molecular weight under similar test conditions. Since this fractionation is based on the size and shape of the macromolecule, it is essential that the degree of branching of the control be similar to that of the unknown polymers.

All these techniques may be used for almost any system. However, there is usually a preferred method based on convenience, ease of operation, know-how, availability of equipment, and the nature of the polymeric system.

REFERENCES

Almin, K. E.: Calibration of GPC Columns, *ACS Div. Polymer Chem., Polymer Preprints,* **9**(1):727 (1968).

Altgelt, K. H., and J. C. Moore: Gel Permeation Chromatography, in M. J. R. Cantow (ed.), "Polymer Fractionation," chap. 4, Academic Press, Inc., New York, 1967.

Battista, O. A.: "Fundamentals of High Polymers," chap. 4, Reinhold Publishing Corporation, New York, 1958.

Benoit, H., Z. Grubisic, et al.: Gel Permeation Chromatography, *J. Polymer Sci.,* **M5**:753 (1967).

Bonnar, R. O., M. Dimbat, and F. H. Stross: "Molecular-Average Molecular Weights," Interscience Publishers, Inc., New York, 1958.

Cragg, L. H., and H. Hammerschlag: The Fractionation of High Polymeric Substances, *Chem. Rev.*, **39**:83 (1946).

Debye, P. J.: Light Scattering Analysis, *J. Appl. Phys.*, **15**:338 (1944).

————: How Giant Molecules Are Measured, *Sci. Am.*, **197**:90 (1957).

Edsall, J. T.: in J. T. Edsall and K. Bailey (eds.), "The Proteins," vol. 1B, p. 549, Academic Press, Inc., New York, 1953.

Flory, P. J.: "Principles of Polymer Chemistry," chap. 7, Cornell University Press, Ithaca, N.Y., 1953.

Goldfinger, G., W. P. Hohenstein, and H. F. Mark: *J. Polymer Sci.*, **2**:503 (1947).

Johnson, J. F., and R. S. Porter: "Analytical Gel Permeation Chromatography," John Wiley & Sons, Inc., New York, 1968.

Kerker, M.: *Ind. Eng. Chem.*, **60**(10):31 (1968).

Kuhn, W.: *Kolloid-Z.*, **68**:2 (1939).

Margerison, D., and G. C. East: "Introduction to Polymer Chemistry," chap. 2, Pergamon Press, New York, 1967.

Mark, H. F., and G. S. Whitby (eds.): "Collected Papers of Wallace Hume Carothers on High Polymeric Substances," Interscience Publishers, Inc., New York, 1940.

————: "Frontiers in Chemistry," vol. 5, Interscience Publishers, Inc., New York, 1948.

McIntyre, D.: Light Scattering, *ASTM, Spec. Techn. Publ.* 247, p. 27, 1948.

Meares, P.: "Polymers—Structure and Bulk Properties," chap. 3, D. Van Nostrand Company, Inc., Princeton, N.J., 1965.

Meyer, K. H., and H. F. Mark: *Ber.*, **61**:593 (1928).

Miller, M. L.: "The Structure of Polymers," chaps. 1 and 2, Reinhold Publishing Corporation, New York, 1966.

Moore, J. C.: Gel Permeation Chromatography, *J. Polymer Sci.*, **A2**:835 (1964).

Morgan, P. W.: "Condensation Polymers by Interfacial and Solution Methods," chap. 10, Interscience Publishers, a division of John Wiley & Sons, Inc., New York, 1965.

O'Driscoll, K. F.: "The Nature and Chemistry of High Polymers," chap. 5, Reinhold Publishing Corporation, New York, 1964.

Price, G. F.: in P. W. Allen (ed.), "Technique of Polymer Characterization," Butterworth & Co. (Publishers), Ltd., London, 1959.

Ravve, A.: "Organic Chemistry of Macromolecules," Marcel Dekker, Inc., New York, 1967.

Rempp, P., and H. Benoit: Determination of Molecular Weight, *Rubber Chem. Technol.*, **41**(1):245 (1968).

Schmidt, A. X., and C. A. Marlies: "Principles of High-polymer Theory and Practice," McGraw-Hill Book Company, New York, 1948.

Staudinger, H.: *Ber;* **61**:2427 (1928).

————: "Die Hochmolekularen Organischen Verbindungen," Springer-Verlag OHG, Berlin, 1932.

Svedberg, T., and K. O. Pederson: "The Ultracentrifuge," Clarendon Press, Oxford, 1940.

Vaughan, M. F.: Gel Permeation Chromatography, *Nature*, **188**:55 (1960).

Weissberg, S. G., S. Rothman, and M. Wales: in G. M. Kline (ed.), "Analytical Chemistry of Polymers," Pt. II, Interscience Publishers, a division of John Wiley & Sons, Inc., New York, 1962.

Zimm, B. H., and R. W. Kelb: *J. Polymer Sci.*, **37**:19 (1959).

4

Naturally
Occurring Polymers

4-1 POLYSACCHARIDES

Carbohydrates are widely occurring compounds containing carbon, hydrogen, and oxygen. These products, which were investigated in the early part of the nineteenth century, were erroneously considered hydrates of carbon with the empirical formula $(CH_2O)_n$. These compounds are now known to be poly(hydroxyaldehydes), poly(hydroxyketones), or related products but the name carbohydrate continues to be used. The classification of these products as *monosaccharides, oligosaccharides,* and *polysaccharides* corresponds to that used for other mers and their polymeric chains.

Thus the monosaccharides are the building blocks (mers) in polysaccharides. Polymers consisting of various pentoses and hexoses are known, but the most widely occurring monosaccharide is D-glucose or β-D-glucopyranose. The early carbohydrate chemists used structural formulas similar to Fischer projections. These were superseded by perspective formulas in which all bond lengths are similar, as shown below. These were used by Boeseken in 1913 and reintroduced by Haworth in 1926.

Since the structure of a six-membered pyranose ring is not planar but resembles that of cyclohexane, one should use a more realistic *strainless nonplanar* structural formula with normal bond angles ($109.5°$). Thus there could be staggered arrangements or *chair forms* and less stable *boat forms.* There are an infinite number of conformations for the boat form, including

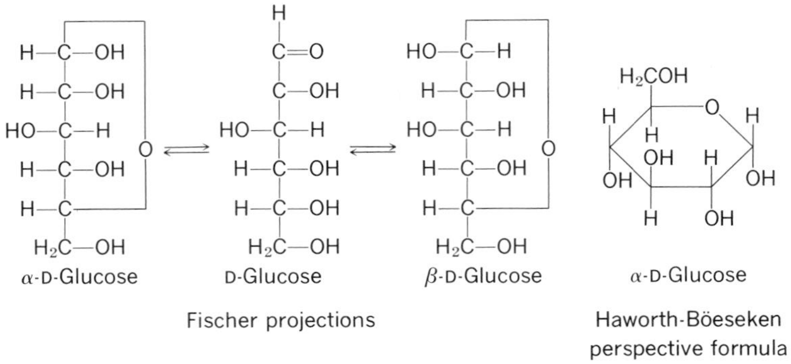

(4-1)

α-D-Glucose   D-Glucose   β-D-Glucose   α-D-Glucose

Fischer projections   Haworth-Böeseken perspective formula

Formulas for D-glucose

the halfway stage, i.e., the twist or skew boat form. However, since an energy barrier of about 11 kcal favors the more stable chair form, this is the predominant conformation.

The analogy of the pyranose and cyclohexane structures is complicated by the ease of cleavage of the acetal link in the pyranose ring and the presence of a methylol substituent on the number 5 carbon atom. In the absence of this substituent, one would expect similar stabilities for the chair forms with *equatorial bonds (planar)* and *axial bonds (perpendicular* to the plane of the ring).

However, substitution favors the conformation with the maximum number of groups in the equatorial position. Thus the equatorial form is more stable than the axial form by about 6 kcal; hence this conformation predominates in polysaccharides. These two arrangements are shown below:

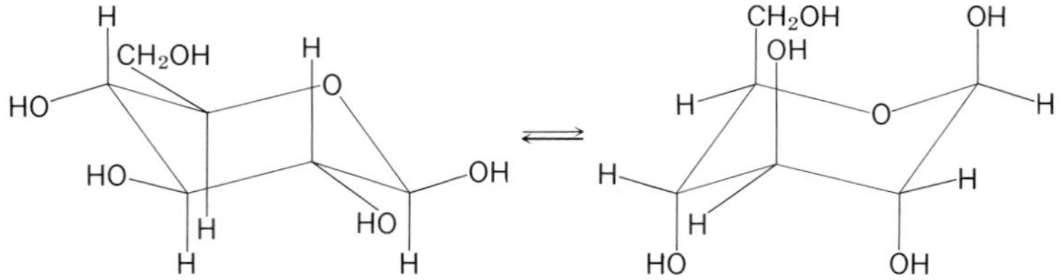

(4-2)

Chair conformations of β-D-glucopyranose

Disaccharides and oligosaccharides are dimers and oligomers of monosaccharides, such as glucose, joined by glycosidic bonds, i.e., *acetal linkages.*

Polysaccharides, like many other polymers, are high-molecular-weight polydisperse macromolecules consisting of many monosaccharide molecules joined together by glycosidic linkages. They may be homopolysaccharides, i.e., made up of only one type of monosaccharide, or heteropolysaccharides consisting of more than one type of building unit. Much of the nomenclature is not systematic because the trivial names given to these products in the eighteenth century are usually preferred to scientific names.

The principal polysaccharides are cellulose and starch. However, many other naturally occurring products such as hemicelluloses, chitin, pectins, dextrans, inulin, alginic acid, xylans, plant gums, and mucilages are also included in this classification.

Cellulose, which is the principal polysaccharide in living plants, is a polydisperse linear poly$((1 \rightarrow 4)$-β-(anhydroglucose)$)$ or poly$((1 \rightarrow 4)$-β-D-(glucopyranose)$)$ in which the $\overline{DP}$ may range from 3,500 to 10,000. Since the molecular weight of each anhydroglucose unit is 162, the molecular-weight range is 58,000 to 1,620,000. Cotton consists of over 98 percent cellulose, and wood contains 40 to 50 percent of this polysaccharide. Cellulose is also found in ramie, flax, hemp, jute, nettle fibers, grass, leaves, moss, ferns, some fungi, and in some sea animals (tunicin). It can be synthesized by *Acetobacter xylinium*.

Cotton is the seed hair of *Gossypium* plants. Wood pulp is obtained by removing lignin and hemicellulose from wood. These cellulose products are termed *native cellulose* to distinguish them from *regenerated cellulose* such as rayon. The latter is produced by the precipitation of dissolved native cellulose.

Electron microscopy shows cellulose to be an aggregate of chains (microfibrils). In the biosynthesis of cellulose by *Acetobacter xylinium*, microstrings form after an induction period of 30 sec and increase in length at the rate of 0.2 μ each minute. The diameter of these growing microstrings remains constant; hence it may be concluded that the growth is at the chain ends.

It is assumed that microfibrils may consist of an association of many cellulose chains but that there is a thermodynamically stable unit consisting of a minimum number of chains. No microstrings with a diameter of less than 50 Å have been observed. Multiple units of these microfibrils may be seen with the naked eye.

The presence of submicroscopic, anisotropic crystalline particles called *micelles* was recognized by Naegeli in 1858. Crystallinity was demonstrated by x-ray diffraction techniques by Nishikawa and Ono in 1913. The monoclinic crystalline unit that is now generally accepted was proposed by Mark and Meyer in 1928.

Hydrolysis of cellulose by enzymes yields cellobiose, which is β-D-glucopyranosyl-$(1 \rightarrow 4)$-β-glucopyranose. This structure meets the size requirement of the unit cell which has an identity period equal to the cellobiose unit (10.3 Å). As shown below, the pyranose rings in cellobiose are in the chair form and the substituents are equatorial.

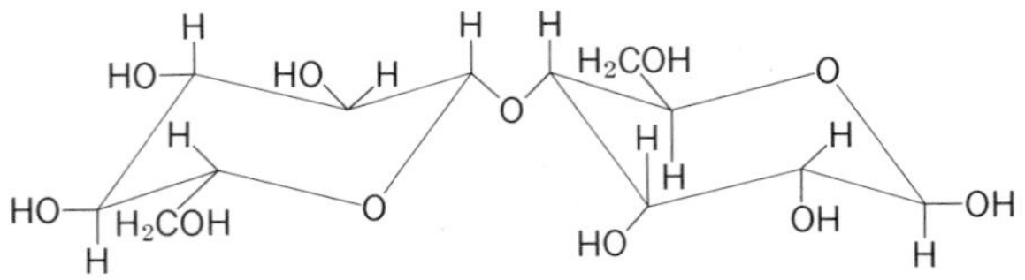

Cellobiose

β-D-Glucopyranosyl-$(1 \rightarrow 4)$-β-glucopyranose

(4-3)

Since cellulose consists of a chain made up of cellobiose units, it is merely an extension of this disaccharide with all linkages being β and in the 1,4 positions. Thus cellulose is a poly($(1 \rightarrow 4)$-β-D-glucopyranose). The empirical formula is usually given as $(C_6H_{10}O_5)_n$ or $C_6H_7O_2(OH)_3$. However, regardless of the magnitude of n there are four hydroxyls on the end pyranose rings and three hydroxyls on each of the other units in the chain. These end groups are obvious in cellobiose and in related oligomers but they are camouflaged and less readily detected in high-molecular-weight polymers.

A model of cellulose with chair conformations and with the substituents in equatorial positions demonstrates that the distances between the hydrogen atoms and the oxygen atoms on different carbons in the same chain are less than 3 Å. Thus there is ample opportunity for intramolecular hydrogen bonding. These bonds serve to anchor the anhydroglucose units and restrict the rotation of the β-acetal linkages. Thus, in contrast to the more flexible amylose which is poly($(1 \rightarrow 4)$-α-D-glucopyranose), cellulose is a stiff-chain macromolecule because of the β linkages.

The monoclinic cellulose cell has a diagonal screw parallel to the fiber axis. This facilitates intermolecular hydrogen bonding between adjacent chains. These forces are in accordance with a high degree of crystallinity and a melting point that is higher than its decomposition temperature. Thus, because of high intramolecular and intermolecular hydrogen bonding, cellulose is not thermoplastic under normal processing conditions. The density of cellulose varies from a highly amorphous polymer with a range of 1.47 to 1.49 to a higher-ordered polymer with a range of 1.59 to 1.63 g/cm^3.

Amorphous cellulose swells in water. Aqueous sodium hydroxide with a concentration greater than 13 percent will penetrate the crystalline lattice to form a loose equimolar compound presumably with the methylol hydroxyl group. This product, called *alkali* or *soda cellulose,* is important for the production of regenerated cellulose and some cellulose derivatives.

Mercerized cotton is produced by removal of the alkali. Cellulose xanthate is produced by adding carbon disulfide to the soda cellulose. The relative solubility of cellulose in controlled concentrations of aqueous sodium hydroxide facilitates the fractionation of this polymer.

The fraction of this β-linked polymer that is insoluble in 17.5 percent sodium hydroxide is called *alpha cellulose*. The soluble fraction, presumably with a lower $\overline{DP}$, is precipitated by subsequent dilution of the filtrate to 8 percent concentration of sodium hydroxide. This precipitate is called *beta cellulose*, and the soluble portion is called *gamma cellulose*. The latter consists of polyuronic acids, plant gums, xylans, mannans, etc.

Cellulose may also be dissolved in other systems capable of breaking the strong hydrogen bonds. This polysaccharide is soluble in calcium thiocyanate, zinc chloride, trifluoroacetic acid, dimethyl dibenzyl ammonium hydroxide, iron-sodium tartrate complex, and Schweitzer's reagent. The latter originally consisted of copper (II) ion and ammonia. A soluble blue solution may also be obtained when ethylene diamine is used in place of the ammonia. A colorless solution results when cadmium (II) ion is used in place of copper.

The average molecular weight of cellulose may be estimated from the viscosity of the Schweitzer's solution by using the Mark-Houwink equation, $[\eta] = K\overline{M}^{A}$. The constants may be determined by the direct measurement of the average molecular weight $\overline{M}$ by using a solution of cellulose trinitrate or cellulose acetate.

Cellulose nitrate is prepared by reacting cellulose with a mixture of nitric and sulfuric acids, which may contain a small excess of SO_3. It is never commercially nitrated to its fullest extent. Since theoretically all three hydroxyls of each anhydroglucose unit could be esterified, the fully nitrated product would have a *degree of substitution* (DS) of 3. When nitrated to DS up to 2.8 it is called guncotton, a principal constituent of smokeless powder. By adjustment of reaction conditions, nitrates with a lower DS may be produced. The nitrates with a DS of about 2.5, which are acetone-soluble, are used in coatings and cements. At a DS of 2.3, they are soluble in a mixture of diethyl ether and ethyl alcohol and are used for plastics. The solvent-soluble types may be hydrolyzed chemically or by steam ("digested") to reduce the $\overline{DP}$ and thus reduce solution viscosity, but this reaction does not appreciably affect DS.

Organic esters of cellulose are prepared by pretreating the polymer with an acid, such as glacial acetic acid, and adding an anhydride of the acid and sulfuric acid to the swollen mass. Cellulose triacetate (DS = 2.8) has an acetyl content of 43.5 percent and is insoluble in acetone. When some of the ester groups are removed by hydrolysis so that $\overline{DP}$ is equal to about 2.4, this so-called "secondary" cellulose acetate is soluble in acetone, methyl acetate, and dioxane.

Alkali cellulose may be reacted with ethyl chloride, chloroacetic acid, or ethylene oxide to produce ethyl cellulose, carboxymethyl cellulose, or hydroxyethyl cellulose. The hydroxyl groups in cellulose may also be oxidized. Cellulose may be depolymerized by ultraviolet or gamma radiation, heat, oxidation, or hydrolysis using acids, enzymes (cellulase), or microbes.

The term *hydrocellulose* is used to describe partially depolymerized cellulose. The term *holocellulose* is used to describe a mixture of cellulose and hemicellulose after all noncellulosic materials have been removed from wood. The term *hemicellulose* is used to describe the celluloselike products that are soluble in 17.5 percent sodium hydroxide, viz., β-cellulose and γ-cellulose.

The shells of crustacea and the exoskeletons of many lower animals such as insects and arachnids and some fungi consist of a linear cellulose-like homopolysaccharide in which the hydroxyl on the number 2 carbon is replaced by the acetylamino group. Thus, as shown by the chain segment below, chitin is a poly((1 → 4)(N-acetyl-2-amino-2-deoxy-β-D-glucopyranose)). Hydrolysis by chitinase from snails yields N-acetyl-2-amino-2-deoxyglucose (N-acetyl-2-glucosamine).

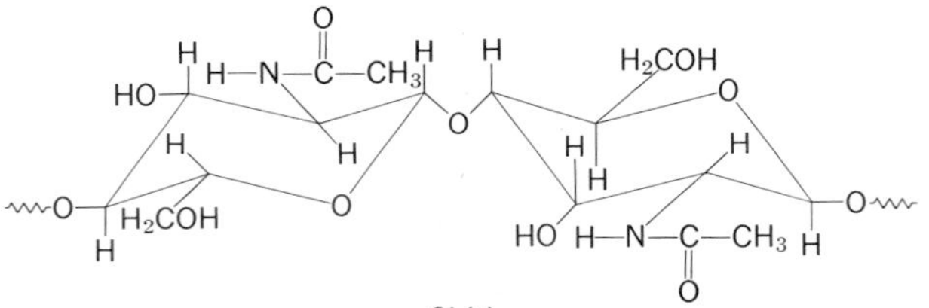

(4-4)

Chitin

Poly((1 → 4)(*N*-acetyl-2-amino-2-deoxy-β-D-glucopyranose))

Chitin, like cellulose, is soluble in Schweitzer's reagent and may be converted to a xanthate by carbon disulfide. It is also soluble in concentrated mineral acids but if the solution is allowed to stand for several hours the polysaccharide is hydrolyzed to an acid salt of D-glucosamine. Chitin has been found in fossils that are over 500 million years old. Both chitin (Kylan) and deacetylated chitin are available commercially as film and fiber.

Starch, the second most abundant polysaccharide, is a reserve carbohydrate which is stored as microscopic granules (2 to 150 μ in diameter) in various parts of plants, such as seeds, roots, tubers, and stems. This homopolysaccharide is formed by photosynthesis in corn (maize), white potatoes (farina), wheat, rice, millet, barley, cassava, tapioca, sago, arrowroot, and sorghum.

An A-type crystalline form of native starch is found in cereal grains, and a B type occurs in tubers. An intermediate C type is obtained when an aqueous paste from either type is evaporated at a temperature of about 35°C. Crystallization of an aqueous starch paste at room temperature or precipitation by freezing also yields B-type crystals. The A-type crystals are also obtained by evaporation of an aqueous starch paste at temperatures just below the boiling point (80 to 90°C). An amorphous polymer is obtained at higher temperatures.

When ethanol or isopropanol is added to aqueous starch paste, the coarse precipitate obtained exhibits an x-ray diffraction pattern and is called the V type which has a simpler structure than the other crystalline types. The V-type crystals are readily dispersible in water but revert to the B type on standing.

There are two types of starch macromolecules, viz., a linear poly((1→4)-α-D-glucopyranose) called the A fraction or amylose and a highly branched poly((1 → 4)-α-D-glycopyranose) called the B fraction or amylopectin. Native starch usually contains 20 to 30 percent of the linear amylose but some mutant varieties of grains contain amylopectin exclusively. In contrast, the starch in a recessive mutant strain of wrinkled pea is predominantly amylose.

Amylose is only slightly soluble in hot water. A 5 percent aqueous solution of amylose sets to a rigid irreversible gel on standing (*retrogradation*). In contrast, the highly branched amylopectin yields viscous but stable aqueous solutions. A suspension of native starch (amylose and amylopectin) may be obtained in cold water. An opalescent colloidal dispersion (starch paste) is obtained when this suspension is poured into hot water. This paste changes to a translucent gel when cooled because the amylopectin serves as a protective colloid and prevents the retrogradation of the amylose portion.

Molecular weights of 100,000 to 200,000 and 1 to 6 million have been reported for the amylose and amylopectin fractions, respectively. The acetal linkages in both forms may be hydrolyzed to D-glucose by acids. Amylose may be hydrolyzed to maltose by diastatic enzymes such as β-maltase. Thus, in contrast to cellulose which is made up of cellobiose units, amylose is a linear polymer made up of maltose units. Branch points are present on some of the methylolic carbons in amylopectin, as shown below:

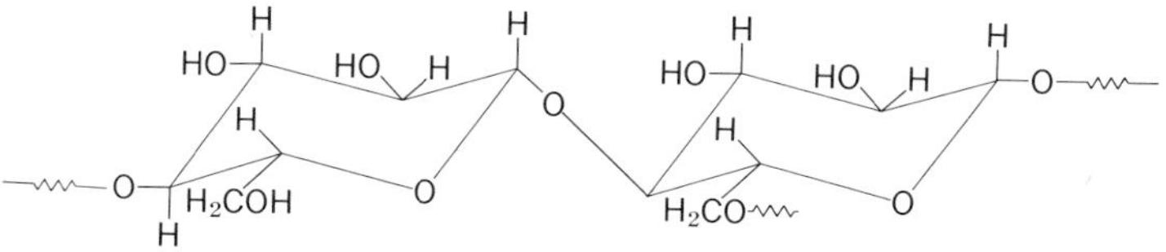

$$(4\text{-}5)$$

Amylopectin starch

The polymer chains in amylose tend to coil through their α-glucosidic linkages to assume a helical conformation. It may be observed from this tubular model that the amylose molecule is able to provide space for an iodine molecule. This accounts for the characteristic blue inclusion compound of amylose and iodine. Such an arrangement is not possible with cellulose or oligosaccharides.

Amylose absorbs as much as 20 percent by weight of iodine. Amylopectin absorbs less than 1 percent of its weight of iodine and yields a violet or pale red color. The lower-molecular-weight polymers (dextrins) obtained by heat or acid hydrolysis also do not yield a blue coloration in the presence of iodine.

The moderate-molecular-weight dextrins (erythrodextrins) turn red when iodine is added but the lower-molecular-weight achrodextrins show no color change. These dextrins, which are produced in the hot pressing of starched clothes, are also used as adhesives for paper such as postage stamps. Some water-soluble carboxyl groups are also produced by the oxidation of the primary hydroxyl groups when starch is heated. Amylase, which is present in the salivary glands, converts amylose to maltose. Exhaustive acid hydrolysis yields D-glucose.

Glycogen, which occurs in mussels, is the reserve polysaccharide in animals. All available evidence indicates that glycogen is a very high-molecular-weight, highly branched poly(α-D-glycopyranose) which resembles amylopectin but has at least twice as much branching.

Highly branched polysaccharides called *dextrans* are produced by the fermentation of sucrose by bacteria, such as *Leuconostoc dextranicum*. Polysaccharides produced by the partial hydrolysis of native dextran have been used as extenders for blood plasma. Synthetic polysaccharides have been prepared by the polymerization of acetone derivatives of D-glucose in the presence of boron trifluoride.

Many plants and some species of seaweed contain polyuronides, a type of polysaccharide in which the methylol groups have been replaced by carboxylic acid groups. This class includes poly(mannuronic acid)(alginic acid) and agar from seaweed and carrageenin (Irish moss). Poly(galacturonic acid)(pectic acid) is obtained from fruits. Gum arabic (acacia), gum tragacanth (astagalus), karaya (*Sterculia urens*), carob seed gum, slippery-elm mucilage, guar gum, cherry gum, and mesquite gum are obtained from plants. Gum olibanum (frankincense) and gum myrrh, which are mentioned in the New Testament, contain polyuronides.

The name *hemicellulose,* used to describe β- and γ-cellulose, also includes pentosans, such as xylans from esparto grass, wheat straw, barley husks, and beech wood. Mannans from vegetable ivory, galactans and glucomannans from conifers, and arabans are also classified as hemicelluloses.

Heparin, an anticoagulant which helps to prevent thrombosis, is a polysaccharide consisting of D-glucuronic acid and D-glucosamine in which the amino groups and an occasional hydroxyl group are sulfated. The structure of chondroitin sulfate found in skeletal tissue and of hyaluronic acid found in synovial fluid is related to heparin. Inulin, which is present in dahlias, dandelions, and Jerusalem artichokes, is a polysaccharide made up primarily of D-fructose units.

Haptans are polysaccharides that are of major biological importance since they have immunological specificity. The polymer chains in haptans contain D-glucuronic acids, glucosamine, and hexoses. These polysaccharides are produced by pneumococci such as pneumococcus type III and streptococci, such as hemolytic streptococcus.

Antibiotics such as streptomycin and neomycin are tri- and tetrasaccharides. These important medicinal products contain more amino groups than chitin. Streptomycin also contains guanidine groups. These and several other antibiotics also contain cyclohexyl groups with hydroxy and amino substituents in addition to the complex aminopyranoses.

REFERENCES

Burger, M.: "Bacterial Polysaccharides," Charles C. Thomas, Publisher, Springfield, Ill., 1950.

Conrad, J.: Chitin, in H. F. Mark, N. G. Gaylord, and N. M. Bikales (eds.), "Encyclopedia of Polymer Science and Technology," vol. 3, p. 695, Interscience Publishers, a division of John Wiley & Sons, Inc., New York, 1965.

Cram, D. J., and G. S. Hammond: "Organic Chemistry," 2d ed., chap. 29, McGraw-Hill Book Company, New York, 1964.

Dyke, S. F.: "The Carbohydrates," Interscience Publishers, Inc., New York, 1960.

Goheen, G. E.: Chemical Reactions of Fibrous Cellulose, *Tappi*, **41**(12):737 (1958).

Guthrie, R. D., and J. Honeyman: "An Introduction to the Chemistry of Carbohydrates," Clarendon Press, Oxford, 1964.

Hermans, P. H.: "Physics and Chemistry of Cellulose Fibers," Elsevier Publishing Company, Amsterdam, 1949.

Heuser, E.: "The Chemistry of Cellulose," John Wiley & Sons, Inc., New York, 1944.

Honeyman, J.: "Recent Advances in the Chemistry of Cellulose and Starch," Interscience Publishers, Inc., New York, 1960.

Kenyon, W. O.: Cellulose Chemistry, *Ind. Eng. Chem.*, **43**(4):820 (1951).

Meyer, K. H.: "Natural and Synthetic High Polymers," 2d ed., Interscience Publishers, Inc., New York, 1959.

Nessan, A. H., G. K. Hunger, and S. S. Sternstein: Cellulose, in H. F. Mark, N. G. Gaylord, and N. M. Bikales (eds.), "Encyclopedia of Polymer Science and Technology," vol. 3, p. 131, Interscience Publishers, a division of John Wiley & Sons, Inc., New York, 1965.

Ott, E., H. M. Spurlin, and M. W. Grafflin: "Cellulose and Cellulose Derivatives," vol. 5, Interscience Publishers, Inc., New York, 1955.

Percival, E. G. V.: "Structural Carbohydrate Chemistry," Prentice-Hall, Inc., Englewood Cliffs, N.J., 1950.

Pigman, W.: "The Carbohydrates," Academic Press, Inc., New York, 1957.

Smith, F., and R. Montgomery: "The Chemistry of Plant Gums and Mucilages," Reinhold Publishing Corporation, New York, 1959.

Whistler, R. L., and C. L. Smart: "Polysaccharide Chemistry," Academic Press, Inc., New York, 1953.

————: "Methods in Carbohydrate Chemistry," vol. 3, Academic Press, Inc., New York, 1963.

4-2 PROTEINS AND NUCLEIC ACIDS

The term *protein* is derived from the Greek word *proteios* which means prime, or chief, or *protos* which connotes of first importance. This is an appropriate name for this diversified group of biopolymers which are essential to all forms of life and are of prime importance in sustaining the life process in plants and animals.

Proteins may be classified as water-soluble, *globular*, spheroid-shaped, monodisperse macromolecules and water-insoluble, *fibrillar*, hairlike proteins. The latter general class includes silk, wool, and hair. Another member of this class, collagen, is converted into water-soluble gelatin when heated in boiling water.

Proteins have also been classified as simple proteins (polyamides) and conjugated proteins (proteids). The simple proteins (polyamides) may be subclassified primarily on the basis of solubility in selected aqueous solutions. These classes range from water-soluble protamines and albumins to prolamines which are insoluble in either water or alcohol but are soluble in aqueous alcohol. The conjugated proteins, such as glycoproteins, yield when hydrolyzed a prosthetic group, such as a saccharide, in addition to the amino acids. Proteins may also be classified in accordance with their activity as enzymes, hormones, etc., or in accordance with specific functions or commercial use.

In addition to their use as food and clothing, proteins were used by the ancients as glues and as binders for pigments. Animal blood, fish protein, soybean protein, zein (maize), and casein are used as glues and sizings today. Casein has also been used in water paints and as a moldable plastic (Galalith or milkstone). The latter, like zein fibers (Vicara), and animal hides (leather) are made more resistant to water and bacterial attack by tanning or embalming in an aqueous solution of formaldehyde or other crosslinking agents. The extensive use of proteinaceous fibers such as silk and wool in previous eras is well known.

Proteins, like polysaccharides, are heteropolymers, since they contain other atoms in the polymer backbone in addition to the carbon atoms. The structure of polyamide chains in proteins is simpler than that of the polysaccharides which contain anhydroglucose groups. All simple proteins contain peptide linkages

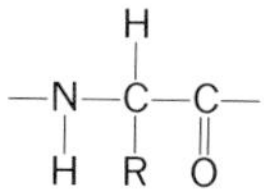

$$-N-\underset{\underset{R}{|}}{\overset{\overset{H}{|}}{C}}-\underset{O}{\overset{||}{C}}-$$

Polyamides having a molecular weight of less than 10,000 are called *peptides* (oligomers). The simplest peptide molecule could be represented by the (dimer) glycyl glycine:

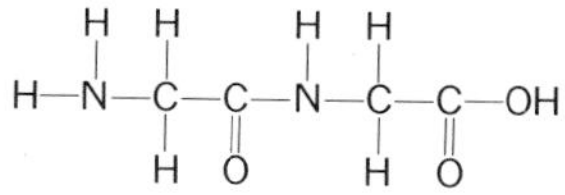

$$H-N-\underset{\underset{H}{|}}{\overset{\overset{H}{|}}{C}}-\underset{O}{\overset{||}{C}}-N-\underset{\underset{H}{|}}{\overset{\overset{H}{|}}{C}}-\underset{O}{\overset{||}{C}}-OH$$

which contains only one peptide link.

There are over 20 different α-amino acids

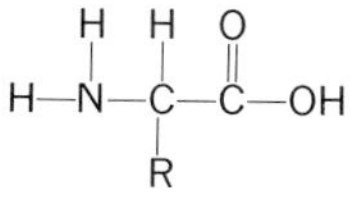

$$H-N-\underset{\underset{R}{|}}{\overset{\overset{H}{|}}{C}}-\underset{O}{\overset{||}{C}}-OH$$

that serve as building blocks for proteins. With the exception of the lowest member of the series, viz., glycine

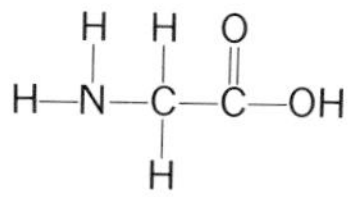

$$H-N-\underset{\underset{H}{|}}{\overset{\overset{H}{|}}{C}}-\underset{O}{\overset{||}{C}}-OH$$

all naturally occurring amino acids are optically active l isomers. The other l-α-amino acids have different R groups which are present as pendant groups on the polypeptide chain. They are often abbreviated, e.g., gly(glycine), ala(alanine), and these abbreviations are shown in appropriate sequence in the chain, e.g., (-gly-ala-gly-). The names and formulas for the other α-amino acids may be found in any elementary organic or biochemistry textbooks.

Proteins, like α-amino acids and peptides, e.g., glycyl glycine

$$H-N-\underset{\underset{H}{|}}{\overset{\overset{H}{|}}{C}}-\underset{\overset{||}{O}}{C}-N-\underset{\underset{H}{|}}{\overset{\overset{H}{|}}{C}}-\underset{\overset{||}{O}}{C}-OH$$

contain both acid and basic groups and hence are *amphoteric electrolytes*. The solid amino acids exist as inner salts or *dipolar ions* (zwitterions)

$$H^+-N-\underset{\underset{H}{|}}{\overset{\overset{H}{|}}{C}}-\underset{\overset{R}{|}}{\overset{\overset{H}{|}}{C}}-\underset{}{\overset{\overset{O}{||}}{C}}-O^-$$

There is an equilibrium between the anion $(-)$ and cation $(+)$ forms in aqueous solutions. The position of the equilibrium is dependent on the relative strengths of the amino and carboxylic acid groups and the pH of the solution.

The pH at which the concentration of the dipolar ion is at a maximum, i.e., the dissociation of the amino acids or polypeptide as an acid and base is equal, is called the *isoelectric point*. The amino acid or protein exhibits minimum solubility, conductivity, osmotic pressure, and index of refraction at the isoelectric point. At either side of this characteristic pH value, additional ions are formed. These ions will move toward oppositely charged electrodes.

This process of migration, called *electrophoresis,* may be used to separate these amphoteric electrolytes. The isoelectric point depends on the relative strengths of the amino and carboxylic groups and is characteristic for each amino acid and polypeptide. The wide distribution of isoelectric points is evident from the following partial list: glutamic acid, 3; tomato bushy stunt virus, 4.1; glycine, 6; lysozyme, 10.7.

Because of the availability of over 20 building blocks (α-amino acids) and their multitudinous potential arrangements in the chain, hundreds of thousands of different polyamides are possible. The variation in properties of proteins found in the body ranges from the elastic keratin in the hair to the horny variety found in the fingernails. The differences in properties are dependent on the sequence and the relative amounts of different amino acids in the chains and the characteristic morphology of the specific proteins.

When proteins are hydrolyzed by acids, alkalies, or proteolytic enzymes, the products consist of mixtures of amino acids or their salts. These acids may be separated by electrophoresis or paper chromatography. Martin and Synge, who developed the latter technique in 1944, were awarded the Nobel Prize in 1952.

The relative movement or travel of amino acids or di- or tripeptides in paper chromatography depends on their relative *hydrophilic* and *lyophilic* character. The technique involves partitioning of these components between the stationary phase (water adsorbed on paper) and the moving phase (an organic solvent such as butanol).

The more lyophilic compounds, which are more compatible with the organic solvent, travel faster and hence farther than the more hydrophilic compounds. The rate of travel of the amino acid to that of the organic solvent, i.e., the rate of flow (R_f), is observed by adding ninhydrin which produces a pigment by reacting with the amine groups in the amino acids. The rate of flow R_f which is characteristic for each amino acid increases with molecular weight and decreases as the number of branches and polar groups increases.

A method for determining the sequences of amino acids in proteins was developed by Sanger who was awarded the Nobel Prize in 1958. This technique consists in labeling the end groups by reacting the free amino chain ends with 2,4-dinitrofluorobenzene to form a bright yellow dinitrophenyl-amino derivative that is stable to hydrolysis. Since hydrolysis yields a dinitrophenylamino acid, the terminal group can be identified. A sequence of 246 amino acid residues in chymotrypsinogen has been identified by this technique. Several other methods for end-group analysis of proteins are also available.

As mentioned previously, proteins, unlike most synthetic polymers, are monodisperse; i.e., they are heterocopolymers with specific molecular weights. Thus the molecular-weight values obtained by osmometry ($\overline{M}_n$) and centrifugation ($\overline{M}_w$) are identical. The molecular-weight values vary from 5,733 for insulin to 40 million for tobacco mosaic virus. The molecular weight of tomato bushy stunt virus is 7,600,000.

When the keratin in wool or hair is hydrolyzed, one of the amino acids produced is cystine. Since this is a tetrafunctional building block

$$\left(-S-\overset{\overset{\displaystyle H}{|}}{\underset{\underset{\displaystyle H}{|}}{C}}-\overset{\overset{\displaystyle H}{|}}{\underset{\underset{\underset{\displaystyle H}{|}}{\overset{\displaystyle N-H}{}}}{C}}-\overset{\overset{\displaystyle O}{\|}}{C}-OH \right)_2$$

its presence in the polymer chain permits crosslinking. The insolubility of wool and hair and many of their properties are related to the disulfide crosslinks present in this network polymer.

Both hot and cold waving of hair can be explained on the basis of the disulfide crosslinks (—S—S—) present. When these crosslinks are cleaved

by steam, pendant sulfhydryl

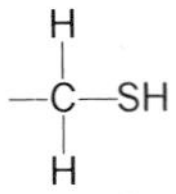

$$\begin{array}{c} H \\ | \\ -C-SH \\ | \\ H \end{array}$$

and unstable sulfenic acid

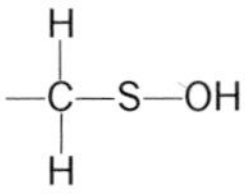

$$\begin{array}{c} H \\ | \\ -C-S-OH \\ | \\ H \end{array}$$

groups are produced. The latter lose hydrogen sulfide (H_2S) and yield aldehyde groups

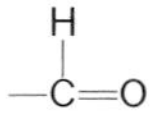

$$\begin{array}{c} H \\ | \\ -C=O \end{array}$$

which form new crosslinks with amino groups on adjacent protein chains. Similar crosslinking takes place when formaldehyde reacts with other proteins:

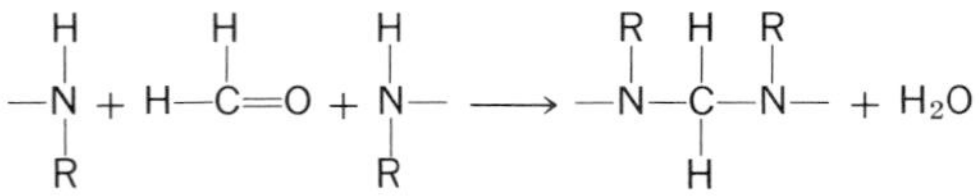

$$\begin{array}{ccccccc} H & & H & & H & & R\ H\ R \\ | & & | & & | & & |\ \ |\ \ | \\ -N & + & H-C=O & + & N- & \longrightarrow & -N-C-N- & + & H_2O \\ | & & & & | & & |\\ R & & & & R & & H \end{array}$$ (4-6)

Reaction of formaldehyde and amino groups

In the cold-waving process, the disulfide crosslinks (—S—S—) are reduced to sulfhydryl groups

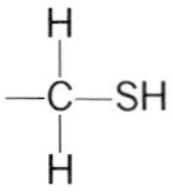

$$\begin{array}{c} H \\ | \\ -C-SH \\ | \\ H \end{array}$$

by thioglycolic acid. The crosslinks are re-formed by oxidation with sodium bromate or by a reaction with an alkylene dibromide, such as ethylene dibromide.

Wool or hair may be softened by hot water or aqueous sodium hydroxide and stretched up to 100 percent of the original length. These fibers obey Hooke's law and return to their original length when the tension is released.

When globular proteins are heated or exposed to acids, alkalies, detergents, or solvents such as alcohol or acetone, a change in properties is noted. The process is called *denaturation,* and the extent of the change depends on the degree of denaturation.   For example, there is little effect at low temperatures.   The denatured proteins are usually less soluble, noncrystalline, and physiologically inactive.

Denaturation, elasticity, and many biological activities are related to protein structure.   By use of x-ray diffraction techniques, Meyer and Mark showed an *identity period* of 7 Å along the fiber axis of fibroin in 1928.   As shown below, this identity period corresponds to a dipeptide link.   The length of an α-amino acid molecule is approximately one-half of this, or 3.5 Å.

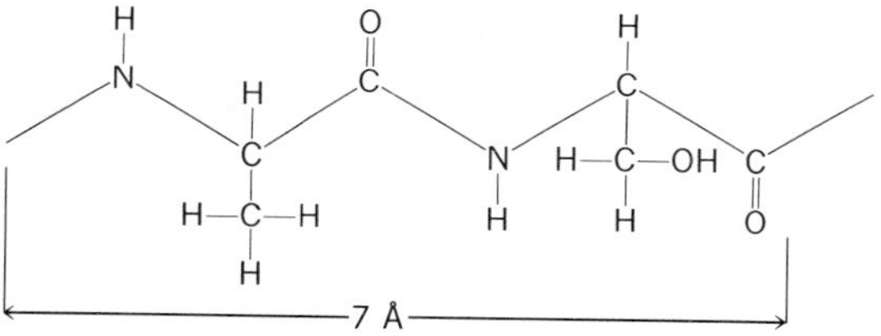

$$(4\text{-}7)$$

Dipeptide link in fibroin

It is of interest to note that the identity period of stretched hair is 3.3 Å and the identity period of collagen is 2.9 Å.   The shorter identity period of collagen is related to the dearth of hydrogen bonding between collagen chains in contrast to the extensive hydrogen bonding in fibrous proteins. The few bonds that are present in collagen are destroyed when it is dissolved in boiling water to form gelatin.

On the basis of interatomic distances calculated from x-ray diffraction data, Pauling and Corey proposed an alpha-helix conformation for fibrous proteins in 1951.   Unlike the flexible carbon-carbon or carbon-oxygen-carbon bonds, the carbon-nitrogen linkage acts as a chain stiffener and restricts rotation.   As a result of the restricted rotation, the amide groups are essentially planar, and intramolecular hydrogen bonding or chelation takes place between the carbonyl (C=O) and amine (HN—) at a distance of 2.79 Å.

The proposed alpha-helix conformation has been shown to be correct for α-keratin and also for many nonproteinaceous polymers.   The hydrogen bonding in keratin is weakened in water because of the hydrogen-bonding properties of this solvent.   Thus, helical and random arrangements may also be observed in solution, depending on the extent of retention of hydrogen bonding.   At least six different helices have been identified but the right-handed alpha helix is the most stable.

Three types of protein structure were proposed by Linderstrøm-Lang in 1952. The primary structure is related to the primary valence bonds, i.e., the sequence of amino acids in the chain. The secondary structure is related to the various conformations associated primarily with intramolecular hydrogen bonding. The tertiary structure is related to intermolecular hydrogen bonding and to crosslinking, which are also related to arrangements such as folding of the polypeptide chain.

Some of the high-molecular-weight proteins previously cited, such as tobacco mosaic virus, are nucleoproteins. The proteins and nucleic acids present in nucleoproteins may be separated in salt solutions. The nucleoproteins, which are essential components of all living matter, were obtained from pus by Miescher in 1869 and were isolated as proteins and pure nucleic acids by Levene in 1900.

The two types of nucleic acids are *deoxyribonucleic acid* (DNA) and *ribonucleic acid* (RNA). These were obtained originally from the thymus gland and yeast, respectively. DNA is found principally in the cell nucleus but RNA occurs both in the cell nucleus and in the cytoplasm.

Nucleic acids may be classified by molecular weight, functionalism, or origin. The molecular-weight range is from 29,000 to 6 million. The function of RNA varies but its best-known function is as a messenger. One of the origins of RNA is intracellular, i.e., ribosomal RNA.

The prosthetic groups in nucleoproteins are called *nucleotides*. These phosphoric acid esters are readily hydrolyzed to *nucleosides* and phosphoric acid. The principal difference between RNA and DNA is the absence of oxygen in the pentoses (D-furanosides) in DNA and a slight difference in the pyrimidine bases obtained by hydrolysis of these nucleosides. One of the pyrimidine bases in DNA has a methyl group (thymine). The composition of nucleoproteins and the structural formulas for the pentoses and the principal pyrimidine and purine bases are as follows:

Nucleoproteins $\longrightarrow$ protein + nucleotide $\longrightarrow$ phosphoric acid + nucleoside $\longrightarrow$ pentose (ribose or deoxyribose) + pyrimidines + purines.

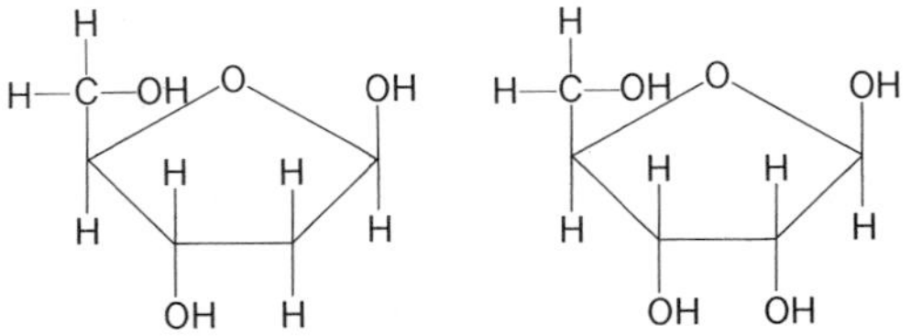

$$(4\text{-}8)$$

D Deoxyribose   D-Ribose

Structural formulas for D-riboses

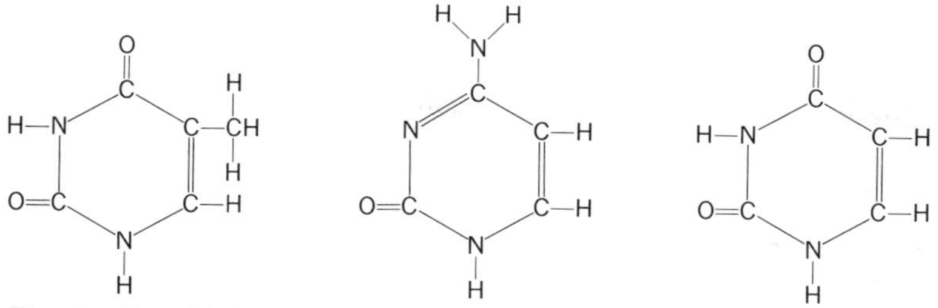

Thymine (from DNA)   Cystosine (from DNA + RNA)   Uracil (from RNA)

(4-9)

Structural formulas for primidine bases

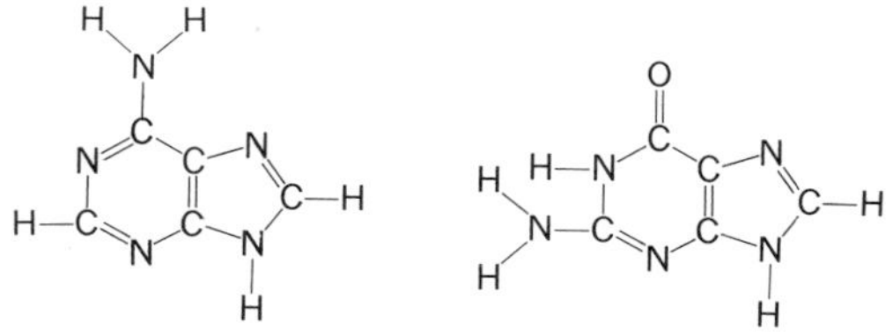

Adenine   Guanine

(4-10)

Structural formulas for purine bases

The structural formula for the nucleotide (adenylic acid) shown below includes the nucleoside (adenosine) and D-ribose. The polynucleotides consist of mononucleotides in which the methylolic pentose groups are esterified by phosphates.

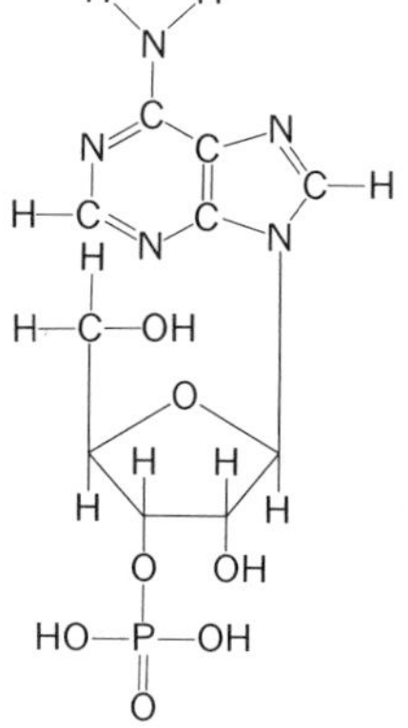

(4-11)

Adenylic acid (adenosine 3'-phosphate)(nucleotide)

Watson and Crick, who were awarded the Nobel Prize, proposed a double-strand helix for DNA. The normal RNA molecule is believed to be a single-strand helix. These structures may be shown by using a cylinder and Dreiding models. One may also purchase an inexpensive kit to show the interlocking spirals and hydrogen bonding in DNA. There are several possible conformations but the most probable one is that with 10 or 11 nucleotides per turn.

The purine and pyrimidine moieties are present as hydrogen-bonded pairs in characteristic sequences in the double-strand helix of DNA. The structural formula of two of the four possible pairs, viz., adenine (A)-thymine (T) and guanine (G)-cytosine (C) are shown below. The deoxyribose is abbreviated as D to maintain simplicity in this structure. A hypothetical arrangement in a double-strand helix is also shown.

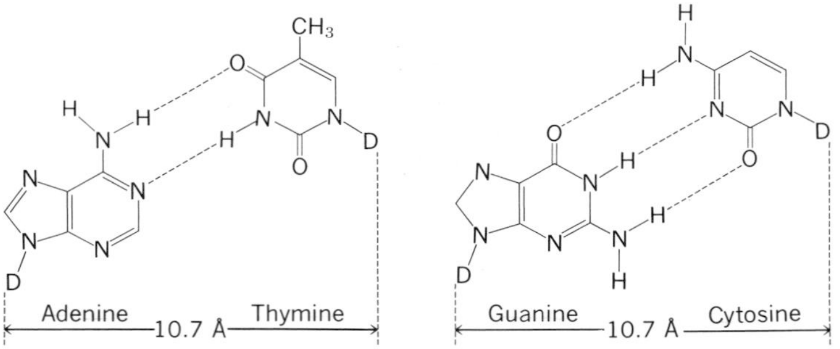

(4-12)

Hydrogen-bonded pairs of purine and pyrimidine bases

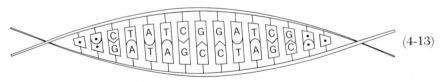

(4-13)

Simulated double-stranded helix in DNA

There is still much to be learned about nucleic acids. However, the following conclusions may be made: Life is a special arrangement of moieties. Biological instructions (heredity) are communicated with mathematical precision by chromatin and DNA nucleoprotein (genes) which are present in the chromosomes. RNA communicates information from DNA to the proteins and enzymes to direct the assembly of amino acids in protein syntheses. The possible arrangements of the four pyrimidine and purine bases yield

20 different combinations which are comparable to the number of available α-amino acids. In spite of the importance of the knowledge of the molecular structure of these biopolymers, this knowledge is but the first step in solving the larger problem of the life process.

REFERENCES

Chargaff, E., and J. N. Davidson: "The Nucleic Acids," vols. I–III, Academic Press, Inc., New York, 1955, 1960.

Doty, P.: *Sci. Am.*, **197**:173 (1957).

Edsall, J. T.: in R. E. Burke and O. Gummit (eds.), "High Molecular Weight Organic Compounds," Interscience Publishers, Inc., New York, 1949.

Fox, S., and J. Foster: "Protein Chemistry," John Wiley & Sons, Inc., New York, 1957.

Kornberg, A.: *Sci. Am.*, **219**(4):64 (1968).

Linderstrøm-Lang, K.: "Proteins and Enzymes," Stanford University Press, Stanford, Calif., 1952.

Meyer, K. H.: "Natural and Synthetic High Polymers," 2d ed., Interscience Publishers, Inc., New York, 1959.

Neurath, H., and K. Bailey: "The Proteins," Academic Press, Inc., New York, 1953.

Pauling, L., and R. B. Corey: *Proc. Natl. Acad. Sci. U.S.*, **37**:729 (1951); **39**:253 (1953).

Perutz, M. F.: "Proteins and Nucleic Acids," Elsevier Publishing Company, Amsterdam, 1962.

Potter, V. R.: "Nucleic Acid Outlines," I, Burgess Publishing Company, Minneapolis, 1960.

Sahyun, M.: "Outline of the Amino Acids and Proteins," Reinhold Publishing Corporation, New York, 1944.

Sanger, F., and H. Tuppy: *Biochem. J.*, **49**:463 (1951).

Scheraga, A. A.: "Protein Structure," Academic Press, Inc., New York, 1961.

Springall, H. D.: "The Structural Chemistry of Proteins," Butterworth Scientific Publications, London, 1954.

Wrinch, D.: "Chemical Aspects of Polypeptide Chain Structures and the Cyclol Theory," Plenum Press, New York, 1965.

4-3 MISCELLANEOUS NATURALLY OCCURRING POLYMERS

Natural rubber is one of the most important biologically inactive, naturally occurring polymers. It is found as an aqueous milky juice or latex in microscopic tubules which are present between the bark and the cambian layer in the hevea plant (*Hevea braziliensis*). Less than 1 percent of the natural rubber used is obtained from wild rubber trees in Central and South America.

The bulk of this product is obtained by tapping hevea plants on the rubber plantations and collecting the latex that seeps out from the cambian layer.

Rubber may also be obtained from several other related plants such as *Ficus elastica*. This rubber plant is a native of Asia and is used principally as a decorative plant. Rubber is also present in vines of the milkweed family (*Cryptostegia grandiflora*), goldenrod (*Solidago*), dandelions (*Taraxacum officinale* and *Kok-saghyz*), and the guayule shrub (*Parthenium argentatum*).

Cahuchu or "weeping wood," which was called *India rubber* by Priestley, was used by the Aztecs for waterproofing clothing and for making tlachtli balls centuries before Columbus arrived in the West Indies. The disadvantageous thermoplasticity of natural rubber was circumvented by Macintosh who used a cloth sandwich-type construction. Charles Goodyear accomplished similar objectives by inserting a few sulfur crosslinks in the rubber macromolecule. Thus the structure of Goodyear's vulcanized rubber was comparable to wool. In contrast, Nelson Goodyear's highly crosslinked ebonite was a hard nonelastic solid.

The empirical formula for rubber (C_5H_8) was suggested by Faraday in 1826. The pyrolytic product (C_5H_8) was named *isoprene* by Williams in 1860. This monomer was converted to an elastic solid by Bouchardat in 1879. Tilden proposed the structural formula

$$H_2C{=}C{-}C{=}CH_2$$
$$\overset{CH_3}{|} \qquad \overset{H}{|}$$

for isoprene in 1892. Harries obtained levulinic aldehyde

$$H_3C{-}\overset{\overset{O}{\|}}{C}{-}\overset{\overset{H_2}{|}}{C}{-}\overset{\overset{H_2}{|}}{C}{-}\overset{\overset{H}{|}}{C}{=}O$$

by the hydrolysis of the reaction product of rubber and ozone in the early part of the twentieth century.

That stretched hevea rubber is crystalline was demonstrated by Katz by use of x-ray diffraction techniques in 1925. Subsequently, Meyer and Mark suggested that this was a cis isomer of polyisoprene and that gutta-percha was a trans isomer. The latter, which is obtained from *Palaquium oblongifolium* trees in the East Indies, is similar to balata from *Mimusops globosa* and the bully tree in South America.

The nonrubbery isomer (gutta-percha or balata) is crystalline because the trans configuration facilitates good fitting of adjacent polymer chains. This isomer may exist as an α form (planar) which has an x-ray identity period of 8.7 Å and a melting point of 74°C. It transforms to the β form (nonplanar) when heated above its transition temperature of 68°C. The β form has an x-ray identity period of 4.8 Å and a melting point of 64°C. As shown in the structural formulas, these identity periods correspond to the monomer and dimer of isoprene.

Hevea rubber is amorphous at room temperature because the steric hindrance in the cis configuration contributes to disorder, i.e., randomly oriented chains. This polydisperse isomer has a $\overline{DP}$ of 1,000 to 5,000 which corresponds to a molecular-weight range of 68,000 to 340,000. The x-ray identity period of stretched rubber is 8.2 Å. It has a glass transition temperature (T_g) of $-85°C$ and a melting point of $28°C$. Projected structural formulas for these isomers of 1,4-polyisoprene are shown below.

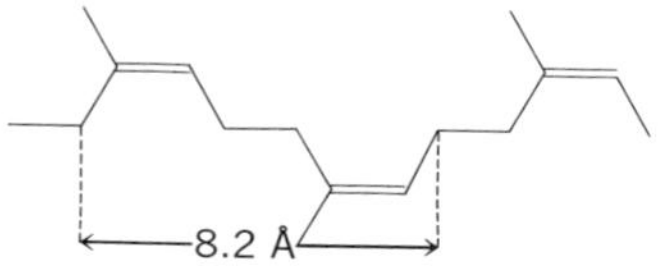

cis-1,4-Polyisoprene (rubber)

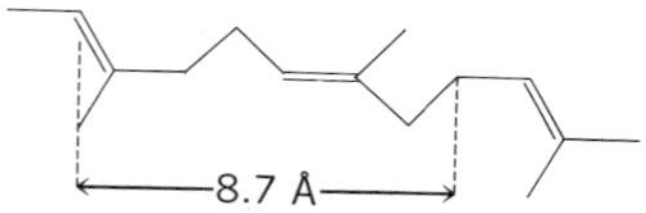

α-trans-1,4-Polyisoprene
(α-gutta-percha)

(4-14)

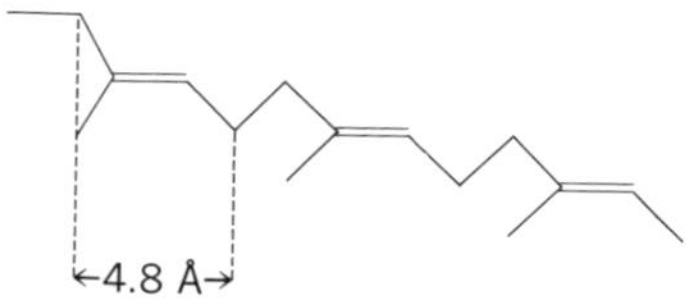

β-trans-1,4-Polyisoprene
(β-gutta-percha)

Abbreviated structural formulas for polyisoprenes

Both the *cis-* and the *trans*-polyisoprene isomers are present in chicle which occurs in the *Achras sapota* tree in Central America. This product, which is used for chewing gum, resembles some of the first synthetic rubber samples which were also mixtures of trans and cis isomers. However, *cis*-polyisoprene, which is synthesized in the presence of coordination catalysts, is highly elastic.

Staudinger showed that a similar polymeric hydrocarbon was obtained when any of the isomers of polyisoprene were hydrogenated. All these isomers of polyisoprene may be vulcanized with sulfur and chlorinated or hydrochlorinated. The saturated reaction products have similar configurations. Chlorinated rubber, rubber hydrochloride, and cyclized rubber are produced commercially. The degree of crystallinity of *cis*-polyisoprene increases as the unsaturation is decreased. When the unsaturation is reduced by about 50 percent, spherulites are evident and the x-ray diffraction pattern resembles that of simple paraffinic hydrocarbons. The degree of ordering of completely hydrogenated hevea rubber at room temperature is similar to that of the unsaturated polymer at the temperature of dry ice.

The term *long-range elasticity* is used to describe the properties of the *cis*-polyisoprene isomer. This elastomer deforms like a liquid when stretched and returns to its original form when the stress is removed.

This high degree of flexibility or internal mobility of the natural-rubber elastomer, in contrast to the nonelasticity of gutta-percha and polyethylene, may be explained by differences in molecular structure. Rotation of a carbon-carbon bond through an arc of 120° requires only 3 kcal/mole. Thus these flexible bonds contribute to a high degree of segmental motion. The internal mobility is increased when a carbon-carbon double bond is adjacent to the single bond. Actually, the rotational energy barrier is reduced from 3 to 1.5 kcal/mole when double bonds are present on adjacent carbon atoms.

The flexibility of the natural-rubber macromolecule is also enhanced by the absence of strong intermolecular forces. The pendant methyl groups and the cis configuration lower the glass transition temperature so that viscoelasticity is assured at temperatures far below room temperature. The glass transition temperature may be lowered further by the addition of small amounts of thiol acids

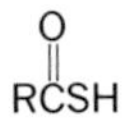

$$\text{R}\overset{\text{O}}{\overset{\|}{\text{C}}}\text{SH}$$

which introduce bulky pendant groups on the chain, as shown by the following reaction:

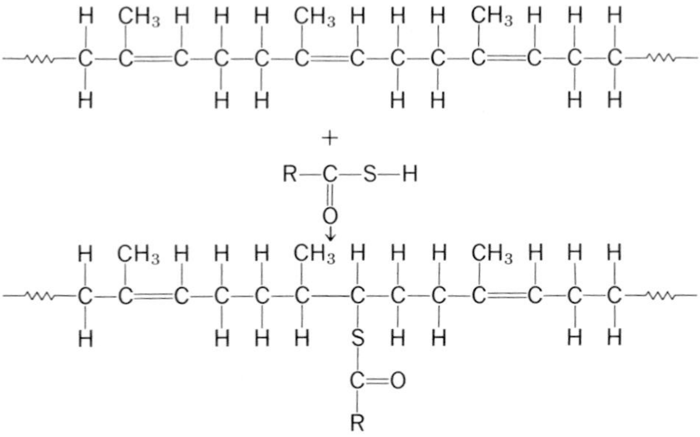

(4-15)

Reaction of rubber molecule with a thiol acid

The characteristic long-range elasticity of vulcanized rubber is dependent on the introduction of a few crosslinks such as sulfur links to produce a network structure with one crosslink for approximately 100 carbon atoms in the polymer chain. Additional crosslinks, such as in ebonite, reduce flexibility but a few crosslinks in the principal section reduce slippage between chains; this enhances reversible recovery (snap) or restoration of the original dimensions when the stress is removed.

Unstretched natural rubber is amorphous above its glass transition temperature T_g. However, because of the regularity of its structure, it does crystallize at ordinary temperatures. Crystallization is possible because of the alignment of the polymer chains along the axis of elongation which occurs after uncoiling of the chain segments. If stretched rubber is cooled quickly (racked rubber), it resembles an inelastic fiber, since the crystals prevent retraction. However, under ordinary temperature conditions, the crystallites melt when the stress is removed and the extended chains return to their normal random coiled conformations.

As stated previously, the shear stress (s) of an ideal elastic solid is proportional to the strain (γ); that is, $s = G\gamma$. However, the proportionality constant (modulus G) for cured gum rubber varies. When rubber is stretched at a constant rate, the stress (tensile) increases slowly until a strain (elongation) of about 500 percent is observed. The tensile then increases rapidly with little change in elongation. It breaks at a stress of about 3,000 psi (based on original unstretched dimensions) and at an elongation (strain) of about 800 percent.

The original high extensibility is associated with the untangling and uncoiling of noncrystalline segments, i.e., the principal sections between the sulfur crosslinks. The increase in modulus G after an elongation of about 500 percent is associated with crystallite formation which is favored by the alignment of the chains along the axis of elongation.

The significance of long-range elasticity may be appreciated by referring to the Gibbs free-energy equation which was used to explain solvency in Chap. 2: $\Delta G = \Delta H - T\Delta S$. Since the changes considered are extremely small, this will be represented as $dG = dH - TdS$.

The work done in the stretching of an elastic bond (W_{el}) is equal to the retractive force (f) multiplied by the change in length (dl), that is,

$$W_{el} = f\,dl \qquad \text{or} \qquad f = \frac{W_{el}}{dl} \qquad (4\text{-}16)$$

Stretching-force relationships

Under conditions of constant temperature and pressure, the free-energy change dG is related to the work function W_{el}, and the change in enthalpy

dH corresponds to the change in internal energy dE of the elastomer. Thus

$$f = \frac{W_{el}}{dl} = \frac{dG}{dl} = \frac{dE}{dl} - T\frac{dS}{dl} \qquad (4\text{-}17)$$

Relationship of retractive force to internal energy

The energy term dE/dl is important during the initial stretching process as the energy barrier is overcome and the chain segments uncoil but still retain considerable randomness. As stretching is continued, there is a significant *decrease in entropy* dS/dl because of a high degree of order and crystallization. Thus the energy term becomes less significant at this stage of the stretching process and $f \cong -T(dS/dl)$.

The temperature of rubber increases as it is stretched because of an irreversible frictional effect of the polymer chains (*hysteresis*) and the reversible decrease in entropy (*Joule effect*). Thus, as demonstrated by Gough in 1805, the retractive force f of an elastomer increases as the temperature is increased.

The relationship of the change in retractive force, df, with change in temperature, dT, at constant length l and pressure was investigated by Kelvin and Clausius in the 1850s. They showed that this change (df/dT) in the adiabatic stretching process was equal to the specific heat of the elastomer (C_p) per degree Kelvin (T) multiplied by the change in temperature (dT) per change in length (dl); that is,

$$\frac{df}{dT} = -\frac{C_p}{T}\frac{dT}{dl} \qquad (4\text{-}18)$$

Relationship of stretching force to temperature

This formula may be rearranged to show that, unlike most solids, an *elastomer contracts when heated*, i.e.,

$$\frac{dT}{df} = -\frac{T}{C_p}\frac{dl}{dT} \qquad (4\text{-}19)$$

Effect of temperature on contraction

The chain length of unvulcanized rubber may be decreased by mastication on a two-roll mill or in a Banbury mixer in the presence of oxygen at elevated temperatures. This mechanical breaking of carbon-carbon bonds yields fragments with unpaired electrons at the chain ends, i.e., *free-radical chains:*

$$-\!\!\!\text{\vphantom{x}}\wedge\!\!\!\wedge\!\!\!\wedge\!-\!\!\underset{\underset{\displaystyle H}{|}}{\overset{\overset{\displaystyle H}{|}}{C}}\!\cdot$$

If rubber is masticated in an oxygen-free atmosphere, the free radicals recombine and there is little if any change in $\overline{DP}$. When oxygen is present, peroxides are produced by the reaction with the free radicals.

The coupling of free radicals may also be prevented by the reaction with compounds such as alkyl mercaptans or phenyl hydrazine. These compounds are *chain transfer agents* which donate labile atoms to the free radicals and thus produce new free radicals, as follows:

$$\underset{\substack{\text{Rubber free}\\\text{radical}}}{R\cdot} \;+\; \underset{\substack{\text{Chain transfer}\\\text{agent}}}{HSR} \;\longrightarrow\; \underset{\text{Stable fragment}}{RH} \;+\; \underset{\text{Free radical}}{\cdot SR}$$

The stable chain fragments that are produced by the reaction with these chain transfer agents (erroneously called *peptizers*) have lower molecular weights than the unmilled rubber and hence are more readily processed (compounded).

The term *compounding* is used to describe the addition of sulfur and other ingredients to rubber. The time of vulcanization is decreased by the addition of organic accelerators such as 2-mercaptobenzothiazole (Captax). The wear resistance is increased by the addition of carbon black as a reinforcing agent, and the resistance to deterioration is increased by the addition of antioxidants such as phenyl-β-napththylamine.

Bitumens were used by the ancients for caulking and waterproofing. Large deposits of natural asphalt were discovered by Raleigh at Trinidad Lake (West Indies) in 1595 and by Gilson (Gilsonite) in Utah in 1870. A large deposit was also discovered at Bermudez Lake (Venezuela). These sources account for less than 5 percent of bitumens used. Petroleum still residues are widely used as alternatives for the native resinous products.

Asphalt is used as a binder for aggregates in highway construction, as an ingredient of roofing and flooring compositions, and for the waterproofing of buildings. In many instances it is converted to a nonnewtonian fluid by blowing air into the hot asphalt melt. Asbestos-filled bitumens are used as cold-molding compositions. The thermoplasticity of these moldings may be reduced by the incorporation of linseed or tung oil plus a metallic salt of an organic acid (drier), such as lead naphthenate.

Approximately 25 percent of all woody material is lignin. This undesirable product is removed in the manufacture of paper but is used advantageously in the manufacture of pressed board (Masonite). Lignin is a complex polyphenolic material with a molecular weight in the 4,000 range.

Lignin sulfonic acid is used as a wetting agent, as an extender of phenolic resins, and for the production of vanillin. This macromolecule consists of propylphenyl units which are linked together through a phenolic oxygen. There is a slight difference in the structure of softwood and hardwood lignins.

Rosin is one of the products of the group called naval stores. Pine and fir resins were used by the ancients. Rosin is one of the constituents of the exudate from pine trees. The principal source today is from southern pine. It may be obtained from the tree, by extraction from stumps, or from tall oil. Rosin is essentially an anhydride of abietic acid. It is used as a paper sizing, as a potting compound, and in the production of linoleum and yellow laundry soap.

Shellac was used as an alcoholic solution (spirit varnish) as one of the pioneer polymer coatings. It was also used as a pioneer molding resin and was the principal polymer used for molding the first phonograph records. Shellac consists of poly(hydroxy aliphatic carboxylic acids) such as aleuritic acid (9,10,16-trihydroxypalmitic acid).

Humic acid is found as a component of recent fossil fuels which have not been converted completely to coal. These acids may be obtained from peat or brown coal or from deposits that are essentially humic acid. Humic acid is used in drilling muds and as a soil conditioner.

Mantell classified natural resins in accordance with their geographical source. These fossil resins include dammar (α- and β-resene) from the East Indies, batu, and a similar resin from Borneo. Manila, Congo, and Kauri, which are included collectively under the term *copals*, are produced in the Philippines and the East Indies. Pontiak, which is produced in Borneo, is also a copal resin.

Other natural resins are the gum accroides from Australia, elemi from Eastern Mediterranean islands, sandarac from Morocco, and amber from the Baltic areas. Recent resins obtained by tapping trees are characterized by a high volatile content. Semifossil resins from dead trees have less volatiles present, and fossil resins from ancient trees are devoid of any volatile solvents. Prior to the introduction of oil-soluble Bakelite resins and alkyds, these natural resins were in great demand for varnish production. Like silk, wool, hevea, and cellulose derivatives, these polymers are still available. However, they must now compete with quality-controlled synthetic resins.

REFERENCES

Abraham, H.: "Asphalts and Allied Substances," 6th ed., D. Van Nostrand Company, Inc., Princeton, N.J., 1960–1963.

Barron, H.: "Modern Rubber Chemistry," Chapman & Hall, Ltd., London, 1947.

Bloomfield, G. F.: in W. J. S. Naunton (ed.), "The Applied Science of Rubber," p. 72, E. Arnold (Publishers) Ltd., London, 1961.

Brauns, F. E.: "The Chemistry of Lignin," Academic Press, Inc., New York, 1952.

Cook, P. G.: "Latex: Natural and Synthetic," Chapman & Hall, Ltd., London, 1956.

Davis, C., and J. T. Blake: "The Chemistry and Technology of Rubber," Reinhold Publishing Corporation, New York, 1937.

Dunbrook, R. F., and V. N. Morris: "The Science of Rubber," Reinhold Publishing Corporation, New York, 1934.

Fisher, H. L.: "Chemistry of Natural and Synthetic Rubbers," Reinhold Publishing Corporation, New York, 1957.

Garvin, G. S.: in C. E. Schildknecht (ed.), "Polymer Processes," chap. 16, Interscience Publishers, Inc., New York, 1956.

Hicks, E.: "Shellac," Chemical Publishing Company, Inc., New York, 1961.

Hoiberg, A. J.: "Bituminous Material: Asphalts, Tar and Pitches," Interscience Publishers, a division of John Wiley & Sons, Inc., New York, 1964.

LeBras, J., R. Pautrat, and C. P. Pinazzi: in E. M. Fettes (ed.), "Chemical Reactions of Polymers," chap. 2, Interscience Publishers, a division of John Wiley & Sons, Inc., New York, 1964.

Mantell, C. L., C. W. Kopf, J. L. Curtis, and E. M. Rogers: "The Technology of Natural Resins," John Wiley & Sons, Inc., New York, 1942.

Meyer, K. H., and H. F. Mark: Cis and Trans Polyisoprene, *Ber.*, **61:**593 (1928).

Moakes, R. C. W., and W. C. Wake: Butterworth Scientific Publications, London, 1957.

Morton, M.: "Rubber Technology," Reinhold Publishing Corporation, New York, 1964.

Sanderman, W.: "Naturharze, Terpentinol, Tallol, Chenio und Technologi," Springer-Verlag OHG, Berlin, 1960.

Stern, H. L.: "Rubber: Natural and Synthetic," Maclaren and Sons, Ltd., London, 1954.

Stevens, H. P., and W. H. Stevens: "Rubber Latex," Chemical Publishing Company, Inc., New York, 1940.

Treloar, L. R. G.: "The Physics of Rubber Elasticity," 2d ed., Clarendon Press, Oxford, 1958.

Weber, C. O.: "The Chemistry of Natural Rubber," Charles Griffin & Company, Ltd., London, 1919.

Winspear, G. G. (ed.): "Rubber Handbook," R. T. Vanderbilt Co., Inc., New York, 1968.

5

Step-reaction Polymerization

(Polycondensation Reactions)

The first polymers to be used as elastomers, plastics, coatings, or fibers were naturally occurring. The pioneer elastomer was hevea rubber. The pioneer plastics and coatings were bitumens and shellac. The pioneer fibers were cotton, flax, wool, and silk.

Derivatives of these naturally occurring polymers, such as vulcanized rubber, cellulose nitrate, and the reaction product of protein with tannic acid, were superior to the unreacted polymers. However, the properties of these modified macromolecules were related to the original polymer backbone as well as to the new pendant groups.

The first useful synthetic macromolecules were obtained by the condensation of low-molecular-weight molecules, such as formaldehyde and phenol. These phenolic resins as well as synthetic polyamides and polyesters were called *condensation polymers* by Carothers. This term and polycondensation are widely used, but the term *step-reaction polymer*, which is descriptive of the mechanism of this type of polymerization, is preferred by many polymer chemists.

The reactions taking place in this type of polymerization are analogous to the condensation reactions described in classic organic chemistry. The intermediate reaction products are relatively stable and may be isolated readily. Fortunately, the kinetics and mechanisms for the polyfunctional reactions are similar to those for simple monofunctional compounds. Hence, much information on this type of polymerization may be obtained from a study of simple condensations involving similar functional groups.

Polypeptides and polysaccharides may be synthesized by step-reaction polymerization. The structure of these polymers is similar to those of synthetic condensation polymers. Hence, much of the information in this chapter may also be applied to naturally occurring proteins and carbohydrates.

5-1 INTERFACIAL POLYCONDENSATIONS

The Schotten-Baumann amidation of a monoacyl chloride, such as acetyl chloride, by a monoamine, such as ethylamine, may be used as a model for the condensation of poly(acyl chlorides) and polyamines. As indicated by the following equation, a protonated amide is formed in the first step of this substitution, nucleophilic, bimolecular reaction (S_N2). The proton is released rapidly to a proton acceptor such as pyridine or hydroxyl ion which may be present in the aqueous phase.

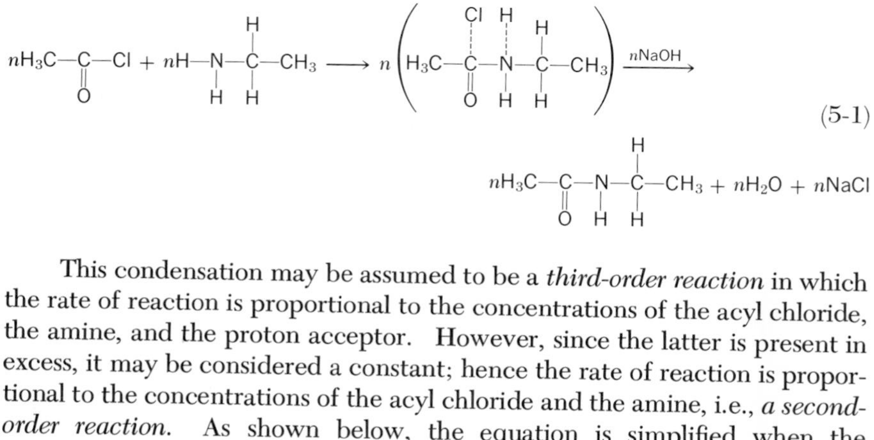

$$n H_3C-\overset{\underset{\|}{O}}{C}-Cl + n H-\overset{\overset{H}{|}}{\underset{\underset{H}{|}}{N}}-\overset{\overset{H}{|}}{\underset{\underset{H}{|}}{C}}-CH_3 \longrightarrow n\left(H_3C-\overset{\overset{Cl}{|}}{\underset{\underset{O}{\|}}{C}}-\overset{\overset{H}{|}}{\underset{\underset{H}{|}}{N}}-\overset{\overset{H}{|}}{\underset{\underset{H}{|}}{C}}-CH_3\right) \xrightarrow{n NaOH}$$

(5-1)

$$n H_3C-\overset{\underset{\|}{O}}{C}-\overset{\overset{H}{|}}{N}-\overset{\overset{H}{|}}{\underset{\underset{H}{|}}{C}}-CH_3 + n H_2O + n NaCl$$

This condensation may be assumed to be a *third-order reaction* in which the rate of reaction is proportional to the concentrations of the acyl chloride, the amine, and the proton acceptor. However, since the latter is present in excess, it may be considered a constant; hence the rate of reaction is proportional to the concentrations of the acyl chloride and the amine, i.e., *a second-order reaction*. As shown below, the equation is simplified when the reactants are present in equimolar concentrations:

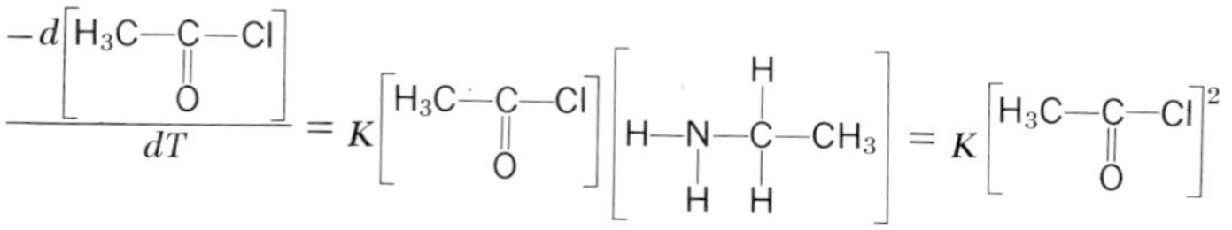

$$\frac{-d\left[H_3C-\overset{\underset{\|}{O}}{C}-Cl\right]}{dT} = K\left[H_3C-\overset{\underset{\|}{O}}{C}-Cl\right]\left[H-\overset{\overset{H}{|}}{\underset{\underset{H}{|}}{N}}-\overset{\overset{H}{|}}{\underset{\underset{H}{|}}{C}}-CH_3\right] = K\left[H_3C-\overset{\underset{\|}{O}}{C}-Cl\right]^2$$

(5-2)

Reaction rate of Schotten-Baumann reaction

If the original concentration of the acetyl chloride is C_0 and its concentration at any time t is C, the fractional yield, i.e., the fraction of molecules that has reacted at time t, may be represented by the parameter p. This parameter p may also be considered the probability that a molecule of acetyl chloride has reacted in time t. This parameter p may be defined mathematically as follows:

$$p = \frac{C_0 - C}{C_0} \quad \text{or} \quad C = C_0(1 - p) \quad \text{or} \quad \frac{C_0}{C} = \frac{1}{1 - p} \quad (5\text{-}3)$$

Relationship of change in concentration to yield

Thus, if the original concentration of acetyl chloride was 1 molar and it decreased to 0.05 molar after 130 sec, $p = 95$ percent yield:

$$p = \frac{C_0 - C}{C_0} = \frac{1 - 0.05}{1} = 0.95$$

The acetamide produced is relatively stable and does not react further with either reactant; i.e., the product is a very short chain in which $\overline{DP} = 1$ or $n = 1$.

When a difunctional acyl chloride, such as sebacyl chloride, dissolved in carbon tetrachloride in a beaker is covered by a layer of an aqueous alkaline solution of a difunctional amine, such as hexamethylenediamine, a reaction takes place at room temperature at the interface. Since both reactants are difunctional, a polyamide is produced which may be withdrawn as a film or filament in the well-known "nylon-rope trick."

The first product is comparable to that formed with monofunctional reactants. Since this reaction is much faster than competing side reactions, the yield is essentially quantitative; that is, $p \cong 1$. However, since this amide has reactive end groups, the condensation may continue stepwise by a similar $S_N 2$ mechanism, as shown below.

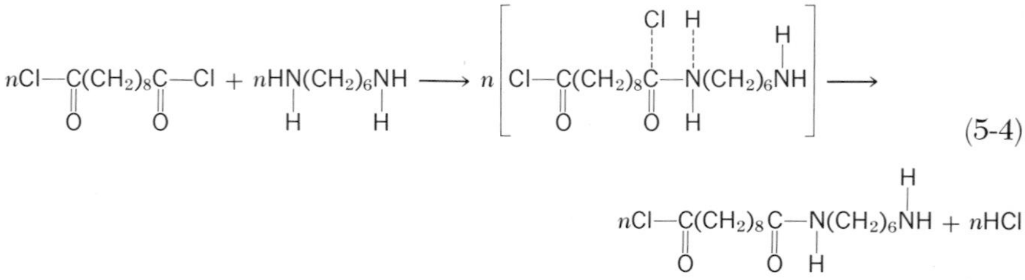

$$n\text{Cl}-\underset{\underset{O}{\|}}{C}(CH_2)_8 \underset{\underset{O}{\|}}{C}-\text{Cl} + n\text{HN}(CH_2)_6\text{NH} \longrightarrow n \left[\text{Cl}-\underset{\underset{O}{\|}}{C}(CH_2)_8\underset{\underset{O}{\|}}{\overset{\overset{\text{Cl}}{|}}{C}}-\underset{\overset{|}{H}}{N}(CH_2)_6\underset{\overset{|}{H}}{N}H \right] \longrightarrow$$

(5-4)

$$n\text{Cl}-\underset{\underset{O}{\|}}{C}(CH_2)_8\,\underset{\underset{O}{\|}}{C}-N(CH_2)_6\underset{\overset{|}{H}}{N}H + n\text{HCl}$$

Reaction of sebacyl chloride and hexamethylenediamine

If this condensation were conducted in a dilute mutual solvent rather than in two immiscible solvents, some 18-membered rings might have been formed in accordance with the *Ruggli high-dilution principle.* Under the conditions used, five- or six-membered strainless rings might form with appropriate reagents. However, under the reaction conditions described, the tendency to form rings with more than seven atoms would be negligible.

The rate of reaction for the first step is similar to that for amidation with monofunctional reactants, as shown below:

$$\frac{-d[\text{Cl}-\underset{\underset{\text{O}}{\|}}{\text{C}}(\text{CH}_2)_8\underset{\underset{\text{O}}{\|}}{\text{C}}-\text{Cl}]}{dT} = K[\text{Cl}-\underset{\underset{\text{O}}{\|}}{\text{C}}(\text{CH}_2)_8\underset{\underset{\text{O}}{\|}}{\text{C}}-\text{Cl}]^2 \tag{5-5}$$

Reaction rate of interfacial polyamidation reaction

This rate constant K also applies to subsequent steps, provided the end groups are far apart, as in the example used. Thus the reactivity of the end groups in this step-reaction-polymerization reaction, and other nucleophilic displacement reactions involving difunctional groups, is *independent of chain length.* The most useful reactions for this type of polymerization are amidation, esterification, and the synthesis of polyurethanes.

If the original concentration of sebacyl chloride is C_0 and the concentration at any time t is C, then as in Eq. (5-3)

$$p = \frac{C_0 - C}{C_0} \quad \text{or} \quad \frac{C_0}{C} = \frac{1}{1-p}$$

Also as stated previously, p is equal to the probability that a molecule of sebacyl chloride has reacted in time t. However, in contrast to the simple amidation reaction cited previously, the degree of polymerization $\overline{DP}$ at time t is equal to the ratio of the original number of molecules of sebacyl chloride (N_0) and the number of unreacted molecules (N):

$$\overline{DP} = \frac{N_0}{N} = \frac{C_0}{C} \tag{5-6}$$

Relationship of chain length to change in concentration

$\overline{DP}$ is a number average and when multiplied by the weight of the amide segment is equal to $\overline{M}_n$. Thus, as shown in Eq. (5-3),

$$\frac{C_0}{C} = \overline{DP} = \frac{1}{1-p} \tag{5-7}$$

Carothers' equation

This simple relationship developed by Carothers may be used to explain why he postponed esterification reactions in favor of amidation polymerization. Because of the inherent flexibility of the carbon-carbon bond in aliphatic polyesters, these products are characterized by low melting points. In the absence of groups which provide *steric hindrance*, these polyesters are hydrolytically unstable. Most important, extremely pure reactants in equimolecular concentrations, which are essential for the production of long-chain polymers by direct esterification, were not readily available to Carothers.

In preparatory organic chemistry, a yield of 98 percent is considered excellent for esterification reactions. However, the Carothers' equation shows that this fractional yield is equivalent to a $\overline{DP}$ of 50:

$$\overline{DP} = \frac{1}{1-p} = \frac{1}{1-0.98} = 50$$

A $\overline{DP}$ of 50 may be above the threshold value for crystalline polymer chains with high intermolecular forces, such as polyamides or polyurethanes, but it is below the threshold value for aliphatic polyester fibers.

In contrast, when an aliphatic diamine, such as hexamethylenediamine, is mixed with a dicarboxylic acid, such as adipic acid, a salt containing stoichiometric proportions of the reactants is formed. This amine salt (nylon salt) may be purified by crystallization. The salt may be heated and converted practically quantitatively to the polyamide (*nylon 6,6*). (The numbers following nylon correspond to the number of carbons in the amine and acid, respectively.)

The application of the Carothers' equation will show that the $\overline{DP}$ for nylon 6,6 (PA) is of the order of 1,000:

$$\overline{DP} = \frac{1}{1-p} = \frac{1}{1-0.999} = 1,000$$

This $\overline{DP}$ value is above the threshold limit for a strong fiber and actually beyond the range required for commercial nylon fibers. The $\overline{DP}$ of these products, called *supermacromolecules* by Carothers, is usually reduced for commercial applications of nylon.

The Schotten-Baumann interfacial condensation was chosen for nylon preparation in this discussion because of ease of preparation. In addition to the value of this experiment for demonstration purposes, the product is a readily obtainable useful polymer. Because side reactions are negligible, the kinetics and statistics of step-reaction polymerization are readily applied to this type of amidation.

Since the rate constant K is independent of $\overline{DP}$, one may apply Eq. (5-5) to the interfacial polycondensation of sebacyl chloride and hexamethylenediamine:

$$\frac{-dc}{dt} = K[C^2]$$

The following relationships are obtained by integration and rearrangement:

$$\frac{1}{C} - \frac{1}{C_0} = KT \tag{5-8}$$

$$\overline{DP} = \frac{1}{1-p} = 1 + KC_0t \qquad p = \frac{KC_0t}{1 + KC_0t}$$

Relationship of chain length to reaction rate

Thus, as shown in Fig. 5-1, straight lines are obtained when one plots $\overline{DP}$ or $1/(1-p)$ against time t. The slopes of the lines (KC_0) increase as the temperature is increased in accordance with the Arrhenius equation

$$K = Ae^{-E_a/RT} \tag{5-9}$$

Arrhenius equation

The activation energies E_a for comparable reactions with monofunctional reactants may be used to calculate the rate constant K for other step-reaction polymerizations.

If the value of the slope, at a specific temperature, is known, one may use Eq. (5-8) to determine $\overline{DP}$ after any reaction time t. Thus $\overline{DP}$ is found to be over 100 after 90 min for a step-reaction polymerization in which $K = 10^{-2}$ liter/mole sec and $C_0 = 2$ moles/liter

$$\overline{DP} = 1 + KC_0t = 1 + (10^{-2})(2)(90)(60) = 109$$

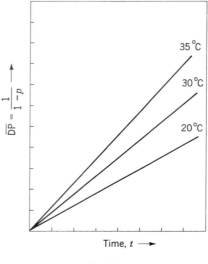

Fig. 5-1

Since p has been defined as the probability that a functional group such as the acetyl

$$\overset{\displaystyle O}{\underset{\displaystyle -CCl}{\|}}$$

has reacted in time t, the probability of finding an unreacted functional group at time t is $1 - p$. If the polymer chain is the result of the reaction of n molecules of the reactants, then $n - 1$ of the reactive groups must have reacted, or in general if the reactants are labeled A-A and B-B, the product is as shown:

$$nAA + nBB \longrightarrow AA(BBAA)_{n-1}BB \qquad (5\text{-}10)$$

General step-reaction polymerization

The probability of finding a single reacted group (mer) in the molecule is p, and the probability of finding $n - 1$ of these mers (BBAA) in time t is p^{n-1}. This probability is equal to the fraction of molecules with n units or mers. Therefore, the total number of molecules of n units (N_n) is as follows: $N_n = Np^{n-1}(1 - p)$. From the Carothers' equation $N = N_0(1 - p)$, the number average N_n and the weight average W_n may be defined as follows:

$$N_n = N_0 p^{n-1}(1 - p)^2 \qquad (5\text{-}11)$$

Relationship of number average to probability

$$W_n = \frac{nN_n}{N_0} = np^{n-1}(1 - p)^2 \qquad (5\text{-}12)$$

Relationship of weight average to probability

The expression for the weight average W_n is in accordance with the information given in Chap. 3. The number of monomer molecules usually exceeds the number of other molecular species. However, because the monomers are low-molecular-weight products, their proportion on a weight basis decreases rapidly as the polymerization proceeds.

The number average $\overline{DP}$ and weight average $\overline{M}_w$ were defined in Chap. 3 as follows:

$$\overline{M}_n = \frac{C_0}{C} = \overline{DP} = \frac{1}{1 - p} \qquad \text{[This is identical to Eq. (5-3)]}$$

$$\overline{M}_w = \frac{1 + p}{1 - p} \qquad (5\text{-}13)$$

Relationship of average molecular weight to probability

Thus the distribution range $\overline{M}_w/\overline{M}_n$ is equal to $1 + p$ as shown:

$$\frac{\overline{M}_w}{\overline{M}_n} = \frac{(1 + p)/(1 - p)}{1/(1 - p)} = 1 + p \qquad (5\text{-}14)$$

Relationship of degree of dispersity to probability

Thus, as p approaches unity, the distribution range $\overline{M}_w/\overline{M}_n$ approaches 2; that is, $1 + 1 = 2$. Typical curves for number and weight distribution for increasing values of p are shown in Figs. 5-2 and 5-3.

Regardless of whether one considers the weight or number average molecular weight, the concentration of short chains, i.e., monomers, dimers, trimers, etc., is negligible as p approaches 1. As stated in Chap. 2, extremely

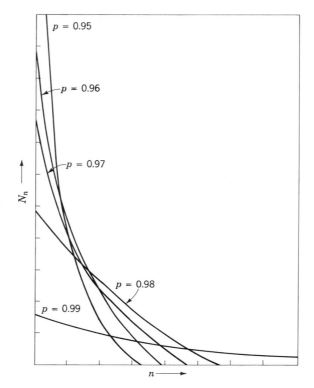

Fig. 5-2   Relationships of N_n and n at different values of p

high-molecular-weight polymers are difficult to process and the slight improvement in physical properties characteristic of very high-molecular-weight products does not justify the use of the temperatures or heavy-duty equipment necessary for processing these long-chained products. In addition, the active chain ends present in step-reaction polymers may react further at elevated temperatures.

Thus, extremely high-molecular-weight products that are readily obtained by amidation reactions may be avoided by quenching the reaction before p exceeds 0.98 or by using a slight excess of one of the reactants. The effects of quenching the reaction before completion are shown in Figs. 5-2 and 5-3. The effect of exceeding the stoichiometric quantity of one of the reactants may be demonstrated by using a modified form of the Carothers' equation.

Thus, if n molecules of sebacyl chloride are reacted with $1.02n$ molecules of hexamethylenediamine, the ratio of the reactants (AA/BB or r) will be 0.98 instead of 1 as when stoichiometric quantities are present. The Carothers' equation becomes

$$\overline{DP} = \frac{1 + r}{1 + r - 2rp}$$

$$\overline{DP} = \frac{\text{total nAA at } p}{\text{total nAA at } rp} = \frac{n(1 + 1/r)/2}{n[1 - p + (1 - rp)]/2}$$

$$= \frac{1 + r}{2r(1 - p) + 1 - r} = \frac{1 + r}{1 + r - 2rp} \qquad (5\text{-}15)$$

Carothers' equation for excess reactants

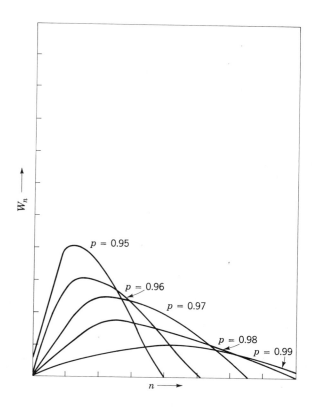

Fig. 5-3   Relationships of W_n and n at different values of p

If this reaction is assumed to be essentially quantitative, that is, $p = 1$, $\overline{DP}$ is equal to 99 instead of 1,000, which was calculated for stoichiometric relationships, i.e.,

$$\overline{DP} = \frac{1 + r}{1 + r - 2r} = \frac{1 + 0.98}{1 - 0.98} = \frac{1.98}{0.02} = 99$$

This value is well above the threshold value of 50 for nylon 6,10 and is much below the $\overline{DP}$ calculated for equimolecular quantities. However, the $\overline{DP}$ may be more readily decreased by adding a measured amount of a monofunctional reactant, such as acetyl chloride, to the difunctional reactants. Thus, as shown in another modification of the Carothers' equation [Eq. (5-16)], the $\overline{DP}$ for the condensation of sebacyl chloride and hexamethylenediamine may be reduced to 101 by the addition of 1 mole percent of acetyl chloride (n_a) to the reaction mixture.

$$\overline{DP} = \frac{1 + n_a/n}{1 - p + n_a/n} \tag{5-16}$$

Carothers' equation for a monofunctional additive

$$\overline{DP} = \frac{1 + n_a/n}{1 - p + n_a/n} = \frac{1 + 0.010}{1 - 1 + 0.010} = \frac{1.010}{0.010} = 101$$

For demonstration purposes, the two immiscible liquids in interfacial polycondensations should be stationary. However, more uniform polymers are produced when this Schotten-Baumann reaction takes place in a high-speed mixer, such as a Waring blender.

Interfacial condensation techniques are also applicable to phosgenation of diamines and dihydric compounds for the production of polyureas and polycarbonates, respectively. Other reactants, such as bischloroformates and sulfonic chlorides, may be used in place of phosgene to produce polyurethanes and polysulfonates.

Because of the simplicity of this reaction, it may be used to form polymers in situ by adding one reactant to a substance, such as cloth, which has been impregnated previously with the other reactant. Some of the general classes of polymers that may be synthesized by this technique are listed with their reactants in Table 5-1.

Table 5-1 General Interfacial Polycondensation Reactions

n reactant AA + n reactant BB $\longrightarrow$ polymer AA (BBAA)$_{n-1}$BB

Amine	Acyl chloride	Amide (PA)
Alcohol	Phosgene	Carbonate (PC)
Alcohol	Acyl chloride	Ester
Alcohol	Aryl sulfonyl chloride	Sulfonamide
Amine	Phosgene	Urea
Amine	Chloroformate	Urethane (PUR)

REFERENCES

Burnett, G. M.: "Mechanism of Polymer Reactions," Interscience Publishers, Inc., New York, 1954.

Flory, P. J.: "Principles of Polymer Chemistry," Cornell University Press, Ithaca, N.Y., 1953.

Lenz, R. W.: "Organic Chemistry of Synthetic High Polymers," Interscience Publishers, a division of John Wiley & Sons, Inc., New York, 1967.

Magat, E. E., and D. R. Strachem: Reactions at the Interface, U.S. Patent 2,708,617, April 17, 1955.

Mark, H. F.: The Mechanism of Polymerization, in R. E. Burke and O. Gummit (eds.), "The Chemistry of Large Molecules," chap. 1, Interscience Publishers, Inc., New York, 1943.

———— and A. V. Tobolsky: "Physical Chemistry of High Polymeric Systems," Interscience Publishers, Inc., New York, 1950.

Morgan, P. W.: "Condensation Polymers by Interface and Solution Methods," Interscience Publishers, a division of John Wiley & Sons, Inc., New York, 1965.

————: "Low Temperature Polycondensation Processes," in R. F. Gould (ed.), "Polymerization and Polycondensation Processes," American Chemical Society, Washington, D.C., 1962.

————: Nylon, SPE J., **15**:485 (1959).

Ravve, A.: "Organic Chemistry of Macromolecules," Marcel Dekker, Inc., New York, 1967

5-2 HOMOGENEOUS POLYCONDENSATIONS

Relatively stable intermediates are produced in homogeneous step-reaction (stepwise) polymerizations. These polycondensations proceed by a series of discrete reaction steps in which all intermediates grow at a similar rate. Some step reactions, like the reaction of isocyanates and alcohols, and ring-opening polymerization reactions produce polymers exclusively. Hence they are not defined by IUPAC as condensation polymers. However, they are produced by step-reaction polymerization and are included in this section.

Nylon 6,6 [poly(hexamethylene adipamide)] is prepared by heating recrystallized nylon 6,6 salt in an inert atmosphere in the presence of a controlled amount of a monofunctional carboxylic acid, such as acetic acid. The principal reactions in the preparation of nylon 6,6 from hexamethylenediamine and adipic acid are shown in the following equation:

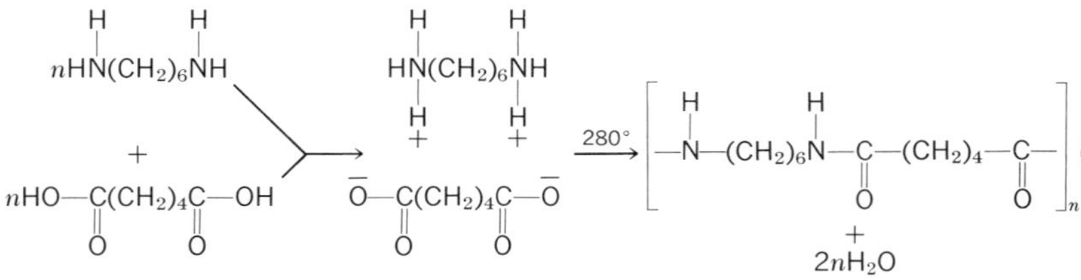

Equation for preparation of nylon 6,6

Nylon 6,6 is characterized by excellent resistance to solvents. It is soluble in phenol, cresols, formic acid, and some complexing agents. It is readily hydrolyzed by acids. When heated in an inert atmosphere, molten nylon 6,6 may be extruded through small orifices (spinnerets) to form unoriented filaments. The latter may be stretched 400 to 500 percent (cold-drawn) to produce strong partially crystalline fibers. Nylon 6,10 is produced commercially from hexamethylenediamine and sebacic acid.

The melting point of polyamides (PA) may be increased by the incorporation of additional stiffening groups such as phenyl or cyclohexyl groups in the polymer backbone. For example, poly(1,4-cyclohexylene dimethylene suberamide) is a commercial temperature-resistant nylon polymer. The melting point may also be increased by decreasing the number of methylene groups between the amide linkages.

When the number of carbons in both the diamine and dicarboxylic acid is even, as in nylon 6,6, there is an optimum opportunity for intermolecular hydrogen bonding. The melting point is lowered when there is an odd number of carbon atoms in either of the reactants. The effect of carbon number of each reactant on melting point is shown in Table 5-2.

When mixtures of dicarboxylic acids or diamines are used as reactants the melting point of polyamides is decreased because of the irregular structure produced. Crystallinity is also hindered when pendant groups are present on the chain. Thus amorphous polymers with lower softening points and increased solubility are obtained when nylon 6,6 is converted to N-methoxymethyl nylon by the reaction with acidified methanolic formalde-

Table 5-2   The Melting Points (°C) of Nylons

CARBON ATOMS IN DIAMINE	CARBON ATOMS IN ACID				
	6	7	8	9	10
4	278	233	250	223	239
5	223	183	202	178	195
6	250	202	215	185	210
7	236	196	200	169	187

hyde. Likewise, the polyamides produced by the condensation of either β-methylhexamethylenediamine or β-methyladipic acid are also amorphous.

Nylon 7, nylon 9, nylon 11, and nylon 13 are produced by the step-reaction polymerization of appropriate ω-amino acids. The reactant for nylon 7 {ω-aminoenanthic acid [$H_2N(CH_2)_6COOH$]} is produced by the partial reduction and hydrolysis of pimelic dinitrile or by the hydrolysis and amination of the telomer obtained from ethylene and carbon tetrachloride [$Cl(CH_2)_6CCl_3$]. *Telomerization* with selected chain transfer agents will be discussed in Chap. 6.

The reactant for nylon 9 is produced by the amidation and reduction of azelaic acid which is obtained by the ozonolysis of oleic acid. Nylon 11 is obtained by step-reaction polymerization of 11-aminoundecanoic acid. The latter is obtained from the methyl ester of undecylenic acid which is one of the pyrolytic products of methyl ricinoleate.

Nylon 13 may be obtained in a similar manner from erucic acid. The step-reaction polymerization takes place readily when the appropriate ω-amino acids are heated. Because of the large number of methylene groups there is little tendency for cyclization.

The difficulties encountered in obtaining crystalline water-resistant polymers by classic esterification of aliphatic dicarboxylic acids may be overcome by ester interchange of terephthalic acid esters. The phenyl groups serve as chain stiffeners and increase resistance to hydrolysis because of steric hindrance. The low-molecular-weight esters such as dimethyl phthalate may be readily purified by distillation.

Poly(ethylene terephthalate) (Terylene, Dacron, Mylar, Kodel) (PETP) may be produced by heating equimolar quantities of ethylene glycol and dimethyl terephthalate in the presence of sodium methoxide. The bis(β-hydroxyethyl) terephthalate which is produced after distillation of volatile alcohols undergoes step-reaction polymerization. This polyester may also be obtained by heating terephthalic acid and ethylene glycol under reduced pressure so that both water and excess ethylene glycol are removed. A small amount of cyclic dimer may also be produced in either esterification process.

The Carothers' equation may be applied to this or any other step-reaction polymerization. The molecular weight is controlled by the addition of a small amount of monofunctional acid (acetic acid). The principal reactions in this type of esterification are shown in the following equation:

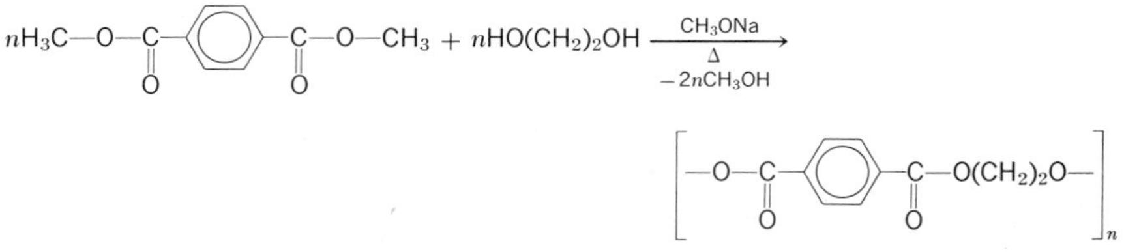

$$(5\text{-}18)$$

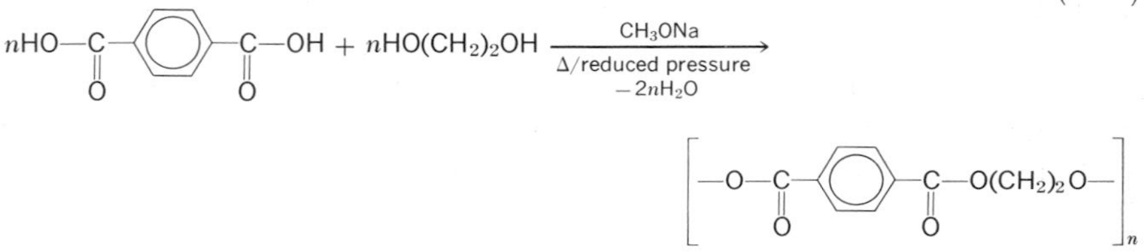

Equation for the preparation of poly(ethylene terephthalate)

As shown by the data in Table 5-3, the melting points of aliphatic polyesters are lower than those of phthalic acid esters. The melting point decreases as the number of methylene groups between carboxyl groups is increased. As stated in Chap. 1, the degree of crystallization in these polyesters depends on whether the number of methylene groups between the carboxyl groups are odd or even. Also, as shown by the data in Table 5-4, the melting points of the terephthalic acid esters decrease as the number of carbon atoms in the glycols increase. The melting point is increased by replacing the phenyl group by biphenyl, diphenyl sulfone, or stilbene. The melting points of the polyesters are decreased when the carboxyls are in the meta or ortho positions and when dicarboxylic acids of diphenyl methylene or diphenyl ether are used in place of the phenyl group.

Table 5-3 The Melting Points (°C) of Aliphatic Polyesters

CARBON ATOMS IN GLYCOL	CARBON ATOMS IN ACID			
	2	4	6	10
2	172	108	50	75
3	69	52	46	58
10	80	70	77	76

Table 5-4   The Melting Points (°C) of Aromatic Polyesters,

$$HO-\underset{O}{\overset{O}{\underset{\|}{C}}}-Ar-\underset{O}{\overset{O}{\underset{\|}{C}}}-OH \qquad\qquad HO(CH_2)_nOH$$

Ar	n						
	2	3	4	5	6	8	10
 (tere) 1,4	265	190	226	150	170	130	135
 (iso) 1,3	143						
 4,4′	355						
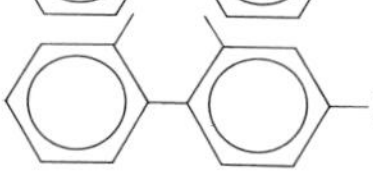 2,2′	132						
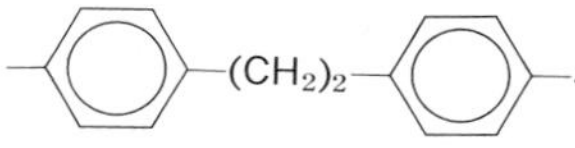 (CH₂)₂ 4,4′	220						
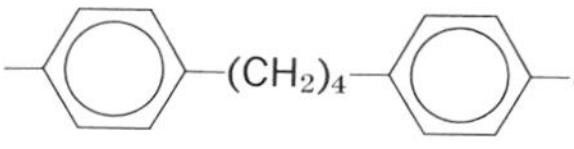 (CH₂)₄ 4,4′	170						
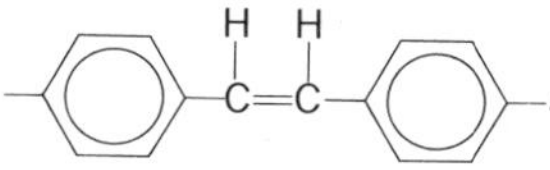 C=C (H,H) 4,4′	420						
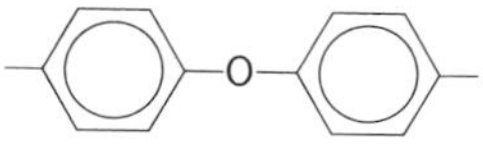 O 4,4′	152						
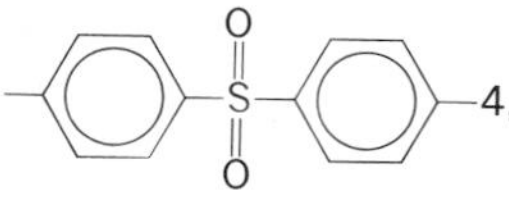 SO₂ 4,4′	380						

Because of the resultant irregular structures, the melting points of polyesters are decreased when mixtures of dicarboxylic acids or glycols are used as reactants. This effect is also observed with mixtures of optical isomers. *meso*-Tartaric acid also yields a polyester with a lower melting point than D-tartaric acid.

Poly(ethylene terephthalate) is the only common linear polyester. It is converted to a filament or film by extrusion of the melt in an inert atmosphere through a spinneret or through a slit. This polyester is resistant to acids and most solvents. It is soluble in phenol and trifluoroacetic acid. It may be hydrolyzed by strong alkalies.

Polycarbonates (Lexan, Merlon) (PC) may be prepared by ester interchange of diphenyl carbonate with bisphenol A [2,2'-bis(4-hydroxyphenyl) propane], as shown in the following equation:

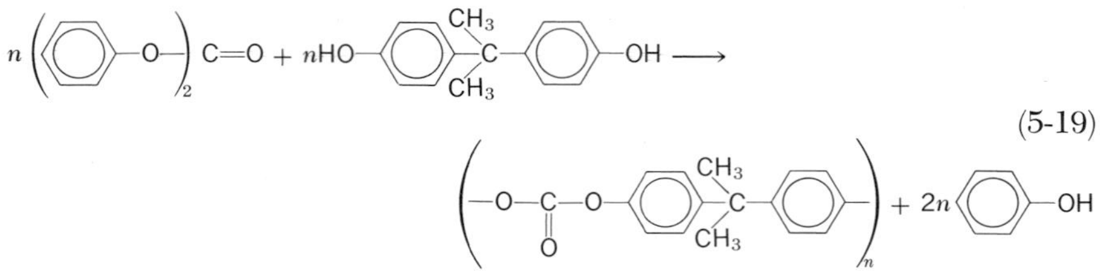

$$n \left(\langle\bigcirc\rangle{-}O{-} \right)_2 C{=}O + nHO{-}\langle\bigcirc\rangle{-}\underset{CH_3}{\overset{CH_3}{C}}{-}\langle\bigcirc\rangle{-}OH \longrightarrow$$

(5-19)

$$\left({-}O{-}\underset{O}{\overset{||}{C}}{-}O{-}\langle\bigcirc\rangle{-}\underset{CH_3}{\overset{CH_3}{C}}{-}\langle\bigcirc\rangle{-} \right)_n + 2n\langle\bigcirc\rangle{-}OH$$

Equation for preparation of polycarbonate from bisphenol A

The melting point of polycarbonates may be increased by replacing the phenyl or methyl groups with cyclohexyl groups. The glass transition temperatures (T_g) and melting points are decreased when 1,1'-bis(4-hydroxyphenyl) ethane or bis(4-hydroxyphenyl) ether is used instead of the bisphenol A. Commercial polycarbonates are characterized by high impact and tensile strengths.

In addition to investigating polyesters and polyamides, Carothers also investigated polyanhydrides. These polymers have been produced by heating a large number of dicarboxylic acids with acetic anhydride (Ac_2O). Fibers may be spun from molten high-molecular-weight polyanhydrides but these filaments are readily hydrolyzed under conditions of high humidity.

In contrast, the polyanhydrides obtained from aromatic acids are more stable to hydrolysis because of steric hindrance. As might be anticipated, the moisture resistance, degree of crystallinity, and glass transition temperature (T_g) decrease as the number of methylene groups between the phenoxy groups increase. In Eq. (5-20), m should not be greater than 3 for the production of stable polymers.

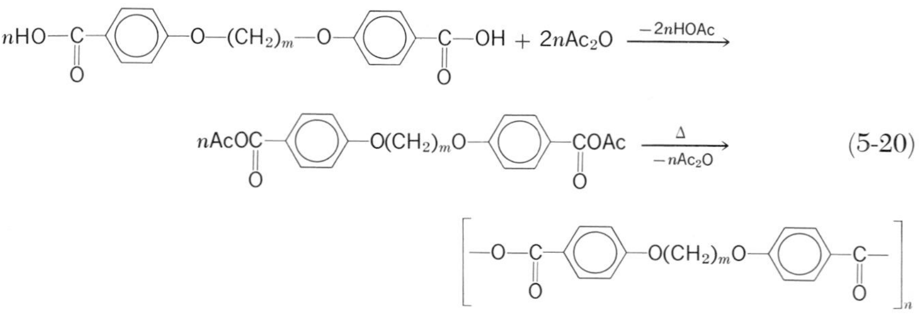

$$nHO{-}\underset{O}{\overset{||}{C}}{-}\langle\bigcirc\rangle{-}O{-}(CH_2)_m{-}O{-}\langle\bigcirc\rangle{-}\underset{O}{\overset{||}{C}}{-}OH + 2nAc_2O \xrightarrow{-2nHOAc}$$

$$nAcO\underset{O}{\overset{||}{C}}{-}\langle\bigcirc\rangle{-}O(CH_2)_mO{-}\langle\bigcirc\rangle{-}\underset{O}{\overset{||}{C}}OAc \xrightarrow[-nAc_2O]{\Delta}$$

(5-20)

$$\left[{-}O{-}\underset{O}{\overset{||}{C}}{-}\langle\bigcirc\rangle{-}O(CH_2)_mO{-}\langle\bigcirc\rangle{-}\underset{O}{\overset{||}{C}}{-} \right]_n$$

Equation for preparation of an aromatic polyanhydride

The Wurtz urethane reaction, which has become a classic qualitative test for alcohols, may be used for the step-reaction polymerization of difunctional alcohols and diisocyanates. The production of polyurethanes (polycarbamates) (PUR) was investigated extensively by Bayer in the 1930s.

The rate of reaction is dependent on the type and concentration of solvent and the catalyst used. An intermediate compound is formed by the reaction either with basic catalysts, such as triethylene diamine, or with metal salts such as di-n-butyl tin diacetate.

As shown by Eq. (5-21), a typical crystalline polymer (Perlon U) may be obtained by the reaction of 1,4-butanediol and 1,6-hexane diisocyanate. Because of hydrogen bonding, polymers with a $\overline{DP}$ of at least 50 are crystalline and have high melting points.

$$n\text{HO(CH}_2)_4\text{OH} + n\text{OCN(CH}_2)_6\text{NCO} \longrightarrow \left[-\text{O} - (\text{CH}_2)_4\text{O} - \overset{\text{H}}{\underset{\text{O}}{\overset{|}{\text{C}}}} - \overset{\text{H}}{\underset{}{\text{N}}}(\text{CH}_2)_6\overset{\text{H}}{\underset{\text{O}}{\text{N}}} - \overset{}{\underset{\text{O}}{\overset{}{\text{C}}}} - \right]_n \qquad (5\text{-}21)$$

Equation for preparation of a polyurethane

The melting point may be increased by incorporating stiffening groups in the polymer backbone. For example, the melting point of the polyurethane from ethylene glycol and biphenylene diisocyanate is about 390°C as compared with a melting point of 180°C for the polyurethane obtained from butanediol and hexane diisocyanate. A similar low melting point is obtained for the polyurethane from ethylene glycol and 2,4-tolylene diisocyanate (TDI). Lower melting points are observed when glycols with an odd number of methylene groups are used.

Elastomers are obtained when diisocyanates are reacted with flexible polymethylenes or polyoxymethylenes with terminal hydroxy groups. Polyureas are obtained from the reaction of alkylene diamines and diisocyanates. The phenol-diisocyanate adduct may be used with dihydric compounds for the production of baked polymer coatings. This adduct decomposes under baking conditions to yield the diisocyanate and phenol.

Any moisture present will react with the diisocyanate to produce an unstable intermediate. As shown by the following equation, the intermediate decomposes to form an active amine and gaseous carbon dioxide. Thus controlled amounts of water may be added for the production of polyurethane-cellular products (plastic foams).

Polyurethanes are less stable than polyamides (nylons) at elevated temperatures. They are used as coatings, fibers, films, foams, adhesives, potting compounds, and elastomers. Resilient polyurethane fibers (Spandex) are used for foundation garments and swim suits.

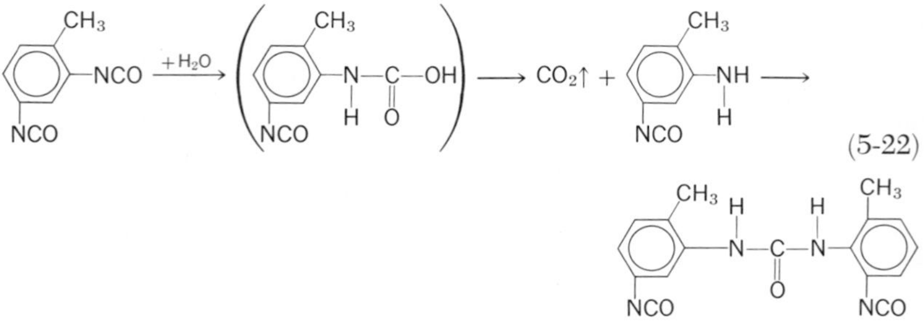

$$(5\text{-}22)$$

Equation showing reaction of water
with 2,4-tolylene diisocyanate (TDI)

One of the first commercial elastomers was a poly(ethylene sulfide) (Thiokol) prepared by Patrick in the 1920s. The simplest polymer is produced by the reaction of an alkylene dichloride, such as ethylene dichloride, with sodium polysulfide. Polysulfides are also obtained by the condensation of bis(2-chloroethyl) formal $[Cl(CH_2)_2OCH_2O(CH_2)_2Cl]$ and sodium polysulfide.

The most useful products are liquid polymers (LP-2) obtained by reduction of the sulfide linkages. Since the liquid polymers contain thiol end groups, they may be oxidized to solid elastomers. Polysulfides may also be obtained by heating aromatic dichlorides, such as p-dichlorobenzene, with sulfur in the presence of sodium carbonate.

Poly(ethylene sulfides) are characterized by excellent resistance to solvents and an inherent disagreeable odor. They are used as caulking materials, sealants, binders for solid rocket propellants, and plasticizers for sulfur. The equation for the preparation of classic poly(ethylene sulfides) is

$$nCl(CH_2)_nCl + nNa(S)_XNa \longrightarrow [-(CH_2)_n-S_X-]_n + 2nNaCl \qquad (5\text{-}23)$$

Silicon atoms may catenate to form chains but the silanes produced are unstable when the number of silicon atoms is greater than six, that is, $H(SiH_2)_6H$. However, high-molecular-weight siloxanes

$$\underset{\underset{R}{|}}{\overset{\overset{R}{|}}{(SiO-)_n}}$$

are readily produced. They are erroneously called silicones. Linear silicone polymers are produced by the hydrolysis of dichlorosilanes. As shown in the following equation, the unstable dialkyl silanols condense rapidly to form cyclic silicones and low-molecular-weight polymers:

$$n(CH_3)_2SiCl_2 + 2H_2O \longrightarrow 2HCl + n[(CH_3)_2Si(OH)_2] \longrightarrow 2H_2O + \left(\begin{array}{c} CH_3 \\ | \\ -O-Si- \\ | \\ CH_3 \end{array}\right)_n \quad (5\text{-}24)$$

Equation for preparation of a linear silicone resin

The hydroxyl end groups on these siloxane chains are stabilized (capping) by reacting with a monofunctional siloxane such as that obtained from hexamethyldisiloxane $[(CH_3)_3SiOSi(CH_3)_3]$ which serves as a chain-length regulator.

Phenylsilicones are brittle, but mixtures of alkyl and arylsiloxanes result in useful products. Softer silicones are obtained when the methyl groups are replaced by bulky groups. An unusual product "bouncing putty" is obtained when dimethylsilicone is heated with boric acid.

Because of the silicon-oxygen backbone, silicones are stable at elevated temperatures. The pendant alkyl groups provide lubricity and water repellancy. Various surfaces may be waterproofed by preparing silicones in situ from chlorosilanes. Elastomers may be obtained by forming a few crosslinks by the addition of some trichlorosilane to the reactants. Silicones are used as heat-resistant polymer coatings, potting compounds, and gaskets.

An elastomeric polymer with *sym*-diphenylethane units in the chain (AXF) was prepared by Shinkle by the condensation of benzene and ethylene dichloride in the presence of aluminum chloride. These poly(arylene alkylenes) have good physical properties but cannot be vulcanized like polyisoprene. The equation for this reaction is as follows:

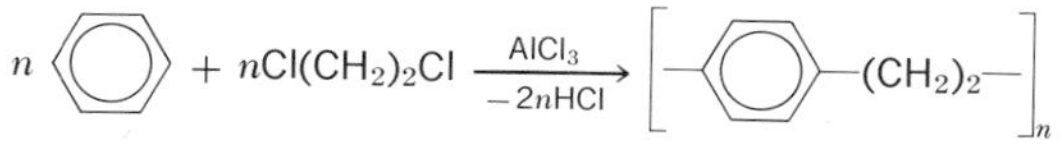

$$n \left\langle \bigcirc \right\rangle + nCl(CH_2)_2Cl \xrightarrow[-2nHCl]{AlCl_3} \left[-\left\langle \bigcirc \right\rangle -(CH_2)_2- \right]_n \quad (5\text{-}25)$$

Equation for preparation of a poly(arylene alkylene)

Similar polymers have also been reported for the self-condensation of phenylethyl chloride.

Crystalline polybenzyls or poly(α-methyl benzyls) are obtained by the condensation of benzyl chloride or 1-chloroethylbenzene in ethyl chloride at $-135°C$ in the presence of aluminum chloride. The $\overline{DP}$ may be regulated by the addition of small amounts of toluene which acts as a chain transfer agent; i.e., it donates a hydride ion which couples with the polybenzyl cation as follows:

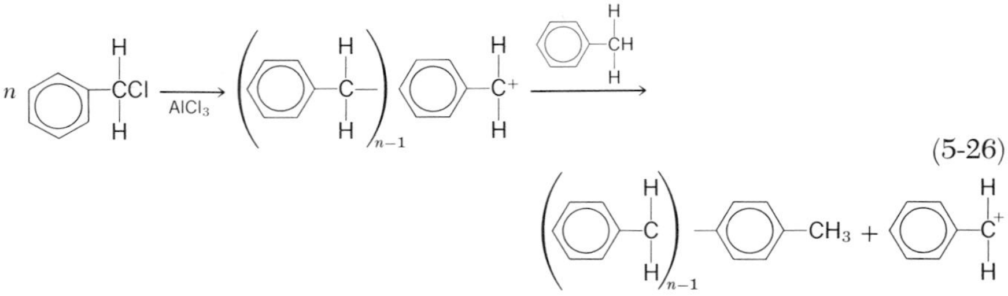

$$(5\text{-}26)$$

Equation for preparation of polybenzyl

These benzyl polymers are more stable at elevated temperatures than polyalkylenes, but they have vulnerable methylene links connecting the phenylene groups in the chain. Marvel prepared polyphenylene by the catalytic hydrogenation of the polycyclohexene obtained by the polymerization of cyclohexadiene. This and the insoluble black polyphenylene described by Kovacic are chain-reaction-type polymerizations which will be discussed in Chap. 6. As shown in the equation below, Marvel used a Ziegler-Natta catalyst; in contrast, Kovacic used a Friedel-Crafts catalyst and oxidized the product with copper (II) chloride.

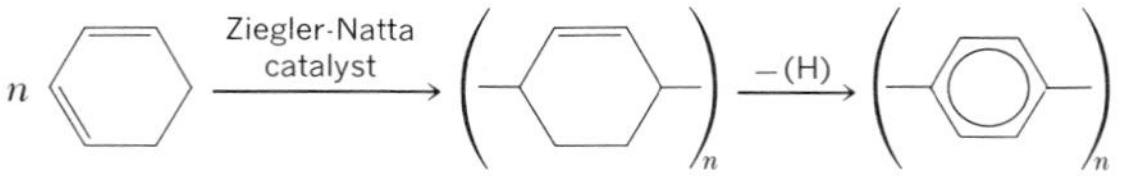

$$(5\text{-}27)$$

Equation for the preparation of polyphenylene

Soluble colorless phenylated polyphenylenes were produced by Mukamal by the Diels-Alder reaction of biscyclopentadiones with diacetylenes.

Poly(phenylene oxide)(PPO, Noryl) is produced by the oxidative coupling of 2,6-xylenol in the presence of copper salts. These linear polymers are characterized by good mechanical properties over a wide temperature range. The equation for this type of polymerization is as follows:

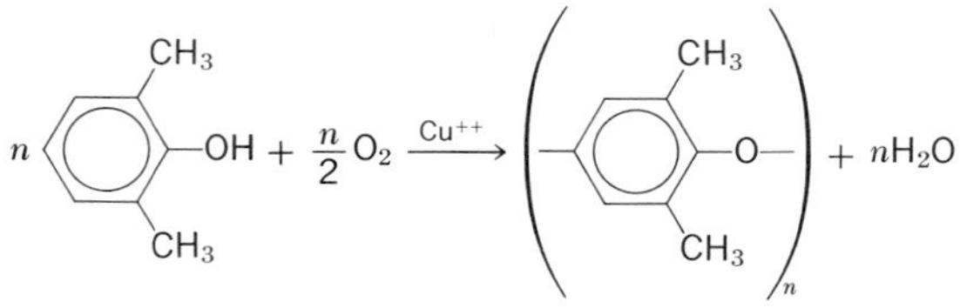

$$(5\text{-}28)$$

Equation for preparation of poly(phenylene oxide)

Poly(p-xylylenes)(Parylene) are produced by the vapor phase (950°C) cyclic dimerization of monochloro-p-xylene or p-xylene. The dimers are obtained by quenching at lower temperatures. High-melting linear polymeric films are deposited on cool surfaces (50°C) when the dimers are pyrolyzed in the vapor phase (550°C), as shown in the following equation:

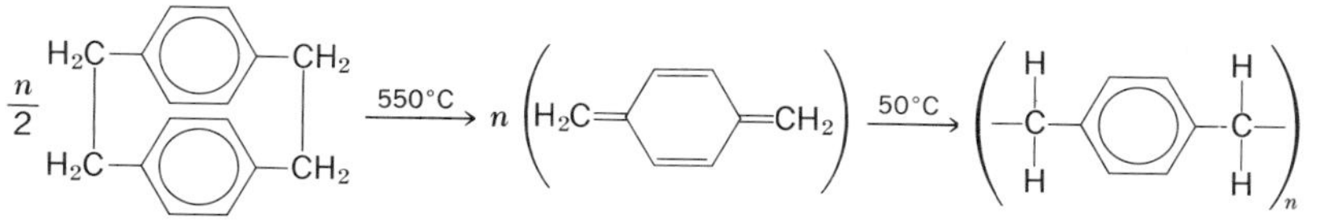

Equation for preparation of poly(p-xylylene) (5-29)

Linear heat-resistant polymers have also been produced by the condensation of alkylenediamines with intraanhydrides of tetracarboxylic acids, such as pyromellitic anhydride. As shown by the following equation, the chains of these *polymellitimides* (Vespel, Kapton) contain five- and six-membered rings.

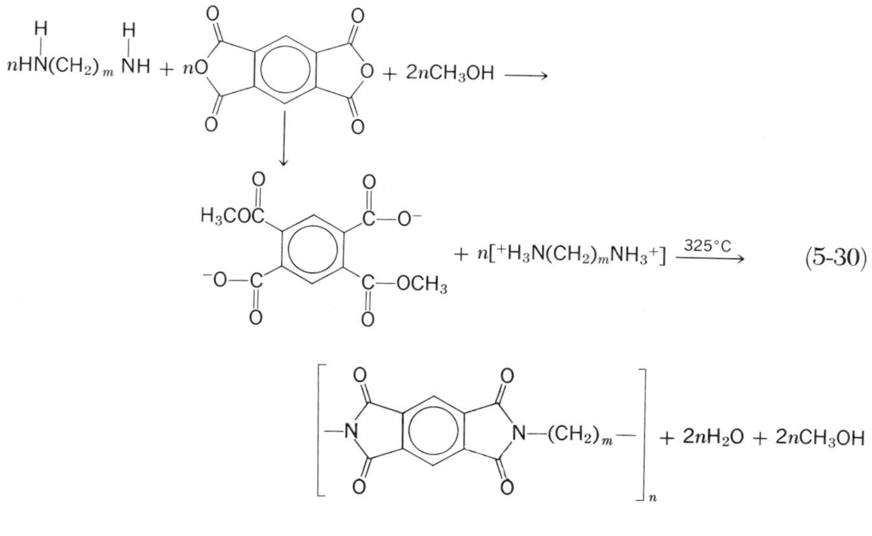

Equation for preparation of a polymellitimide

Linear polyimidazoles are obtained by the condensation of aliphatic dicarboxylic acids and aromatic tetraamines in the presence of phosphoric acid. Polymers with superior heat resistance are produced when both reactants are aromatic. Linear, gold-colored, semiladder-type polybenzimidazoles may be produced by the melt condensation of 3,3'-diaminobenzidine and diphenylisophthalate.

Higgins and Marvel also produced polyimidazoles by the condensation of 3,3'-diamobenzidine and salts of disulfonic acids by heating a solution of these reactants in dimethylacetamide at 70 to 160°C. These polymers may be cast as films or spun into fibers from the solutions of these polymers. The equation for this type of reaction is as follows:

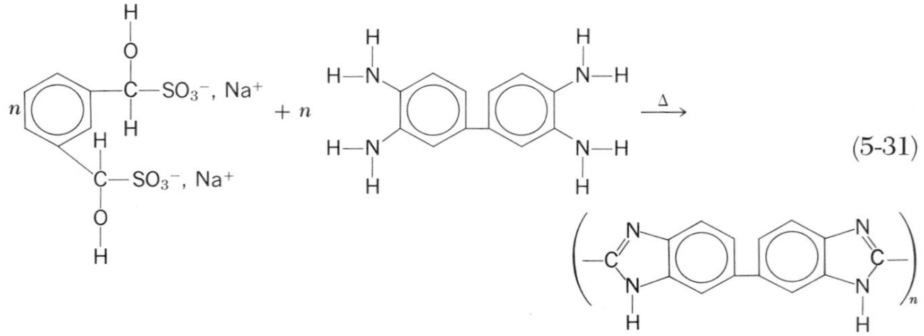

$$(5\text{-}31)$$

Equation for preparation of a polyimidazole

These and related linear heterocyclic polymers such as polythiazoles, poly(benzoxazoles), and poly(quinoxalines) in the form of films and fabricated parts are of great interest for aerospace applications. They are insoluble in most solvents and stable to thermal degradation at temperatures as high as 500°C and are called *semiladder polymers.*

In spite of their improved resistance to high temperatures, semiladder polymers have a vulnerable single link connecting the ladder-type segments of the chain. The excellent high-temperature resistance of graphite, which is a ladder-type polymer of carbon, suggests that superior products could be obtained by the synthesis of ladder- or spiro-type polymers which are simulated below:

Simulated ladder- and spiro-type polymers

Silicone ladder polymers (phenyl T) as shown below were described by Edwards in 1955.

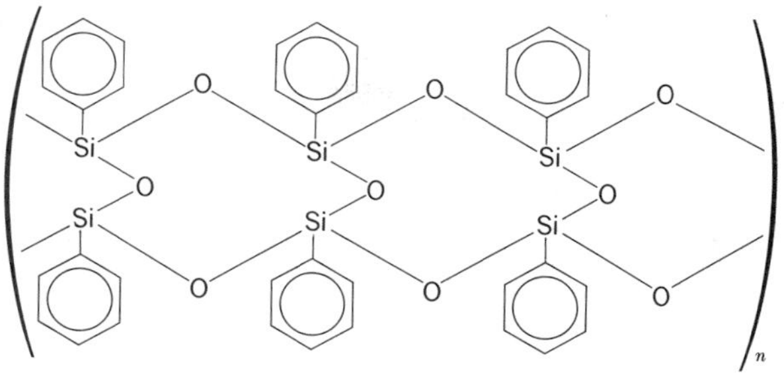

Silicone ladder polymers

$$(5\text{-}32)$$

As shown in the following equation, inorganic spiro polymers have been produced by the alkaline condensation of phosphinic acids and zinc salts of organic acids.

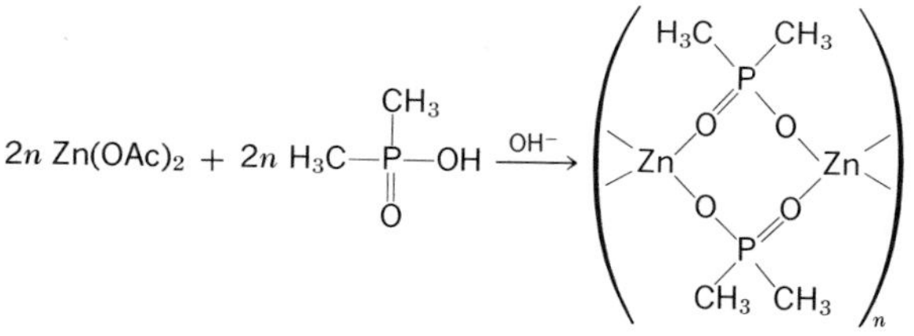

$$(5\text{-}33)$$

Inorganic spiro polymer

The oldest organic ladder polymer (fiber **AF**) was produced by the pyrolysis and oxidation of polyacrylonitrile, as shown by the following equation:

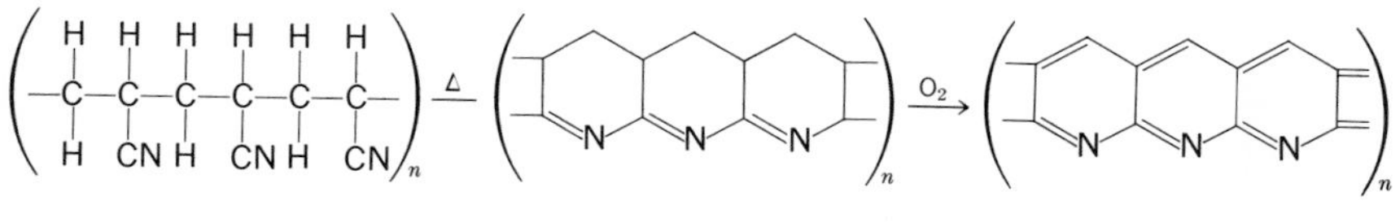

Equation for preparation of a ladder polymer $$(5\text{-}34)$$

Stille prepared other ladder polymers by heating 3,3,6,6-tetramethyl cyclohexane-1,2,4,5-tetrone with 1,2,4,5-tetraaminobenzene in dioxane and by heating 4,6-diaminoresorcinol dichloride with 3,6-dichloro-p-benzoquinone in hexamethyl phosphoramide.

REFERENCES

Allcock, H. R.: "Heteroatom Ring Systems and Polymers," Academic Press, Inc., New York, 1967.

Bannerman, D. G., and E. E. Magat: Polyamides and Polyesters, in C. E. Schildknecht (ed.), "Polymer Processes," chap. 7, Interscience Publishers, Inc., New York, 1951.

Bayer, O.: Polyurethanes, *Ann.*, **549**:286 (1941).

—— and E. Muller: Polyurethanes, *Angew. Chem.*, **72**:934 (1960).

Bertozzi, E. R.: Polysulfide Elastomers, *Rubber Chem. Technol.*, **41**(1):114 (1968).

Bjorksten, J., H. Tovey, B. Harker, and J. Henning: "Polyesters and Their Applications," Reinhold Publishing Corporation, New York, 1956.

Carothers, W. H.: Nylon, U.S. Patent 2,130,947, 1938.

—— and J. A. Arvin: Polyesters, *J. Am. Chem. Soc.*, **51**:2560 (1929).

Christopher, W. F., and D. W. Fox: "Polycarbonates," Reinhold Publishing Corporation, New York, 1962.

Courtright, J. R., and C. K. Ikeda: Polyimides, *Soc. Plastics Engrs.*, *RETEC*, Stability of Plastics, Washington, D.C., June, 1964.

Delman, A. D., A. A. Stein, and B. B. Simms: C. L. Segal (ed.), "High Temperature Polymers," Marcel Dekker, Inc., New York, 1967.

Dombrow, B. A.: "Polyurethanes," Reinhold Publishing Corporation, New York, 1957.

Eaborn, C.: "Organosilicon Compounds," Academic Press, Inc., New York, 1960.

Edwards, W. M. W., and V. M. Robinson: Silicone Ladder Polymers, U.S. Patent 2,710,853, 1955.

Fettes, E. M., and J. S. Jorczak: Polysulfides, in C. E. Schildknecht (ed.), "Polymer Processes," chap. 11, Interscience Publishers, Inc., New York, 1956.

Floyd, D. E.: "Polyamide Resins," Reinhold Publishing Corporation, New York, 1958.

Heacock, J. F., and C. E. Berr: Polyimides, *Soc. Plastics Engrs.*, *RETEC*, Stability of Plastics, Washington, D.C., June, 1964.

Hill, J. W., and W. H. Carothers: Polyanhydrides, *J. Am. Chem. Soc.*, **54**:1569 (1932); **55**:5023 (1933).

Hill, R.: "Fibers from Synthetic Polymers," Elsevier Publishing Company, Amsterdam, 1953.

Inderfurth, K. H.: "Nylon Technology," McGraw-Hill Book Company, New York, 1953.

Jorczak, J. S.: Polysulfide Polymers, in M. Morton (ed.), "Introduction to Rubber Technology," chap. 15, Reinhold Publishing Corporation, New York, 1959.

Kennedy, J. P., and R. B. Isaacson: Polybenzyl, *ACS Div. Polymer Chem.*, **7**(2):419 (1966).

Kovacic, P., and A. Kyriakis: Polyphenylenes, *J. Am. Chem. Soc.*, **83**:1697 (1961).

Lawrence, John R.: "Polyester Resins," Reinhold Publishing Corporation, New York, 1960.

Mark, H. F., and G. S. Whitby (eds.): "The Collected Papers of Wallace Hume Carothers," Interscience Publishers, Inc., New York, 1940.

—— and S. M. Atlas: Principles of Polymer Stability, *Soc. Plastics Engrs.*, *RETEC*, Stability of Plastics, Washington, D.C., June, 1964.

Martin, S. M., and J. C. Patrick: Thiokol, *Ind. Eng. Chem.*, **28**:1144 (1936).

Marvel, C. S.: Polyaromatic Heterocycles, *Soc. Plastics Engrs.*, Stability of Plastics, Washington, D.C., June, 1964.

——: Polyaromatic Heterocycles, *Proc. Robert A. Welch Found. Conf. Chem. Res.*, *10th Polymers, Houston*, 1967.

McGregor, R. R.: "Silicones and Their Uses," McGraw-Hill Book Company, New York, 1954.

Meals, R. N., and F. M. Lewis: "Silicones," Reinhold Publishing Corporation, New York, 1959.

Mukamal H., F. W. Harries, and J. K. Stille: Polyphenylenes, *J. Polymer Sci.*, *Pt. A-1*, **5**(1):2721 (1967).

Mulvaney, J. W.: Heat-resistant Polymers, in H. F. Mark, N. G. Gaylord, and N. M. Bikales (eds.), "Encyclopedia of Polymer Science and Technology," vol. 7, Interscience Publishers, a division of John Wiley & Sons, Inc., New York, 1967.

Post, H. W.: "Silicones and Other Organic Silicon Compounds," Reinhold Publishing Corporation, New York, 1940.

Ravve, A.: "Organic Chemistry of Macromolecules," Marcel Dekker, Inc., New York, 1967.

Rochow, E. G.: "An Introduction to the Chemistry of Silicones," John Wiley & Sons, Inc., New York, 1951.

Saunders, J. H., and K. C. Frisch: "Polyurethanes, Chemistry and Technology," vols. I and II, Interscience Publishers, a division of John Wiley & Sons, Inc., New York, 1964.

Seymour, R. B.: Nylon, Polyurethanes, in G. L. Clark and G. G. Hawley (eds.), "Encyclopedia of Chemistry," Reinhold Publishing Corporation, New York, 1966.

Stille, J. F., and M. E. Freeburger: Polyquinoxalines, *J. Polymer Sci.*, **5B**(11):989 (1967).

———— and ————: Ladder Polymers, *J. Polymer Sci.*, **6A-1**(1):161 (1968).

Whinfield, J. R.: Terylene, *Nature,* **158**:930 (1946).

5-3 RING-OPENING POLYMERIZATION

As stated previously, the condensation of compounds with two monofunctional groups may produce a linear polymer or a cyclic compound. In dilute solutions, the controlling reaction may be ring formation, provided strainless configurations are possible. In contrast, under appropriate conditions, strained rings may be opened and polymerization may take place preferentially. Thus, heterocyclic compounds, such as oxiranes, oxetanes, furans, lactams, and lactones, may be cleaved by aqueous alkalies or acids to yield intermediates which may add the cyclic compound in a so-called "step-addition" polymerization process. All intermediates may react with the reactants or with each other; almost all chains are initiated simultaneously in this step-addition polymerization. The chains with active ends propagate or grow at a similar rate by continuing to add cyclic molecules.

As shown in the following equations, the heterocyclic oxirane ring is cleaved by sodium methoxide dissolved in dioxane in the presence of a trace of methanol. The anion formed by this S_N2 reaction will cleave another oxirane ring which will add (propagate) to form a higher-molecular-weight anion. When large proportions of the oxirane to sodium methoxide (initiator) are present, long-chained molecules are formed; that is, n becomes a large number.

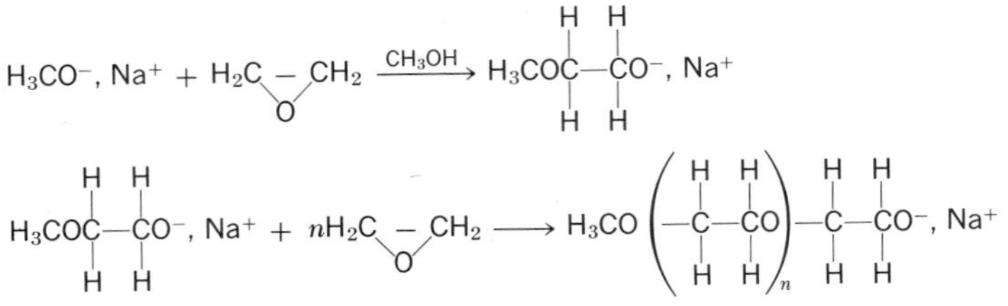

$$H_3CO^-, Na^+ + H_2C\underset{O}{\overset{}{-}}CH_2 \xrightarrow{CH_3OH} H_3CO\overset{\overset{H}{|}\overset{H}{|}}{\underset{\overset{|}{H}\overset{|}{H}}{C-C}}O^-, Na^+$$

$$(5\text{-}35)$$

$$H_3CO\overset{\overset{H}{|}\overset{H}{|}}{\underset{\overset{|}{H}\overset{|}{H}}{C-C}}O^-, Na^+ + nH_2C\underset{O}{\overset{}{-}}CH_2 \longrightarrow H_3CO\left(\overset{\overset{H}{|}\overset{H}{|}}{\underset{\overset{|}{H}\overset{|}{H}}{-C-C}O-}\right)_n\overset{\overset{H}{|}\overset{H}{|}}{\underset{\overset{|}{H}\overset{|}{H}}{C-C}}O^-, Na^+$$

Equations for the preparation of a polyoxirane

It may be shown that $\overline{M}_w/\overline{M}_n = 1 + n/(1 + n)^2$. Thus monodispersity is approached as n increases. The n or $\overline{DP}$ value is governed by the relative concentration of cyclic monomer and initiator. The polymer produced has hydroxyl end groups and is water-soluble. The degree of crystallinity increases and the hygroscopicity decreases as $\overline{DP}$ increases. These polymers may be prepared with $\overline{M}_n$ values ranging from 2 to 20 million. These products are available commercially (Carbowax, Polyox).

The ring opening of aziridine rings such as ethylene imine is much more complicated. The polymer produced (Montrek) is highly branched and is soluble in aqueous acid solutions. The equation for this ionic ring-opening polymerization is as follows:

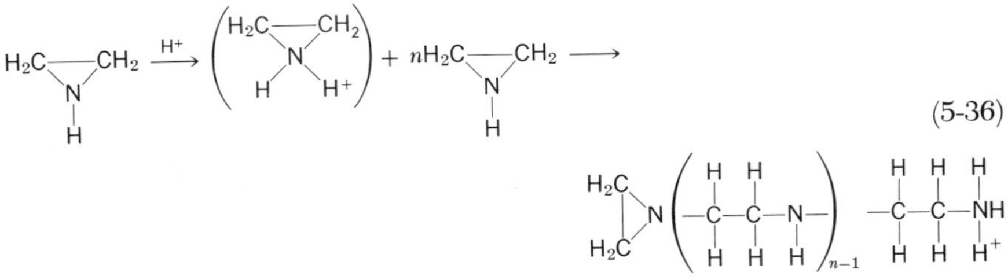

$$(5\text{-}36)$$

Equation for preparation of a polyaziridine

Oxetanes such as 3,3-bis(chloromethyl)-1-oxacyclobutane may be polymerized by initiators such as boron trifluoride etherate in a solvent such as chloroform. The rate of propagation is increased in the presence of an epoxide (oxirane) which serves as a promotor.

As shown in the following equation, the oxetane may be produced by the dehydrochlorination of trichlorinated pentaerythritol monoacetate. The latter is obtained by the hydrochlorination of the tetraacetate of pentaerythritol.

$$2n \left(AcO-\overset{\overset{H}{|}}{\underset{\overset{|}{H}}{C}} \right)_3 \overset{\overset{H}{|}}{\underset{\overset{|}{H}}{C}}-\overset{H}{\underset{\overset{|}{H}}{C}}-OAc \xrightarrow{6nHCl} 2n \left(ClC \overset{\overset{H}{|}}{\underset{\overset{|}{H}}{}} \right)_3 \overset{H}{\underset{\overset{|}{H}}{C}}-\overset{H}{\underset{\overset{|}{H}}{C}}-OAc \xrightarrow{2nNaOH}$$

$$(5\text{-}37)$$

$$2n \left(ClC \overset{\overset{H}{|}}{\underset{\overset{|}{H}}{}} \right)_2 -C \underset{\underset{H_2}{C}}{\overset{\overset{H_2}{C}}{\diagdown}} O \xrightarrow{BF_3} \left(\begin{matrix} Cl & Cl \\ | & | \\ H & HCH & H & H & HCH & H \\ -C-C-C-O- & C-C-C-O- \\ H & HCH & H & H & HCH & H \\ | & | \\ Cl & Cl \end{matrix} \right)_n$$

Equation for preparation of a polyoxetane

These linear polyoxetanes (Penton) have a high degree of crystallinity and are characterized by excellent resistance to solvents and corrosives.

Ring opening of tetrahydrofuran by Lewis acids such as boron trifluoride etherate also yields high-molecular-weight linear polymers. These polymerizations may be accelerated by the addition of traces of oxiranes which serve as promotors for cleavage of the relatively stable five-membered rings.

Nonlinear polymers of formaldehyde may be formed when aqueous solutions of formaldehyde are heated in the presence of aqueous acids or alkalies. This polymerization is inhibited by methanol, and the products are readily decomposed by heat. Commercial polymers of formaldehyde (Delrin, Celcon)(POM) are produced by the ring opening of a pure trioxane in the presence of Lewis acid initiators such as boron trifluoride etherate.

It has been postulated that a resonance-stabilized zwitterion results from the reaction of the initiator and these active complexes at low temperatures in inert solvents such as hexane. As shown in the following equation, the polymers have hydroxyl end groups and hence are readily depolymerized.

Esterification by acetic anhydride (capping) produces a more stable polymer. Polymerization in the presence of small amounts of ethylene oxide or dioxolane yields a stable copolymer. The molecular weight is controlled by the addition of a small amount of water which serves as a chain transfer agent.

$$n\,H\overset{\overset{H}{|}}{C}{=}O \longrightarrow \frac{n}{3} O \underset{\underset{H_2}{C-O}}{\overset{\overset{H_2}{C-O}}{\diagup}} CH_2 \longrightarrow HO-\overset{H}{\underset{\overset{|}{H}}{C}} \left(O-\overset{H}{\underset{\overset{|}{H}}{C}} \right)_{n-2} -O-\overset{H}{\underset{\overset{|}{H}}{C}}-OH \xrightarrow{Ac_2O}$$

$$(5\text{-}38)$$

$$AcO-\overset{H}{\underset{\overset{|}{H}}{C}} \left(O-\overset{H}{\underset{\overset{|}{H}}{C}} \right)_{n-2} -O-\overset{H}{\underset{\overset{|}{H}}{C}}-OAc$$

Equation for preparation of a polymer from formaldehyde

Polymers of formaldehyde (acetals) are characterized by a high degree of crystallinity and solvent resistance. The crystalline structure is similar to that of polyethylene. However, acetal polymers are denser, harder, and higher melting than ethylene polymers. Both the polymer and copolymer are readily hydrolyzed by aqueous acids.

That polymers of amino acids (polypeptides) could be produced by heating carboanhydrides was demonstrated by Leuchs in 1908. These carboanhydrides may be produced by the phosgenation of α-amino acids. In the mechanism proposed by Woodward, alkalies such as sodium methylate in dioxane serve as initiators for the ionic polymerization, as shown in the following equation:

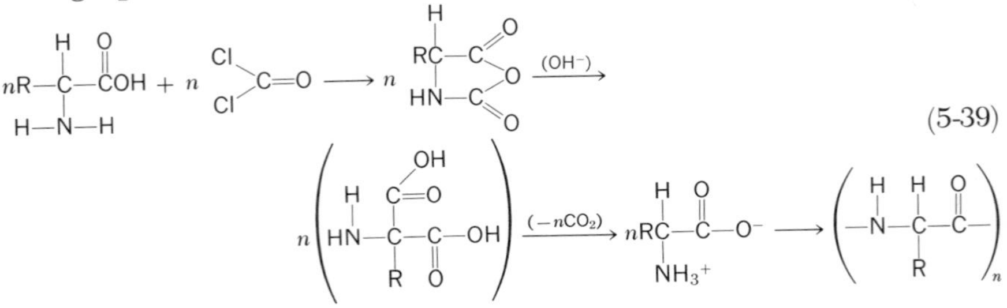

$$(5\text{-}39)$$

Equation for preparation of a synthetic polypeptide (nylon 2)

This polymerization technique has been used to produce a polymer of D-glutamic acid [$HOOC(CH_2)_2CH(NH_2)COOH$] which, like the polypeptide present in *B. subtilus*, is resistant to proteolytic enzymatic hydrolysis. This polymer may be called nylon 2 since it has two carbon atoms in each unit in the chain.

Nylon 5, nylon 6, nylon 8, and nylon 12 have also been produced by ring-opening polymerization of appropriate lactams. As shown by the following equation, nylon 5 is produced by the aqueous alkaline opening of valerolactam. The latter is obtained by the Beckmann rearrangement of cyclopentanone oxime. Acetic acid is used as a chain-length regulator.

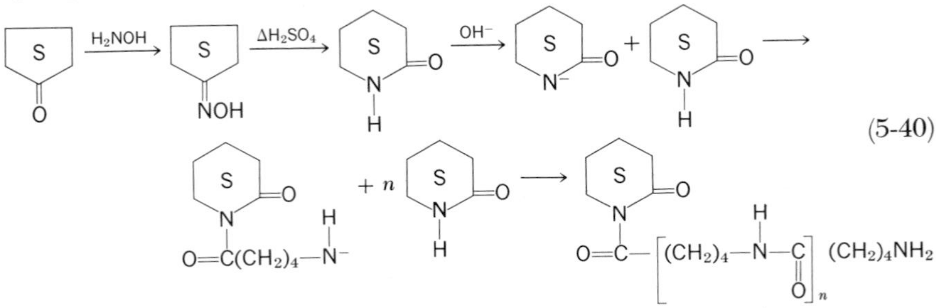

$$(5\text{-}40)$$

Equation for preparation of nylon 5

As shown by the following equation, nylon 6 is produced by the ring-opening polymerization of ε-caprolactam which is obtained by the Beckmann rearrangement of cyclohexanone oxime.

$$ n \underset{}{\overset{}{\bigcirc}}=NOH \xrightarrow{\Delta H_2SO_4} n \underset{}{\overset{}{\bigcirc}}=O \xrightarrow{OH^-} \left[-(CH_2)_5-\overset{H}{\underset{}{N}}-\overset{}{\underset{O}{C}}- \right]_n \qquad (5\text{-}41) $$

Equation for preparation of nylon 6

Because of the odd number of methylene groups in each unit, the melting point of nylon 6 is less than that of nylon 5. To achieve hydrogen bonding without distortion, the nylon 6 chains must be aligned in opposite directions (antiparallel). In the absence of this arrangement the chains must be twisted to permit hydrogen bonding. These conformations are more readily attained as the number of methylene groups is increased in nylons from higher-molecular-weight lactams.

Nylon 8 and nylon 12 are prepared by ring-opening polymerization of capryllactam and lauryllactam. The corresponding cyclic oximes are obtained from the cyclic dimer and trimer of butadiene. This polymerization takes place readily when caprolactam is heated at 150°C in the presence of sodium hydroxide and sodium acetate. Thus, propellant binders or large castings may be produced readily by in situ polymerization. Higher temperatures are required for ring-opening polymerization of higher-molecular-weight lactams. The melting points of these polymers are as follows: nylon 5, 260°C; nylon 6, 220°C; nylon 8, 195°C; and nylon 12, 180°C.

Lactones with 3, 4, 5, and 8 atoms may be polymerized by ring opening in the presence of aqueous alkaline solutions. In contrast, five-membered rings like γ-valerolactone are relatively free from strain and have little tendency to open and form linear polymers. The six-membered rings like δ-valerolactone have more strain and may yield some polymer. However, the tendency to produce linear polymers is reduced if substituents are present on the lactone ring.

Even those polyesters produced from lactones in good yields are unstable and have a tendency to revert to lactones. Carothers prepared polyesters from cyclic carbonates, glycolates, and oxalates by ring-opening polymerization.

Cyclic anhydrides like phthalic anhydrides react readily with difunctional alcohols to yield polyesters. However, the step-reaction polymerization that results is similar to that with the dicarboxylic acids discussed previously under polyesterifications.

REFERENCES

Akin, R. B.: "Acetal Resins," Reinhold Publishing Corporation, New York, 1962.

Bailey, W. J., and R. E. Hartz: Polymethylene Imine, ACS *Div. Polymer Chem., Polymer Preprints,* **9**(1):404 (1968).

Blout, E. R., R. H. Karlson, P. Doty, and B. Hargitay: Polypeptides, *J. Am. Chem. Soc.,* **76**:4492 (1954).

Boardman, H.: Oxetanes, in W. M. Smith (ed.), "Manufacture of Plastics," chap. 15, Reinhold Publishing Corporation, New York, 1964.

Burrows, R. C.: Polytetrahydrofuran, ACS *Div. Polymer Chem., Polymer Preprints,* **6**(2):600 (1965).

Davidson, R. L., and M. Sittig: "Water Soluble Resins," Reinhold Publishing Corporation, New York, 1962.

Farthing, A. C.: Oxetanes, *J. Appl. Chem.,* **8**:188-8 (1958).

Furukawa, J., and T. Saegusa: "Polymerization of Aldehydes and Oxides," Interscience Publishers, a division of John Wiley & Sons, Inc., New York, 1962.

Hall, H. K.: Nylons, Polyesters, *J. Am. Chem. Soc.,* **80**:6404, 6412 (1958).

McDonald, R. N.: Polyformaldehyde, U.S. Patent 2,768,994, Oct. 30, 1956.

Seymour, R. B.: Acetals, Polyoxyethylenes, in G. L. Clark and G. G. Hawley (eds.), "Encyclopedia of Chemistry," Reinhold Publishing Corporation, New York, 1966.

Sittig, M.: "Polyacetal Resins," Gulf Publishing Company, Houston, 1963.

Vogl, O.: "Polyaldehydes," Marcel Dekker, Inc., New York, 1967.

Woodward, R. B., and C. H. Schramm: Polypeptides, *J. Am. Chem. Soc.,* **69**:1552 (1947).

5-4 NONLINEAR STEP-REACTION POLYMERIZATION

When a trifunctional alcohol such as glycerol condenses with a dibasic acid or anhydride, such as phthalic acid or phthalic anhydride, the chain contains active hydroxyl pendant groups which may react independently of the chain ends. The extent of theoretical crosslinking or network polymer formation may be predicted from a modification of the Carothers' equation (5-7).

The modification includes a functionality factor (f) which is equal to the average number of functional groups present per reactive molecule. Thus, in this modification, when the average degree of functionality is 2, the equation $p = (C_0 - C)/C_0$ becomes $p = 2[(C_0 - C)/C_0 f]$ and Eq. (5-3) for number average

$$\overline{DP} = \frac{N_0}{N} = \frac{C_0}{C} = \frac{1}{1 - p}$$

becomes

$$\overline{DP} = \frac{C_0}{C_0[(1-pf)/2]} = \frac{2}{2-pf} \qquad (5\text{-}42)$$

Carothers' equation for polymerization of multifunctional reactants

This equation incorrectly assumes that all groups are equally reactive and that no cyclization occurs. However, the equation may be used to predict the degree of crosslinking in step-reaction polymerization. Thus, in the esterification of 1 mole of phthalic anhydride by 0.9 mole of ethylene glycol and 0.1 mole of glycerol, $f = 2.1$ (1.8 + 0.3). Therefore, for a 95 percent yield, the $\overline{DP}$ would be 200.

$$\overline{DP} = \frac{2}{2-pf} = \frac{2}{2-0.95(2.1)} = 200$$

This high molecular weight may be contrasted to the same step-reaction polymerization in the absence of glycerol. Thus, with stoichiometric quantities of the difunctional reactants, a 95 percent yield would produce a $\overline{DP}$ of 20. A $\overline{DP}$ of 25 would result from a 96 percent yield in the absence of glycerol.

However, a $\overline{DP}$ of infinity is obtained theoretically with a 96 percent yield in the presence of 0.1 mole of glycerol. If the concentration of glycerol is increased to 0.2 so that $f = 2.4$, incipient gel formation (that is, $\overline{DP} = \infty$) should occur with a 87.5 percent yield. However, the practical gel points differ from those calculated because of erroneous assumptions and the lack of detectability of the initial microgel by ordinary techniques.

In contrast, even a 98 percent yield should not cause gel formation in the presence of glycerol when f is not greater than 2,

$$\overline{DP} = \frac{2}{2-pf} = \frac{2}{2-0.98(2)} = 50$$

Thus, by control of the relative number of functional groups, it is theoretically possible to obtain polymers of finite molecular weight when trifunctional groups are present in the reactants.

When glycerol and phthalic anhydride are condensed, the first step reaction involves a preferential esterification of the primary hydroxyl groups. Thus, as shown in the equations below, linear glyceryl mono- and diphthalates may be produced. These esters contain unreacted secondary hydroxyl groups which may react further to produce network polyesters (glyptals).

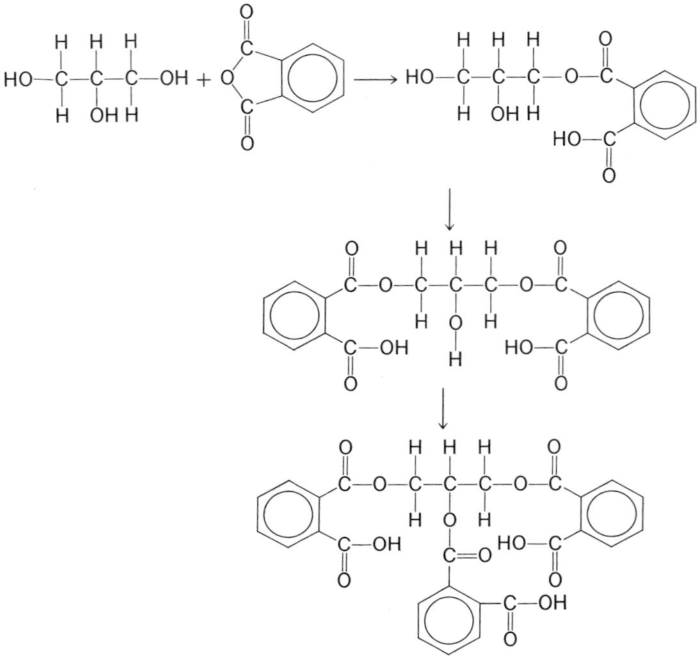

$$(5\text{-}43)$$

Equations for preparation of a network polyester resin

The general reaction for the step-reaction polymerization of a bifunctional monomer AA and a trifunctional monomer BBB may be illustrated by the following equation:

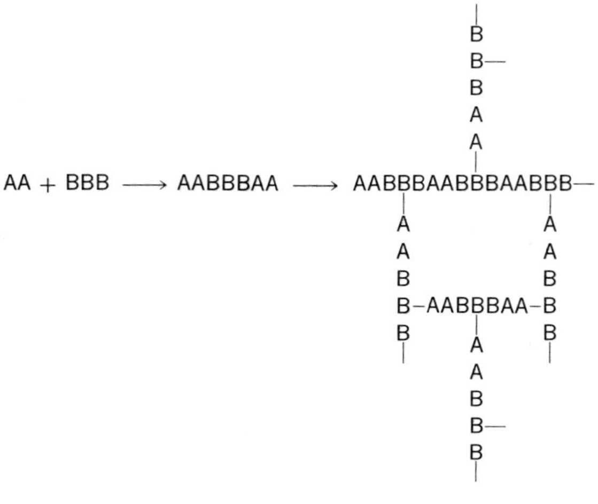

$$AA + BBB \longrightarrow AABBBAA \longrightarrow AABBBAABBBAABBB—$$

```
                                          |
                                          B
                                          B—
                                          B
                                          A
                                          A
AA + BBB ⟶ AABBBAA ⟶ AABBBAABBBAABBB—
                          |                 |
                          A                 A
                          A                 A
                          B                 B
                          B—AABBBAA—B
                          B        |        B
                          |        A        |
                                   A
                                   B
                                   B—
                                   B
                                   |
```

$$(5\text{-}44)$$

Illustration of a simulated network polymer

The degree of crosslinking of saturated polyesters may be controlled by the functionality, i.e., the relative amounts of functional groups present in the reactants. The functionality may be reduced by the addition of mono-functional reactants such as monobasic acids or monohydric alcohols.

The functionality of polyesters from difunctional reactants may be increased by the addition of unsaturated reactants. Kienle coined the term *alkyds* to describe polyesters produced from phthalic anhydride, glycerol, and unsaturated acids such as oleic or linoleic acid. The linear unsaturated esters are thermoplastic and soluble, but they may be crosslinked by *chain-reaction polymerization* through the double bonds present.

This polymerization (curing) in the presence of oxygen is catalyzed by metallic salts such as lead naphthenate (driers). Ellis showed that comparable unsaturation could be introduced in the molecule by using maleic anhydride in place of part of the phthalic anhydride. The curing of these unsaturated polyesters by initiators such as benzoyl peroxide is also a chain-reaction polymerization, which is discussed in Chap. 6.

Part of the glycerol may be replaced by ethylene glycol, glyceryl esters, or pentaerythritol [$(HOCH_2)_4C$]. The degree of unsaturation of the alkyds is expressed in the paint trade as short, medium, and long oil alkyds in accordance with the relative amount of unsaturated acid added. Alkyds may be prepared in inert atmospheres as solvent-free melts or as solutions in solvents, such as xylene. Their use varies from printing-ink resins to protective coatings, such as refrigerator enamels.

The so-called "polyester resins," which are polyfunctional because of the presence of ethylenic groups, are usually prepared from propylene glycol, phthalic anhydride, and maleic anhydride. These unsaturated polyesters are usually dissolved in styrene and polymerized by a chain-reaction mechanism. In one modification, isophthalic acid is used in place of phthalic anhydride. Another commercial polyester resin (Atlac 382) is produced by the condensation of fumaric acid and prodendro bisphenol A, as shown below:

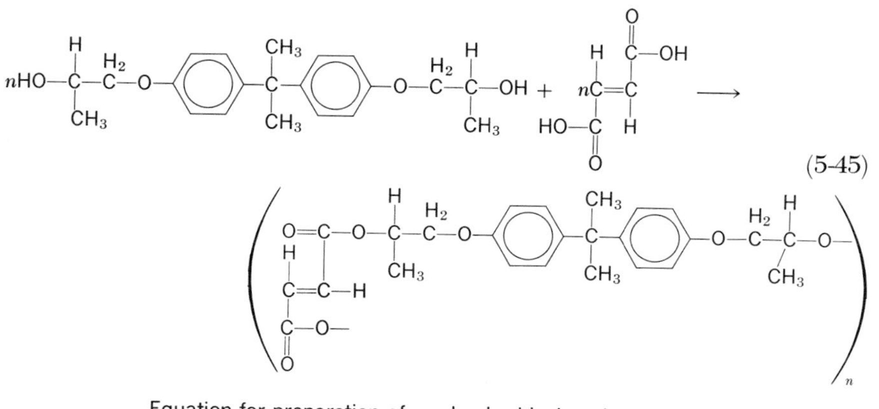

$$(5\text{-}45)$$

Equation for preparation of prodendro bisphenol A fumarate

The difunctionality of formaldehyde was demonstrated in the first part of this chapter by the preparation of linear polymers or acetals. Thus network polymers may be produced when formaldehyde is condensed with phenol since the latter has three reactive positions (two ortho and one para). Several eminent chemists such as Von Baeyer and Tollens produced network polymers by this reaction over a century ago.

Since these scientists were unfamiliar with the importance of the concept of functionality, they avoided polymer synthesis. Their decision to concentrate their research efforts on crystalline low-molecular-weight products affected potential contributions in polymer chemistry by several generations of chemists. Modern chemists. who consider courses in polymer chemistry unimportant, should remember that the phenolic "gunk" that was discarded by Von Baeyer is now produced at an annual rate of over 1 billion pounds.

This large-scale production, which exceeds that of almost all crystalline compounds, is a tribute to Baekeland's understanding of functionality. Over two decades before the development of the Carothers' equation, Baekeland produced linear polymers of phenol and formaldehyde (PF) under both alkaline and acid conditions.

Baekeland obtained thermoplastic resoles (one-stage resins) by adding stoichiometric quantities of formaldehyde to phenol under alkaline conditions. He also produced thermoplastic novolacs (two-stage resins) by using less than stoichiometric quantities of formaldehyde under acid conditions. Berend prepared oil-soluble thermoplastic resins (Albertols) by adding rosin to the reactants.

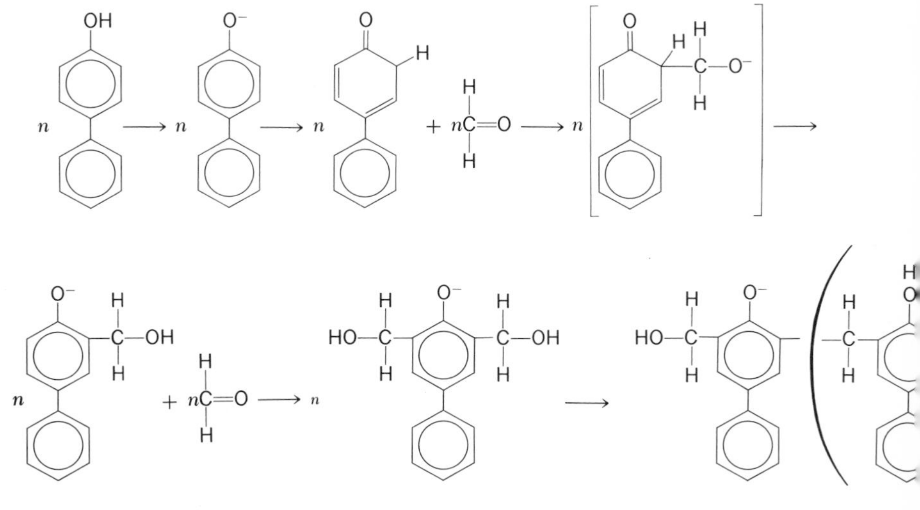

Equation for preparation of an oil-soluble phenolic resin

The significance of these reactions may now be appreciated through the use of Carothers' equation. The typical condensation reaction may be interpreted from a study of oil-soluble phenolic resins. These polymers may be prepared by the condensation of formaldehyde with p-phenyl phenol. As shown by the preceding equation (5-46), the blocking of the para position reduces the functionality of phenol to 2. Hence the reaction is similar to those discussed previously under step-reaction polymerization.

These oil-soluble resins, which have average molecular weights of less than 2,000, are used by the paint and varnish industry as replacements for natural resins. The mechanism for the formation of resoles by the alkaline condensation of phenol and formaldehyde is similar to that for the preparation of oil-soluble resins. These resoles crosslink on standing or when heated. The addition of acid accelerates the formation of network polymer from resoles. These resins are used for laminating and casting.

Hultszch suggested that novolacs result from the reaction of an electrophilic formaldehyde-proton complex and phenol under acid conditions. As shown by the following equation, the cation produced reacts with the oxonium form of phenol to produce a bishydroxy(diphenyl methane).

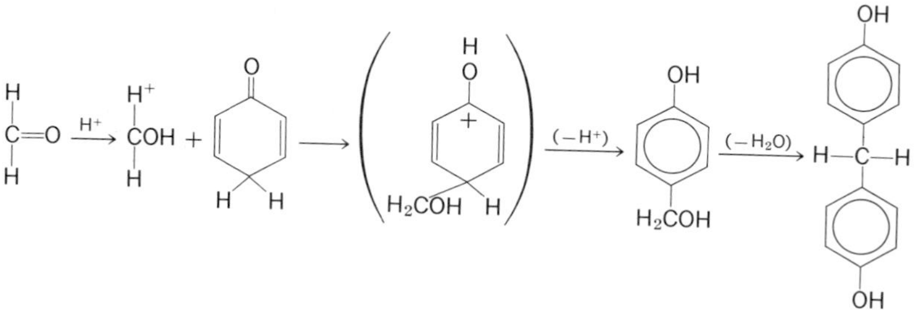

Equation for preparation of bishydroxy(diphenyl methane)

When less than stoichiometric quantities of formaldehyde are present, A-stage thermoplastic resins with molecular weights of 1,000 to 1,500 are obtained. These novolac resins may be admixed (compounded) with fillers such as wood flour, pigments, and hexamethylene tetramine to produce moldable resins. When the mixture is heated, the hexamethylene tetramine decomposes to yield formaldehyde which methylolates the available reactive centers in the benzene rings.

The moldings that result are insoluble and infusible. However, unlike the comparable products prepared by Von Baeyer, these end products are in the desired shape of the mold cavity. Phenolic moldings are used for electrical parts and for other applications where resistance to boiling water is essential and where the dark color is not objectionable. Phenolic resins are resistant to nonoxidizing acids such as hydrochloric acid but they are not resistant to nitric acid nor to alkalies, such as aqueous sodium hydroxide solutions.

Resorcinol (*m*-hydroxyphenol) has the same functionality but, like other meta-substituted phenols, is much more reactive than phenol. Resorcinol condenses with paraformaldehyde when admixed at room temperature. Another meta-substituted phenol (cardinol), which is obtained from cashew nuts, may also be condensed with paraformaldehyde to produce a solid flexible infusible condensate. Since cardinol is related to urushiol, found in poison ivy, it is irritating to the skin.

Since paraformaldehyde yields formaldehyde under the conditions used for the production of novolacs or resoles, it may be used in place of formaldehyde. Acrolein and chloral have been used experimentally. Furfural has been used commercially to produce phenolic resins (Durite) with improved flow properties. Aniline has also been used in place of phenol to produce an acid-soluble yellow resin (Cibanite).

The term *aminoplast* has been used as a general name to describe step-reaction-polymerization products of aldehydes, such as formaldehyde, and nitrogen compounds, such as urea, melamine, and guanidine. Each urea molecule contains four reactive hydrogens but only two are methylolated by formaldehyde under alkaline conditions. As shown by the following equation, crosslinking of the dimethylol urea occurs under acid conditions to form infusible urea resins (UF). Marvel suggested that the network polymerization is preceded by the formation of a cyclic trimer, as shown below:

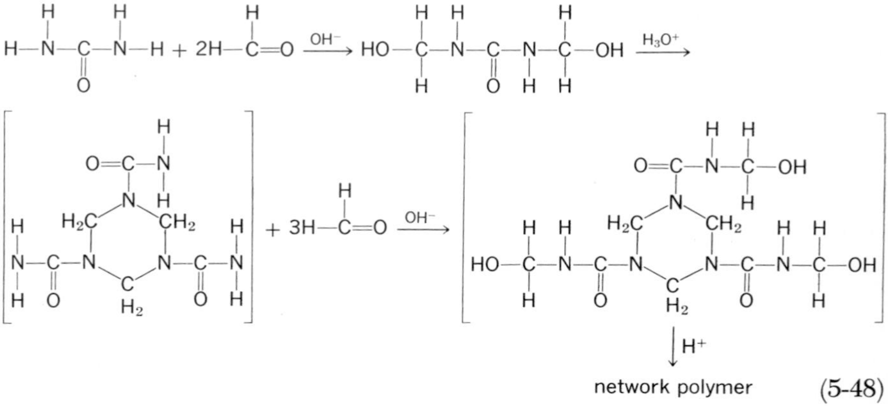

network polymer   (5-48)

Equation for the preparation of a urea resin

The crosslinking reaction may be delayed by the addition of hexamethylene tetramine, ammonium carbonate, or phenyl silicate. The addition of monohydric alcohols such as *n*-butanol yields a more soluble ether-type resinous product, with a bulky pendant group, that is used for coatings. The unfilled urea resins are also used as adhesives for the production of wet-strength paper and for laminates.

Molding powders are prepared by adding α-cellulose or wood flour as fillers. Urea-formaldehyde moldings (Plaskon, Beetle) are less expensive and lighter in color than phenolic moldings. They are more resistant to electrical tracking but have lower resistance to heat and moisture.

Guanidine

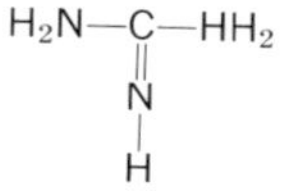

$$H_2N-\underset{\underset{H}{\overset{\|}{N}}}{C}-HH_2$$

and thiourea

$$H_2N-\underset{\overset{\|}{S}}{C}-NH_2$$

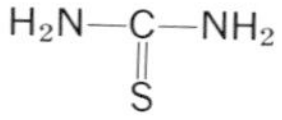

also contain four potentially reactive hydrogen atoms. These compounds react with formaldehyde to yield aminoplasts which may be used as substitutes or as supplements for urea resins. *p*-Toluenesulfonamide ($H_3CC_6H_4SO_2NH_2$) also condenses with formaldehyde to produce a thermoplastic resin (Santolite).

Melamine resins (Cymel, Melmac, Resimene) (MF) are produced by the formylation of melamine (2,4,6-triamino-1,3,5-triazine). This compound has six active hydrogen atoms and hence forms mono-, di-, tri-, tetra-, penta-, and hexamethylol melamines. The methylol derivatives may be etherified with alcohols such as *n*-butanol. A hexamethyl ether (hexamethoxymethyl melamine) is commercially available and may be used as an intermediate. The reactions leading to resinification of melamine are shown in the following equation:

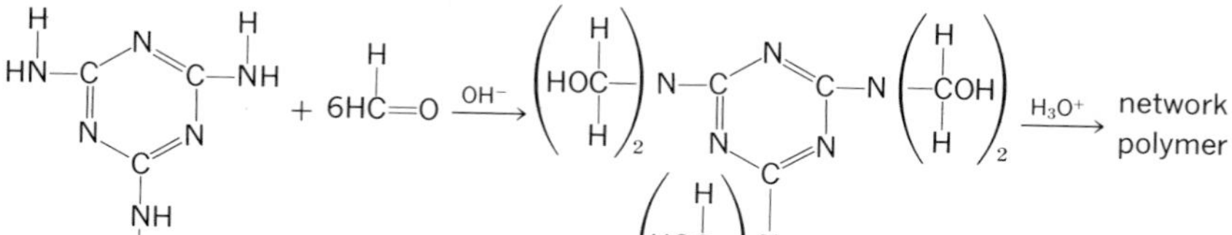

$$(5\text{-}49)$$

Equation for preparation of a melamine resin

Melamine resins are more heat-resistant than urea resins. They are used as coatings, adhesives, and molding powders. Guanamines (2,4-diamino-6-alkyl-1,3,5-triazine) have four reactive hydrogen atoms and also react with formaldehyde. Guanamines also react with acetaldehyde to form hydroxyethyl guanamines which undergo subsequent resinification.

The terms *epoxy resin* (EP) and *ethoxyline resin* are used to describe polyphenols or other compounds which resinify by ring opening of oxirane rings. The polyphenols may be diphenylolmethane (bisphenol F), the reaction product of resorcinol and acetone, or bisphenol A. The latter, 2,2-bis(4-hydroxyphenyl)propane, which is obtained by the condensation of phenol and acetone is the most widely used polyphenol for epoxy resin production.

Glycidyl ethers were prepared from phenols and epichlorohydrin by Lindermann in the last part of the nineteenth century. Glycidyl ethers of polyphenols were investigated by Schlack in the 1930s and by Castan and Greenlee in the 1940s. It is of interest to note that a moldable thermoplastic polymer related to epoxy resins (Phenoxy) was introduced commercially in the 1960s.

The most widely used epoxy resin intermediates (Araldite, Epon, Epi-Rez) are produced from the reaction of bisphenol A and epichlorohydrin, as shown in the following equation:

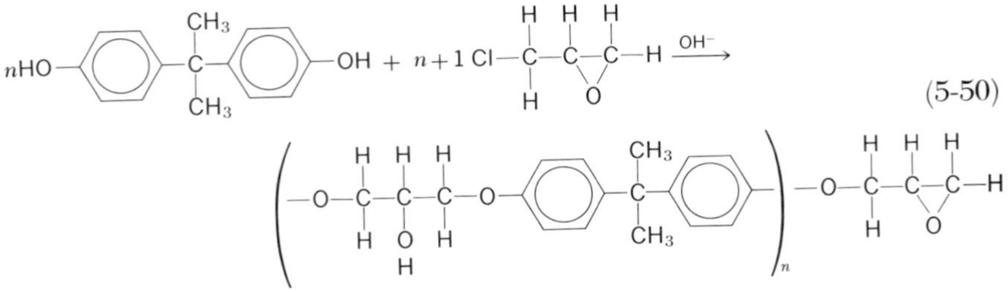

$$(5\text{-}50)$$

Equation for preparation of an epoxy resin intermediate

Liquids are produced when high ratios of epichlorohydrin to bisphenol A are used. Solids with n values of 10 to 12 are produced by using higher proportions of the polyphenol.

Compounds with oxirane rings may also be produced by the reaction of peracetic acid with unsaturated compounds. The epoxidized oils obtained by the reaction of peracetic acid and vegetable oils are used as stabilizers for poly(vinyl chloride) resins. The epoxides obtained from butadiene oligomers or cyclohexenes may be used for resin production.

These oxiranes may undergo ring-opening polymerization similar to ethylene oxide in the presence of acidic or basic catalysts. Polyamines such as diethylene triamine are widely used for the production of network polymers at room temperature. Amides with amine end groups (Versamids) obtained from the reaction of diamines and dicarboxylic acids are also used as room-temperature curing agents for epoxy resins.

These ring-opening reactions take place in the presence of traces of proton donors such as water or methanol. The essential reactions in this type of polymerization are shown in the following equations:

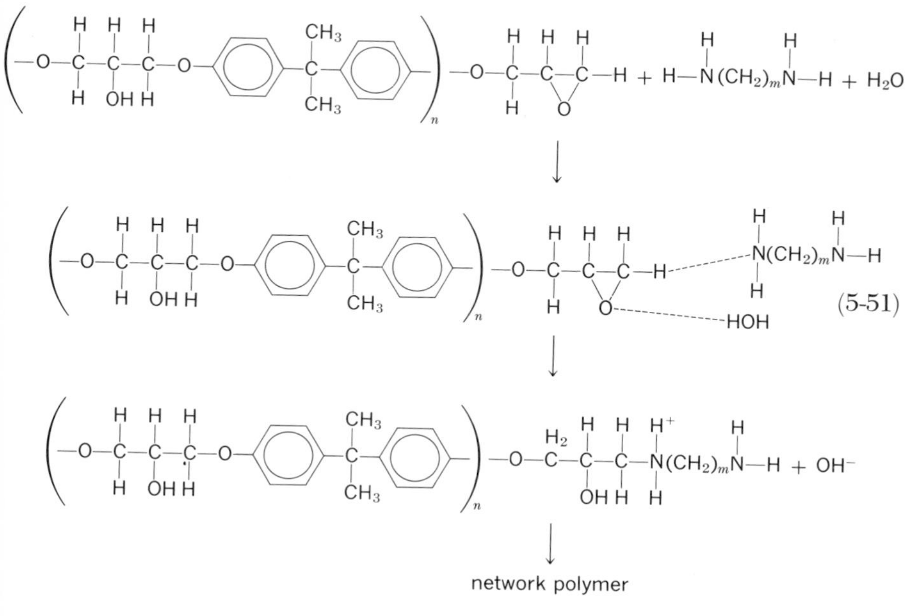

$$
\left(-O-\overset{H}{\underset{H}{C}}-\overset{H}{\underset{OH}{C}}-\overset{H}{\underset{H}{C}}-O-\bigcirc-\overset{CH_3}{\underset{CH_3}{C}}-\bigcirc\right)_n \quad -O-\overset{H}{\underset{H}{C}}-\overset{H}{C}\overset{H}{\underset{O}{\diagdown}}C-H \; + \; H-\overset{H}{N}(CH_2)_m\overset{H}{N}-H \; + \; H_2O
$$

$$\downarrow$$

$$
\left(-O-\overset{H}{\underset{H}{C}}-\overset{H}{\underset{OH}{C}}-\overset{H}{\underset{H}{C}}-O-\bigcirc-\overset{CH_3}{\underset{CH_3}{C}}-\bigcirc\right)_n \quad -O-\overset{H}{\underset{H}{C}}-\overset{H}{C}\overset{H}{\underset{O\text{-----}}{\diagdown}}C-H\text{-----}\overset{H}{\underset{H}{N}}(CH_2)_m\overset{H}{N}-H
$$
$$\text{-----HOH}$$
(5-51)

$$\downarrow$$

$$
\left(-O-\overset{H}{\underset{H}{C}}-\overset{H}{\underset{OH}{C}}-\overset{H}{\underset{H}{C}}-O-\bigcirc-\overset{CH_3}{\underset{CH_3}{C}}-\bigcirc\right)_n \quad -O-\overset{H_2}{C}-\overset{H}{\underset{OH}{C}}-\overset{H}{\underset{H}{C}}-\overset{H^+}{\underset{}{N}}(CH_2)_m\overset{H}{N}-H \; + \; OH^-
$$

$$\downarrow$$

network polymer

Equations for the curing of an epoxy resin

Epoxy resins may also be cured by heating with cyclic anhydrides such as phthalic anhydride. A half ester is formed by the reaction of the hydroxyl group in the epoxy resin. The carboxyl group formed may then react with either a hydroxyl group or an oxirane ring.

Filled epoxy resins are used for the manufacture of tools for aircraft and automobiles. The catalyzed liquid resins may be used as potting compounds, adhesives, and components of asphalt or coal-tar coatings. Skidproof surfaces are produced by sprinkling coarse aggregates on partly cured epoxy resin surfaces.

Furan resins are produced by the polymerization of furfural or furfuryl alcohol in the presence of acids. Furfural is produced by the acid hydrolysis of hemicellulose from corncobs or bagasse. It may be reduced to the alcohol by catalytic hydrogenation. It is assumed that the first step in the resinification of furfuryl alcohol is dehydration to form methylene bridges between the furan rings. As shown in the following equation, this is followed by a chain-reaction polymerization of the double-bonded carbons. The kinetics of this type of polymerization will be discussed in Chap. 6.

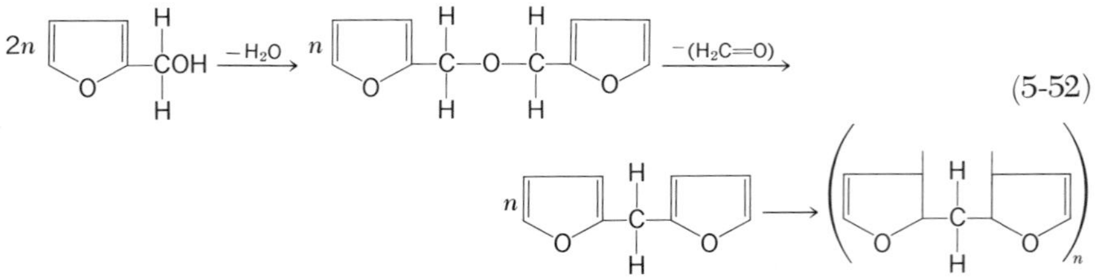

$$(5\text{-}52)$$

Equation for preparation of a furan resin

These dark-colored resins are characterized by excellent resistance to alkalies and nonoxidizing acids. They have been used for laminates, as impregnants, and as cements.

REFERENCES

Baeyer, A.: Phenol-Formaldehyde Condensates, *Ber.*, **5**:280, 1094 (1878).

Bjorksten, J., H. Tovey, B. Harker, and J. Henning: "Polyesters and Their Applications," Reinhold Publishing Corporation, New York, 1956.

Bradgon, C. R.: "Film Formation, Film Properties and Film Deterioration," Interscience Publishers, a division of John Wiley & Sons, Inc., New York, 1958.

Carswell, T. S.: "Phenoplasts, Their Structure, Properties and Chemical Technology," Interscience Publishers, Inc., New York, 1947.

Corkum, R. T., W. F. Herbes, L. C. Lane, and W. N. Oldham: Melamines, in W. M. Smith (ed.), "Manufacture of Plastics," chap. 9, Reinhold Publishing Corporation, New York, 1964.

Dunlap, A. P., and F. N. Peters: "The Furans," Reinhold Publishing Corporation, New York, 1953.

Delmonte, John: Furane Resins, *Mod. Plastics*, **44**(1A):172 (1966).

Gould, D. F.: "Phenolic Resins," Reinhold Publishing Corporation, New York, 1959.

Hutz, C. E.: Epoxy Resins, in W. M. Smith (ed.), "Manufacture of Plastics," chap. 13, Reinhold Publishing Corporation, New York, 1964.

Kienle, R. H.: Alkyds, *Ind. Eng. Chem.*, **22:**590 (1930); **55:**229T (1936).

Lawrence, J. R.: "Polyester Resins," Reinhold Publishing Corporation, New York, 1960.

Lee, H., and K. Neville: "Epoxy Resins: Their Application and Technology," McGraw-Hill Book Company, New York, 1957.

——— and ———: "Handbook of Epoxy Resins," McGraw-Hill Book Company, New York, 1966.

Martens, C. R.: "Alkyd Resins," Reinhold Publishing Corporation, New York, 1961.

Martin, R. W.: "The Chemistry of Phenolic Resins," John Wiley & Sons, Inc., New York, 1956.

Megson, N. J. L.: "Phenolic Resin Chemistry," Academic Press, Inc., New York, 1958.

Patton, T. C.: "Alkyd Resins Technology," Interscience Publishers, a division of John Wiley & Sons, Inc., New York, 1962.

Payne, C. R., and R. B. Seymour: Furan Resins, U.S. Patent 2,366,049, Dec. 26, 1944.

Raff, R. A. V., and B. H. Silvermann: Resorcinol Resins, *Ind. Eng. Chem.*, **43:**1423 (1951).

Robitschek, P., and A. Lewin: "Phenolic Resins," Iliffe Books, Ltd., London, 1900.

Seymour, R. B.: Alkyd Resins, Furan Resins, in G. L. Clark and G. G. Hawley (eds.), "Encyclopedia of Chemistry," Reinhold Publishing Corporation, New York, 1966.

Shechter, L., J. Wynstra, and R. P. Kurkjy: Epoxy Resins, *Ind. Eng. Chem.*, **48:**86, 94 (1956).

Skeist, I.: "Epoxy Resins," Reinhold Publishing Corporation, New York, 1958.

Solomon, D. H.: "The Chemistry of Organic Film Formers," John Wiley & Sons, Inc., New York, 1967.

Spitzer, W. C.: Alkyd Resins, *Offic. Dig., Fed. Soc. Paint Technol.,* **36:**16 (1964).

Stivala, S. S.: Epoxy Resins, in C. E. Schildknecht (ed.), "Polymer Processes," chap. 10, Interscience Publishers, Inc., New York, 1956.

Suen, T. J.: Condensations with Formaldehyde, in C. E. Schildknecht (ed.), "Polymer Processes," chap. 8, Interscience Publishers, Inc., New York, 1956.

Turkington, V. H., and W. H. Butler: Oil Soluble Phenolic Resins, U.S. Patent 2,017,877, Oct. 22, 1935; 2,375,964, May 15, 1945.

Vale, C. P.: "Aminoplastics," Cleaver-Hume Press, Ltd., London, 1950.

Walker, F. J.: "Formaldehyde," Reinhold Publishing Corporation, New York, 1964.

Whitehouse, A. A. K., and E. G. K. Pritchett: "Phenolic Resins," Plastics Institute, London, 1955.

Wismer, M.: Epoxides, in E. M. Fettes (ed.), "Chemical Reactions of Polymers," chap. 11B, Interscience Publishers, a division of John Wiley & Sons, Inc., New York, 1964.

6

Chain-reaction Polymerization

(Addition Polymerization)

Ethylenic compounds are characterized by unusual activity because of the π orbitals which result from incomplete overlapping of the p orbitals. The reactivity of these π bonds, which are about 60 percent as strong as the σ bonds, is discussed in introductory organic chemistry textbooks. It was also demonstrated by the reactivity of alkyds and furans discussed in Chap. 5. The chain-reaction-polymerization reactions of π bonds may involve free radicals, i.e., atoms or molecules (with unpaired electrons) or ions (charged molecules or atoms).

The initiation of *free-radical reactions* is usually dependent on unimolecular homolytic dissociation of weak bonds by irradiation or heat. Organic peroxides, such as benzoyl peroxide, and azo compounds such as 2,2′-bisazoisobutyronitrile readily dissociate to form free radicals $(R \cdot)$, as shown in the following equations:

$$C_6H_5-\underset{\underset{O}{\|}}{C}-OO-\underset{\underset{O}{\|}}{C}C_6H_5 \xrightarrow{\Delta} 2C_6H_5-\overset{\overset{O}{\|}}{C}-O\cdot \xrightarrow{\Delta} 2C_6H_5\cdot + 2CO_2$$

$$(CH_3)_2\underset{\underset{CN}{|}}{C}-N{=}N-\underset{\underset{CN}{|}}{C}(CH_3)_2 \xrightarrow[\substack{or \\ 3600\ \text{Å}}]{\Delta} 2(CH_3)_2\underset{\underset{CN}{|}}{C}\cdot + N_2$$

or, in general,

$$R\cdot/\cdot R \longrightarrow 2R\cdot \qquad (6\text{-}1)$$

Equation for synthesis of free radicals

Ions may be produced when the ethylenic double bonds are subjected to electrophilic or nucleophilic attack. As shown in the following equations, the complex formed from a Lewis acid, such as boron trifluoride, and a proton-donating *cocatalyst* such as water is the first step in *cationic polymerization*. The proton in this complex may add to ethylenic monomers, such as ethyl vinyl ether, at low temperature ($-80°C$). The resultant carbonium ion may add additional molecules of the ethylenic monomers rapidly in a chain-reaction type of polymerization:

$$BF_3 + H_2O \longrightarrow H/:BF_3 + H-\overset{\overset{\displaystyle H}{\overset{\displaystyle O}{|}}}{\underset{\underset{\displaystyle H}{|}}{C}}-\overset{\overset{\displaystyle H}{|}}{\underset{\underset{\displaystyle H}{|}}{C}}-O-\overset{\overset{\displaystyle H}{|}}{\underset{\underset{\displaystyle H}{|}}{C}}\overset{\displaystyle H}{\underset{\displaystyle }{\text{∹}}}C \longrightarrow H-\overset{\overset{\displaystyle H}{|}}{\underset{\underset{\displaystyle H}{|}}{C}}-\overset{\overset{\displaystyle H}{|}}{\underset{\underset{\displaystyle H}{|}}{C}}-O-\overset{\overset{\displaystyle H}{|}}{\underset{\underset{\displaystyle H}{|}}{C}}-\overset{\overset{\displaystyle H}{|}}{\underset{\underset{\displaystyle H}{|}}{C^+}}, (HOBF_3)^-$$

$$\qquad (6\text{-}2)$$

or, in general,

$$H/:B + \overset{\overset{\displaystyle H}{|}}{\underset{\underset{\displaystyle H}{|}}{C}}\overset{\overset{\displaystyle H}{|}}{\underset{\underset{\displaystyle X}{|}}{\text{∹}C}} \longrightarrow H-\overset{\overset{\displaystyle H}{|}}{\underset{\underset{\displaystyle H}{|}}{C}}-\overset{\overset{\displaystyle H}{|}}{\underset{\underset{\displaystyle X}{|}}{C^+}}, B:^-$$

Equation for cationic initiation

As shown in the following equations, nucleophilic attack on an ethylenic double bond yields a *carbanion*. For example, the amide ion may add to methacrylonitrile, and the anion formed may add additional molecules of monomer.

$$Na/:NH_2 + \overset{\overset{\displaystyle H \quad CH_3}{|\qquad|}}{\underset{\underset{\displaystyle H \quad CN}{|\qquad|}}{C\text{∹}C}} \longrightarrow H-\overset{\overset{\displaystyle H}{|}}{\underset{\underset{\displaystyle NH_2}{|}}{C}}-\overset{\overset{\displaystyle CH_3}{|}}{\underset{\underset{\displaystyle CN}{|}}{C}}:^-, Na^+$$

or, in general,

$$B:/M + \overset{\overset{\displaystyle H \quad H}{|\quad|}}{\underset{\underset{\displaystyle H \quad X}{|\quad|}}{C\text{∹}C}} \longrightarrow H-\overset{\overset{\displaystyle H}{|}}{\underset{\underset{\displaystyle B}{|}}{C}}-\overset{\overset{\displaystyle H}{|}}{\underset{\underset{\displaystyle X}{|}}{C}}:^-, M^+ \qquad (6\text{-}3)$$

Equations for anionic initiation

Ionic polymerizations are discussed in Sec. 6-3.

Vinyl monomers may also be polymerized by *complexing catalysts* (Ziegler-Natta catalysts), reduced transition metal oxides on a support such as aluminum oxide, and alfin catalysts. These will be discussed in Sec. 6-4.

The driving force in free-radical or ionic polymerization is the energy difference between the σ bonds in the product and the π and σ bonds in the reactants. The term *addition* was used to characterize these reactions in classic organic chemistry and by Carothers to describe this type of polymerization. However, as stated in Chap. 5, nomenclature based on polymerization mechanisms is preferred by many polymer chemists instead of the term *addition polymerization*. Hence, the addition of active centers (free radicals or ions) to π bonds in a rapid reaction is usually called *chain-reaction polymerization* as distinguished from step-reaction polymerization.

The principal differences between these two types of polymerization are the reaction velocities and the molecular-weight distribution at various stages in the polymerization process. Chain-reaction polymerization is extremely rapid and many times faster than step-reaction polymerization.

As demonstrated by the Carothers' equation in Chap. 5, a fractional yield (p) of 0.98 is required for a $\overline{DP}$ of 50 in step-reaction polymerization. At this stage, none of the reactants remains, and the $\overline{DP}$ of most of the chains is approximately 50. In contrast, the first active center produced in chain-reaction polymerization yields a long-chain polymer. The monomer molecules which constitute the bulk of the mixture will continue to react with the growing chain ends to form additional long chains so that, prior to completion, the mixture consists of both polymer and monomer molecules. Thus, when the yield is 98 percent, 2 percent of the mixture by weight is present as monomer molecules. Chain reactions include three principal steps, viz., initiation, propagation of reactive centers, and termination.

6-1 RADICAL CHAIN POLYMERIZATION

Free radicals $(R \cdot)$ may be produced when a labile organic compound (initiator) is decomposed by heat, light, or particulate radiation. When styrene or methyl methacrylate is heated, free radicals are readily formed. The original suggestion that diradicals were produced when these monomers were heated is not completely in accordance with experimental data. However, the following mechanism proposed by Dulong for styrene suggests a reasonable path for the bimolecular radical production.

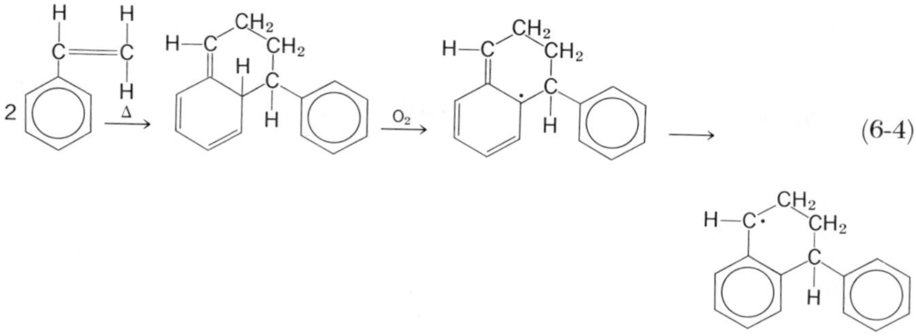

Equation for proposed thermal initiator of styrene

When heated at 125°C for 10 hr, styrene generates enough free radicals to assure almost quantitative yields of high-molecular-weight polymer. Free radicals may also be produced from monomers by photolysis and radiolysis. However, most investigations of high-energy radical formation have been associated with the grafting of monomers on polymer chains and crosslinking (curing) reactions. The use of high-energy sources for depolymerization will be discussed in a subsequent chapter.

The principal source of free radicals for polymerization reactions is by the homolytic decomposition of labile compounds called *initiators* (I). The equations for this first-order reaction were described earlier in this chapter. As shown in the following equations, the rate of decomposition is proportional to the concentration of the initiator and to the temperature. The temperature relationship is shown by the Arrhenius equation. As is true for all first-order reactions, the half-life ($t_{1/2}$) is inversely proportional to the rate constant (K_d) which may be called a *decay constant*.

$$I \xrightarrow{K_d} 2R\cdot \tag{6-5}$$

$$R_d = \frac{-d[I]}{dt} = K_d[I] \tag{6-6}$$

$$t_{1/2} = \frac{\ln 2}{K_d} = \frac{0.693}{K_d} \tag{6-7}$$

$$K_d = Ae^{-E_a/RT} \tag{6-8}$$

Equations for kinetics of free-radical formation

The decomposition of organic peroxides such as benzoyl peroxide may be accelerated by the addition of tertiary amines such as *N,N*-dimethyl aniline. Azo compounds such as 2,2′-bisazoisobutyronitrile (Vazo) (AIBN) may be decomposed at low temperatures by ultraviolet radiation (3600 Å). The yield of free radicals is not quantitative because of cage effects (primary recombinations) and secondary recombination of the free radicals. Hence an *efficiency factor* (f) may be used to show the effective radical concentration in these reactions.

The ceiling temperatures, i.e., the highest temperatures at which free radicals are stable, rate constants and half-lives are shown in Table 6-1.

The decomposition of initiators is also affected by the solvent present. As shown in Table 6-2, the percent decomposition varies from 35 percent in tetrachloroethylene to 85 percent in ethyl acetate.

As shown in the following equations, the free radicals produced by decomposition of typical initiators may add to monomers (M) such as vinyl chloride to form new free radicals in the initiation step.

$$C_6H_5\overset{\displaystyle O}{\overset{\|}{C}}\!-\!O\cdot \;+\; \underset{\substack{|\\H}}{\overset{\substack{H\\|}}{C}}\cdots\underset{\substack{|\\Cl}}{\overset{\substack{H\\|}}{C}} \;\xrightarrow{K_i}\; C_6H_5\!-\!\overset{\displaystyle O}{\overset{\|}{C}}\!-\!O\!-\!\underset{\substack{|\\H}}{\overset{\substack{H\\|}}{C}}\!-\!\underset{\substack{|\\Cl}}{\overset{\substack{H\\|}}{C}}\cdot$$

$$(CH_3)_2\overset{}{C}\cdot \;+\; \underset{\substack{|\\H}}{\overset{\substack{H\\|}}{C}}\cdots\underset{\substack{|\\Cl}}{\overset{\substack{H\\|}}{C}} \;\xrightarrow{K_i}\; (CH_3)_2\underset{\substack{|\\CN}}{C}\!-\!\underset{\substack{|\\H}}{\overset{\substack{H\\|}}{C}}\!-\!\underset{\substack{|\\Cl}}{\overset{\substack{H\\|}}{C}}\cdot \qquad (6\text{-}9)$$

or, in general,

$$R\cdot \;+\; \underset{\substack{|\\H}}{\overset{\substack{H\\|}}{C}}\cdots\underset{\substack{|\\X}}{\overset{\substack{H\\|}}{C}} \;\xrightarrow{K_i}\; R\!-\!\underset{\substack{|\\H}}{\overset{\substack{H\\|}}{C}}\!-\!\underset{\substack{|\\X}}{\overset{\substack{H\\|}}{C}}\cdot \qquad R\cdot \;+\; M \;\xrightarrow{K_i}\; RM\cdot$$

Equations for the initiation of chain-reaction polymerization

Table 6-1   **Rate Constants, Half-life, and Ceiling Temperatures of Various Initiators in Benzene**

INITIATOR	$K_d \times 10^{-8}$/sec	$t_{1/2}$, hr	CEILING TEMPERATURE, °C
Azobisisobutyronitrile	210 @ 50°C	83 @ 50°C	
Dibenzoyl peroxide	42 @ 50°C	190 @ 50°C	70
Diacetyl peroxide	120 @ 50°C	158 @ 50°C	
Di-*tert*-butyl peroxide	7.8 @ 80°C	218 @ 100°C	100
Cumyl peroxide	1600 @ 115°C	25 @ 150°C	100
Dilauroyl peroxide	220 @ 50°C	54 @ 50°C	60

Table 6-2   The Effect of Solvents
            on the Percent Decomposition
            of Benzoyl Peroxide
            at Reflux Temperature (4 hr)

SOLVENT	PERCENT DECOMPOSITION
Ethyl acetate	85
Cyclohexane	84
Ethyl chloride	65
Benzene	50
Ethylbenzene	45
Carbon tetrachloride	40
Cyclohexene	39
Tetrachloroethylene	35

As shown in Eq. (6-10), the initiation rate (R_i) is proportional to the concentration of free radical $[R\cdot]$ and monomer $[M]$.

$$R_i = \frac{-d[M]}{dt} = \frac{d[RM\cdot]}{dt} = K_i[R\cdot][M] = 2K_d f[I] \qquad (6\text{-}10)$$

Equation for initiation rate

The new free radical $[RM\cdot]$ may add to another molecule of vinyl monomer M in a manner similar to the initiation step. The rate constant K_p in this propagation may be affected slightly by the initiator fragment on the chain end when the $\overline{DP}$ is very small (less than 3). However, for all subsequent steps, which are the major steps, the propagation rate R_p is considered to be independent of chain length.

A sequence of head-to-tail arrangements of monomers is shown in the following propagation or *chain-carrying equation* because the substituents (X) are better stabilizers than hydrogen atoms for the growing chain radicals.

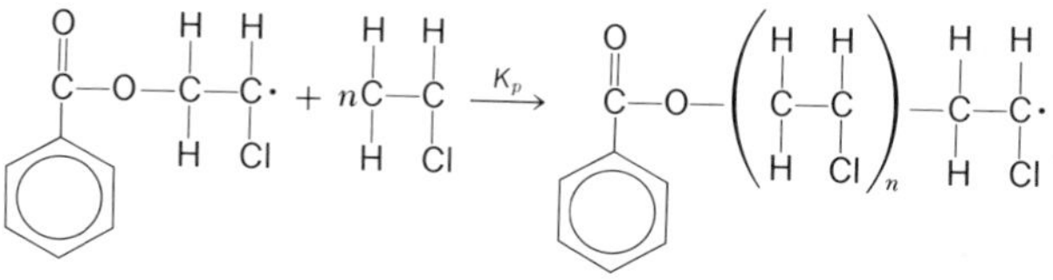

$$(6\text{-}11)$$

or, in general,

$$RM\cdot + {}_nM \xrightarrow{K_p} RM_nM\cdot \quad \text{or} \quad P\cdot$$

Equations for propagation in chain-reaction polymerization

As shown in Eq. (6-12), the propagation rate R_p is proportional to the concentration of monomer [M] and the concentration of reactive centers [M·]:

$$R_p = \frac{-d[M]}{dt} = K_p[M][M\cdot] \tag{6-12}$$

Equation for propagation rate

Termination of growing polymer chains may result from the coupling of two growing chains, as illustrated by the following equations:

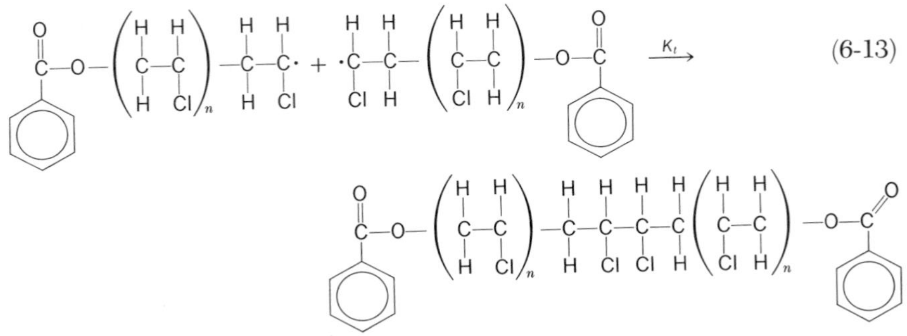

$$\tag{6-13}$$

or, in general,

$$RM_nM\cdot + \cdot MM_nR \xrightarrow{K_t} RM_nM{:}MM_nR \quad \text{or} \quad P\cdot + \cdot P \xrightarrow{K_t} P{:}P$$

Equations for termination by coupling

The rate of termination R_t by coupling is proportional to the square of the concentration of reactive centers ([M·]), as shown below:

$$R_t = \frac{-d[M\cdot]}{dt} = 2K_t[M\cdot]^2 \tag{6-14}$$

Equation for rate of termination by coupling

Thus the rates of propagation (R_p) and termination by coupling (R_t) are proportional to the concentration of active centers ([M·]), but [M·] is not easily determined. However, one may assume a *steady-state condition;*

i.e., the rate of initiation (R_i) is equal to the rate of termination (R_t). Thus one may equate Eqs. (6-10) and (6-14) and solve for the rate of propagation R_p, using values which are readily determined experimentally.

$$R_i = 2K_d f[\text{I}] = R_t = 2K_t[\text{M}\cdot]^2$$

(6-15)

$$[\text{M}\cdot]^2 = \frac{2K_d f[\text{I}]}{2K_t} \qquad [\text{M}\cdot] = \left(\frac{K_d f[\text{I}]}{K_t}\right)^{1/2}$$

Equation for free-radical chain concentration

Then, solving for R_p with this expression for $[\text{M}\cdot]$, one obtains the following:

$$R_p = K_p[\text{M}][\text{M}\cdot]$$

(6-16)

$$R_p = K_p[\text{M}]\left(\frac{K_d f[\text{I}]}{K_t}\right)^{1/2}$$

Equations for propagation rate of free-radical-initiated reactions

Thus, as shown in Eq. (6-16) and in Fig. 6-1, the rate of polymerization is proportional to the concentration of monomer and the square root of the concentration of the initiator. However, these relationships are only approximate since several variables have been overlooked for convenience. For example, a head-to-tail arrangement throughout the entire chain has been assumed, only termination by coupling has been considered, and an *autoacceleration* (*Trommsdorff effect*) has been neglected. The latter causes a deviation when the viscosity increases. Since the diffusion of active chain ends in a viscous media is decreased, the rate of termination decreases and thus the chain length ($\overline{\text{DP}}$) increases.

The Trommsdorff effect can be avoided by restricting the investigation of propagation rates to nonviscous systems. Head-to-tail arrangement is the normal sequence for most polymer systems. However, in addition to coupling, one must consider other termination mechanisms of active chain ends.

Propagation may also be terminated by abstraction of atoms by the free-radical chain ends. If an atom is abstracted from another growing chain, two dead polymer chains result from this *disproportionation* process. As

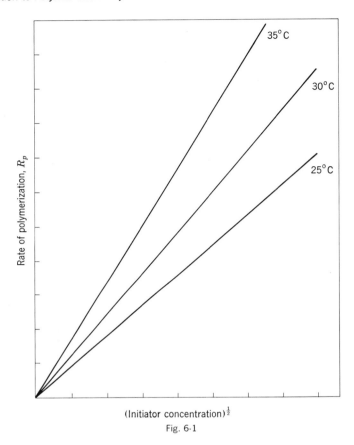

Fig. 6-1

shown in the following equation, one of the polymer chains resulting from this bimolecular termination process will have an unsaturated chain end.

(6-17)

Equation for termination by disproportionation

Table 6-3 **Propagation and Termination Constants for Free-radical Polymerization**

MONOMER	K_p, liter/mole-sec	K_t, liter/mole-sec $\times 10^{-6}$	TEMPERATURE, °C
Styrene	123	65	50
Vinyl chloride	11,000	2,100	50
Vinyl acetate	2,640	117	50
Methyl methacrylate	410	24.1	50
Ethylene	242	540	83
Acrylonitrile	32,500	4,400	30
Methyl acrylate	1,000	3.55	50

Both coupling and disproportionation types of termination take place in the polymerization of methyl methacrylate at ordinary temperatures. However, the disproportionation process predominates for methyl methacrylate at above 60°C. In contrast, coupling is the predominant termination process for styrene. Propagation (K_p) and termination (K_t) constants for free-radical polymerizations are given in Table 6-3.

As shown in the preceding equations, the chain length ($\overline{DP}$) differs for the two termination processes. This difference may be expressed in terms of the *average kinetic chain length* (ν), that is, the number of monomer molecules consumed by an active center. Thus the average kinetic chain length is equal to the ratio of the rate of propagation (R_p) to the rate of initiation (R_i) or termination (R_t), i.e.,

$$\frac{R_p}{R_i} = \frac{R_p}{R_t} = \nu \tag{6-18}$$

Equation for average kinetic chain length

The $\overline{DP}$ is proportional to twice the average kinetic chain length (ν) for termination by coupling, that is, $\nu = \overline{DP}/2$, and equal to the average kinetic chain length for termination by disproportionation, that is, $\overline{DP} = \nu$. As shown by Eq. (6-21), the average kinetic chain length ν is directly proportional to the concentration of monomer [M] and indirectly proportional to the square root of the concentration of the initiator [I].

$$R_i = 2K_{df}[I] \tag{6-19}$$

$$R_p = K_p[M]\left(\frac{K_{df}[I]}{K_t}\right)^{1/2} \tag{6-20}$$

$$\nu = \frac{R_p}{R_i} = \frac{K_p[M](K_{df}[I]/K_t)^{1/2}}{2K_{df}[I]} = \frac{K_p[M]}{2(K_{df}[I]K_t)^{1/2}} \tag{6-21}$$

Equations for average kinetic chain length

Thus, if all other means of termination are excluded, the kinetic-chain-length value ν may be used to estimate the relative amount of each type of termination.

Growing chains may also be terminated by a phenomenon which Flory and Mayo designated as *chain transfer*. In the process, the active center abstracts an atom from the same chain (*backbiting*), another chain, the monomer, the initiator, or other compounds present such as a solvent or additive. The active center becomes inactive, and a new free radical $(R\cdot)$ is produced in each of these chain transfer reactions. These additives (chain transfer agents) may be classified as inhibitors, retarders, or modifiers in accordance with the activity of the new free radicals produced. In all chain transfer reactions, the growth of individual polymer molecules is terminated but the number of active centers remains unchanged, as shown for the following reaction of a general chain transfer agent (RH).

$$M\cdot + RH \longrightarrow MH + R\cdot \tag{6-22}$$

General equation for a chain transfer reaction

Chain transfer between an active center and another polymer chain produces an active center on the chain which serves as a *branch point*. Thus *long-chain branching* results as monomer molecules add to this active center, as shown below:

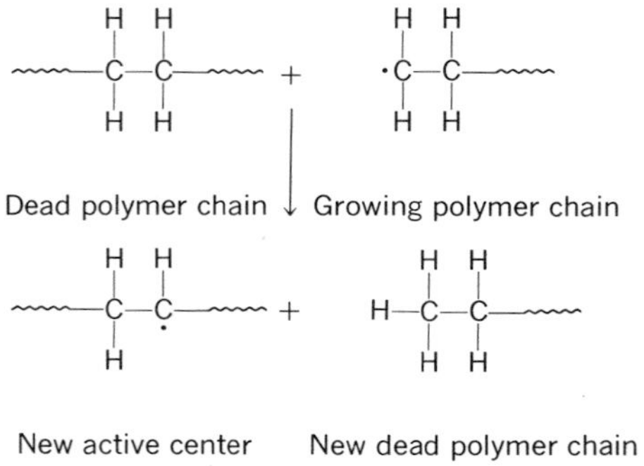

Dead polymer chain | Growing polymer chain $\quad$ (6-23)

New active center $\quad$ New dead polymer chain

Equation for typical long-chain branching

Backbiting takes place when an active chain end doubles back and abstracts a labile atom from its own backbone and thus produces a new active center near the chain end. *Short-chain branching* may result since there is usually a relatively short distance between the chain end and the branch point. This type of chain transfer reaction may be illustrated as follows:

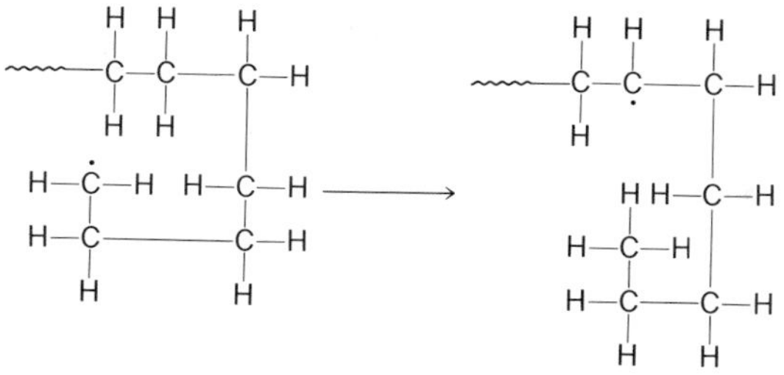

Growing polymer chain   Polymer chain with new active
center

Typical short-chain branching

The degree of polymerization $\overline{DP}$ is equal to the rate of propagation R_p divided by the combined rates of all termination reactions, viz., termination by coupling and disproportionation, and chain transfer to monomer M, initiator I, and solvent S. This complicated equation is simplified by polymerizing under controlled conditions in the presence of a solvent and using the reciprocal relationship $1/\overline{DP}$. Since it may be assumed that, under these conditions, transfer to all molecules except solvent [S] is negligible, all terms except that for the solvent may be combined as $1/\overline{DP}_0$. Thus, this expression may be reduced to the Mayo equation, i.e.,

$$\frac{1}{\overline{DP}} = \frac{1}{\overline{DP}_0} + C_S \frac{[S]}{[M]} \tag{6-25}$$

Mayo equation for chain transfer

The chain transfer constant C_S, which is the ratio of the rate of cessation to the rate of propagation, is related to the relative bond strengths in the labile solvent molecules and the stability of the products. As shown in Eq. (6-25) and Fig. 6-2, the chain transfer constant C_S is the slope of the line obtained when the reciprocal of the degree of polymerization $(1/\overline{DP})$ is plotted against the ratio of the concentrations of solvent [S] and monomer [M]. The intercept is $1/\overline{DP}_0$. The chain transfer constant for very active chain transfer agents is equal to the derivative of the ratio of the logarithms of solvent and monomer concentrations.

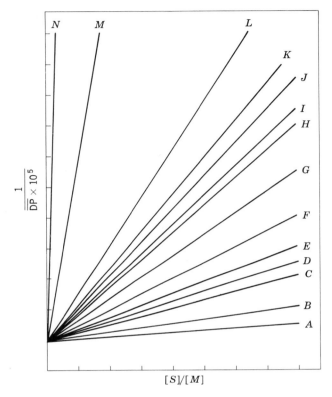

Fig. 6-2 A = Benzene, B = Toluene, C = n-Heptane, D = Chloroform, E = Ethylbenzene, F = Cumene, G = sec-Butylbenzene, H = Phenol, I = m-Cresol, J = p-Cresol, K = o-Cresol, L = Carbon tetrachloride, M = Carbon tetrabromide, N = n-Butylmercaptan, $[S]$ = Concentration of chain-transfer agent, $[M]$ = Concentration of styrene monomer

Chain transfer constants (calculated from the Mayo equation) for various compounds to styrene and those for solvents with selected monomers are shown in Tables 6-4 and 6-5. Effective chain transfer constants are used to control the degree of polymerization. Hence they are called modifiers or *regulators*. When used in larger proportions, they are usually called *telogens*, since they form *telomers* (low-molecular-weight polymers) in *telomerization* reactions. The following is an example of the telomerization of styrene with the telogen carbon tetrabromide.

A chain transfer agent like nitrobenzene which yields a radical with low activity is called a *retarder* for styrene. The limiting case for retarder is an inhibitor such as tert-butyl catechol. Potent inhibitors such as hydroquinone

may be used to quench polymerization reactions and are called
chain stoppers.

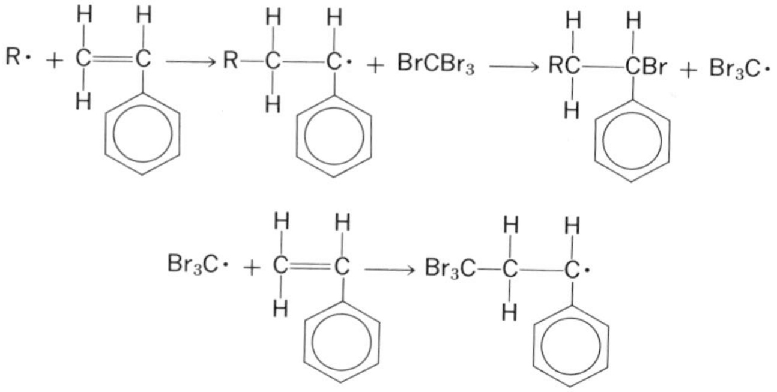

$$(6\text{-}26)$$

Equation for telomerization with carbon tetrabromide

**Table 6-4   Chain Transfer Constants of Solvents
to Styrene at 60°C**

TRANSFER AGENT	$C_S \times 10^4$
Benzene	0.018
Cyclohexane	0.024
n-Butyl chloride	0.04
tert-Butylbenzene	0.04
n-Butyl bromide	0.06
Toluene	0.125
Methylene chloride	0.15
Ethylene chloride	0.32
n-Heptane	0.42
Chloroform	0.50
Ethylbenzene	0.67
Isopropylbenzene	0.82
n-Butyl iodide	1.85
2-Heptene	2.7
sec-Butylbenzene	6.22
p-Dibutylbenzene	7.02
sec-Amylbenzene	9.43
Phenol	8.1
m-Cresol	11
Ethyl benzoate	
o-Cresol	33
p-Cresol	22.1
Carbon tetrachloride	90
Carbon tetrabromide	13,600
n-Butyl mercaptan	400,000

Table 6-5 Transfer Constants of Solvents to Selected Monomers at 60°C

SOLVENT	MONOMER	$C_S \times 10^4$
Benzene	Acrylonitrile	2.5
	Methyl acrylate	0.10
	Methyl methacrylate	0.04
	Styrene	0.02
	Vinyl acetate	1.1
Ethylbenzene	Acrylonitrile	36
	Methyl acrylate	1.5
	Methyl methacrylate	0.77
	Styrene	0.67
	Vinyl acetate	55.2
Carbon tetrachloride	Acrylonitrile	500
	Methyl acrylate	1.3
	Methyl methacrylate	0.90
	Styrene	90
	Vinyl acetate	7,300
Carbon tetrabromide	Acrylonitrile	500
	Methyl acrylate	4,100
	Methyl methacrylate	2,700
	Styrene	13,600
	Vinyl acetate	7,400,000

REFERENCES

Alter, H., and A. D. Jenkins: Chain-reaction Polymerization, in H. F. Mark, N. G. Gaylord, and N. M. Bikales (eds.), "Encyclopedia of Polymer Science and Technology," Interscience Publishers, a division of John Wiley & Sons, Inc., New York, 1965.

Bamford, C. H., W. G. Barb, A. D. Jenkins, and P. F. Onyon: "Kinetics of Vinyl Polymerization by Radical Mechanisms," Butterworth Scientific Publications, London, 1958.

Bawn, C. E. H.: "The Chemistry of High Polymers," Interscience Publishers, Inc., New York, 1948.

Bevington, J. C.: "Radical Polymerization," Academic Press, Inc., New York, 1961.

Billmeyer, F. W.: "Textbook of Polymer Science," Interscience Publishers, a division of John Wiley & Sons, Inc., New York, 1962.

Burnett, G. M.: "Mechanism of Polymer Reactions," John Wiley & Sons, Inc., New York, 1954.

Flory, P. J.: "Principles of Polymer Chemistry," Cornell University Press, Ithaca, N.Y., 1953.

Frith, E. M., and R. F. Tuckett: "Linear Polymers," Longmans, Green & Co., Ltd., London, 1951.

Gaylord, N. G., and H. F. Mark: "Linear and Stereoaddition Polymers," Interscience Publishers, Inc., New York, 1958.

Ham, G. E.: "Vinyl Polymerization," vol. I, Marcel Dekker, Inc., New York, 1967.

Hine, J.: "Physical Organic Chemistry," 2d ed., McGraw-Hill Book Company, New York, 1962.

Kennedy, J. P., and A. W. Langer: Recent Advances in Cationic Polymerization, *Fortschr. Hochpolymer.-Forsch.*, **3**:508 (1964).

Lenz, R. W.: Polymer Mechanisms and Processes, in A. Standen (ed.), "Encyclopedia of Chemical Technology," Interscience Publishers, a division of John Wiley & Sons, Inc., 1968.

Mark, H. F.: Polymers, in A. Standen (ed.), "Encyclopedia of Chemical Technology," Interscience Publishers, a division of John Wiley & Sons, Inc., New York, 1968.

——— and A. V. Tobolsky: "Physical Chemistry of High Polymeric Systems," John Wiley & Sons, Inc., New York, 1950.

Masson, J. C.: Decomposition Rates of Free Radical Initiators, in J. Brandrup and E. H. Immergut (eds.), "Polymer Handbook," chap. 2-1, Interscience Publishers, a division of John Wiley & Sons, Inc., New York, 1966.

Mayo, F. R.: Chain Transfer, *J. Am. Chem. Soc.*, **65**:2324 (1943).

Moore, W. R.: "An Introduction to Polymer Chemistry," Aldine Publishing Company, Chicago, 1963.

Palit, S. R., S. R. Chatterjee, and A. R. Mukherjee: Chain Transfer, in H. F. Mark, N. G. Gaylord, and N. M. Bikales (eds.), "Encyclopedia of Polymer and Science Technology," vol. 3, Interscience Publishers, a division of John Wiley & Sons, Inc., New York, 1965.

Plesch, P. H., "The Chemistry of Cationic Polymerization," Pergamon Press, New York, 1963.

Schmidt, A. X., and C. A. Marlies: "Principles of High-polymer Theory and Practice," McGraw-Hill Book Company, New York, 1948.

Seymour, R. B.: Chain Transfer Agents, *La Scuola in Azione*, (8)**32**(1309): 71 (1969).

Stille, J. K.: "Introduction to Polymer Chemistry," John Wiley & Sons, Inc., New York, 1962.

Trommsdorff, E., H. Kohle, and P. Lagally: Viscous Polymerization, *Makromol. Chem.*, **1**:169 (1948).

Trotman-Dickenson, A. F.: The Abstraction of Hydrogen Atoms by Free Radicals, in G. H. Williams (ed.), "Advances in Free Radical Chemistry I, Logos Press, London, 1965.

Ulbricht, J.: Propagation and Termination Constants in Free Radical Polymerization, in J. Brandrup and E. H. Immergut (eds.), "Polymer Handbook," chap. 2-2, Interscience Publishers, a division of John Wiley & Sons, Inc., New York, 1966.

Walling, C.: "Free Radicals in Solution," John Wiley & Sons, Inc., New York, (1957).

Young, L. J., G. Brandrup, and J. Brandrup: Transfer Constants, in J. Brandrup and E. H. Immergut (eds.), "Polymer Handbook," chap. 2, Interscience Publishers, a division of John Wiley & Sons, Inc., New York, 1966.

6-2 POLYMERIZATION TECHNIQUES

The degree of polymerization ($\overline{DP}$) is inversely proportional to the concentration of the initiator and the temperature. Since the propagation is exothermic, it is necessary to remove the heat produced and to control the temperature in order to obtain polymers of relatively uniform molecular weight. Temperature control in bulk polymerization is dependent on heat transfer between the environment and the monomer-polymer mixture. The other processes—suspension, solution, and emulsion—utilize water or solvents for heat transfer. The choice of technique is governed by economics and end use. Polystyrenes (PS), poly(vinyl chloride) (PVC), poly(vinyl acetate) (PVAC), and poly(methyl methacrylate) (PMMA) may be produced by all four techniques but there is a preferred process for the production of each polymer.

Bulk-polymerization methods for chain-reaction polymerization are similar to those used for potting, casting, or encapsulation of step-reaction (condensation) polymers. This technique may be used for the production of polystyrene and for the production of sheet, rod, tubing, and various articles from methyl methacrylate. Since the temperature in the early stages of polymerization of liquid monomers can be controlled by agitation, it is customary to polymerize the monomer, in an oxygen-free atmosphere, to a syrup consisting of a solution of polymer in the monomer. There is some additional increase in chain length as the viscosity increases because of the reduced tendency for coupling of the growing radical chains (Trommsdorff effect).

The unreacted monomer may be removed by evaporation on vacuum drum driers, or the syrup may be transferred to molds with thin cross sections for further polymerization. This final step may be conducted in the chambers of a modified plate and frame filter press or in multichambered polymerization towers from which the final product is extruded and chopped to form discrete particles of moldable resin.

The production of polystyrene (PS) from styrene monomer is shown in the following equation:

$$R\cdot + n\underset{\underset{H}{|}}{\overset{\overset{H}{|}}{C}}=\underset{}{\overset{\overset{H}{|}}{C}} \xrightarrow{\Delta} R\left(\underset{\underset{H}{|}}{\overset{\overset{H}{|}}{C}}-\underset{}{\overset{\overset{H}{|}}{C}}-\right)_n \qquad (6\text{-}27)$$

Equation for polymerization of styrene

Polystyrene (Dylene, Lustrex, Styron) is an atactic, amorphous, transparent polymer. It has a glass transition temperature of 80°C and a solubility parameter of 9.1. This brittle polymer is soluble in benzene and other solvents with solubility parameters in the 8.5 to 9.5 range. In general, substituents in the para position have little effect on the glass transition temperature. However, the value is lowered when the substituent is in the meta position and raised when the substituent is in the ortho position. Polystyrene is produced at an annual rate of over 3 billion pounds. It is characterized by good optical and electrical properties.

The production of poly(methyl methacrylate) (PMMA) from methyl methacrylate monomer is shown in the following equation:

$$
R\cdot + n\underset{\underset{\displaystyle H}{|}}{\overset{\overset{\displaystyle H}{|}}{C}}=\underset{\underset{\displaystyle \underset{|}{C}=O}{|}}{\overset{\overset{\displaystyle CH_3}{|}}{C}}\xrightarrow{\Delta} R\left(\underset{\underset{\displaystyle H}{|}}{\overset{\overset{\displaystyle H}{|}}{C}}-\underset{\underset{\displaystyle \underset{|}{C}=O}{|}}{\overset{\overset{\displaystyle CH_3}{|}}{C}}\right)_n
$$

$$OCH_3 \qquad OCH_3$$

(6-28)

Equation for polymerization of methyl methacrylate

This polymer is atactic and amorphous and has a high glass transition temperature (110°C). Its solubility parameter is 9.2; hence low-molecular-weight polymers of methyl methacrylate are soluble in ethyl acetate or chloroform and in other solvents with comparable solubility-parameter values. Poly(methyl methacrylate) (Lucite, Plexiglas) is characterized by high light transmission (92 percent) and good resistance to attack by aqueous acids. These properties are related to the morphology and molecular structure of this polymer.

In contrast to the rigidity and alkaline resistance of poly(methyl methacrylate), the isomeric poly(ethyl acrylate)

$$
\left(\underset{\underset{\displaystyle H}{|}}{\overset{\overset{\displaystyle H}{|}}{C}}-\underset{\underset{\displaystyle \underset{|}{C}=O}{|}}{\overset{\overset{\displaystyle H}{|}}{C}}\right)_n
$$

$$OC_2H_5$$

is flexible and readily saponifiable. These differences may be attributed to the α-methyl group which stiffens the poly(methyl methacrylate) chains and hinders hydrolysis by alkaline media. The glass transition temperature of both polyacrylates and polymethacrylates decreases as the size of the ester pendant group is increased. When this pendant group becomes sufficiently long to cause independent side-chain crystallization, i.e., when 12 or more carbons are present in a linear pendant group, the glass transition temperature increases because of molecular attractions between these long pendant groups.

The grinding step required in some forms of bulk polymerization may be omitted, and better temperature control may be attained by *suspension polymerization*. In this process, the monomer, such as vinyl chloride, is suspended as discrete droplets in a dilute aqueous solution containing protective colloids, such as poly(vinyl alcohol), or the sodium salts of carboxymethylcellulose or poly(acrylic acid). Other ingredients such as surfactants (sodium dodecylbenzene sulfonate), insoluble salts (tricalcium phosphate), or viscous liquids (ethylene glycol) may be present.

The production of poly(vinyl chloride) (PVC) from vinyl chloride monomer is shown in the following equation:

$$R\cdot \; + \; n\underset{\substack{|\\H}}{\overset{\substack{H\\|}}{C}}{=}\underset{\substack{|\\Cl}}{\overset{\substack{H\\|}}{C}} \longrightarrow R\left(\!\!-\underset{\substack{|\\H}}{\overset{\substack{H\\|}}{C}}{-}\underset{\substack{|\\Cl}}{\overset{\substack{H\\|}}{C}}{-}\!\!\right)_{n} \tag{6-29}$$

Equation for polymerization of vinyl chloride

Because of the high intermolecular attraction forces present, commercial poly(vinyl chloride) (Exon, Geon, Marvinol, Pliovic, Tygon, Velon, Vinylite) is a hard and stiff amorphous plastic. The solubility parameter of poly(vinyl chloride) is 9.5. It has glass transition temperature ($T_g = 81\,°C$) and is soluble in cyclohexanone ($\delta = 9.9$) and tetrahydrofuran ($\delta = 9.5$).

PVC is characterized by excellent flame resistance and low cost. Over 3 billion pounds of poly(vinyl chloride) is produced annually in the United States. Flexible films may be obtained by the addition of plasticizers, such as dioctyl phthalate, which have similar solubility-parameter values. The plasticized polymer is used for wire coating, upholstery, film, and tubing. The unplasticized rigid polymer is used for the production of pipe, sheet, and molded parts.

The polymerization mechanism of suspension polymerization is similar to that in the bulk process. The size of the beads is controlled by the concentration of monomer and suspension agents and the type of agitation. Finely divided poly(vinyl acetate) (Elvacet, Gelva), or poly(methyl methacrylate) may be produced by this technique and separated from the aqueous phase by filtration or spray drying.

The production of poly(vinyl acetate) is shown in the following equation:

$$R\cdot \; + \; n\underset{\substack{|\\H}}{\overset{\substack{H\\|}}{C}}{=}\underset{\substack{|\\O\\|\\C{=}O\\|\\CH_3}}{\overset{\substack{H\\|}}{C}} \longrightarrow R\left(\!\!-\underset{\substack{|\\H}}{\overset{\substack{H\\|}}{C}}{-}\underset{\substack{|\\O\\|\\C{=}O\\|\\CH_3}}{\overset{\substack{H\\|}}{C}}{-}\!\!\right)_{n} \tag{6-30}$$

Equation for polymerization of vinyl acetate

This linear, amorphous, atactic polymer has a low glass transition temperature (28°C). It has a solubility parameter of 9.5 and is soluble in solvents, such as benzene and chloroform, which have similar solubility parameters. The principal uses of the polymer are as hot melts, adhesives, and lacquers and for the production of poly(vinyl alcohol) (Elvanol) (PVAL) and its derivatives, such as poly(vinyl butyral) (Butacite, Butvar, Saflex).

The initial polymerization step in bulk polymerization is essentially a *solution polymerization* in which the monomer serves as the solvent and provides a means of temperature control in the early stages of polymerization. Additional nonpolymerizable solvents provide this type of control throughout the entire process. The polymer obtained by solution techniques usually has a lower molecular weight than that produced by bulk polymerization because of chain transfer with the solvent. These solvent fragments are present in the polymer chain.

When the polymer is soluble in the solvent system used, it may be recovered by evaporation of this solvent or by precipitation in a miscible nonsolvent such as ethanol. Solutions of polymers such as poly(methyl methacrylate) may be used directly for adhesives or polymer coatings. When the monomer is soluble and the polymer is insoluble in the solvent system used, the product precipitates as formed. This process is called *precipitation polymerization.*

The latter type of solution polymerization is an extremely interesting process since presumably the active chains precipitate when they become long enough so that they are no longer soluble. Thus, the kinetic chain length ν is equal to the degree of polymerization $\overline{DP}$, and the insoluble product is a macroradical. The rate of propagation is lower than in a homogeneous-solution polymerization but the effect is masked by the marked decrease in the rate of termination.

Thus, the overall polymerization rate in precipitation polymerization is much faster than in that of homogeneous solutions. In addition, the molecular weight of the freshly prepared product may be controlled by the solubility-parameter value of the solvents. However, propagation may continue in the swollen precipitated polymer if it is not removed as formed.

Since polyacrylonitrile is insoluble in monomeric acrylonitrile, its production may be used as an example of precipitation polymerization. The presence of trapped free radicals in this polymer may be readily demonstrated. The production of this polymer is shown in the following equation:

$$R\cdot + n\underset{\underset{H}{|}}{\overset{\overset{H}{|}}{C}}=\underset{\underset{CN}{|}}{\overset{\overset{H}{|}}{C}} \longrightarrow R\left(-\underset{\underset{H}{|}}{\overset{\overset{H}{|}}{C}}-\underset{\underset{CN}{|}}{\overset{\overset{H}{|}}{C}}-\right)_n \tag{6-31}$$

Equation for polymerization of acrylonitrile

Because of a high degree of hydrogen bonding, polyacrylonitrile has a high glass transition temperature (107°C) and a high solubility-parameter value (15.4). It is soluble in dimethyl formamide, dimethyl sulfoxide, and concentrated aqueous solutions of sodium thiocyanate. It is widely used as a synthetic fiber (Acrilan).

The rate of polymerization is also faster for the *emulsion polymerization* of water-insoluble vinyl monomers. The kinetics and mechanisms for this two-phase type of polymerization are not completely understood but it is known that the mechanism for this process differs from that discussed for bulk, suspension, and solution polymerizations. Much of the present theory is based on investigations by Harkins and Smith.

Water-soluble initiators, such as potassium persulfate, are used to produce free radicals ($SO_4^-\cdot$). The emulsion system also contains a surface active agent, such as soap. Relatively large amounts of soap are used (up to 5 percent based on the monomer), and it is present as oriented clusters of

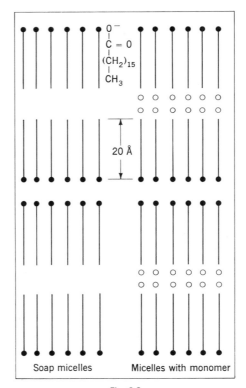

Fig. 6-3

molecules (micelles) which are assumed to be spherical, to have a diameter of about 50 Å, and to consist of 100 or more soap molecules. The molecules of soap in the micelles are oriented so that the polar carboxyl ends are on the outside and the nonpolar hydrocarbon ends are inside the aggregate. The concentration of micelles is approximately 10^{18} aggregates per milliliter of water.

As in other emulsions, the soap emulsifies or solubilizes a small fraction of nonpolar (monomer) molecules which are oriented toward the nonpolar ends of the soap molecules in the micelles. The presence of monomer molecules causes the size of the micelles to increase considerably. However, most of the monomer is dispersed as soap-stabilized droplets which are over 1,000 times larger than micelles. The size of monomer droplets is influenced by the temperature and the rate of agitation. If these droplets are 1000 Å in diameter, their concentration would be 10^{11} per milliliter of water compared with 10^{18} micelles for the same volume.

Simple arithmetic will show that there are 10 million times more micelles than droplets in a milliliter of water. Hence, the probability of a collision of a free radical with a swollen micelle rather than with a droplet is strongly favored. Initiation occurs in the aqueous phase, as shown in the following equation. However, there are essentially no collisions of free radicals in the aqueous phase; hence propagation takes place exclusively in the micelles.

$$S_2O_8^{--} \longrightarrow 2SO_4 \cdot^-, \quad SO_4 \cdot^- + \underset{\underset{\bigcirc}{H}}{\overset{H}{C}} = \underset{H}{\overset{H}{C}} \longrightarrow O = \underset{O}{\overset{-O}{\underset{\parallel}{S}}} - O - \underset{\underset{\bigcirc}{H}}{\overset{H}{C}} - \overset{H}{\underset{H}{C}} \cdot$$

(6-32)

Equation for initiation of polymerization of styrene
in emulsion technique

The propagation step is similar to that discussed for the bulk, suspension, and solution processes. However, the growing chains are in a protected environment in the emulsion process. Each micelle accommodates only one free radical; hence a second radical is terminated immediately on entering the previously inoculated micelle. Thus, from a statistical viewpoint, only half the micelles will contain growing chains at any specified time.

The rate of radical production is about 10^{13} per milliliter per second at 50°C. Thus, since there are 10^{18} micelles per milliliter originally, inoculation by free radicals is infrequent. Hence there is ample opportunity for the propagation of long chains without much interference by coupling-type termination under these conditions of high viscosity. More monomer molecules are supplied, as needed, to the inoculated micelles from the droplets which serve as reservoirs. More soap molecules from uninoculated micelles are also supplied to the activated micelles. Thus, the number of micelles decreases from 10^{18} per milliliter of water to 10^{15} during the polymerization cycle. The monomer content in the droplets decreases, and the inoculated micelles expand as much as 250 times as a result of polymer formation and swelling by the monomer.

The rate of propagation R_p is proportional to the monomer concentration [M] and initiator concentration [I]. The latter is related to the number of activated micelles per milliliter $N/2$.

$$R_p = K_p[\text{M}][\text{I}] = K_p[\text{M}]\frac{N}{2} \tag{6-33}$$

Rate of propagation in emulsion polymerization

The chain length is directly proportional to the concentration of monomer [M] and the number of activated micelles $N/2$ and inversely proportional to the rate of initiation R_i, that is,

$$\overline{\text{DP}} = K_p\frac{N}{2}\frac{[\text{M}]}{R_i} \tag{6-34}$$

Relationship of chain length to variables in emulsion process

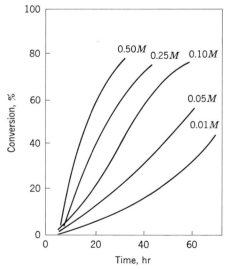

Fig. 6-4 Effect of concentration of surfactant on the rate of emulsion polymerization

The number of micelles is proportional to the concentration of soap, and both the rate of propagation R_p and the chain length ($\overline{DP}$) are proportional to the concentration of soap provided the other variables remain constant.

After about 20 percent conversion, all soap micelles disappear, and all soap is present in the dispersed polymer particles. As noted previously, the number of these particles is 10^{15} per milliliter. Since the polymer chains are initiated by sulfate free radicals, the polymer contains sulfate end groups.

As was discussed previously for water-insoluble initiators, such as benzoyl peroxide, the rate of production of free radicals from persulfate ions is increased by the addition of reducing agents. The effect of iron (II) ions and thiosulfate ions on persulfate ions and hydrogen peroxide is shown in the following equations:

$$H_2O_2 + Fe^{++} \longrightarrow OH^- + Fe^{3+} + OH\cdot$$
$$Fe^{++} + OH\cdot \longrightarrow Fe^{3+} + OH^-$$
$$H_2O_2 + OH\cdot \longrightarrow H_2O + HOO\cdot \qquad (6\text{-}35)$$
$$Fe^{++} + HOO\cdot \longrightarrow Fe^{3+} + HOO^-$$
$$Fe^{3+} + HOO\cdot \longrightarrow Fe^{++} + O_2 + H^+$$
$$S_2O_8^{--} + S_2O_3^{--} \longrightarrow SO_4^{--} + SO_4\cdot^- + S_2O_3\cdot^-$$

Equations for free-radical reactions in emulsion process

Since emulsion polymerization yields unusually high-molecular-weight products, chain transfer agents, such as dodecyl mercaptan, are often added to reduce the chain length. As shown in the following general equation, the logarithm of the ratio of the concentration of a modifier [RSH] at any specific time and its initial concentration [RSH$_0$] is proportional to the logarithm of the ratio of the concentration of the monomer [M] at any specific time and its original concentration [M$_0$], that is,

$$\log \frac{[RSH]}{[RSH_0]} = C_S \log \frac{[M]}{[M_0]} \qquad (6\text{-}36)$$

Relationships of change in concentrations of chain transfer agent and monomer to chain transfer constant

The proportionality factor C_S is the chain transfer constant.

The low degree of chain branching found in many polymers prepared by the emulsion process would be expected in the early stages of polymerization but would not be expected in later stages if all the propagation took place in the interior of the micelles. Much backbiting and short-chain branching might be expected on the basis of the Harkins-Smith theory. Accordingly,

Brodnyan suggested that propagation takes place at the micelle or particle surface rather than in the interior of the micelle.

Emulsion polymerization of vinyl monomers has also been conducted in nonaqueous systems such as formamide or ammonia. Hydrophilic monomers, such as acrylic acid, may be polymerized by using an oil-soluble initiator, such as benzoyl peroxide, and a water-in-oil emulsifier, such as sorbitol monostearate. This *inverse-emulsion-polymerization* process yields a viscous latex consisting of hydrophilic polymer particles swollen by water in the continuous oil phase.

The aqueous-emulsion-polymerization process yields an aqueous dispersion which may be used directly for adhesives and coatings. The polymeric product may be separated by spray or drum drying or by coagulation. The addition of electrolytes, such as sodium sulfate, or dehydrating agents, such as ethanol, or freezing will cause the emulsion to coagulate. Since the surface active agent is intimately mixed with the polymer, it is difficult to obtain a soap-free product when the emulsion-polymerization technique is used.

An oxygen-free atmosphere is a prerequisite for the routine radical-chain polymerization of vinyl compounds. Oxygen forms explosive hydroperoxides with methyl methacrylate and vinylidene chloride. It copolymerizes with styrene and serves as an initiator for the polymerization of ethylene.

Fawcett and Gibson produced polyethylene (PE) in 1934 by using extremely high pressures (500 atm) and elevated temperatures (150°C) in the presence of traces of oxygen (0.075 percent). Since higher pressures reduce branching tendencies and increase the chain length, an essentially linear high-density polymer is produced at 5,000 atm. However, a lower-density highly branched polymer is obtained under normal operating pressures (1,500 atm).

Organic peroxides may also be used as initiators. The polymer chain length ($\overline{DP}$) is inversely proportional to the concentration of either oxygen or the peroxide. It is customary to polymerize ethylene in a tubular reactor or autoclave in a solvent such as benzene. The polyethylene produced at high pressures contains both long and short branches. It has a high degree of crystallinity (50 to 60 percent), a low density (0.91 to 0.94 g/cm^3), and a solubility-parameter value of 7.9. Polyethylene is soluble in hot solvents with similar values but because of its crystallinity is not soluble at room temperature. The polymerization of ethylene is illustrated by the following equation:

$$n\underset{\substack{|\\H}}{\overset{\substack{H\\|}}{C}}=\underset{\substack{|\\H}}{\overset{\substack{H\\|}}{C}} \longrightarrow \left(-\underset{\substack{|\\H}}{\overset{\substack{H\\|}}{C}}-\underset{\substack{|\\H}}{\overset{\substack{H\\|}}{C}}- \right)_n \tag{6-37}$$

Equation for polymerization of ethylene

Commercial polyethylene is available in several viscosity ranges. These are characterized on the basis of *melt index* which is related inversely to melt viscosity. The index is equal to the weight of polymer extruded through an orifice at 190°C under controlled conditions during a 10-min interval. Low-density polyethylene has excellent electrical properties and good resistance to corrosive environments. The annual rate of production in the United States is in excess of 3 billion pounds. It is used as film, tubing, cable coatings, paperboard coatings, and blow-molded containers.

Polytetrafluoroethylene (Teflon, Halon) (PTFE) was discovered accidentally by Plunkett who was investigating the use of tetrafluoroethylene as an aerosol. The polymerization may be initiated by succinic peroxide in the presence of traces of oxygen, as shown in the following equation:

$$ R\cdot + n\,{\underset{\underset{F}{|}}{\overset{\overset{F}{|}}{C}}}={\underset{\underset{F}{|}}{\overset{\overset{F}{|}}{C}} \longrightarrow R\left({\underset{\underset{F}{|}}{\overset{\overset{F}{|}}{C}}}-{\underset{\underset{F}{|}}{\overset{\overset{F}{|}}{C}}}- \right)_n $$

(6-38)

Equation for polymerization of tetrafluoroethylene

The polymer exists in two different crystalline forms which differ in the number of CF_2 groups in the unit cell. Unlike polyethylene, in which there is ample room for the hydrogen atoms in a normal chain structure, the polytetrafluoroethylene chain must assume a twisted, zigzag structure to provide space for the larger fluorine atoms. The glass transition temperature is low for one crystalline form ($-113°C$) and much higher for the other ($127°C$). The difference is related to the extent of interlocking of the fluorine atoms in the two different spirals.

Because of its low solubility-parameter value ($\delta = 6.2$), polytetrafluoroethylene is insoluble in most solvents. However, it is soluble in perfluorinated kerosene at elevated temperatures ($300°C$). This polymer has little tendency to flow even at elevated temperatures and hence cannot be processed by normal extrusion and molding techniques. Powdered polytetrafluoroethylene may be preformed and sintered to produce various shapes. It may be extruded when softened with a solvent such as naphtha. Processing difficulties may be reduced by replacing one fluorine atom by a larger chlorine atom or by replacing two or more fluorine atoms by smaller hydrogen atoms. Polymonochlorotrifluoroethylene (Kel-F, Halon), poly(vinylidene fluoride) (Kynar), and poly(vinyl fluoride) (Tedlar) are more flexible, more transparent, lower melting, and hence more readily processed than polytetrafluoroethylene.

Poly(vinylidene fluoride) is soluble in N,N-dimethylacetamide. Poly(vinyl fluoride) is more crystalline than poly(vinyl chloride) because of its smaller pendant group. All polyfluorocarbons are characterized by good resistance to heat, solvents, and corrosive compounds. Since they have excellent lubricity qualities, polyfluorocarbons are used as nonadhesive coatings and bearings. They are also used as heat-resistant tubing and gaskets.

As shown by the following equation, poly(vinylidene chloride) (Saran) (PVDC) is produced by the suspension polymerization of vinylidene chloride in the presence of initiators such as benzoyl peroxide.

$$n\underset{\underset{\text{H}}{|}}{\overset{\overset{\text{H}}{|}}{C}}=\underset{\underset{\text{Cl}}{|}}{\overset{\overset{\text{Cl}}{|}}{C}} \longrightarrow \left(\underset{\underset{\text{H}}{|}}{\overset{\overset{\text{H}}{|}}{C}} - \underset{\underset{\text{Cl}}{|}}{\overset{\overset{\text{Cl}}{|}}{C}} \right)_n \tag{6-39}$$

Equation for polymerization of vinylidene chloride

Because the regular structure permits close packing, the polymer has a high degree of crystallinity. Its high density (1.875) is related to the high chlorine content and to the structure. It has a solubility-parameter value of 9.8 but the strong intermolecular forces reduce the solubility of Saran at room temperature. Poly(vinylidene chloride) is characterized by good resistance to flame and corrosive environment. It is used as transparent film (Saran Wrap), as a pipe lining, and as extruded monofilaments.

REFERENCES

Bamford, C. H., W. G. Barb, A. D. Jenkins, and P. F. Onyon: "The Kinetics of Vinyl Polymerization by Radical Mechanism," Academic Press, Inc., New York, 1958.

Boundy, R. H., and R. F. Boyer: "Styrene," Reinhold Publishing Corporation, New York, 1952.

Bovey, F. A., I. M. Kolthoff, A. I. Medalia, and E. J. Meehan: "Emulsion Polymerization," Interscience Publishers, Inc., New York, 1955.

Brodnyan, J. G., E. Chon-Ginsberg, and T. Konen: Mechanism of Emulsion Polymerization, ACS Div. Polymer Chem., Polymer Preprints, **5**(1):99 (1964).

Burk, R. E., H. E. Thompson, A. J. Weith, and I. Williams: "Polymerization," Reinhold Publishing Corporation, New York, 1937.

Duck, E. W.: Emulsion Polymerization, in H. F. Mark, N. G. Gaylord, and N. M. Bikales (eds.), "Encyclopedia of Polymer Science and Technology," Interscience Publishers, a division of John Wiley & Sons, Inc., 1966.

Fawcett, E. W., R. O. Gibson, et al.: British Patent, 471, 590, Sept. 6, 1937.

Fryling, C. F.: Emulsion Polymerization Systems, in G. S. Whitby, C. C. Davis, and R. F. Dunbrook (eds.), "Synthetic Rubber," chap. 7, John Wiley & Sons, Inc., New York, 1954.

George, M. H.: Styrene, in G. E. Ham (ed.), "Vinyl Polymerization," vol. I, chap. 3, Marcel Dekker, Inc., New York, 1967.

Gould, R. F. (ed.): "Polymerization and Polycondensation Processes," American Chemical Society, Washington, D.C., 1962.

Harkins, W. D.: Emulsion Polymerization, *J. Am. Chem. Soc.,* **69:**1429 (1947); *J. Polymer Sci.,* **5:**217 (1950).

Hohenstein, W. P., and H. Mark: "High Molecular Weight Organic Compounds," John Wiley & Sons, Inc., New York, 1949.

Horn, M. B.: "Acrylic Resins," Reinhold Publishing Corporation, New York, 1960.

Jenkins, A. D.: Acrylonitrile, in G. E. Ham (ed.), "Vinyl Polymerization," vol. I, chap. 6, Marcel Dekker, Inc., New York, 1967.

Kresser, T. O. J.: "Polyethylene," Reinhold Publishing Corporation, New York, 1966.

Lindemann, M. K.: The Mechanism of Vinyl Acetate Polymerization, in G. E. Ham (ed.), "Vinyl Polymerization," vol. I, chap. 4, Marcel Dekker, Inc., New York, 1967.

Miles, D. C., and J. H. Briston: "Polymer Technology," Chemical Publishing Company Inc., New York, 1965.

Newkirk, A. E.: Poly(vinyl fluoride), *J. Am. Chem. Soc.,* **68:**2467 (1946).

Penn, W. S.: "PVC Technology," MacLaren and Sons, Ltd., London, 1962.

Pinner, S. H., "A Practical Course in Polymer Chemistry," Pergamon Press, New York, 1961.

Plunkett, R. J.: Polytetrafluoroethylene, U.S. Patent 2,230,654, Feb. 4, 1941.

Powers, P. O.: "Synthetic Resins and Rubber," John Wiley & Sons, Inc., New York, 1943.

Raff, R. A. V., and J. B. Allison: "Polyethylene," Interscience Publishers, a division of John Wiley & Sons, Inc., New York, 1964.

Renfrew, A., and P. Morgan: "Polyethene—The Technology and Uses of Ethylene Polymers," Iliffe Books, Ltd., London, 1960.

Richardson, H. M., and J. W. Wilson; "Fundamentals of Plastics," McGraw-Hill Book Company, New York, 1946.

Riddle, E. H.: "Monomeric Acrylic Esters," Reinhold Publishing Corporation, New York, 1961.

Ringsdorf, H.: Bulk Polymerization, in H. F. Mark, N. G. Gaylord, and N. M. Bikales (eds.), "Encyclopedia of Polymer Science and Technology," Interscience Publishers, a division of John Wiley & Sons, Inc., New York, 1965.

Rudner, M. A.: "Fluorocarbons," Reinhold Publishing Corporation, New York, 1958.

Scott, W., and R. B. Seymour: Emulsion Polymerization, U.S. Patent 2,328,748, Sept. 7, 1943.

Seymour, R. B.: Plastics Technology, in W. O. Standen (ed.), "Encyclopedia of Chemical Technology," Interscience Publishers, a division of John Wiley & Sons, Inc., New York, 1968.

———: Polymerization Techniques, *Plastics World,* **25:**(2):54 (1967).

Schildknecht, C. E. (ed.): "Polymer Processes," Interscience Publishers, Inc., New York, 1956.

———: "Vinyl and Related Polymers," John Wiley & Sons, Inc., New York, 1952.

Smith, W. M.: "Vinyl Resins," Reinhold Publishing Corporation, New York, 1958.

Smith, W. V., and R. H. Ewart: Emulsion Polymerization, *J. Chem. Phys.,* **16:**592 (1948).

Talamini, G., and E. Peggion: Vinyl Chloride, Vinylidene Chloride, in G. E. Ham (ed.), "Vinyl Polymerization," vol. I, chap. 5, Marcel Dekker, Inc., New York, 1967.

Teach, W. C., and G. C. Kiessling: "Polystyrene," 2nd ed., Reinhold Publishing Corporation, New York, 1963.

Topchiev, A. V., and B. A. Krentsel: "Polyolefins," Pergamon Press, New York, 1962.

Trommsdorff, E., and C. E. Schildknecht: Polymerization in Suspension, in C. E. Schildknecht (ed.), "Polymer Processes," chap. 3, Interscience Publishers, Inc., New York, 1956.

Van der Hoff, B. M. E.: Kinetics of Emulsion Polymerization in R. F. Gould (ed.), "Polymerization and Polycondensation Processes," American Chemical Society, Washington, D.C., 1962.

VanderHoff, J. W., E. B. Bradford, et al.: Inverse Emulsion Polymerization, in R. F. Gould (ed.), "Polymerizations and Polycondensation Processes," American Chemical Society, Washington, D.C., 1962.

Wheeler, O. L., E. Lavin, and R. N. Crozier: Poly(vinyl acetate), *J. Polymer Sci.*, **9:**157 (1952).

Winding, C. C., and R. L. Hasche: "Plastics, Theory and Practice," McGraw-Hill Book Company, New York, 1947.

6-3 IONIC POLYMERIZATION

Ionic or *polar polymerization* may be *anionic* when electron-withdrawing groups, such as chlorine, are present, or *cationic* when electron-donating groups, such as methyl, are present. When the propagating chain is a free ion and not an ion pair, the polymer ion may be coordinated; hence the chain growth may be stereospecific. This type of polymerization is discussed in Sec. 6-4 under complex catalyst systems.

Anionic (*carbanion*) polymerization and cationic (*carbonium ion*) polymerization are more complex and more versatile than free-radical chain polymerization. These polar reactions are characterized by the rapid production of high-molecular-weight polymers at very low temperatures. Both these types of polar polymerization were discussed previously in Chap. 5 under ring-opening polymerization of cyclic compounds, such as oxiranes, and addition to the double bond in carbonyls ($C{=}O$), as in the polymerization of formaldehyde.

The anionic polymerization of olefins was investigated by Matthews in the early part of the twentieth century but the principles of this type of polymerization were not recognized until the 1950s. The initiators are electropositive metallic compounds, and the cations may become the *counterions* (gegenions) paired with the polymer carbanions. The rates of the initiation and propagation steps in the anionic polymerization of vinyl compounds are dependent on the electropositivity of the initiators, the electronegativity of the substituents on the monomer, the dielectric constant of the solvent, the resonance stability of the polymeric carbanion produced, and the degree of solvation of the cation. Thus it is advantageous to use highly electropositive metals, such as lithium, and solvents with high solvating power, such as ethers or amines.

Since both the initiators and the polymeric carbanions react with water, alcohols, carbon dioxide, and oxygen, the polymerization must be conducted in the absence of these compounds. However, water or alcohols may be added to terminate the polymerization.

Monomers with highly electronegative substituents such as acrylonitrile, vinyl chloride, and methyl methacrylate may be polymerized by weak electropositive initiators, such as *n*-butyl magnesium bromide or other Grignard reagents. Monomers with less electronegative substituents such as styrene and α-methyl styrene require more electropositive initiators such as *n*-butyl lithium. In the following scheme proposed by Higginson and Wooding, the partial negative charge on the polymer chain, and hence the tendency to form ion pairs, is dependent on the electropositivity of the initiator, the electronegativity of the substituents on the monomer, etc., as discussed earlier in this section.

$$C/{:}A \xrightarrow{K_d} C^+ + A^- \qquad K/{:}NH_2 \xrightarrow{K_d} NH_2^- + K^+$$

Initiation:

$$A^- + M \xrightarrow{K_i} AM^-$$

$$NH_2^- + \underset{\substack{|\\H}}{\overset{\substack{H\\|}}{C}}{=}\underset{\substack{|\\CN}}{\overset{\substack{H\\|}}{C}} \xrightarrow{K_i} H_2N{-}\underset{\substack{|\\H}}{\overset{\substack{H\\|}}{C}}{-}\underset{\substack{|\\CN}}{\overset{\substack{H\\|}}{C}}{}^-$$

Propagation: $AM^- + nM \xrightarrow{K_p} AM_nM^-$

$$.H_2N{-}\underset{\substack{|\\H}}{\overset{\substack{H\\|}}{C}}{-}\underset{\substack{|\\CN}}{\overset{\substack{H\\|}}{C}}{}^- + n\underset{\substack{|\\H}}{\overset{\substack{H\\|}}{C}}{=}\underset{\substack{|\\CN}}{\overset{\substack{H\\|}}{C}} \xrightarrow{K_p}$$

$$H_2N\left(\underset{\substack{|\\H}}{\overset{\substack{H\\|}}{C}}{-}\underset{\substack{|\\CN}}{\overset{\substack{H\\|}}{C}}{-}\right)_n\underset{\substack{|\\H}}{\overset{\substack{H\\|}}{C}}{-}\underset{\substack{|\\CN}}{\overset{\substack{H\\|}}{C}}{}^-$$

Termination: $AM_nM^- + HA \xrightarrow{K_t} AM_nMH + A^-$

$$H_2N\left(\underset{\substack{|\\H}}{\overset{\substack{H\\|}}{C}}{-}\underset{\substack{|\\CN}}{\overset{\substack{H\\|}}{C}}{-}\right)_n\underset{\substack{|\\H}}{\overset{\substack{H\\|}}{C}}{-}\underset{\substack{|\\CN}}{\overset{\substack{H\\|}}{C}}{}^- + HNH_2 \xrightarrow{K_t} H_2N\left(\underset{\substack{|\\H}}{\overset{\substack{H\\|}}{C}}{-}\underset{\substack{|\\CN}}{\overset{\substack{H\\|}}{C}}{-}\right)_n\underset{\substack{|\\H}}{\overset{\substack{H\\|}}{C}}{-}\underset{\substack{|\\CN}}{\overset{\substack{H\\|}}{C}}H + NH_2^- \qquad (6\text{-}40)$$

Equations for anionic polymerizations

Thus, as shown in the equations above, and summarized in Eq. (6-41), the rate of propagation R_p is directly proportional to the concentration of the anion $[A^-]$ and the square of the monomer concentration $[M]$ and inversely proportional to the concentration of the initiator $[CA]$:

$$R_p = \frac{K_p K_i}{K_t} \frac{[A^-][M^2]}{[CA]} \tag{6-41}$$

Equation for propagation rate in anionic polymerization

The degree of polymerization $\overline{DP}$ is proportional to the ratio of the concentration of monomer [M] and initiator [CA].

$$\overline{DP} = \frac{K_p}{K_t} \frac{[M]}{[CA]} \tag{6-42}$$

Equation for average chain length in anionic polymerization

Szwarc showed that in the absence of reactive contaminants, such as water and ethanol, anionic polymerization systems initiated by a sodium-aromatic hydrocarbon couple do not terminate unless quenched. Propagation in these "living polymers" involves a transient *radical ion* which dimerizes to a dianion which may propagate from both ends, as shown below:

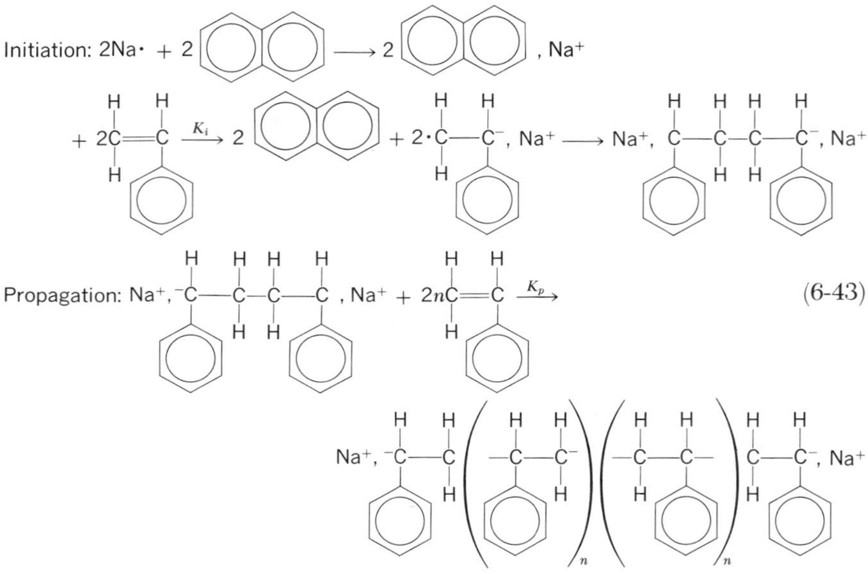

Equations for initiation and propagation of "living polymers"

These reactions may be terminated by the addition of reactive compounds such as ethanol which "quench" the active chain ends and produce dead polymers. Polymers produced by anionic techniques are characterized by a narrow molecular-weight distribution range, that is, $\overline{M_w}/\overline{M_n} \cong 1.1$.

The principal use of this technique is for the production of polybutadienes as discussed in Sec. 6-5.

Both styrene and methyl methacrylate have been polymerized by passing an electric current through solutions of these monomers. Gamma rays have also been used to initiate the polymerization of styrene in dilute solutions.

The first step in *cationic polymerization,* as in the classic Friedel-Crafts reaction, is an electrophilic attack on the π electrons by a Lewis-type acid, such as aluminum chloride, in the presence of a cocatalyst. As shown in the following equations, the electrophile is a carbonium ion which acts as a chain carrier in the propagation step. The rates of initiation and propagation are dependent on the electropositivity of the substituents on the vinyl monomer, the dielectric constant of the solvent, and the stability of the carbonium ion or ion pair. A counterion (gegenion) is essential for cationic polymerization.

$$A + RH \rightleftharpoons ARH \qquad AlCl_3 + HOH \rightleftharpoons H^+, AlCl_3OH^-$$

Initiation: $ARH + M \xrightarrow{K_i} HM^+, AR^-$

$$H^+, AlCl_3OH^- + \underset{\substack{| \\ H}}{\overset{\substack{H \\ |}}{C}}=\underset{\substack{| \\ CH_3}}{\overset{\substack{CH_3 \\ |}}{C}} \xrightarrow{K_i} H-\underset{\substack{| \\ H}}{\overset{\substack{H \\ |}}{C}}-\underset{\substack{| \\ CH_3}}{\overset{\substack{CH_3 \\ |}}{C}}{}^+, AlCl_3OH^-$$

Propagation: $HM^+, AR^- + nM \xrightarrow{K_p} HM_nM^+, AR^-$

$$H-\underset{\substack{| \\ H}}{\overset{\substack{H \\ |}}{C}}-\underset{\substack{| \\ CH_3}}{\overset{\substack{CH_3 \\ |}}{C}}{}^+, AlCl_3OH^- + nC=C \xrightarrow{K_p} H\left(-\underset{\substack{| \\ CH_3}}{\overset{\substack{CH_3 \\ |}}{C}}-\right)_n \underset{\substack{| \\ CH_3}}{\overset{\substack{CH_3 \\ |}}{C}}-C^+, AlCl_3OH^-$$

Termination: $HM_nM^+, AR^- \xrightarrow{K_t} M_nM + ARH$

$$H\left(-\underset{\substack{| \\ H}}{\overset{\substack{H \\ |}}{C}}-\underset{\substack{| \\ CH_3}}{\overset{\substack{CH_3 \\ |}}{C}}-\right)_n \overset{\substack{H \\ |}}{C}-C^+, AlCl_3OH^- \xrightarrow{K_t} H\left(-\overset{\substack{H \\ |}}{C}-\overset{\substack{CH_3 \\ |}}{C}-\right)_n C=C + H^+, AlCl_3OH^-$$

Chain transfer: $HS + HM_nM^+AR^- \xrightarrow{K_{tr}} HM_nMH + S^+, AR^-$

$$H\left(-\overset{\substack{H \\ |}}{C}-\overset{\substack{CH_3 \\ |}}{C}-\right)_n \overset{\substack{H \\ |}}{C}-C^+, AlCl_3OH^- + H-\overset{\substack{H \\ |}}{\underset{\substack{| \\ H}}{C}}-\bigcirc \xrightarrow{K_{tr}} \qquad\qquad (6\text{-}44)$$

$$H\left(-\overset{\substack{H \\ |}}{C}-\overset{\substack{CH_3 \\ |}}{C}-\right)_{n+1} H + \overset{+}{H}\overset{}{C}H \bigcirc, AlCl_3OH^-$$

Equations for cationic polymerization

Because the chain carrier is a carbonium ion, it directs the propagation so that the sequence is head to tail, as shown above. The reaction time varies from a fraction of a second for strong acid catalysts, like boron trifluoride, to several days for weak acid catalysts, such as stannic chloride. Higher-molecular-weight polymers are obtained and a tendency toward stereospecificity is observed at low temperatures ($-100°C$). Liquids with high dielectric constants accelerate the rate of polymerization, but they are generally unsatisfactory as solvents at extremely low temperatures. Hence, a compromise in choice of solvents is often made to assure solubility.

The rate of initiation (R_i) is proportional to the concentrations of the catalyst (ARH) and monomer [M], that is,

$$R_i = K_i(\text{ARH})[\text{M}] \tag{6-45}$$

Equation for rate of initiation of cationic polymerization

As shown in Eq. (6-46), termination is first order:

$$R_t = K_t[\text{HM}^+] \tag{6-46}$$

Equation for rate of termination of cationic polymerization

Hence, with a steady-state assumption, that is, $R_i = R_t$,

$$[\text{HM}^+] = \frac{K_i}{K_t}(\text{ARH})[\text{M}] \tag{6-47}$$

Relation of cation concentration to other variables in cationic polymerization

Thus the rate for propagation R_p is as follows:

$$R_p = K_p[\text{HM}^+][\text{M}] = \frac{K_p K_i}{K_t}[\text{ARH}][\text{M}^2] \tag{6-48}$$

Relation of rate of propagation to other variables in cationic polymerization

If the rate of termination predominates over chain transfer, the degree of polymerization $\overline{\text{DP}}$ is equal to the concentration of monomer and the ratio of the rates of propagation and termination, i.e.,

$$\overline{DP} = \frac{R_p}{R_t} = \frac{K_p[HM^+][M]}{K_t[HM^+]} = \frac{K_p}{K_t}[M] \qquad (6\text{-}49)$$

Relation of chain length to monomer concentration for termination reactions

In contrast, if chain transfer is the predominant reaction leading to a "dead polymer," the degree of polymerization is equal to the ratio of the rate constants for propagation and transfer, as shown below:

$$\overline{DP} = \frac{R_p}{R_{tr}} = \frac{K_p}{K_{tr}} \frac{[HM^+][M]}{[HM^+][M]} = \frac{K_p}{K_{tr}} \qquad (6\text{-}50)$$

Relationship of chain length to reaction rate constants for chain transfer reactions

The production of polyisobutylene (Vistanex) (IM) has been used to illustrate cationic polymerization, since this technique is used for the commercial production of this tacky polymer with a low glass transition temperature. The commercial product is available in several different molecular-weight ranges. It is used as a tacky adhesive and as an additive for paraffin wax.

Schildknecht is credited with the production of the first synthetic stereoregular polymer. As shown in the following equation, he prepared poly(vinyl isobutyl ether) using a boron trifluoride etherate catalyst in liquid propane at −40°C.

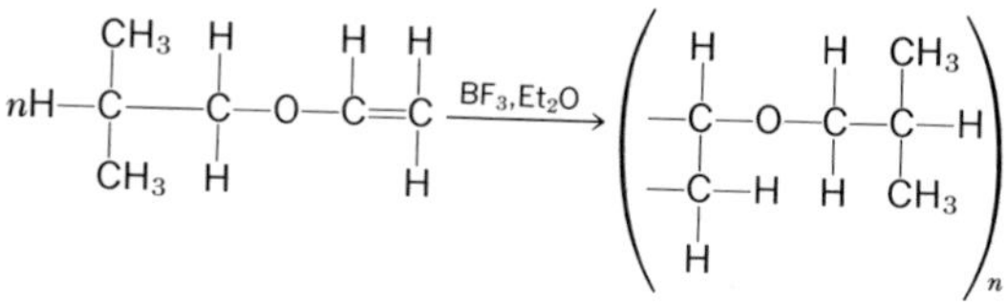

$$n H-\underset{\underset{CH_3}{|}}{\overset{\overset{CH_3}{|}}{C}}-\underset{\underset{H}{|}}{\overset{\overset{H}{|}}{C}}-O-\underset{}{\overset{\overset{H}{|}}{C}}{=}\underset{\underset{H}{|}}{\overset{\overset{H}{|}}{C}} \xrightarrow{BF_3,Et_2O} \left(\begin{array}{c} \overset{H}{\underset{}{}} \quad \overset{H}{\underset{}{}} \ CH_3 \\ -C-O-C-C-H \\ -C-H \ H \ CH_3 \\ H \end{array} \right)_n \qquad (6\text{-}51)$$

Equation for polymerization of vinyl isobutyl ether

This polymer and other poly(vinyl alkyl ethers) have been used as adhesives and impregnating resins.

Polyterpenes are produced by the low-temperature polymerization of dipentene in the presence of aluminum chloride, as shown below:

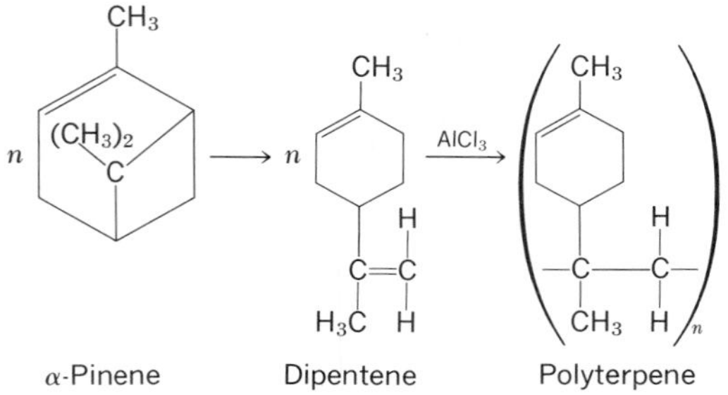

$$(6\text{-}52)$$

α-Pinene   Dipentene   Polyterpene

Equation for polymerization of dipentene

Coumarone-indene resins (Cumar, Nevindene, Paradene, Picco-cumaron) and other hydrocarbon resins (Piccolite) are produced by the polymerization of coal tar or petroleum fractions in the presence of sulfuric acid or aluminum chloride at low temperature ($-70°C$) in solvents such as methylene chloride. A typical polymerization of this type is shown below:

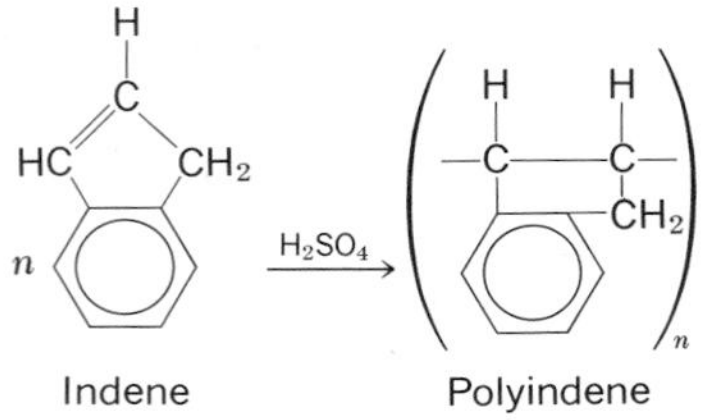

$$(6\text{-}53)$$

Indene   Polyindene

Equation for polymerization of indene

These petroleum resins are produced at an annual rate of over 300 million pounds. They are used as coatings, floor coverings, adhesives, and additives (mineral rubber) for the compounding of rubber.

REFERENCES

Bywater, S.: Anionic Copolymerization, *ACS Div. Polymer Chem.*, (1):114 (1966).

Cram, D. J.: Carbanions, *Pure Appl. Chem.*, **7**:155 (1963).

Eastham, A. M.: Cationic Polymerization, in H. F. Mark, N. G. Gaylord, and N. M. Bikales (eds.), "Encyclopedia of Polymer Science and Technology," Interscience Publishers, a division of John Wiley & Sons, Inc., New York, 1965.

Gaylord, N. G., and H. F. Mark: "Linear and Stereoregular Addition Polymers," Interscience Publishers, Inc., New York, 1959.

Higginson, W. C. E., and N. S. Wooding: Ionic Polymerization, *J. Chem. Soc.*, pp. 760, 774, 1178 (1952).

Kennedy, J. P., and A. W. Langer: Recent Advances in Cationic Polymerization, *Advan. Polymer. Sci.*, **3**:508 (1964).

Margerison, D., and G. C. East: "Introduction to Polymer Chemistry," chap. 5, Pergamon Press, New York, 1967.

Matthews, F. E., and E. H. Strange: *Brit. Patent*, **24**:790 (1910).

McClelland, B. J.: Carbanions, *Chem. Rev.*, **64**:301 (1964).

Overberger, G. G., J. E. Mulvaney, and A. M. Schiller: Anionic Polymerization, in H. F. Mark, N. G. Gaylord, and N. M. Bikales (eds.), "Encyclopedia of Polymer Science and Technology," Interscience Publishers, a division of John Wiley & Sons, Inc., New York, 1965.

Plesch, P. H.: "Cationic Polymerization and Related Complexes," W. Heffer & Sons, Ltd., Cambridge, England, 1953.

————: "The Chemistry of Cationic Polymerization," Pergamon Press, New York, 1963.

Powers, P. O.: Coumarone-Indene Resins, in H. F. Mark, N. G. Gaylord, and N. M. Bikales (eds.), "Encyclopedia of Polymer Science and Engineering," Interscience Publishers, a division of John Wiley & Sons, Inc., New York, 1966.

Ravve, A: "Organic Chemistry of Macromolecules," chap. 5, Marcel Dekker, Inc., New York, 1967.

Schildknecht, C. E.: Ionic Polymerization, "Polymer Processes," chap. 6, Interscience Publishers, Inc., New York, 1956.

————: Poly(vinyl ethers), *Ind. Eng. Chem.*, **40**:404 (1948).

————, S. T. Gross, et al.: Poly(vinyl isobutyl ethers), *Ind. Eng. Chem.*, **40**:2104 (1948).

Szwarc, M.: Anionic Polymerization, *ACS Div. Polymer Chem., Polymer Preprints*, **7**(1): (1966).

————: Living Polymers, *J. Am. Chem. Soc.*, **82**:521 (1960).

Thomas, R. M., W. J. Sparks, et al.: Polyisobutylene, *J. Am. Chem. Soc.*, **62**:276 (1940).

6-4 COMPLEX CATALYST SYSTEMS

A heterogeneous catalysis system consisting of lithium alkyl and nickel oxide on silica was used by Ellis to produce polyethylene (PE) in 1941. However, Ziegler was the first to recognize the linearity of these high-molecular-weight ethylene polymers (Alathon, Hi-Fax, Marlex, Petrothene). Ziegler produced linear polyethylene, in the early 1950s, by bubbling ethylene through xylene in the presence of diethyl aluminum chloride and titanium tetrachloride at low pressures (2 to 3 atm) and moderate temperatures (25 to 50°C).

Shortly thereafter, Natta observed that crystalline polypropylene (PP) could be produced by proper catalyst selection. He pioneered investigations of molecular structure and is responsible for much of our present knowledge of tacticity, which was discussed in Chap. 1. These heterogeneous catalyst systems are now called *Ziegler-Natta catalysts*. These two scientists were awarded the Nobel Prize in 1963 for their outstanding contributions to modern polymer chemistry.

Schildknecht suggested the broad term *stereopolymerization* to describe any process that yields polymers with ordered structure. The term *coordination polymerization* has been used to describe these reactions because the coordination complex between the monomer and the organometallic compound regulates the polymer structure through coordination.

In spite of many empirical investigations, a general theory for the mechanism of Ziegler-Natta catalysis has not been developed. However, considerable information has been supplied for specific catalyst-monomer systems. It is now known that the effective catalyst systems must contain metal-carbon bonds such as are present in triethyl aluminum. A transition metal compound in a lower than maximum valence state, such as titanium trichloride, must also be present. This component of the catalyst system reduces the activation energy required for the insertion of the monomer at the metal-carbon bond.

Some of the other transition metal compounds that have been used successfully are the reaction products of aluminum metal and titanium tetrachloride, titanium tetraalkoxide, titanium tribromide, and titanium dichloride. Halides of vanadium, zirconium, chromium, molybdenum, and tungsten have also been used. These compounds must be paired with specific organometallic compounds.

Some of the other organometallic compounds that have been used successfully with specific transition metal compounds are diethyl aluminum chloride, diethyl zinc, dimethyl phenyl silane, tetrabutyl tin, tetraethyl lead, ethyl magnesium bromide, phenyl lithium, diethyl beryllium, and diethyl cadmium. These compounds are usually present in larger amounts than the transition compounds. It is important that the atomic radii of the metals in the system be similar in size, as is the case for titanium and aluminum.

Aluminum alkyls are extremely reactive. They burn in air and react violently with compounds containing active hydrogen atoms, such as ethanol. When the alkyls are branched, the organometallic compounds exist as monomers in solution but form dimers when the alkyls are linear. Trimers are formed when dialkyl aluminum hydrides are used. Suggested structures for these compounds are as follows:

$$\text{(6-54)}$$

Suggested structures for aluminum alkyls

There are four different crystalline forms of titanium trichloride. All have lattice structures with octahedrally coordinated titanium ions. The alpha, gamma, and delta forms are more active and may be used to produce over 85 percent of isotactic polypropylene in the presence of triethyl aluminum. Finely ground crystals increase the propagation rate. The beta form of titanium trichloride is fibrous and gives low yields of isotactic polypropylene.

The original polymerizations by Ziegler and Natta took place in aromatic solvents, such as xylene, but better yields are obtained when aliphatic hydrocarbons are used. For example, a 95 percent yield of isotactic polypropylene may be produced in a heptane solution of α-titanium trichloride and diethyl aluminum chloride. The yield is decreased with larger halides such as titanium bromide and iodide. Other transition trichlorides such as vanadium, zirconium, and chromium give lower yields of the isotactic polymer.

The yield of isotactic polypropylene in the presence of titanium trichloride is also decreased when the size of the alkyl group on the aluminum atom is increased. The size of the alkylated metal ion is also important. For example, the yields of isotactic polypropylene decrease when magnesium and zinc are used in place of aluminum alkyls in the presence of titanium trichloride. The yield of isotactic polymer has been increased by the addition of small amounts of triethyl amine to the catalyst system.

The use of the Ziegler-Natta catalyst system is usually restricted to the polymerization of nonpolar unsaturated monomers such as ethylene, propylene, butene-1, 3-methylpentene-1, and 4-methylpentene-1. Styrene, butadiene, isoprene, 1,3-pentadiene, and 1,5-hexadiene have also been polymerized in an inert atmosphere by this type of catalysis. Copolymers of ethylene with propylene, butene-2, and butadiene have also been prepared. The subject of copolymers is discussed in Chap. 7.

More polar monomers, such as vinyl chloride, vinyl acetate, and acrylonitrile, may be polymerized by Ziegler-Natta type of catalysts under special conditions. For example, the addition of a more active solvent (tetrahydrofuran) will prevent the reaction of triethyl aluminum and vinyl chloride so that a polymer of vinyl chloride can be prepared. Poly(vinyl acetate) may be obtained in the presence of ethyl acetate. Copolymers of ethylene and tert-butyl acrylate have been prepared in the presence of butyl lithium and titanium tetrachloride but this propagation may follow a different mechanism from that proposed for Ziegler-Natta catalysis.

A variety of polymers of cycloolefins may be obtained in good yield by the solvent polymerization of the cycloalkene in the presence of chromium triacetate and diethyl aluminum chloride. A mixture of cyclic and linear polymers is obtained from cyclopentene. Larger rings, such as cyclohexene, cycloheptene, cyclooctene, and cyclododecene, yield linear polymers in which the trans opening is preferred over the cis type. However, cis opening of cyclopentene takes place exclusively in the presence of molybdenum trichloride and triethyl aluminum. Equal yields of all three types of polymer may be obtained when this specific catalyst system is used with cyclobutene.

As shown in Eqs. (6-55), the reaction of titanium tetrachloride and trialkyl aluminum produces titanium trichloride and several alkyl metal chlorides.

$$
\begin{aligned}
TiCl_4 + AlR_3 &\longrightarrow RTiCl_3 + R_2AlCl \\
TiCl_4 + R_2AlCl &\longrightarrow RTiCl_3 + RAlCl_2 \\
TiCl_4 + RAlCl_2 &\longrightarrow RTiCl_3 + AlCl_3 \\
RTiCl_3 &\longrightarrow TiCl_3 + R\cdot \\
\end{aligned}
$$

$$
\begin{aligned}
&\overset{\displaystyle Cl}{\underset{\displaystyle |}{}} \\
TiCl_4 \cdot Al(C_2H_5)_3 &\longrightarrow TiCl_3 \cdot (C_2H_5)\overset{|}{Al}(C_2H_4\cdot) + C_2H_6 \\
2(C_2H_5)TiCl_3 &\longrightarrow 2TiCl_3 + C_2H_4 + C_2H_6 \\
TiCl_3 + AlR_3 &\longrightarrow RTiCl_2 \cdot R_2AlCl \\
RTiCl_2 &\longrightarrow R\cdot + TiCl_2 \\
R\cdot + TiCl_4 &\longrightarrow TiCl_3 + RCl
\end{aligned}
\tag{6-55}
$$

Suggested reactions of aluminum alkyl and titanium chloride

X-ray data show the presence of a crystalline complex containing both aluminum and titanium ions, as shown below.

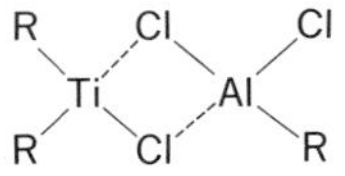

$$
\begin{array}{ccccc}
R & & Cl & & Cl \\
 & \diagdown & \diagup & \diagdown & \diagup \\
 & Ti & & Al & \\
 & \diagup & \diagdown & \diagup & \diagdown \\
R & & Cl & & R
\end{array}
\tag{6-56}
$$

Structure of crystalline complex from Ziegler catalyst ($AlR_3 + TiCl_3$)

It is generally agreed that the catalyst site is a metal-carbon bond similar to that available in the crystalline complex. The catalyst site must contain at least one empty orbital to permit complexation with the π electrons in the monomer by a cationic attack. According to Natta's *insertion hypothesis,* the initiation and subsequent propagation steps require the simultaneous breaking and re-forming of two metal-carbon bonds. This "locking in" of the monomer provides steric control in the propagation steps. The proposed bimetallic mechanism for anionic insertion polymerization is shown below:

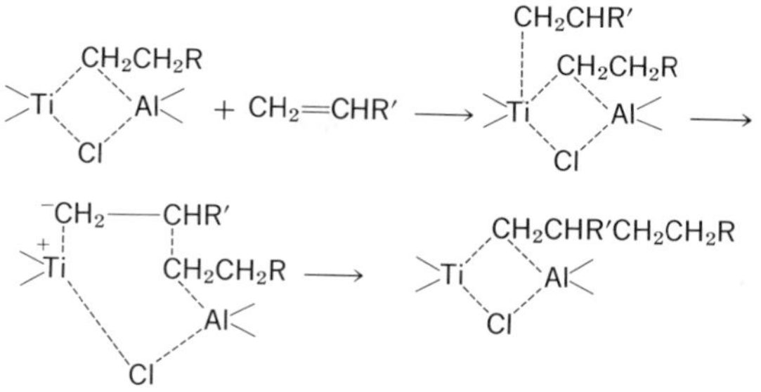

(6-57)

Equation showing insertion of monomer in Natta catalyst

As shown in Eqs. (6-58), termination may be accomplished by the addition of an active hydrogen compound. Hydrogen gas may be used as a chain transfer agent. Molecular weight may also be controlled by the use of a metal alkyl such as diethyl zinc as a chain transfer agent:

Initiation:

$$\text{Cat.—R}' + \text{CH}_2\text{=CHR} \xrightarrow{K_i} \text{Cat.—CH}_2\text{CH(R)R}'$$

Propagation:

$$\text{Cat.—CH}_2\underset{\text{R}}{\underset{|}{\text{C}}}\text{HR}' + n\text{CH}_2\text{=CHR} \xrightarrow{K_p} \text{Cat.—CH}_2\underset{\text{R}}{\underset{|}{\text{C}}}\text{H—}\left(\text{CH}_2\underset{\text{R}}{\underset{|}{\text{C}}}\text{H}\right)_n\text{—R}'$$

Transfer with metal alkyl:

$$\underset{(\text{M}'')}{\text{Cat.}}\text{—CH}_2\text{—}\underset{\text{R}}{\underset{|}{\text{C}}}\text{H—}\left(\text{CH}_2\text{—}\underset{\text{R}}{\underset{|}{\text{C}}}\text{H}\right)_n\text{—R}' + \text{R}''\text{M}' \xrightarrow{K_{tr}}$$

$$\underset{(\text{M}')}{\text{Cat.}}\text{—R}'' + \text{M}''\text{CH}_2\text{—}\underset{\text{R}}{\underset{|}{\text{C}}}\text{H—}\left(\text{CH}_2\text{—}\underset{\text{R}}{\underset{|}{\text{C}}}\text{H}\right)_n\text{—R}' \quad (6\text{-}58)$$

Transfer with hydrogen:

$$\text{Cat.—CH}_2\text{—}\underset{\text{R}}{\underset{|}{\text{C}}}\text{H—}\left(\text{CH}_2\text{—}\underset{\text{R}}{\underset{|}{\text{C}}}\text{H}\right)_n\text{—R}' + \text{H}_2 \xrightarrow{K_{tr}}$$

$$\text{Cat.—H} + \text{CH}_3\text{—}\underset{\text{R}}{\underset{|}{\text{C}}}\text{H—}\left(\text{CH}_2\text{—}\underset{\text{R}}{\underset{|}{\text{C}}}\text{H}\right)_n\text{—R}'$$

Termination with active hydrogen compound:

$$\text{Cat.—CH}_2\text{—}\underset{\text{R}}{\underset{|}{\text{C}}}\text{H—}\left(\text{CH}_2\text{—}\underset{\text{R}}{\underset{|}{\text{C}}}\text{H}\right)_n\text{—R}' + \text{HX} \xrightarrow{K_t}$$

$$\text{Cat.—X} + \text{CH}_3\text{—}\underset{\text{R}}{\underset{|}{\text{C}}}\text{H—}\left(\text{CH}_2\text{—}\underset{\text{R}}{\underset{|}{\text{C}}}\text{H}\right)_n\text{—R}'$$

Polymerization in coordination polymerization

Natta suggested that termination results from the spontaneous dispro-portionation of the growing chain or by chain transfer to the monomer. The rate of propagation is proportional to the concentration of monomer and cat-alyst. The polymer systems may be homogeneous (soluble) or heterogeneous. The latter are preferred for stereospecificity. However, syndiotactic poly-propylene has been obtained at $-78\,°C$ with a soluble catalyst system con-sisting of vanadium tetrachloride and diethyl aluminum chloride.

Polyethylene (PE) produced by using Ziegler-Natta catalysis has a high density (0.945 to 0.965), a glass transition temperature of $-120\,°C$, and a high degree of crystallinity. It has a solubility parameter of 7.9 but is not affected by solvents at ordinary temperatures because of its high degree of crystallinity. The "linear" polymer may have as few as 7 methyl groups per 1,000 atoms in contrast to the 30 methyl groups per 1,000 atoms found in the low-density nonlinear polyethylene. Linear polyethylene is characterized by excellent electrical properties and excellent resistance to stress cracking, solvents, and corrosive environment.

The annual production of linear polyethylene in the United States is in excess of 1 billion pounds. The principal uses are as pipe, blow-molded con-tainers, electrical applications, and monofilaments.

Isotactic polypropylene (Escon, Hostalen, Moplen, Pro-fax) (PP) is produced by the polymerization of propylene in the presence of titanium trichloride and diethyl aluminum chloride at $50\,°C$. The methyl groups are all on the same side of the chain, i.e., isotactic placement (-dd- or -ll-), as shown below:

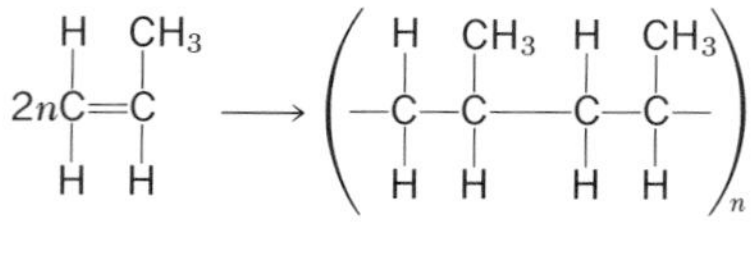

$$2n\overset{\displaystyle H}{\underset{\displaystyle H}{C}}=\overset{\displaystyle CH_3}{\underset{\displaystyle H}{C}} \longrightarrow \left(-\overset{\displaystyle H}{\underset{\displaystyle H}{C}}-\overset{\displaystyle CH_3}{\underset{\displaystyle H}{C}}-\overset{\displaystyle H}{\underset{\displaystyle H}{C}}-\overset{\displaystyle CH_3}{\underset{\displaystyle H}{C}}- \right)_n \qquad (6\text{-}59)$$

Equation for polymerization of propylene

Since n-heptane is a selective solvent for atactic polypropylene, the degree of isotacticity may be determined approximately by measuring the amount of polymer not extracted by n-hexane. The isotactic index of the commercial propylene polymer is greater than 90 percent.

The ordered methyl groups stiffen the chain; hence the melting point of polypropylene is about $50\,°C$ higher than that of polyethylene. This pendant methyl group also increases the volume of the polymer chains so that the density (0.90) is lower than that of polyethylene. However, the presence of the methyl group provides a site which is more susceptible to oxidation than the methylene groups in linear polyethylene.

Polypropylene is used for molded parts that are resistant to autoclave sterilization and for parts where its characteristic hinge effect may be used advantageously. It is also extruded as pipe, sheet, and filaments and blow-molded to produce containers. Over 1 billion pounds of polypropylene is produced annually in the United States.

Other polyolefins such as poly(3-methylbutene-1), poly(4-methylpentene-1), poly(4,4-dimethylpentene-1), and polyvinylcyclohexane have also been produced. Poly(4-methylpentene-1) (TPX) has an unusually low density (0.83) because of the presence of a large pendant group. It is transparent and has a high melting point. The structural formulas and melting points for these polyolefins are shown below:

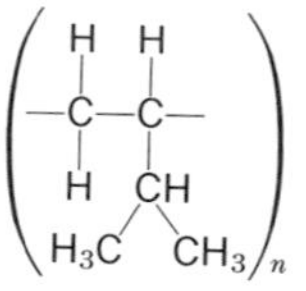

Poly(3-methylbutene-1)   Poly(4-methylpentene-1)
T_m 240°C T_m 300°C

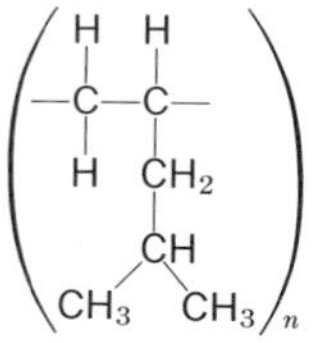

(6-60)

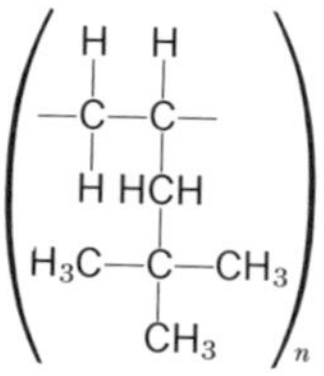

Poly(4,4-dimethylpentene-1)   Polyvinylcyclohexane
T_m 325°C T_m 342°C

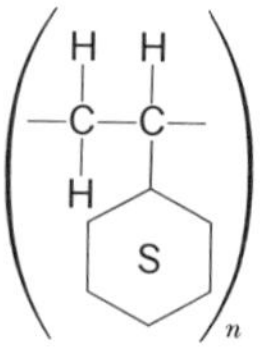

Structures of hydrocarbon polymers with nonlinear
pendant groups

The melting point increases as the size of the branched pendant groups increases since the packing ability of these chains improves as the branching increases in the pendant groups. As stated previously, the melting point of isotactic polypropylene is higher than that of polyethylene because the effect of the small pendant group on chain stiffening is predominant over its effect on the reduction in symmetry.

However, as the size of the pendant group increases from ethyl to heptyl, the melting point decreases because the larger pendant group reduces the packing ability. Yet, when the linear pendant groups contain at least eight carbons, the melting points increase as the size of the groups increases. This effect is attributable to side-chain crystallization, which is comparable to that cited previously for poly(alkyl methacrylates).

Linear polyolefins may also be produced by the polymerization of monomers in the presence of reduced transition metal oxides on appropriate supports. Aluminum alkyls may be used as promotors for these systems. Some of the supports employed are molybdenum oxide, nickel oxide, vanadium oxide, and chromic oxide. Charcoal, silica, and alumina have also been used as supports.

Alfin catalysts consist of a suspension of amyl sodium, sodium isopropoxide, and sodium chloride in pentane. An anionic mechanism has been proposed for this catalyst system. The molecular-weight distribution for polymers produced in the presence of alfin catalysts at low temperatures $(-15°C)$ is much wider than would be anticipated for a heterogeneous anionic catalyst. The principal use for alfin catalysis is for the polymerization of butadiene, which is discussed in Sec. 6-5.

REFERENCES

Bawn, C. E. H., and A. Ledwith: Ziegler Catalyst Mechanism, *Quart. Rev. (London)*, **16**:361 (1962).

Bywater, S., and D. J. Worsfold: Mechanisms, *ACS Div. Polymer Chem., Polymer Preprints*, **5**(2):1108 (1964).

Boor, J.: Ziegler Catalyst Mechanisms, *J. Polymer Sci.*, CI, 257 (1963); B2, 265 (1964); *ACS Div. Polymer Chem., Polymer Preprints*, **6**(2):890 (1965).

Cooper, W.: Stereospecific Polymerization, in J. C. Robb and F. W. Peaker (eds.), "Progress in High Polymers," vol. I, Academic Press, Inc., New York, 1961.

Cossee, P.: in S. Kirschner (ed.), "Advances in the Chemistry of Coordination Compounds," The Macmillan Company, New York, 1961.

Ellis, C.: Lithium Alkyl-metal Oxide Catalysts, U.S. Patent 2,212,155, 1941.

Feay, D. C.: Heterogeneous Chain Growth Polymerization, in R. W. Lenz (ed.), "Organic Chemistry of Synthetic High Polymers," sec. IV, Interscience Publishers, a division of John Wiley & Sons, Inc., New York, 1967.

Field, E., and M. Feller: Polymer Synthesis, *Ind. Eng. Chem.*, **49**:1883 (1957).

Gaylord, N. G., and H. F. Mark: "Linear and Stereoregular Addition Polymers," Interscience Publishers, Inc., New York, 1959.

Hamada, M. M., and V. H. Gary: Ziegler-Natta Polymerization of Isobutylene, *ACS Div. Polymer Chem., Polymer Preprints*, **9**(1):413 (1968).

Hogan, J. P., and R. L. Banks: (Philips Process), U.S. Patent 2,717,888, 1955.

Kresser, T. O. J.: "Polypropylene," Reinhold Publishing Corporation, New York, 1960.

Morton, A. A., and E. J. Lanpher: Alfin Catalyst, *J. Polymer Sci.*, **44:**233 (1960).

Morton, M.: Organometallic Polymerization, *ACS Div. Polymer Chem., Polymer Preprints,* **5**(2):1092 (1964).

————: The Nature of Organometallic Polymerization, in R. F. Gould (ed.), "Elastomer Stereospecific Polymerization," American Chemical Society, Washington, D.C., 1966.

Natta, G.: Ziegler Catalysts, *J. Inorg. Nucl. Chem.*, **8:**589 (1958).

———— and G. Møzzanti: Propagation Mechanism, *Tetrahedron,* **8:**86 (1960).

———— and V. Giannini: Coordinate Polymerization, in H. F. Mark, N. G. Gaylord, and N. M. Bikales (eds.), "Encyclopedia of Polymer Science and Technology," Interscience Publishers, a division of John Wiley & Sons, Inc., New York, 1965.

Overberger, C. G.: Stereospecificity, *ACS Div. Polymer Chem., Polymer Preprints,* **6**(1):1 (1965).

Raff, R. A. V., and K. W. Doak (eds.): "Crystalline Olefin Polymers," Interscience Publishers, a division of John Wiley & Sons, Inc., New York, 1964.

Schildknecht, C. E.: Stereoregular Polymers, in G. L. Clark and G. G. Hawley (eds.), "Encyclopedia of Chemistry," Reinhold Publishing Corporation, New York, 1966.

Szwarc, M., and J. Smid: "Progress in Reaction Kinetics," vol. 2, Pergamon Press, New York, 1964.

Topchiev, A. V., and B. A. Krentsel: "Polyolefins," Pergamon Press, New York, 1962.

Ziegler, K.: Catalysis, *Ann.*, **473:**59 (1929); **511:**1(1934); **542:**40 (1940).

————: Ziegler Catalysts, *Angew Chem.,* **64:**323 (1952); **67:**541 (1955).

6-5 POLYENES

The structure and properties of naturally occurring poly(2-methylbutadienes) were considered in Chap. 4. However, the discussion of synthetic polydienes was postponed until after polymerization techniques and relationships of molecular structure to physical and chemical properties had been described.

Dienes are classified in accordance with the sequence of the multiple ethylenic carbons as *cumulative double bonds* or *allenes* ($-C=C=C-$), *isolated double bonds* ($C=C-C-C-C=C-C$), and alternating or *conjugated double bonds* ($-C=C-C=C-$). The latter undergo 1,2 and 1,4 additions and are more stable and more reactive than the other types. As discussed in introductory organic chemistry textbooks, these additions are dependent on the delocalization of the charge which spreads over all four carbon atoms in 1,3-dienes.

In contrast, double bonds, such as those present in p-divinylbenzene, behave as isolated vinyl groups. Since the functionality of these polyenes is greater than 2, network polymers may be produced. However, linear saturated polymers may be obtained through the use of special techniques; for example, the reaction of p-divinylbenzene and diphenyl tin dihydride yields a linear polymer with tin atoms in the polymer backbone, as shown below:

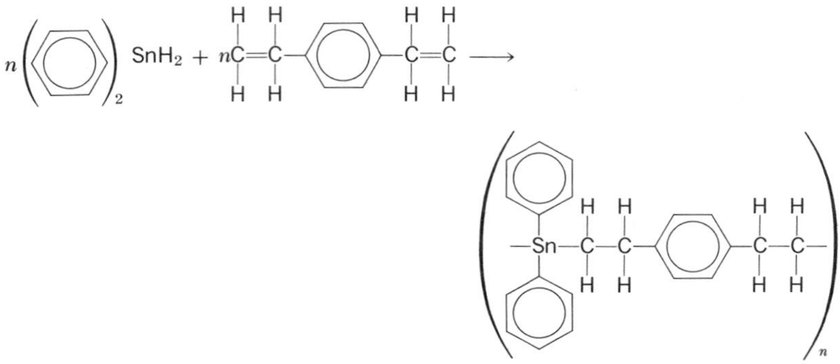

$$
n\left(\!\!\left(\!\bigcirc\!\right)\!\!\right)_2 \text{SnH}_2 + n\text{C}=\text{C}-\!\!\left(\!\bigcirc\!\right)\!\!-\text{C}=\text{C} \longrightarrow \tag{6-61}
$$

Equation for reaction of p-divinylbenzene and diphenyl tin dihydride

Polyene monomers with isolated double bonds may be polymerized by the techniques previously described for radical chain polymerization. The structure of the network polymers produced is similar to that described for network polymers obtained by step-reaction polymerization as discussed in Chap. 4. The extent of crosslinking may be reduced by the addition of vinyl monomers, such as styrene, or methyl methacrylate. For example, cast objects, films, or beads of network polymers may be obtained by casting mixtures of initiator, styrene, and p-divinylbenzene or by the suspension polymerization of these mixtures. Ion-exchange resins may be produced by sulfonation of poly(styrene-co-p-divinylbenzene) beads.

In contrast to the reactivity of vinyl monomers such as styrene, allyl compounds, such as allyl benzene

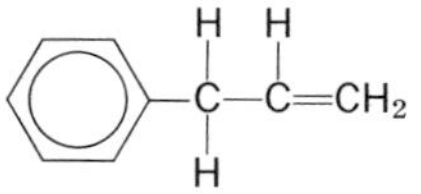

are usually stable to polymerization because of resonance stability. Thus, in chain transfer reactions, a hydrogen atom on a carbon atom adjacent to a double bond is readily abstracted to yield a resonance-stabilized allyl radical, as shown below:

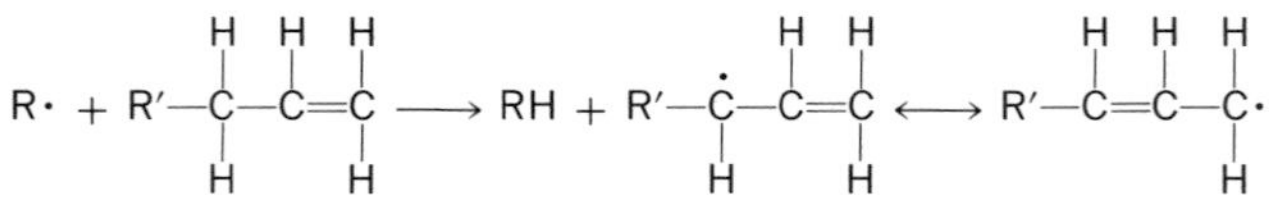

$$
\text{R}\cdot + \text{R}'-\text{C}-\text{C}=\text{C} \longrightarrow \text{RH} + \text{R}'-\text{C}-\text{C}=\text{C} \longleftrightarrow \text{R}'-\text{C}=\text{C}-\text{C}\cdot \tag{6-62}
$$

Equation for formation of resonance-stabilized allyl radical

Hence low-molecular-weight compounds (telomers) are obtained because of chain transfer preference when attempts are made to polymerize monoallyl compounds.   However, radical chain polymerization yields useful polymers of diallyl phthalate (Dapon), diethylene glycol bisallyl carbonate (CR-39), and triallyl cyanurate.   The structures for these polyfunctional monomers are as follows:

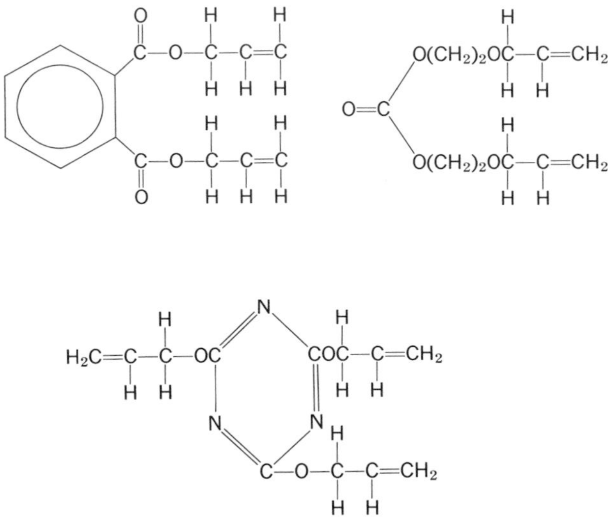

$$(6\text{-}63)$$

Structural formulas for polyallyl compounds

These monomers may be used to produce casting resins and thermosetting molding compounds.

As stated in Chap. 5, esters with multiple double bonds (alkyds), furans, and unsaturated fatty acids may be converted to network polymers.   The classic use of paint and varnish is dependent on the polymerization of the polyenes in these products.   According to Kahn, oxygen reacts with the double bonds to form an activated complex in the presence of driers, such as lead naphthenate.   This complex decomposes to form a hydroperoxide which initiates radical chain polymerization of the unsaturated groups present.

Linear polymers may be produced by the condensation of propylene glycol, or ethylene glycol, and maleic anhydride.   Ellis used benzoyl peroxide as an initiator to polymerize styrene solutions of these unsaturated polyesters.   These so-called polyester resins, which were discussed in Sec. 5-4, are widely used as casting resins and as impregnants for fibrous glass. Reinforced polyesters are used for the construction of boats, aircraft, automobile bodies, pipe, and building panels.

Since it is advantageous to polymerize (cure) these mixtures at room temperature, reducing agents, such as N,N-dimethylaniline, are usually added to accelerate the production of free radicals. The general reactions involved in the production of these useful polymeric compositions are shown below:

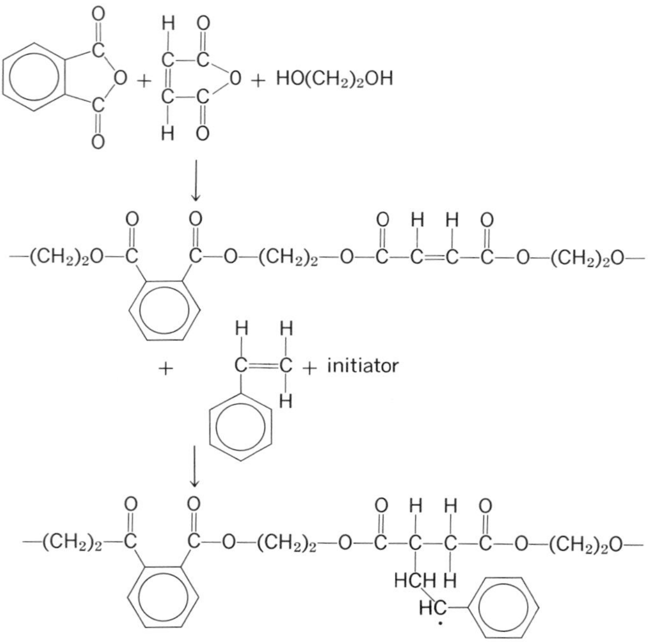

$$(6-64)$$

Equations showing proposed propagation of "polyester" and styrene

Commercial polyesters are heterogeneous products consisting of some polystyrene and network polymer. Empirical formulations for polyesters that have been developed are acceptable for a wide variety of applications. Over 500 million pounds of the polyester plastics are used annually in the United States.

Comparable polyene structures may be obtained by radiolysis or photolysis of dead polymers, such as polyethylene. These techniques may be used to crosslink molded, extruded, or coated resins to form infusible products.

The addition of a free radical (R·) to a conjugated diene such as 1,3-butadiene produces an allyl free radical in which the unpaired electron is delocalized or spread over more than one carbon atom, as shown in the following equation:

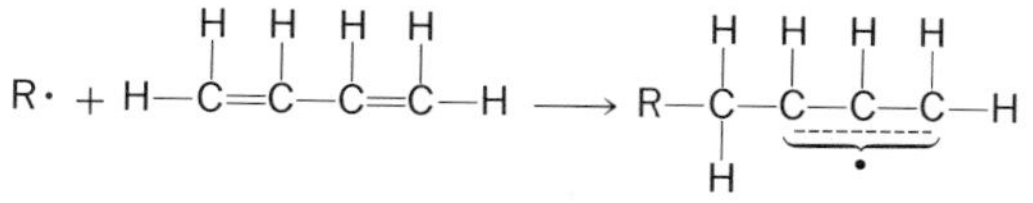

$$R\cdot \;+\; H-\underset{H}{\overset{H}{C}}=\underset{}{\overset{H}{C}}-\underset{}{\overset{H}{C}}=\underset{}{\overset{H}{C}}-H \;\longrightarrow\; R-\underset{H}{\overset{H}{C}}-\underset{}{\overset{H}{C}}-\underset{}{\overset{H}{C}}-\underset{\cdot}{\overset{H}{C}}-H \qquad (6\text{-}65)$$

Formation of allyl free radical from butadiene

This allyl free radical may undergo either 1,2 or 1,4 addition, as shown in the following equation:

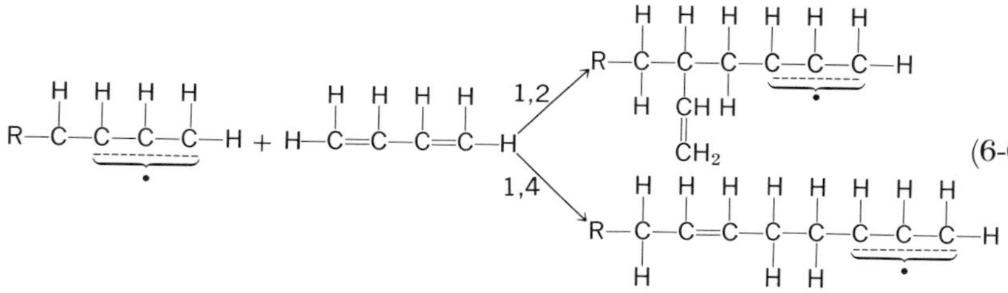

$$(6\text{-}66)$$

Equations showing 1,2 and 1,4 additions of dienes

As discussed previously in Chap. 4, the configurations of the 1,4 polymer chains may be either cis or trans, as shown below:

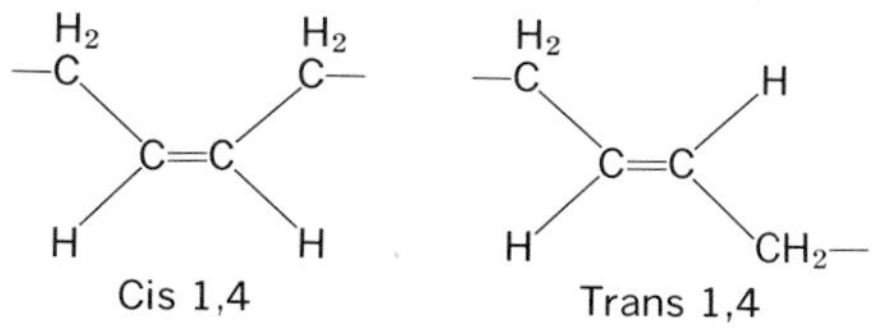

$$(6\text{-}67)$$

Cis 1,4   Trans 1,4

Structures for chain segments of *cis-* and *trans*-polydienes

cis-1,4-Polybutadiene may be prepared by using the heterogeneous catalysis system titanium tetrachloride and triethyl aluminum. *trans*-1,4-Polybutadiene is obtained at 25°C when vanadium trichloride and triethyl aluminum are used as the catalyst system. Poly(1,2-isotactic butadiene) is obtained when hexacarbonyl chromium is used with triethyl aluminum at 25°C. The syndiotactic polymer may be obtained by increasing the ratio of the chromium compound to the aluminum compound in the catalyst system.

Comparable isomers of polyisoprene may be obtained by using similar catalyst systems. However, since different products are obtained from the 1,2 and 3,4 addition reaction of isoprene, a larger variety of polyisoprenes is possible.

The pioneer synthetic rubber Neoprene (CR) (originally called Duprene) was produced by the emulsion polymerization of 2-chloro-1,3-butadiene (chloroprene). Nieuwland had previously synthesized the dimer (vinyl acetylene) and the explosive trimer, using copper (I) chloride and ammonium chloride as catalysts. Collins used aqueous hydrochloric acid to obtain chloroprene, as shown in the following equation:

$$2HC\equiv CH \xrightarrow[\text{NH}_4\text{Cl}]{\text{Cu}_2\text{Cl}_2} \underset{\underset{H}{|}\ \underset{H}{|}}{HC=C-C\equiv CH} \xrightarrow[\text{Cu}_2\text{Cl}_2]{\text{HCl}} \underset{\underset{H}{|}\ \underset{Cl}{|}\ \underset{H}{|}\ \underset{H}{|}}{HC=C-C=CH} \qquad (6\text{-}68)$$

Equation for preparation of chloroprene

This monomer may be polymerized at 40°C by the emulsion technique, with potassium persulfate as the initiator and sulfur as a chain transfer agent or chain-length regulator. As discussed in Chap. 5, both sulfate groups and sulfur atoms are present in the polymer chain. The polymer is stabilized by the addition of tetraethyl thiuram disulfide to the emulsion. The unstable emulsion produced by the addition of acetic acid is then coagulated on chilled rolls.

This polymer has a trans configuration and an identity period of 4.89 Å, which is similar to that of β-gutta-percha. The extent of 1,2 addition increases from none at below 10°C to a high percentage at 90°C. Cross-linked nonelastomeric gels are obtained at temperatures above 100°C. As shown in the following equation, an allylic rearrangement takes place when Neoprene is cured in the presence of zinc oxide.

$$2n\underset{\underset{H}{|}}{\overset{\overset{H}{|}}{C}}=\underset{}{\overset{\overset{Cl}{|}}{C}}-\underset{\underset{H}{|}}{\overset{\overset{H}{|}}{C}}=\underset{}{\overset{\overset{H}{|}}{C}} \xrightarrow{\text{K}_2\text{S}_2\text{O}_8} 2\left(-\underset{\underset{H}{|}}{\overset{\overset{H}{|}}{C}}-\underset{}{\overset{\overset{Cl}{|}}{C}}-\underset{\underset{H}{|}}{\overset{\overset{H}{|}}{C}}=\underset{}{\overset{\overset{H}{|}}{C}}\right)_n \xrightarrow{\text{ZnO}} 2\left(-\underset{\underset{H}{|}}{\overset{\overset{H}{|}}{C}}-\underset{}{\overset{\overset{H}{|}}{C}}=\underset{}{\overset{\overset{H}{|}}{C}}-\underset{\underset{Cl}{|}}{\overset{\overset{H}{|}}{CH}}\right)_n \longrightarrow$$

$$\left(\begin{array}{c}-\underset{\underset{H}{|}}{\overset{\overset{H}{|}}{C}}-\underset{}{\overset{\overset{H}{|}}{C}}=\underset{}{\overset{\overset{H}{|}}{C}}-CH \\ \underset{\underset{H}{|}}{\overset{\overset{|}{H}}{}} \\ -\underset{\underset{H}{|}}{\overset{\overset{}{C}}{}}-C=C-CH \\ H\ H \end{array}\right)_n \qquad (6\text{-}69)$$

Equation for production and curing of polychloroprene

Neoprene is characterized by excellent resistance to flame and hydrocarbon solvents. It has a high modulus of elasticity even in the absence of reinforcing agents.

The principles of emulsion polymerization were patented by Hofman in 1912. However, the potentials of this polymerization technique were overlooked until the 1930s when Tschunker prepared copolymers of butadiene (Buna S, Buna N). The poly(butadiene-co-styrene) elastomer (GRS), selected as a general-purpose rubber, was produced according to a mutual recipe prescribed by the Office of Rubber Reserves of the World War II War Production Board.

The properties of this borderline elastomer were superior to those of methyl rubber, produced during World War I, but were inferior to natural rubber and to the poly(butadiene-co-styrene) elastomers prepared in the laboratories of several rubber corporations in the late 1930s. The recipe included potassium persulfate, 5 percent soap, and 0.3 percent dodecyl mercaptan.

The propagation was terminated by the addition of 0.1 percent hydroquinone (*short stop*) after 12 to 16 hr at 50°C. Phenyl-β-naphthylamine was added as an antioxidant, and the unreacted monomers were removed by distillation. The emulsion was coagulated by the addition of sodium chloride and sulfuric acid.

The elastomer produced was predominantly a trans 1,4-copolymer (60 percent) with equal amounts of 1,4 cis and 1,2 isomers. Attempts to obtain higher than 70 percent yields resulted in a high degree of branching and crosslinking. An idealized chain segment of Buna S (SBR) would have the following structure:

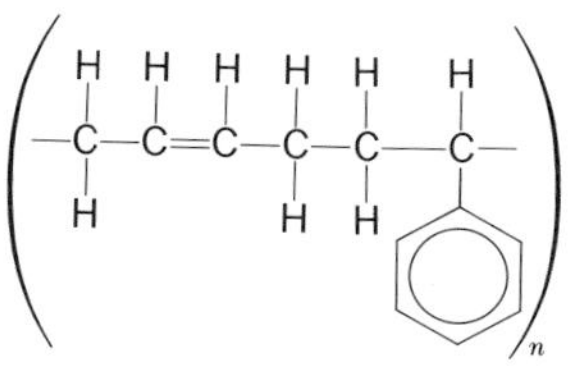

$$(6\text{-}70)$$

Structure of idealized chain segment of SBR elastomer

After cessation of hostilities in 1945, the polymerization temperature was lowered to 5°C (*cold rubber*) and more active initiators were used in the presence of reducing agents. Free radicals were obtained at extremely low temperatures by adding tetraethylene pentamine to cumene hydroperoxide or *p*-menthane hydroperoxide in aqueous systems. The proportion of 1,2 polymer (17 percent) was independent of temperatures. However, the ratio of trans to cis isomer was increased by lowering the temperature.

Poly(butadiene-co-acrylonitrile) (Hycar, Butaprene, Buna N, Paracryl) (NBR) is a specialty rubber which is characterized by excellent resistance to solvents. Over 100 million pounds of this elastomer is produced annually in the United States. An idealized chain segment would have the following structure:

$$
\left(
\begin{array}{c}
\text{H} \quad \text{H} \quad \text{H} \quad \text{H} \quad \text{H} \quad \text{H} \\
\mid \quad \mid \quad \mid \quad \mid \quad \mid \quad \mid \\
-\text{C}-\text{C}=\text{C}-\text{C}-\text{C}-\text{C}- \\
\mid \qquad\qquad \mid \quad \mid \quad \mid \\
\text{H} \qquad\qquad \text{H} \quad \text{H} \quad \text{CN}
\end{array}
\right)_n
$$

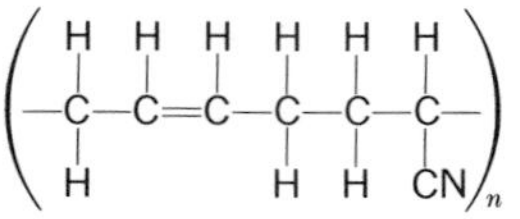

(6-71)

Structure of idealized chain segment of Buna N

Thomas and Sparks used cationic-polymerization techniques to produce a poly(isobutylene-co-isoprene) (butyl rubber) (IIR) in the 1930s. The catalyst was aluminum chloride in the presence of a trace of water. Because only 3 percent isoprene was used with 97 percent isobutylene, the copolymer could be cured (vulcanized) but was resistant to oxidation and ozone attack. The short pendant groups present promoted good flexibility. Since butyl rubber has excellent resistance to gaseous diffusion, it is used for inner tubes. An idealized chain segment would have the following structure:

$$
\left[
\left(
\begin{array}{c}
\text{H} \quad \text{CH}_3 \\
\mid \quad \mid \\
-\text{C}-\text{C}---- \\
\mid \quad \mid \\
\text{H} \quad \text{CH}_3
\end{array}
\right)_{50}
\left(
\begin{array}{c}
\text{H} \quad \text{CH}_3 \quad \text{H} \quad \text{H} \\
\mid \quad \mid \quad \mid \quad \mid \\
--\text{C}-\text{C}=\text{C}-\text{C}- \\
\mid \qquad\qquad \mid \\
\text{H} \qquad\qquad \text{H}
\end{array}
\right)
\right]_n
$$

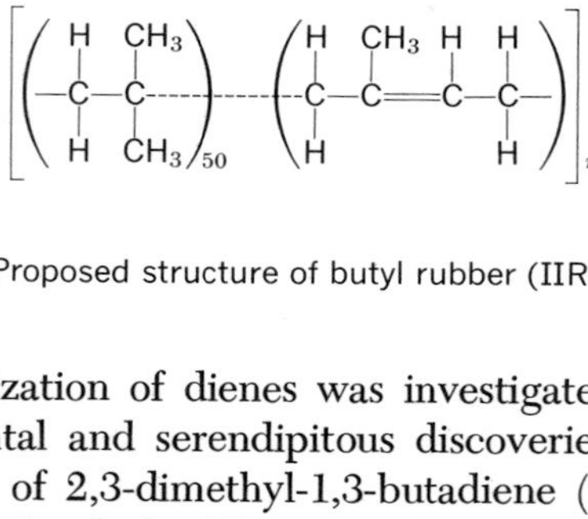

(6-72)

Proposed structure of butyl rubber (IIR)

Anionic polymerization of dienes was investigated in the early 1900s as a result of accidental and serendipitous discoveries by Weizmann and Matthews. Polymers of 2,3-dimethyl-1,3-butadiene (methyl rubber) were also produced independently by Harries in Germany. History shows that the sociological, political, and scientific implications of this discovery rival those of Wöhler, Perkin, and the Curies.

Matthews added sodium metal to isoprene in an attempt to reverse the conditions used unsuccessfully by Weizmann in his attempt to synthesize this monomer. This polymer was patented by Matthews and Strange. A related polymer, poly(2,3-dimethyl-1,3-butadiene), was produced commercially in Germany during World War I. Similar techniques were used by the Russians in the 1930s. The names of the products indicated that the butadiene monomer was produced from petroleum (SKA) or ethanol (SKE).

The sodium was deposited on iron combs which were dipped in the molten metal. This catalyst was replaced by finely divided sodium metal, eutectic alloys, and other active metals. The addition was almost exclusively 1,2 at $-70°C$, but 1,4 addition was favored as the temperature was increased.

The tendency for lithium metal or butyl lithium to produce cis-1,4-polyisoprene (Ameripol SN, Coral rubber) (IR) may be attributed to a chelate formed with a π complex. It is assumed that when sufficient energy is available the carbanion adds to isoprene to yield a trans configuration. Considerable 1,2 and 3,4 addition also occurs because of the high reactivity of the number 2 carbon atom.

The isomeric forms in a polydiene may be controlled by the ratio of aluminum alkyl and titanium trichloride in the Ziegler-Natta catalyst system. Other effective modifications include increasing the size of the alkyl groups, replacing an alkyl by hydrogen or chlorine, and using titanium iodide or cobalt halides in place of the titanium trichloride. Schoenberg suggested that some of the variations in stereospecificity with catalyst modifications are associated with the reducing power and adsorption characteristics of the aluminum compounds toward titanium trichloride.

Morton produced predominantly trans high-molecular-weight polydienes by using catalysts derived from an *al*-(cohol) (isopropanol) and an (ole)-*fin* (propylene). The reactions taking place in the preparation of these *alfin* catalysts are as follows:

$$C_5H_{11}Cl + 2Na \longrightarrow C_5H_{11},{}^-Na^+ + Na^+, Cl^-$$

$$C_5H_{11},{}^-Na^+ + H_3C-\underset{\underset{OH}{|}}{\overset{\overset{H}{|}}{C}}-CH_3 \longrightarrow H_3C-\underset{\underset{O,^-Na^+}{|}}{\overset{\overset{H}{|}}{C}}-CH_3 + C_5H_{12}$$

$$C_5H_{11},{}^-Na^+ + H_2C=\overset{\overset{H}{|}}{C}-CH_3 \longrightarrow H_2C=\underset{\underset{H}{|}}{\overset{\overset{H}{|}}{C}}-\overset{\overset{H}{|}}{C},{}^-Na^+ + C_5H_{12}$$

(6-73)

Proposed reactions in preparation of alfin catalysts

The catalyst is prepared and the diene is polymerized in an inert atmosphere at 30°C. Because of the extremely high molecular weight (9 million), petroleum oil is added to assist the processibility of these elastomers.

When ethylene is polymerized in the presence of propylene with a Ziegler-Natta type of catalyst ($AlEt_2Cl + VOCl_3$) at 25°C, an amorphous ethylene propylene copolymer (EPM) is obtained. A small amount of side-chain unsaturation may be incorporated in these random copolymers by the addition of about 1 percent of a diene, such as a norbornadiene, to the feed. These unsaturated elastomers (EPDM, Nordel, Vistalon, Royalene, Epsyn) may be cured by heating in the presence of sulfur. These vulcanized elastomers are characterized by excellent resistance to ozone, heat, and corrosive environment. They are used for automotive seals and hose. Copolymerization is discussed in the next chapter.

REFERENCES

Anderson, D. E., and P. Kovacic: Neoprene, *Ind. Eng. Chem.*, **47:**171, 1090 (1955).

Bjorksten, J., H. Tovey, B. Harker, and J. Henning: "Polyesters and Their Applications," Reinhold Publishing Corporation, New York, 1960.

Boenig, H. V.: "Unsaturated Polyesters," Elsevier Publishing Company, Amsterdam, 1964.

Brogdon, C. R.: "Film Formation, Film Properties and Film Deterioration," Interscience Publishers, Inc., New York, 1958.

Fischer, H. L.: "Chemistry of Natural and Synthetic Rubbers," Reinhold Publishing Corporation, New York, 1957.

Hofman, F.: Emulsion Polymerization, German Patent 254,672, Jan. 26, 1912.

Horne, S. E., J. P. Kiehl, et al.: Amerpol SN, *Ind. Eng. Chem.*, **48:**784 (1956).

Khan, N. A.: Autoxidation of Unsaturated Oils, *Can. J. Chem.*, **37:**1029 (1959).

Laible, R. C.: Allyl Compounds, *Chenkev*, **58:**807 (1958).

Makowski, H. S., and M. Lynn: Butyl Lithium Polymerization of Butadiene, *ACS Div. Polymer Chem., Polymer Preprints*, **9**(1):420, 427 (1968).

Marvel, C. S.: "An Introduction to Organic Chemistry of High Polymers," John Wiley & Sons, Inc., New York, 1959.

Morton, A. A., F. H. Bolton, et al.: Alfin Catalysis, *Ind. Eng. Chem.*, **40:**2876 (1952).

Morton, M.: "Introduction to Rubber Technology," Reinhold Publishing Corporation, New York, 1959.

Natta, G., and F. Danusso: "Stereoregular Polymers and Stereospecific Polymerization," Pergamon Press, New York, 1967.

——— and L. Porri: Poly-1,3-pentadiene, in R. F. Gould (ed.), "Elastomer Stereospecific Polymerization," chap. 3, American Chemical Society, Washington, D.C., 1966.

Schoenberg, E., D. L. Chalfant, and T. L. Hanlon: Ziegler-Natta Catalytic Polymerization of Isoprene, in R. F. Gould (ed.), "Elastomer Stereospecific Polymerization," chap. 2, American Chemical Society, Washington, D.C., 1966.

Seymour, R. B.: Divinylbenzene Copolymers, U.S. Patent 2,408,690, Oct. 1, 1946.

———: Divinylbenzene Copolymers, U.S. Patent 2,533,635, Dec. 12, 1950.

Solomon, D. H.: "The Chemistry of Organic Film Formers," John Wiley & Sons, Inc., New York, 1967.

Stavely, F. W., et al.: Coral Rubber, *Ind. Eng. Chem.*, **48:**778 (1956).

Talalay, A., and M. Magat: "Synthetic Rubber from Alcohol," Interscience Publishers, Inc., New York, 1945.

Vale, C. P.: Unsaturated Polyesters, in P. Morgan (ed.), "Glass Reinforced Plastics," chap. 2, Iliffe Books, Ltd., London, 1957.

Van Amerongen, G. J.: Catalyst System for Dienes, in R. F. Gould (ed.), "Elastomer Stereospecific Polymerization," chap. 11, American Chemical Society, Washington, D.C., 1966.

Vorlander, D.: Unsaturated Polyesters, *Ann.*, **280:**167 (1894).

Wexler, H.: Paint Films, *Chem. Rev.*, **64:**591 (1964).

Whitby, G. S.: "Synthetic Rubber," John Wiley & Sons, Inc., New York, 1959.

7

Copolymerization

Copolymerization may be defined as a process by which two or more monomers such as styrene and methyl methacrylate or, in general, M_1 and M_2 are joined to form a polymer chain, which may be represented as $\sim M_1 M_2 M_1 M_2 \sim$. This involves a definite chemical reaction between M_1 and M_2 and is not a simple mixing process of two different polymers, such as that used to produce polyblends, that is, $\sim M_1 M_1 \sim + \sim M_2 M_2 \sim$. The components of these mixtures may be separated by physical means, such as solvent extraction. The terms *interpolymer, mixed polymer,* and *heteropolymer* have been used but IUPAC has selected the term *copolymer* to describe these versatile polymeric products.

The general term copolymer includes all polymeric products in which two or more monomers are present as integral parts. Hence it includes those produced by step-reaction, radical-chain, and ionic polymerization processes. Many naturally occurring polymers, such as cellulose, starch, and natural rubber, are *homopolymers.* However, proteins, which are the most important naturally occurring polymers, are complex copolymers of different amino acids.

Synthetic polyamides and polyesters produced by the condensation of mixtures of dicarboxylic acids are also copolymers. The effect of this structural heterogeneity on softening points, degree of crystallinity, and second-order transition temperatures was discussed in Chap. 5. The contribution of copolymerization to the thermal stability of polyacetals was also discussed in that chapter.

190

Copolymers prepared by the anionic polymerization of mixtures of 2-methyl-1,3-butadiene (isoprene) and 2,3-dimethyl-1,3-butadiene were investigated in the early 1920s. The art of bulk copolymerization of vinyl monomers was also practiced many years before the theory of copolymerization was developed. However, the opportunity for the production of different copolymers in the 1920s was limited since only five vinyl monomers were available, viz., ethyl acrylate, methyl methacrylate, styrene, vinyl acetate, and vinyl chloride.

Nevertheless, many of the pioneer developments in the polymer field were associated with copolymers of vinyl chloride, butadiene, and isobutylene. The most widely used commercial polymers are homopolymers such as polyethylene, polystyrene, and poly(vinyl chloride). However, the utility of many other polymers is dependent on the copolymerization process. Butyl rubber (IIR), which was discussed in Chap. 6, is an excellent example of improvement of properties by copolymerization.

The introduction of a comonomer reduces the tendency for crystallization. Copolymerization may also be used to introduce reactive groups, e.g., the addition of vinyl pyridine and maleic anhydride to a polymer chain. As was discussed previously, the addition of a minor amount of a comonomer such as isoprene to isobutylene in the production of butyl rubber may have a substantial effect on the properties of the polymeric product. In a broad sense, most chain-reaction polymers are copolymers since they contain free-radical and telogen fragments. However, since these segments represent less than 1 percent of the polymeric composition, they are overlooked in high-polymer chemistry. Of course, they are of considerable importance in oligomers and telomers.

The biochemist designates the relative content of amino acids in a specific protein by the use of exponents, for example, (gly[66], ala[33]). IUPAC suggests the insertion of "co" to indicate a copolymer such as poly(butadiene-co-styrene). The number of different monomers present in the chain is indicated by the terms *bipolymer* ($\sim M_1M_2M_1M_2 \sim$), *terpolymer* ($\sim M_1M_2M_3M_1M_2M_3 \sim$), *quadripolymer* ($\sim M_1M_2M_3M_4M_1M_2M_3M_4 \sim$), etc.

The following terms used to describe various types of copolymers are explained in the accompanying illustrations as follows: *alternating copolymers* ($\sim M_1M_2M_1M_2 \sim$), *random copolymers* ($\sim M_1M_1M_2M_1M_2M_2M_1 \sim$), *block* (*b*) *copolymers* ($\sim M_1M_1M_1M_1M_2M_2M_2M_2M_2 \sim$), and *graft* (*g*) *copolymers*

$$(\sim M_1M_1M_1\underset{|}{M_1}M_1M_1M_1 \sim)$$
$$(\sim M_2M_2M_2M_2M_2 \sim)$$

The term *run number* (R) is used to express the average number of monomer sequences in 100 monomer units. An azeotropic copolymer is one that has the same composition as its reactants. The composition of the copolymer may be expressed as $M_1/M_2 = n$ and that of the reactants or feed as $m_1/m_2 = X$.

7-1 KINETICS OF COPOLYMERIZATION AND COMPOSITION OF COPOLYMERS

In one of the pioneer empirical approaches to the study of copolymerization, Wall showed that the composition of the copolymer was related to the composition of the reactants. As shown in Eq. (7-1), the *reactivity ratio r* (the ratio of the propagation rate constants) is the slope of the line obtained when M_1/M_2 is plotted against X. This relationship is useful for a few copolymer systems but is not a general equation.

$$n = \frac{M_1}{M_2} = r\,X \tag{7-1}$$

Wall equation

The more general copolymer equation developed by Alfrey, Dostal, Ham, Mayo, Simha, Wall, and others is based on assumptions similar to those used to develop the kinetics for simple radical chain polymerizations. These investigators assumed that the reactivity of a monomer adding to a growing chain end is governed exclusively by the nature of the end group and is unaffected by other variables. Thus it is assumed that the composition of the copolymer is independent of temperature, concentration or type of solvents present, or polymerization method used and that steady-state conditions exist.

Fortunately, these assumptions are acceptable for many radical chain copolymerizations at normal temperatures (25 to 100°C). The polarity of solvents in homogeneous or precipitation copolymerization does not affect the composition because of the close proximity of the monomer and the growing chain free radical. The compositions of copolymers obtained from bulk, solution, and emulsion techniques are similar for water-insoluble monomers. The composition of emulsion copolymers of a water-soluble monomer is related to the solubility of that monomer.

The copolymerization of M_1 and M_2 may take place by two different homopolymerization and heteropolymerization steps. Thus there are four different propagation rates, as shown by the following equations:

$$M_1\cdot + M_1 \xrightarrow{K_{11}} M_1M_1\cdot \qquad \text{homopolymerization} \qquad (7\text{-}2)$$

$$M_2\cdot + M_2 \xrightarrow{K_{22}} M_2M_2\cdot \qquad \text{homopolymerization} \qquad (7\text{-}3)$$

$$M_1\cdot + M_2 \xrightarrow{K_{12}} M_1M_2\cdot \qquad \text{heteropolymerization} \qquad (7\text{-}4)$$

$$M_2\cdot + M_1 \xrightarrow{K_{21}} M_2M_1\cdot \qquad \text{heteropolymerization} \qquad (7\text{-}5)$$

Typical steps in propagation of copolymer chains

The mole fractions of monomers M_1 and M_2 in the copolymer chain may be designated by the symbols F_1 and F_2. These are related to the rate of disappearance of M_1 and M_2 in the feed, as shown below:

$$F_1 = \frac{-d[M_1]}{dt} = K_{11}[M_1\cdot][M_1] + K_{21}[M_2\cdot][M_1] \qquad (7\text{-}6)$$

$$F_2 = \frac{-d[M_2]}{dt} = K_{22}[M\cdot_2][M_2] + K_{12}[M_1\cdot][M_2] \qquad (7\text{-}7)$$

Relationship of copolymer composition to rate constants and concentrations

One may assume a steady-state condition during the early stages of the reaction; i.e., the rate of conversion of $\sim\!M_2\cdot$ to $\sim\!M_2M_1\cdot$ is equal to the rate of conversion of $\sim\!M_1\cdot$ to $\sim\!M_1M_2\cdot$. Thus,

$$K_{21}[M_2\cdot][M_1] = K_{12}[M_1\cdot][M_2] \qquad (7\text{-}8)$$

Steady-state condition

The ratios of the propagating rate constants may be expressed as *monomer reactivity ratios* $r_1 = K_{11}/K_{12}$ and $r_2 = K_{22}/K_{21}$.

The composition of the copolymer (F_1/F_2) may be expressed in terms of Eqs. (7-6) and (7-7) as follows:

$$\frac{F_1}{F_2} = \frac{K_{11}[M_1\cdot][M_1] + K_{21}[M_2\cdot][M_1]}{K_{22}[M_2\cdot][M_2] + K_{12}[M_1\cdot][M_2]} \qquad (7\text{-}9)$$

Equation for copolymer composition

This relationship may be described in terms of monomer reactivity ratios in order to obtain the copolymer equation. In spite of its limitations and empirical development, this general equation is much more useful than the Wall equation (7-1):

$$\frac{F_1}{F_2} = \frac{r_1[M_1]/M_2 + 1}{r_2[M_2]/[M_1] + 1} \tag{7-10}$$

General copolymer equation

$$n = \frac{M_1}{M_2} = \frac{r_1X + 1}{(r_2/X) + 1} \tag{7-11}$$

Copolymer equation

This copolymer equation (7-11) may be used to show the effect of the composition of the feed on the composition of the copolymer. When these compositions are different, the monomer ratio in the feed must be maintained by the continuous addition of monomers in order to produce a copolymer with uniform composition.

For example, as shown in Table 7-1, the monomer reactivity values for butadiene and styrene are $r_1 = 1.40$ and $r_2 = 0.78$, respectively. This indicates that the butadiene would be consumed at a faster rate than the styrene and that the composition of the feed would change rapidly unless butadiene were added continuously to maintain a constant composition.

Thus, as shown in the following illustration, an equimolar ratio of reactants would produce a copolymer with three butadiene units for every two styrene units.

$$n = \frac{r_1X + 1}{(r_2/X) + 1} = \frac{1.40(1) + 1}{0.78/1 + 1} = \frac{2.40}{1.78} = 1.5$$

The monomer reactivity ratios (r_1 and r_2) may be determined by analysis of the change in the composition of the feed during early stages of copolymerization, e.g., at 3, 5, 7, and 10 percent polymerization. It was shown in Chap. 6 that the very first propagation reaction produced a high-molecular-weight polymer. Thus the monomer content in these early stages would be at least 90 percent.

Table 7-1 Selected Copolymerization Reactivity Ratios

M_1	M_2	r_1	r_2	r_1r_2
Acrylic acid	Acrylonitrile	1.15	0.35	0.40
	Styrene	0.25	0.15	0.038
	Vinyl acetate	2	0.1	0.02
Acrylonitrile	Butadiene	0.04	0.40	0.016
	Methyl acrylate	0.84	0.83	0.70
	Methyl methacrylate	0.15	1.45	0.22
	Styrene	0.01	0.40	0.004
	Vinyl acetate	6	0.07	0.042
	Vinyl chloride	3.6	0.05	0.018
1,3-Butadiene	Methyl methacrylate	0.70	0.32	0.22
	Styrene	1.40	0.78	1.1
Ethylene	Propylene	17.8	0.065	1.17
Isobutylene	Isoprene	2.27	0.44	1.22
	Styrene	9.0	2.0	18
Maleic anhydride	Acrylonitrile	0	6	0
	Methyl acrylate	0.02	3.5	0.07
	Styrene	0	0.02	0
Methyl acrylate	Styrene	0.20	0.75	0.15
	Vinyl acetate	9	0.1	0.9
	Vinyl chloride	4	0.06	0.024
Methyl methacrylate	Styrene	0.44	0.50	0.22
	Vinyl acetate	22.2	0.07	1.55
	Vinyl chloride	10	0.1	1.0
Styrene	m-Chlorostyrene	0.64	1.09	0.70
	o-Chlorostyrene	0.56	1.6	0.90
	p-Chlorostyrene	0.74	1.025	0.76
	2,5-Dichlorostyrene	0.30	1.8	0.54
	p-Fluorostyrene	1.5	0.7	1.05
	Methylisopropenyl ketone	0.44	0.29	0.13
	α-Methylstyrene	2.3	0.38	0.87
	p-Methylstyrene	0.82	1.15	0.94
	Vinyl acetate	55	0.01	0.55
	Vinyl chloride	5.7	0.035	0.20
	Vinylidene chloride	2.0	0.14	0.28
	2-Vinyl pyridine	0.55	1.14	0.63
Tetrafluoroethylene	Monochlorotrifluoroethylene	1.0	1.0	1.0
Trichloroethylene	Styrene	0	16	0
Vinyl acetate	Vinyl bromide	0.35	4.5	0.15
	Vinyl chloride	0.65	1.35	0.88
	Vinylidene chloride	0.1	6	0.6
Vinyl chloride	Vinylidene chloride	0.5	0.001	0.0005

The tendency for randomness in the chain is greatest when $r_1 r_2 = 1$. This has been called *ideal copolymerization,* that is,

$$(\sim\!\!\sim M_1 M_2 M_1 M_1 M_2 M_1 M_2 M_2\!\!\sim\!\!\sim).$$

The conditions for perfect randomness are $r_1 = r_2 = 1$. The copolymer equation is identical to the Wall equation for ideal copolymerizations. It may be noted that there is no tendency for alternation when tetrafluoroethylene and monochlorotrifluoroethylene are copolymerized since $r_1 \cong r_2 \cong 1$.

In contrast, when $r_1 = r_2 = 0$, there is perfect alternation regardless of the composition of the feed. Thus the copolymer equation is simplified to $n = M_1/M_2 = 1$. As shown in the following equation, this condition is approached for the copolymerization of styrene and maleic anhydride.

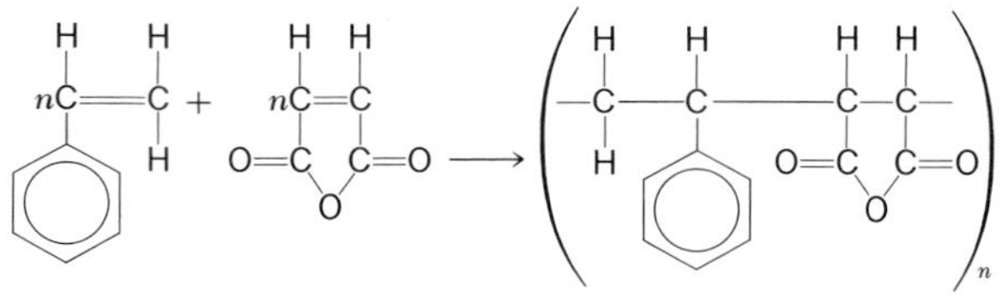

$$(7\text{-}12)$$

Equation for copolymerization of styrene and maleic anhydride

Most copolymer compositions are between these two extremes of perfect alternation and ideal randomness. Thus the values of $r_1 r_2$ may be used to estimate the extent of randomness. When the product of $r_1 r_2$ is greater than 1, two homopolymers may be formed independently. When both r_1 and r_2 are greater than 1, a long sequence of each monomer will be found in the chain. The last two cases are rare and generally associated with ionic rather than free-radical copolymerizations.

In the development of the copolymer equation, it was assumed that the reactivity of a monomer adding to the growing chain end was governed exclusively by the nature of the end group. This assumption is not valid when steric or polar restrictions are present. For example, Ham and Fordyce showed that polar groups, such as the cyano groups in fumaronitrile, influence the addition of fumaronitrile units in the poly(styrene-co-fumaronitrile) chain.

Since this effect extends beyond the *penultimate units,* it is not possible to prepare a copolymer of styrene (M_2) with more than 40 mole percent fumaronitrile (M_1). This limiting structure is consistent with molecular model structures since a copolymer with 50 mole percent of fumaronitrile would be highly strained. The limiting structure is $M_1M_2M_2M_1M_2M_1M_2M_2$, as shown below:

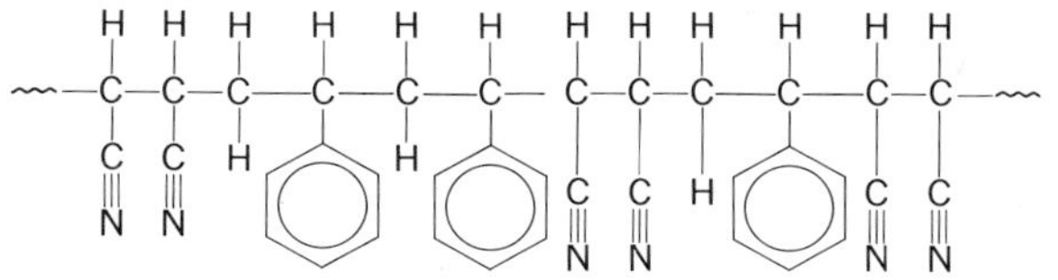

$$(7\text{-}13)$$

Proposed structure for styrene-fumaronitrile copolymer chain

Provided the temperatures are below that at which the rate of depropagation is significant, temperature has little effect on the composition of copolymers. It has also been shown that pressure and the size of lone pendant groups have little effect on copolymerization rates. In general, solvents have little effect unless there is a preferential chemical interaction between the solvent and one of the monomers or preferential adsorption of monomer on the precipitated copolymer

Since the rate of propagation in ionic polymerization is related to the charge on the monomer and the catalyst, the composition of copolymers is influenced by the polarity of the monomers. Styrene is neither strongly electrophilic or nucleophilic. It may be polymerized by both free-radical, cationic, and anionic techniques. Thus the copolymerization of styrene and selected monomers may be used to illustrate the effect of the polymerization method on composition.

As shown in Table 7-1, the monomer reactivity ratios for styrene and methyl methacrylate are $r_1 = 0.50$ and $r_2 = 0.44$. Thus the propagation rates for this system are similar, and approximately equimolar proportions of these monomers would be present in the copolymer when equimolar proportions were present in the feed. In contrast, the reactivity values in the anionic copolymerization of these monomers are $r_1 = 0.12$ and $r_2 = 6.4$. These reactivity values are $r_1 = 10.5$ and $r_2 = 0.1$ for cationic polymerization. Hence the product obtained by anionic polymerization would have a high methyl methacrylate content and that obtained by cationic polymerization would have a high styrene content.

The effect of a substituent (X) in a vinyl monomer

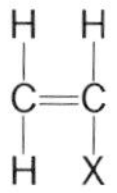

on reactivity is shown in order of decreasing activity as follows:

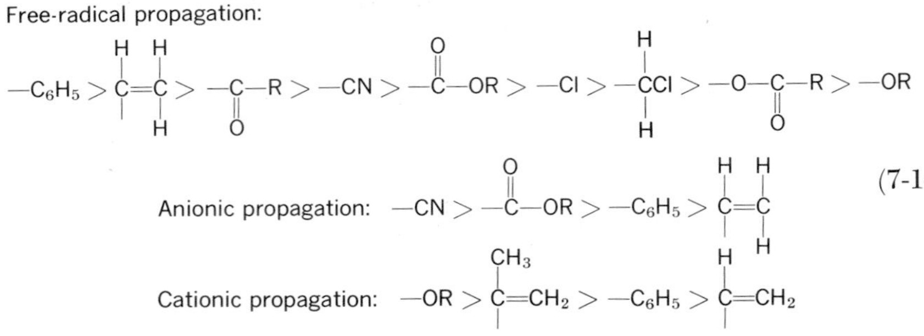

Free-radical propagation:

$$-C_6H_5 > \underset{\underset{H}{|}}{\overset{\overset{H}{|}}{C}}=\underset{\underset{O}{|}}{\overset{\overset{H}{|}}{C}} > -\underset{\underset{O}{\parallel}}{C}-R > -CN > -\overset{\overset{O}{\parallel}}{C}-OR > -Cl > -\underset{\underset{H}{|}}{\overset{\overset{H}{|}}{C}}Cl > -O-\underset{\underset{O}{\parallel}}{C}-R > -OR$$

$$\text{(7-14)}$$

Anionic propagation: $-CN > -\overset{\overset{O}{\parallel}}{C}-OR > -C_6H_5 > \underset{\underset{H}{|}\ \underset{H}{|}}{\overset{\overset{H}{|}\ \overset{H}{|}}{C}}=C$

Cationic propagation: $-OR > \underset{\underset{CH_3}{|}}{C}=CH_2 > -C_6H_5 > C=CH_2$

Relative activities of substituents in vinyl monomers

The order of reactivity ratios of vinyl monomers may be correlated with resonance stability. The resonance stability of a styryl radical is high (20 kcal) because three different quinoid structures may be shown for these radicals, as follows:

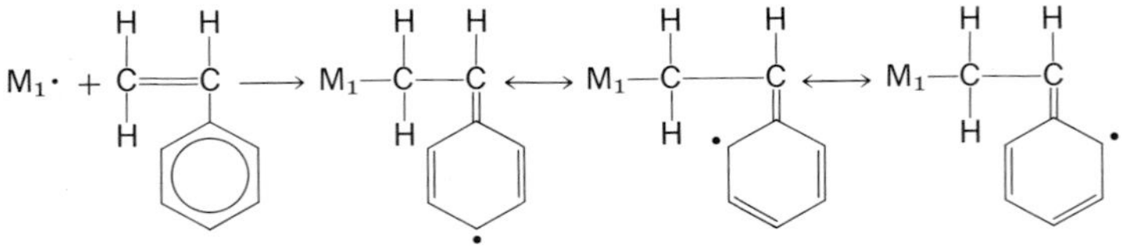

$$\text{(7-15)}$$

Resonance-stabilized styryl radicals

Accordingly, there is little tendency for copolymerization of styrene with other monomers with *high resonance stability*, such as vinyl acetate. In general, the effect of an additional substituent on the substituted carbon atom of a vinyl monomer is additive. Thus the reactivity of methyl methacrylate is much greater than the reactivity of methyl acrylate, and the reactivity of vinylidene chloride is greater than that of vinyl chloride.

In contrast, substituents on the other carbon atom usually decrease the reactivity. Thus stilbene is much less reactive than styrene, and symmetrical dichloroethylene is much less reactive than vinyl chloride. Actually, few 1,2 disubstituted vinyl monomers form homopolymers in free-radical chain polymerization. However, inactive disubstituted ethylenes such as maleic anhydride, fumaronitrile, and dialkyl maleates copolymerize with the active monomers such as styrene to produce alternating copolymers.

Alfrey and Price used the empirical parameters Q and e to represent

Table 7-2 *Q-e* **Values for Selected Monomers**

MONOMERS	Q	e
Acrylic acid	1.15	0.77
Acrylonitrile	0.60	1.20
1,3-Butadiene	2.39	−1.05
Isobutylene	0.033	−0.96
Trichloroethylene	0.019	1.86
Monochlorotrifluoroethylene	0.020	1.48
m-Chlorostyrene	1.03	−0.36
o-Chlorostyrene	1.28	−0.36
p-Chlorostyrene	1.03	−0.33
2,5-Dichlorostyrene	1.60	0.09
Ethylene	0.015	−0.20
p-Fluorostyrene	0.83	−0.12
Isoprene	3.33	−1.22
Maleic anhydride	0.23	2.25
Methyl acrylate	0.42	0.60
Methyl methacrylate	0.74	0.40
α-Methylstyrene	0.98	−1.27
p-Methylstyrene	1.27	−0.98
Propylene	0.002	−0.78
Styrene (reference)	1.0	−0.80
Vinyl acetate	0.026	−0.22
Vinyl bromide	0.047	−0.25
Vinyl chloride	0.044	0.20
Vinylidene chloride	0.23	0.36

the resonance stability of the monomer (M_1) and the polarity of the radical ($M_1\cdot$). Early investigators assigned the arbitrary values of $Q = 1.0$ and $e = -0.80$ for styrene but Zutty showed that it is preferable to assign the arbitrary values of $Q = 1$ and $e = 0$ for ethylene. As shown in Table 7-2, relative values have also been assigned to other monomers.

The Alfrey-Price equation (7-16) is related to the Hammett equation used to predict the effect of nuclear substituents on the reactivity of aromatic compounds. In this equation, the parameter P_1 is related to the reactivity of the radical $\sim\sim M_1\cdot$, Q_2 is related to the reactivity of the monomer M_2, and e_1 and e_2 are characteristic polarities of the radical $\sim\sim M_1\cdot$ and the monomer M_2.

$$K_{12} = P_1 Q_2 e^{-e_1 e_2} \tag{7-16}$$

Alfrey-Price equation

Thus, from the previous definitions, r_1 and r_2 may be related to Q-e values as follows:

$$r_1 = \frac{K_{11}}{K_{12}} = \frac{Q_1}{Q_2} e^{-e_1(e_1-e_2)} \qquad (7\text{-}17)$$

$$r_2 = \frac{K_{22}}{K_{21}} = \frac{Q_2}{Q_1} e^{-e_2(e_2-e_1)} \qquad (7\text{-}18)$$

$$r_1 r_2 = e^{-(e_1-e_2)^2} \qquad (7\text{-}19)$$

Relationships of reactivity ratios to polarity of substituents

In spite of its empirical derivation and its inadequacy in predicting the reactivities of all monomer systems, the Alfrey-Price Q-e scheme is extremely useful. It can be used for bipolymers, terpolymers, etc., and is a valuable tool for predicting the reactivity of copolymer systems. A more reliable relationship has been proposed by Ham. However, this and other improved reactivity parameters are also related to resonance stability and polarity.

In addition to the previously mentioned copolymers, viz., poly(styrene-co-maleic anhydride), poly(styrene-co-fumaronitrile), and poly(isobutylene-co-isoprene), there are many important commercially available copolymers.

For example, nonelastomeric copolymers of styrene and butadiene in which the former is the major component are available. The copolymer containing 70 percent styrene is tough and leathery. The use of higher percentages of butadiene is not justified by the additional increase in toughness. The reactivity values shown in Table 7-1 apply to this emulsion polymerization system. Hence, monomers must be added continuously to the feed to maintain a uniform copolymer composition.

Blends of polystyrene and SBR (copolymer of 70 percent butadiene and 30 percent styrene) have higher resistance to impact and lower tensile strengths than polystyrene. These "styrene-rubber blends" are widely used as extruded pipe and molded parts for applications in which polystyrene is too brittle and where clarity is not essential. This approach has been extended to blends of polystyrene with poly(cis-butadiene), polyisoprene, and ethylene-propylene copolymers.

When both components are produced by the emulsion process, the blended product may be obtained by mixing the emulsions before coagulation. As discussed later in this chapter, superior products are obtained by grafting the styrene on the polydiene backbone.

Poly(styrene-co-acrylonitrile) (SAN) containing 20 to 30 percent of acrylonitrile has a higher softening point, higher impact resistance, and bet-

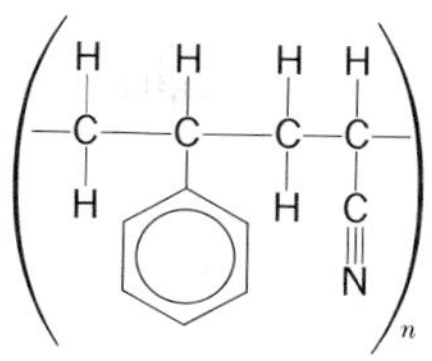

$$(7\text{-}20)$$

Poly(styrene-co-acrylonitrile)

ter resistance to hydrocarbon solvents than polystyrene. Blends of this copolymer and poly(butadiene-co-acrylonitrile) elastomers are included in the broad class of ABS polymers. However, as discussed later in the chapter, graft copolymers obtained from these three monomers (acrylonitrile, butadiene, and styrene) are also included in the ABS copolymer classification.

Fibers from copolymers of acrylonitrile and vinyl pyridine are much more readily dyed than the polyacrylonitrile homopolymer. Poly(styrene-co-maleic anhydride) may be readily hydrolyzed by alkaline solutions to produce water-soluble salts (Stymer). These and poly(vinyl ethyl ether-co-maleic anhydride) (Gantrez) may be used as polymeric dispersants and sizing agents.

Copolymers of methyl methacrylate with styrene or α-methyl styrene are transparent and are more heat-resistant than poly(methyl methacrylate). Elastomeric copolymers of ethyl acrylate and ethyl-2-chloroacrylate may be vulcanized by poly(alkylene amines). Copolymers of ethyl acrylate and acrylonitrile (Acrylon) (ANM) are also used as elastomers. The latter may be cured when heated in the presence of sodium metasilicate or lead oxide. Presumably, ethyl alcohol is eliminated in an intermolecular Claisen-type condensation.

Poly(vinyl chloride-co-vinyl acetate) (Vinylite) was one of the pioneer copolymers and is the most important copolymer of vinyl chloride. The most popular copolymer of this type contains 87 percent vinyl chloride. Its principal use is as a polymeric coating. The adhesive properties of these products are improved by the addition of a small amount of maleic anhydride to the feed or by partial hydrolysis of the vinyl acetate copolymer. These copolymers are more readily processed than poly(vinyl chloride). They are also used for flooring, fibers, and phonograph records.

Poly(vinyl chloride-co-acrylonitrile) in which the acrylonitrile content is 10 percent or less (Vinyon N, Dynel) is soluble in acetone. Flame-resistant thermoplastic fibers may be spun from this solution. Saran is presumably a copolymer of vinylidene chloride and vinyl chloride in which the latter is the minor constituent.

Both uniform and nonuniform copolymers have been produced by copolymerization of ethylene and other monomers at high pressures but most copolymers of ethylene are produced with Ziegler-Natta type of catalysts. Poly(ethylene-co-butene-1) contains pendant groups which interfere with chain mobility; hence resistance to creep and stress cracking is improved in accordance with the content of the comonomer (butene-1). This copolymer may be used for the production of pipe and blow-molded bottles.

Poly(ethylene-co-vinyl acetate) (Elvax) is tougher and more flexible than the polyethylene. The degree of crystallinity may be controlled by the content of the comonomer (vinyl acetate). This product, which is more soluble than the homopolymer, is used as a component of waxes and adhesives.

Poly(ethylene-co-propylene) (EPM) elastomers are produced by adding the monomers to a suspension of Ziegler-Natta catalyst in heptane at 30 to 60°C and 50 to 150 psi pressure. Superior products are obtained when conjugated or unconjugated dienes are included in the reactant mixture.

These terpolymers contain 3 or 4 double bonds per 100 olefin monomer units in the chain. Butadiene and isoprene are representative of the conjugated dienes used. Other dienes used are 1,4-pentadiene, cyclic polyenes such as cyclooctadiene, and endomethylenic dienes such as norbornene [bicyclo(2,2,1)-heptene]. The latter is obtained by the addition of acetylene to cyclopentadiene.

Ionomers such as poly(ethylene-co-methacrylic acid) (Surlyn) produced by high-pressure copolymerization of ethylene and methyacrylic acid may be partially converted to sodium or magnesium salts. These copolymer salts act like thermosetting plastics at low temperatures. These ionomers are transparent, glossy, tough, solvent-resistant polymers at ordinary temperatures and are readily processed in conventional molding and extrusion equipment at higher temperatures. The products are used as film, tubing, blow-molded and injection-molded containers, and injection-molded articles.

REFERENCES

Alfrey, T., and G. Goldfinger: Copolymer Equations, *J. Chem. Phys.*, **12**:205 (1944).
———— and C. C. Price: *Q-e* Scheme, *J. Polymer Sci.*, **101**:(1947).
Burnett, G. M.: "Mechanisms of Polymer Reactions," Interscience Publishers, Inc., New York, 1954.
Ham, G.: "Copolymerization," Interscience Publishers, a division of John Wiley & Sons, Inc., New York, 1964.

————: Copolymerization, in H. F. Mark, N. G. Gaylord, and N. M. Bikales (eds.), "Encyclopedia of Polymer Science and Technology," Interscience Publishers, a division of John Wiley & Sons, Inc., New York, 1966.

Harwood, H. J.: Copolymer, in G. L. Clark and G. G. Hawley (eds.), "Encyclopedia of Chemistry," Reinhold Publishing Corporation, New York, 1966.

Igarashi, S.: Copolymer Composition, *Polymer Letters,* **1:**359 (1963).

Lenz, R.: Polymerization Processes, in H. F. Mark, N. G. Gaylord, and N. M. Bikales (eds.), "Encyclopedia of Polymer Science and Technology," Interscience Publishers, a division of John Wiley & Sons, Inc., New York, 1968.

Mark, H. F., B. Immergut, E. H. Immergut, L. J. Young, and K. I. Beynon: Copolymerization Reactivity Ratios, in J. Brandrup and E. H. Immergut (eds.), "Polymer Handbook," Interscience Publishers, a division of John Wiley & Sons, Inc., New York, 1966.

Margerison, D., and G. C. East: "Introduction to Polymer Chemistry," chap. 4, Pergamon Press, New York, 1967.

Mayo, F. R., and F. M. Lewis: Copolymer Equation, *J. Am. Chem. Soc.,* (502) **66:**1594 (1944).

———— and C. Walling: Copolymer Equation, *Chem. Rev.,* **46:**191 (1950).

Miller, M. L.: "The Structure of Polymers," chap. 8, Reinhold Publishing Corporation, New York, 1966.

Price, C. C.: "Mechanisms of Reactions at the Carbon-Carbon Double Bond," Interscience Publishers, Inc., New York, 1946.

Reich, L., and A. Schindler: "Polymerization by Organometallic Compounds," Interscience Publishers, a division of John Wiley & Sons, Inc., New York, 1966.

Staudinger, H., and J. Schneider: Vinyl Chloride–Vinyl Acetate Copolymers, *Ann.,* **151:**(1939).

Stockmayer, W. H.: Copolymerization, *J. Chem. Phys.,* **13:**199 (1945).

Vollmart, B.: "Grundriss Der Makromolekularen Chemie," Springer-Verlag OHG, Berlin, 1962.

Wall, F. T.: Copolymer Composition, *J. Am. Chem. Soc.,* **63:**1862 (1941).

Wall, L. A.: Q-e Scheme, *J. Polymer Sci.,* **2:**542 (1947).

Young, L. J.: Q-e Values, in J. Brandrup and E. H. Immergut (eds.), "Polymer Handbook," vol. II, p. 341, Interscience Publishers, a division of John Wiley & Sons, Inc., New York, 1966.

————: Reactivity Ratios, *J. Polymer Sci.,* **54:**411 (1961); **62:**S15 (1962).

Zutty, N. L., and R. D. Burkhart: Q-e Scheme, *J. Polymer Sci.,* (A)**1:**1137 (1963).

7-2 BLOCK COPOLYMERS

By definition, a *block copolymer* is a linear copolymer that contains long sequences of one monomer plus another monomer in the polymer backbone. The components of these blocks may be step-reaction polymers, chain-reaction polymers, or copolymers. The term block copolymer also includes stereoblock polymers which are homopolymers with long sequences of similar structures. Typical block-copolymer chains are illustrated below:

Block M_1—Block M_2: $\qquad M_1M_1M_1M_1M_1M_1M_2M_2M_2M_2M_2M_2$

Block M_1—Coupling M_2: $\qquad M_1M_1M_1M_1M_1M_1M_2M_1M_1M_1M_1M_1$ $\quad$ (7-21)

Stereoblock polymers: $\qquad d\ \ d\ \ d\ \ d\ \ d\ \ d\ \ l\ \ l\ \ l\ \ l\ \ l\ \ l$

Block-copolymer chains

Homopolymers with reactive end groups may be converted to block copolymers by reactions with the active end groups, such as hydroxyl, carboxyl, and amine groups. Poly(ethylene oxides) with hydroxyl terminal groups may react with propylene oxide to produce chains with different blocks of alkylene oxides. These products (Pluronics) are surface active agents and are effective additives to soil-removing formulations.

Hydrogen peroxide and specific initiators, such as 4,4'-azobis(4-cyano-n-pentanol), yield polymers with hydroxyl terminals as shown below:

$$H_2O_2 + Fe^{++} \longrightarrow Fe^{3+} + OH^- + HO\cdot$$

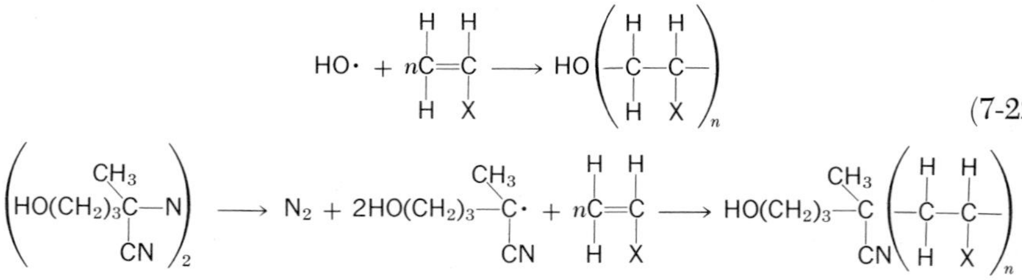

$$(7\text{-}22)$$

Synthesis of polymers with terminal hydroxyl groups

Polyesters with hydroxyl end groups may be obtained when a slight excess of glycol is condensed with a dicarboxylic acid.

Block copolymers may be produced by reacting these products with ethylene oxide, anhydrides of dicarboxylic acids, or diisocyanates. Segmented polyurethane fibers (Spandex) are obtained by the reaction of diisocyanates with polyethers with hydroxyl terminals. Elastomers (Vulcollans) are obtained by the reaction of diisocyanates and polyesters with hydroxyl terminals. Block copolymers are also obtained when chains with hydroxyl end groups, such as polyacetals and silicones, are capped with difunctional derivatives.

Polyesters or polyamides with carboxyl terminals may be obtained by condensing an excess of dicarboxylic acid with a glycol or alkylene diamine. Polymers with carboxyl end groups are also obtained when 4,4'-azobis(4-cyanovaleric acid) or succinic acid peroxide is used as initiator. These reactions are shown below:

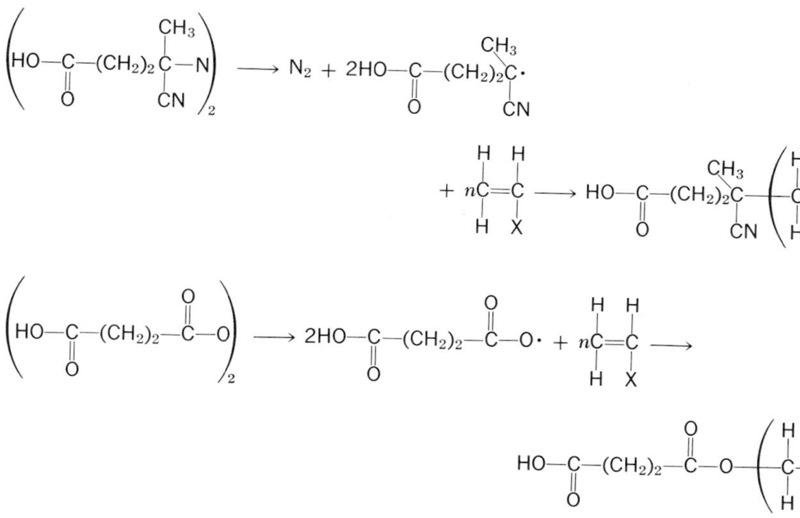

$$\left(HO-\underset{\underset{O}{\|}}{C}-(CH_2)_2\underset{\underset{CN}{|}}{\overset{\overset{CH_3}{|}}{C}}-N\right)_2 \longrightarrow N_2 + 2HO-\underset{\underset{O}{\|}}{C}-(CH_2)_2\underset{\underset{CN}{|}}{\overset{\overset{CH_3}{|}}{C}}\cdot$$

$$+ n\underset{\underset{H}{|}}{\overset{\overset{H}{|}}{C}}=\underset{\underset{X}{|}}{\overset{\overset{H}{|}}{C}} \longrightarrow HO-\underset{\underset{O}{\|}}{C}-(CH_2)_2\underset{\underset{CN}{|}}{\overset{\overset{CH_3}{|}}{C}}-\left(\underset{\underset{H}{|}}{\overset{\overset{H}{|}}{C}}-\underset{\underset{X}{|}}{\overset{\overset{H}{|}}{C}}\right)_n$$

$$\left(HO-\underset{\underset{O}{\|}}{C}-(CH_2)_2-\underset{\overset{O}{\|}}{C}-O\right)_2 \longrightarrow 2HO-\underset{\underset{O}{\|}}{C}-(CH_2)_2-\underset{\overset{O}{\|}}{C}-O\cdot + n\underset{\underset{H}{|}}{\overset{\overset{H}{|}}{C}}=\underset{\underset{X}{|}}{\overset{\overset{H}{|}}{C}} \longrightarrow \qquad (7\text{-}23)$$

$$HO-\underset{\underset{O}{\|}}{C}-(CH_2)_2-\underset{\overset{O}{\|}}{C}-O-\left(\underset{\underset{H}{|}}{\overset{\overset{H}{|}}{C}}-\underset{\underset{X}{|}}{\overset{\overset{H}{|}}{C}}\right)_n$$

Synthesis of polymers with carboxyl end groups

Telomers or oligomers formed by chain transfer with carbon tetrachloride may be hydrolyzed to produce carboxyl terminal groups. Carboxyl end groups may be produced when living polymers are quenched by carbon dioxide.

Polymer chains with carboxyl end groups may be reacted with diamines or with glycols to produce block copolymers. Fibers from block polyesters have improved dyeability and higher softening points than the homopolymers.

Block copolymers from ethylene diamine and propylene oxide (Tetronics) have slight cationic properties as a result of the presence of tertiary nitrogen atoms in the polymer chain. A representative structure for these surface active polymers is shown below:

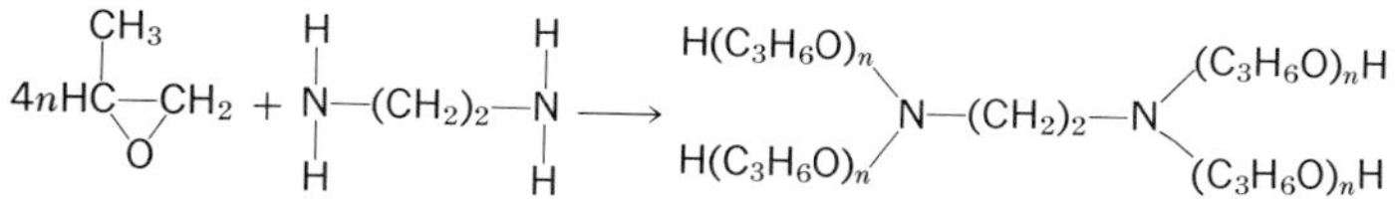

$$4n\underset{\underset{O}{\diagdown}}{\overset{\overset{CH_3}{|}}{H}C}-CH_2 + \underset{\overset{|}{H}}{\overset{\overset{H}{|}}{N}}-(CH_2)_2-\underset{\overset{|}{H}}{\overset{\overset{H}{|}}{N}} \longrightarrow \underset{H(C_3H_6O)_n}{\overset{H(C_3H_6O)_n}{\diagup\diagdown}}N-(CH_2)_2-N\underset{(C_3H_6O)_nH}{\overset{(C_3H_6O)_nH}{\diagup\diagdown}} \qquad (7\text{-}24)$$

Synthesis of a surface active polymer

As shown in the following equation, triethylamine acts as a chain transfer agent in the polymerization of methyl methacrylate. Acrylonitrile will form a block copolymer with these polymeric products.

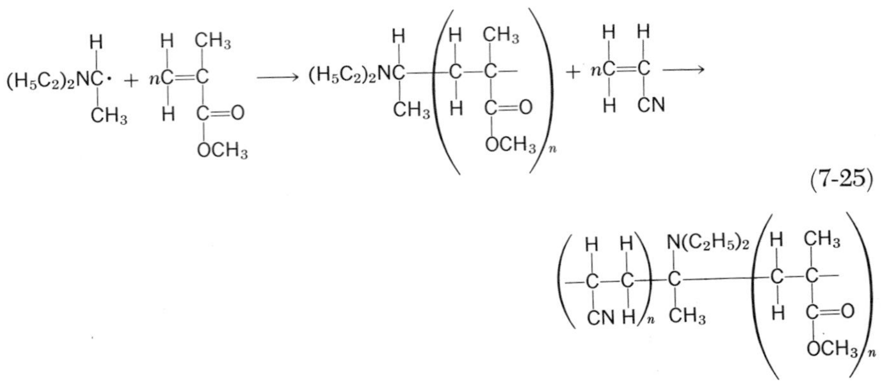

$$(7\text{-}25)$$

Synthesis of an acrylic copolymer with amine groups

Polymers with amine terminal groups are also obtained when living polymers are quenched with p-aminoethyl benzoate and when nylons are produced by using an excess of alkylene diamine.

Living polymers produced by anionic polymerizations and discussed in Chap. 6 may add monomers or cyclic compounds which are polymerizable under similar conditions. For example, as shown in the following equation, a living polystyrene chain may add ethylene oxide or monomer to form a block copolymer.

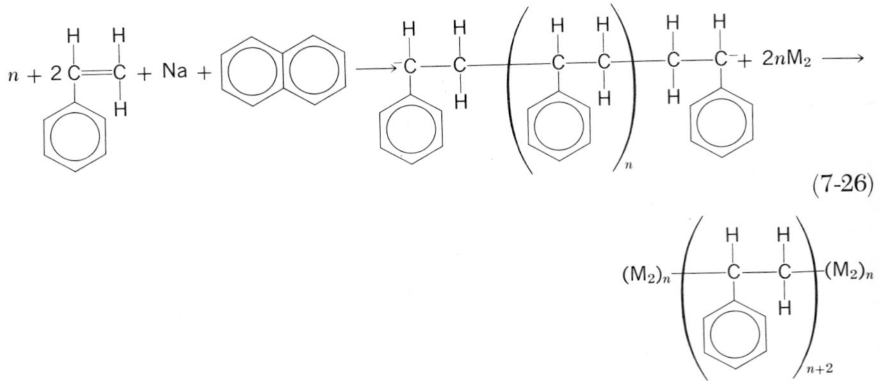

$$(7\text{-}26)$$

Synthesis of a block copolymer from a living polystyrene chain

Polymeric phthaloyl peroxide

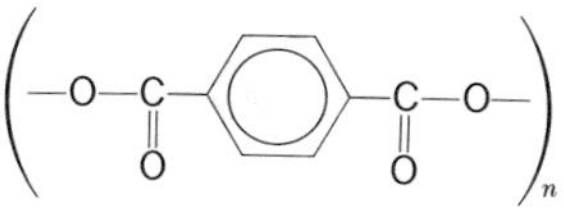

$$\left(-O-\underset{\underset{O}{\|}}{C}--\underset{\underset{O}{\|}}{C}-O- \right)_n$$

may be used as an initiator for vinyl polymerization at low temperature. The homopolymer produced may be dissolved in another monomer and copolymerized at a higher temperature. This technique has been used to produce poly(styrene-*b*-methyl methacrylate), poly(vinyl acetate-*b*-styrene), and poly(vinyl acetate-*b*-ethyl acrylate).

Block copolymers may also be produced when diisopropylbenzene monohydroperoxide is used as an initiator in radical chain polymerization. As shown in the following equation, the polymer obtained may be oxidized by oxygen to produce a free-radical chain which may add other monomers (M_2) to produce a block copolymer.

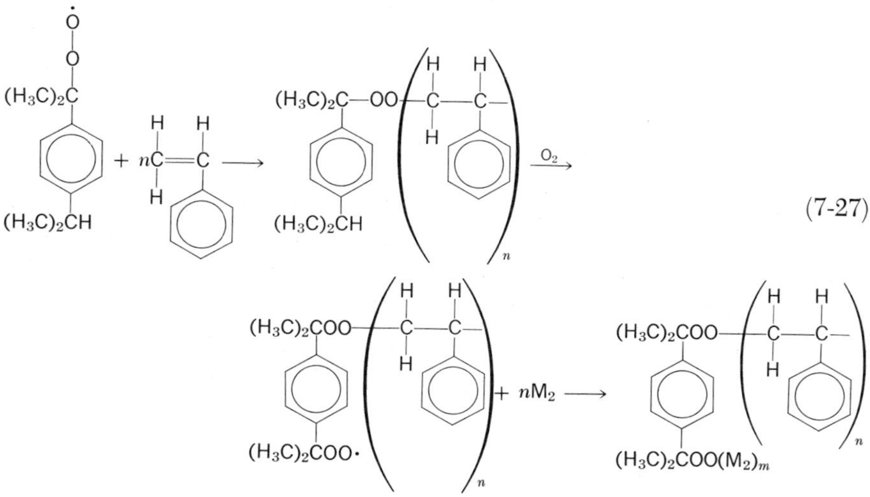

(7-27)

Synthesis of block copolymers from diisopropylbenzene monoperoxide

Crystalline block copolymers of ethylene and propylene (Polyallomers) have the hinge properties of polypropylene and many of the desirable properties of polyethylene. These block copolymers are used as calendered and extruded sheets, extruded profiles, and injection-molded objects.

As stated in Chap. 5, precipitation solution polymerization yields polymer chains with trapped free radicals. Block copolymers may be produced when these polymers are redissolved or swollen in other vinyl monomers

(M_2), as illustrated below:

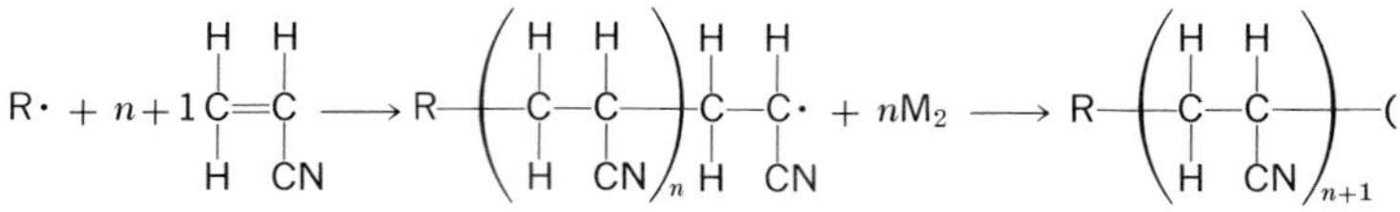

$$R\cdot + n+1\underset{\underset{\text{CN}}{\overset{|}{\text{H}}}}{\overset{\overset{\text{H}}{|}}{\text{C}}}=\underset{\underset{\text{CN}}{\overset{|}{\text{H}}}}{\overset{\overset{\text{H}}{|}}{\text{C}}} \longrightarrow R-\left(\underset{\underset{\text{H}}{\overset{|}{\text{C}}}}{\overset{\overset{\text{H}}{|}}{\text{C}}}-\underset{\underset{\text{CN}}{\overset{|}{\text{C}}}}{\overset{\overset{\text{H}}{|}}{\text{C}}}\right)_n\underset{\overset{|}{\text{H}}}{\overset{\overset{\text{H}}{|}}{\text{C}}}-\underset{\underset{\text{CN}}{\overset{|}{\text{C}}}}{\overset{\overset{\text{H}}{|}}{\text{C}}}\cdot + nM_2 \longrightarrow R-\left(\underset{\underset{\text{H}}{\overset{|}{\text{C}}}}{\overset{\overset{\text{H}}{|}}{\text{C}}}-\underset{\underset{\text{CN}}{\overset{|}{\text{C}}}}{\overset{\overset{\text{H}}{|}}{\text{C}}}\right)_{n+1}\!\!\!(M_2)_n \quad (7\text{-}28)$$

Synthesis of block copolymers from trapped free radicals

Polymer chains may be cleaved by mechanical, electromagnetic, ultrasonic, or particulate energy to produce free-radical chains. Thus, when rubber or other polymers are masticated on a mill or in a mechanical mixer in the absence of oxygen or chain transfer agents, polymer chains are broken and free-radical chains are produced. Mixtures of different polymers or mixtures of polymer and monomer will yield block copolymers. The degradation is accelerated in the presence of inorganic salts. This technique has been used to produce block copolymers of polystyrene and poly(methyl methacrylate) and of natural rubber and poly(methyl methacrylate). The general reaction is illustrated below:

$$\sim\!\!\sim M_1M_1\!\sim\!\!\sim + \sim\!\!\sim M_2M_2\!\sim\!\!\sim \longrightarrow \sim\!\!\sim M_1\cdot + \cdot M_2\!\sim\!\!\sim \longrightarrow \sim\!\!\sim M_1M_2\!\sim\!\!\sim \quad (7\text{-}29)$$

Synthesis of block copolymers by cleavage of homopolymer chains

Poly(styrene-b-methyl methacrylate) has been produced by the action of ultrasonic radiation on a solution of the two homopolymers. Block copolymers are also obtained when a solution of poly(methyl vinyl ketone) in methyl methacrylate is irradiated at a wavelength of 3130 Å.

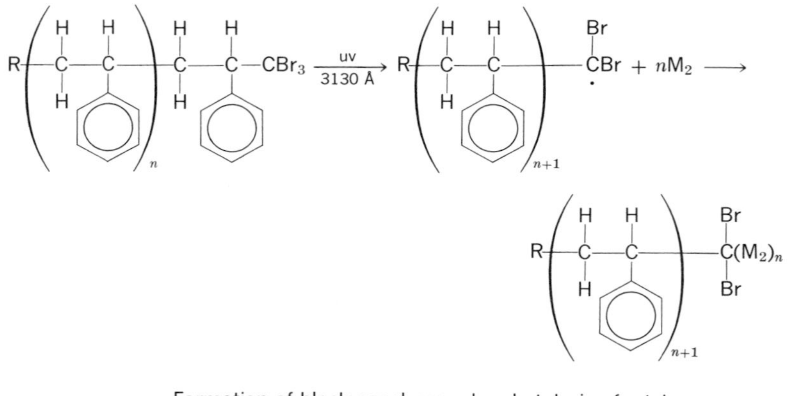

$$(7\text{-}30)$$

Formation of block copolymers by photolysis of a telomer

Similar effects are noted when telomers from carbon tetrabromide are irradiated with ultraviolet radiation. As shown in the above equation, block copolymers may be produced when a bromine atom is removed by photolysis. Similar results are noted when polystyrene is heated with a photosensitizer, such as tetraethyl thiuram disulfide, and this adduct is irradiated with ultraviolet radiation in the presence of other monomers.

A section of the polymer backbone of a stereoblock propylene polymer is shown below:

Chain segment of a stereoblock propylene polymer   (7-31)

REFERENCES

Allen, P. E. M., R. Hardy, J. R. Major, and P. Molyneux: Block Copolymer Wetting Agents, *Makromol. Chem.*, **39**:52 (1960).

Bunn, C. J.: Polyester-Urethane Block Copolymers, *J. Polymer Sci.*, **16**:323 (1955).

Burlant, W. J., and A. S. Hoffman: "Block and Graft Copolymers," Reinhold Publishing Corporation, New York, 1960.

Ceresa, R. J.: "Block and Graft Copolymers," Butterworth Scientific Publications, London, 1962.

————: Block and Graft Copolymers, in H. F. Mark, N. G. Gaylord, and N. M. Bikales (eds.), "Encyclopedia of Polymer Science and Technology," Interscience Publishers, a division of John Wiley & Sons, Inc., New York, 1965.

Coleman, D.: Block Step Reaction Copolymers, *J. Polymer Sci.*, **14**:15 (1959).

Dunn, A. S., and H. W. Melville: Photolysis of Carbon Tetrabromide Telomers, *Nature*, **169**:699 (1952).

Gaylord, N. G.: Block Copolymers, *SPE J.*, **14**(1):31 (1958).

Gobran, R. H.: Polymers with Reactive Terminals, in E. M. Fettes (eds.), "Chemical Reactions of Polymers," Interscience Publishers, a division of John Wiley & Sons, Inc., New York, 1964.

Henglein, A.: Block Copolymers via Ultrasonic Irradiation, *Makromol. Chem.*, **18**:37 (1957).

Hicks, E. M.: Polyether-Urethane Block Copolymers, *Am. Dyestuff Reptr.*, **52**:18 (Jan. 7, 1963).

Hoffman, A. S., and R. Bacskai: in G. E. Ham (ed.), "Copolymerization," chap. 5, Interscience Publishers, a division of John Wiley & Sons, Inc., New York, 1964.

Immergut, E. H., and H. F. Mark: Block and Graft Copolymers, *Makromol. Chem.*, **18/19**:322 (1956).

Morawetz, H.: Trapped Radicals in High Polymer Systems, in A. M. Bass and H. P. Broida (eds.), "Formation and Trapping of Free Radicals," chap. 12, Academic Press, Inc., New York, 1960.

Segal, L.: Block Copolymers, in E. M. Fettes (ed.), "Chemical Reaction of Copolymers," Interscience Publishers, a division of John Wiley & Sons, Inc., New York, 1964.

Smets, G., and A. E. Woodward: Polyphthaloyl Peroxide, *J. Polymer Sci.*, **14**:126 (1954).

Swarc, M.: Block Copolymerization with Living Polymers, *Nature*, **178**:1168 (1956).

Urwin, J. R.: Diisopropylbenzenemonohydroperoxide Initiated Polymers, *J. Polymer Sci.*, **27**:580 (1958).

Vaughn, T., D. Jackson, and L. Lundsted: Polyalkylene Oxide Block Copolymers, *J. Am. Oil Chemists' Soc.*, **29**:240 (1952).

Vermillion, J. L.: Polyallomers, *Mod. Plastics*, **45**(1A):187 (1967).

Watson, W. F.: Mechanochemical Reactions, in E. M. Fettes (ed.), "Chemical Reactions of Polymers," Interscience Publishers, a division of John Wiley & Sons, Inc., New York, 1964.

Zelinski, R., and C. W. Childers: Linear Block Copolymers, *Rubber Chem. Technol.*, **41**(1):161 (1968).

7-3 GRAFT COPOLYMERS

Unlike linear block copolymers, *graft copolymers* are branched structures in which the monomer segments on the branches and on the backbone differ, as illustrated below:

$$M_1—M_1—M_1—M_1—M_1—M_1—M_1—M_1 \atop \qquad\ \ M_2—M_2—M_2—M_2—M_2—M_2—M_2 \tag{7-32}$$

Typical structure of a graft copolymer

A typical graft copolymer such as poly(butadiene-co-acrylonitrile-g-poly(styrene-co-acrylonitrile)) (ABS) may be produced by numerous techniques using a wide variety of formulations.

As stated earlier in this chapter, the pioneer ABS plastics were obtained by coflocculation of blends of poly(styrene-co-acrylonitrile) and poly(butadiene-co-acrylonitrile). However, superior products are obtained when styrene and acrylonitrile are grafted on a polybutadiene backbone or spine. Some commercial products are mechanical blends of graft copolymers with additional plastics or rubber.

The polydienes may be produced by emulsion polymerization or by alfin catalysis. The grafting may take place in emulsion or suspension processes. Benzoyl peroxide is the preferred initiator since azobisisobutyronitrile is not capable of chain transfer reactions.

This free-radical grafting is similar to the process for long-chain branching described in Chap. 6. However, since a dead polymer and second monomer plus an initiator are used in the grafting process, a different monomer propagates at the branch sites, which result from the chain transfer process.

A commercial modified rubber (Heveaplus) may be produced by the emulsion copolymerization of methyl methacrylate in rubber latex. Some homopolymer [poly(methyl methacrylate)] is produced in this and comparable grafting copolymerizations. Both natural and synthetic polydienes have been used as the flexible spines for the commercial production of high-impact plastics by the grafting process. For example, polystyrene may be grafted on polybutadiene produced by alfin catalysis. The chemical and physical properties of these graft copolymers are superior to polystyrene-rubber blends.

Other similar copolymers may be produced by heating ethylene and poly(vinyl acetate), acrylonitrile and polyacrylamide, 2-vinyl pyridine and poly(ethyl acrylate), or vinyl chloride and copolymers of methyl methacrylate and acrylic acid in the presence of initiators.

The so-called "polyester plastics" produced by the polymerization of a solution of an unsaturated polyester in a liquid monomer are graft copolymers. When methyl methacrylate is used as the monomer, poly(methyl methacrylate) grafts are formed. Since these chains terminate almost exclusively by disproportionation, any crosslinking that takes place must involve the unsaturated groups in the polyester backbone.

In contrast, as shown by the following equation, crosslinking by coupling termination of the polystyrene branches may occur when styrene is used as the polymerizable solvent for unsaturated polyesters.

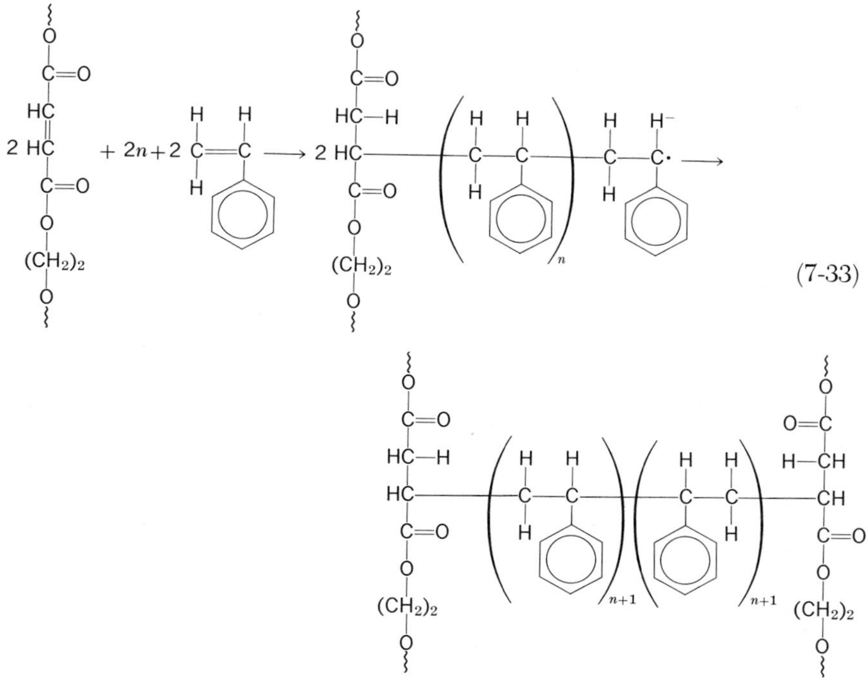

$$(7\text{-}33)$$

Equation for production of polyester plastics

Graft copolymers may also be produced when labile groups such as hydroxyls or halogens are present on the polymer chain. For example, step-reaction polymers produced by the condensation of adipic acid and pentaerythritol dibromide provide active sites for graft copolymerization, as shown below:

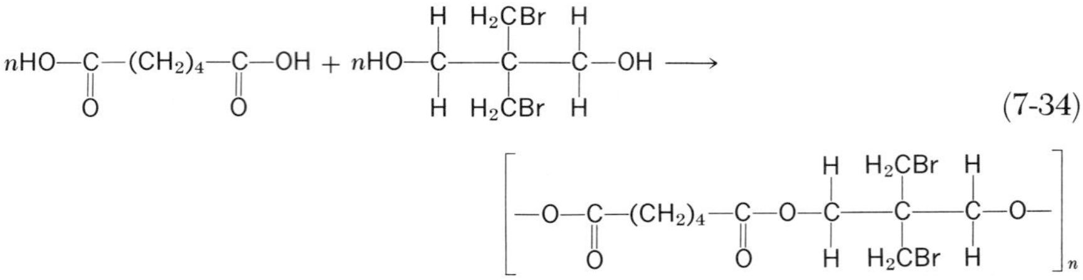

$$n\text{HO}-\underset{\text{O}}{\overset{\text{O}}{\text{C}}}-(\text{CH}_2)_4-\underset{\text{O}}{\overset{\text{O}}{\text{C}}}-\text{OH} + n\text{HO}-\underset{\text{H}}{\overset{\text{H}}{\text{C}}}-\underset{\text{H}_2\text{CBr}}{\overset{\text{H}_2\text{CBr}}{\text{C}}}-\underset{\text{H}}{\overset{\text{H}}{\text{C}}}-\text{OH} \longrightarrow$$

$$\left[-\text{O}-\underset{\text{O}}{\overset{}{\text{C}}}-(\text{CH}_2)_4-\underset{\text{O}}{\overset{}{\text{C}}}-\text{O}-\underset{\text{H}}{\overset{\text{H}}{\text{C}}}-\underset{\text{H}_2\text{CBr}}{\overset{\text{H}_2\text{CBr}}{\text{C}}}-\underset{\text{H}}{\overset{\text{H}}{\text{C}}}-\text{O}-\right]_n$$

(7-34)

Equation for production of linear polymer with active grafting sites

Poly(vinyl chloride-co-vinyl acetate-g-methyl methacrylate) is produced when a solution of the vinyl chloride–vinyl acetate copolymer in methyl methacrylate is heated in the presence of benzoyl peroxide. Poly(vinyl chloride) or Neoprene may also be used as spines for grafting of monomers in a similar manner.

Active pendant groups may also be introduced by the reaction of thioglycolic acid or hydrogen sulfide with pendant epoxide groups, as shown in the following equation:

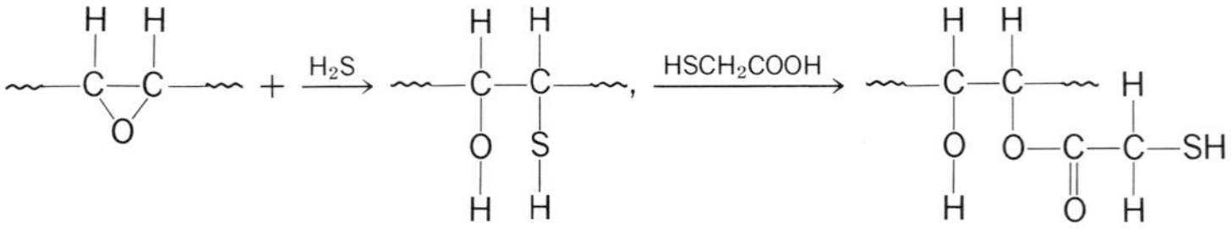

$$\sim\sim\underset{\text{O}}{\overset{\text{H} \quad \text{H}}{\text{C}-\text{C}}}\sim\sim + \text{H}_2\text{S}, \longrightarrow \sim\sim\underset{\underset{\text{H} \quad \text{H}}{\text{O} \quad \text{S}}}{\overset{\text{H} \quad \text{H}}{\text{C}-\text{C}}}\sim\sim, \xrightarrow{\text{HSCH}_2\text{COOH}} \sim\sim\underset{\underset{\text{H} \quad \text{O} \quad \text{H}}{\text{O} \quad \text{O}-\text{C}-\text{C}-\text{SH}}}{\overset{\text{H} \quad \text{H}}{\text{C}-\text{C}}}\sim\sim \text{H}$$

(7-35)

Reaction of ethylene oxide groups with hydrogen sulfide or thioglycolic acid

Because of their high chain transfer activity, graft copolymers are readily formed when monomers and initiators are added to these chains. Ethylene sulfide may be used to produce comparable reactive sites on cellulose or cellulose derivatives.

Poly(isopropyl phenylethylene) may be oxidized by benzoyl peroxide to produce peroxy groups on the polymer backbone. These groups are potential centers for graft polymerization, as shown below:

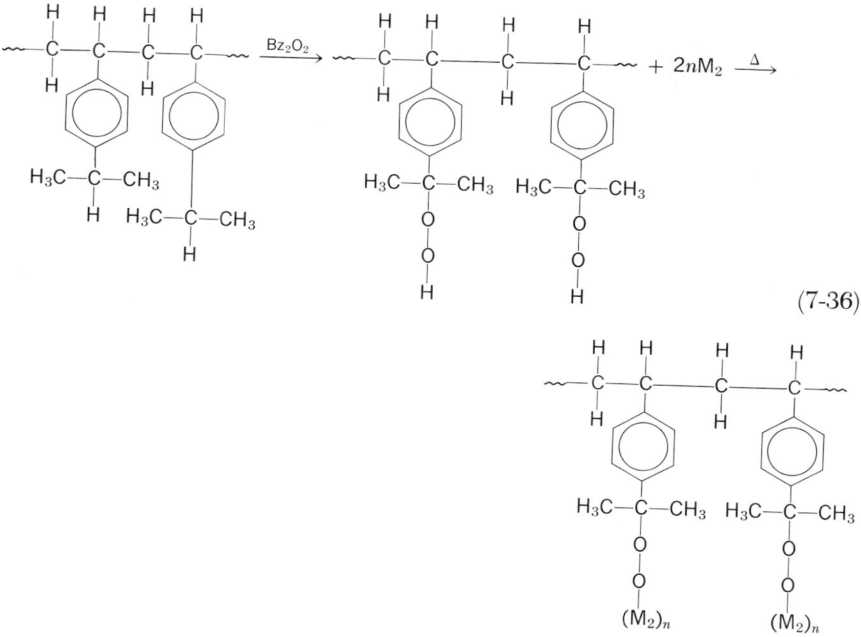

$$(7\text{-}36)$$

Preparation of graft copolymers from polymers containing
isopropylbenzene groups

Reactive sites for copolymerization may also be produced by ozonolysis of polyesters or polyamides. Ultraviolet irradiation in the presence of oxygen will also produce hydroperoxide groups which are reactive sites. Thus, methyl methacrylate may be grafted on natural rubber when a mixture of the monomer and polymer is irradiated by ultraviolet light in the presence of oxygen. These reactions are accelerated in the presence of photosensitizers such as benzophenone.

High-energy irradiation of at least 100 ev is more effective than ultraviolet irradiation. When polymers are irradiated in air, the hydroperoxides or peroxides formed may serve as active sites for graft copolymerizations. Irradiation in vacuo yields trapped free radicals. The depth of penetration may be controlled by the energy of the irradiation and the relative amount of liquid monomer absorbed. Thus, it is possible to graft polymers at a controlled depth from the surface by varying the radiation energy and the amount of monomer.

This technique has been used to increase the adhesion of polytetrafluoroethylene by grafting styrene on the surface of this polymer. Permselective membranes have been produced by grafting polystyrene on the surface of polyethylene films and sulfonating the surface layer.

Most investigations have been conducted by the irradiation of polymers swollen with monomers. Homopolymerization also occurs when this technique is used. Graft copolymers of starch, cellulose, rubber, poly(vinyl chloride), and polyethylene with styrene, acrylonitrile, and vinyl acetate have been investigated. Since these reactions are exothermic, provisions must be taken to dissipate the heat of reaction.

Cationic polymerization may be used for graft copolymerization of monomers that are polymerizable by this technique. As shown by the following typical equation, ethyl vinyl ether, n-vinyl pyrrolidone, or isobutylene may be grafted on polystyrene, poly(p-methoxystyrene), or poly(p-chloromethyl styrene) by aluminum tribromide in carbon disulfide.

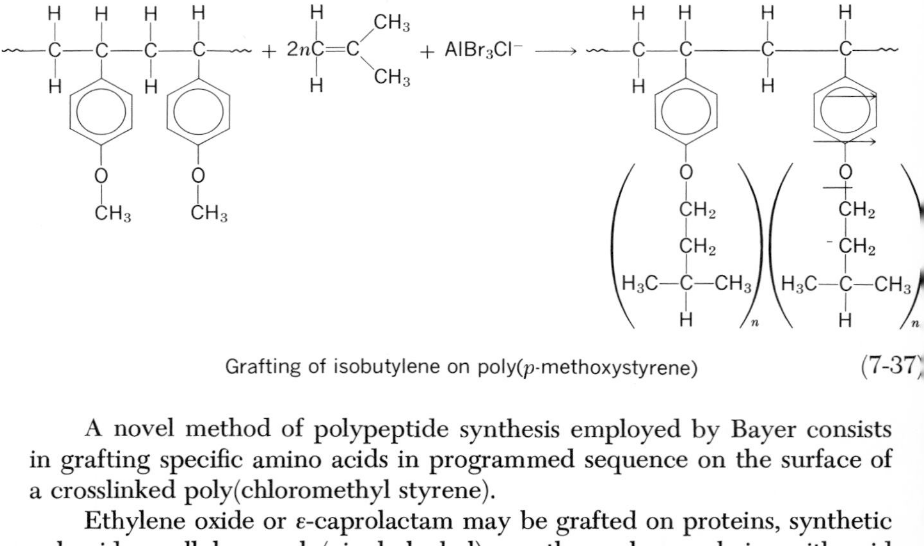

Grafting of isobutylene on poly(p-methoxystyrene)　　　　　(7-37)

A novel method of polypeptide synthesis employed by Bayer consists in grafting specific amino acids in programmed sequence on the surface of a crosslinked poly(chloromethyl styrene).

Ethylene oxide or ε-caprolactam may be grafted on proteins, synthetic polamides, cellulose, poly(vinyl alcohol), or other polymer chains with acid or ester pendant groups. A typical reaction of ethylene oxide and a nylon is shown below:

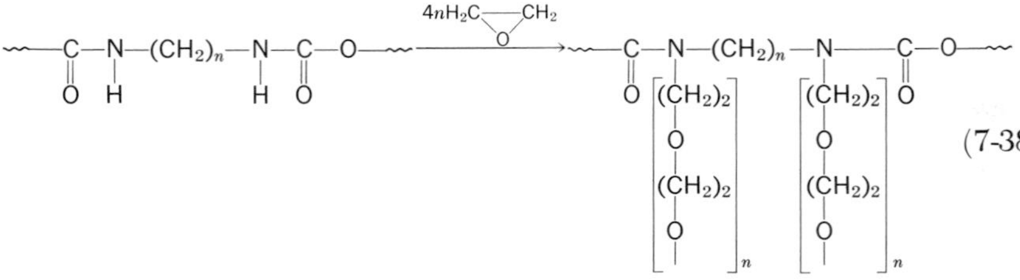

(7-38)

Reaction of ethylene oxide and a nylon

These typical reactions serve to indicate the tremendous potential for graft polymerization.

REFERENCES

Angier, D. J.: Grafting on Polymer Surfaces, *ACS Div. Polymer Chem., Polymer Preprints,* **5**(2):504 (1964).

Basdekis, C. H.: "ABS Plastics," Reinhold Publishing Corporation, New York, 1964.

Ceresa, R. J.: Block and Graft Copolymers, in H. F. Mark, N. G. Gaylord, and N. M. Bikales (eds.), "Encyclopedia of Polymer Science and Technology," Interscience Publishers, a division of John Wiley & Sons, Inc., New York, 1965.

————: in P. W. Allen (ed.), "Block and Graft Copolymers," Butterworth Scientific Publications, London, 1962.

Chapiro, A.: "Radiation Chemistry of Polymeric Systems," Interscience Publishers, a division of John Wiley & Sons, Inc., New York, 1962.

———— and A. Matsumoto: Poly(vinyl chloride)-styrene Graft Copolymers, *J. Polymer Sci.,* **57**:743 (1962).

Charlesby, A.: "Atomic Radiation and Polymers," Pergamon Press, New York, 1960.

Cooper, W., G. Vaughan, S. Miller, and M. Fielden: Rubber–Methyl Methacrylate Graft Copolymers, *J. Polymer Sci.,* **34**:651 (1959).

Gaylord, N. G.: Graft Copolymers, *SPE J.,* **13**(12):34 (1957).

———— and F. S. Ang: Graft Copolymerization, in E. M. Fettes (ed.), "Chemical Reactions of Polymers," chap. 10, Interscience Publishers, a division of John Wiley & Sons, Inc., New York, 1964.

Haas, H. C., P. M. Kamath, and N. W. Schuler: Cationic Graft Copolymers, *J. Polymer Sci.,* **24**:85 (1957).

Hahn, W., and H. Lechtenbohmer: Polyisopropyl Styrene, *Makromol. Chem.,* **16**:50 (1955).

Houtz, R. C., and H. Adkins: Graft Copolymers, *J. Am. Chem. Soc.,* **55**:1609 (1933).

Nelb, R. G.: The ABS Plastics, in W. M. Smith (ed.), "Manufacture of Plastics," chap. 11, Reinhold Publishing Corporation, New York, 1964.

Odian, G., and R. L. Kruse: Reactivity Ratios in Radiation Graft Polymerization, *ACS Div. Polymer Chem., Polymer Preprints,* **9**(1):668 (1968).

Restaino, A. J.: Radiation Induced Graft Copolymerization, in J. J. Harwood et al. (eds.), "Effects of Radiation on Materials," Reinhold Publishing Corporation, New York, 1958.

Roland, J. R., and L. M. Richards: Polyvinyl acetate–ethylene Graft Copolymers, *J. Polymer Sci.,* **9**:61 (1952).

Schonfeld, E., and I. Waltcher: Graft Copolymers from Polyesters, *J. Polymer Sci.,* **48**:159 (1960).

Walrath, R. L., Z. Reyes, and C. R. Russell: Graft Copolymers of Wheat Starch, in R. F. Gould (ed.), "Polymerization and Polycondensation Processes," chap. 5, American Chemical Society, Washington, D.C., 1962.

$$8$$

Inorganic Polymers

In a broad sense, almost all inorganic compounds are polymers. However, in keeping with the covalent-bonding concept that is characteristic of organic polymers, one should not include materials with metallic or ionic bonding. When these materials are eliminated, the principal remaining inorganic polymers are silicates. This limiting classification includes most minerals, glasses, and hydraulic cements. The study of these complex structures may be simplified by considering their relations to more simple structures discussed in the preceding chapters.

The backbone of most organic compounds consists of a chain of catenated carbon atoms. The strength of these covalent bonds and the bonds in heterocarbon polymers such as carbon-oxygen and carbon-nitrogen polymers is of the order of 80 kcal/mole. These covalent bonds may be cleaved at high temperatures but they meet the strength requirements for most services up to the boiling point of water. In contrast, the bond strengths of catenated silicon, germanium, and tin atoms are less than 45 kcal/mole.

Since the ability to form long catenated chains is a function of bond strength, it is not surprising that high-molecular-weight catenated compounds of silicon, germanium, and tin are unknown. Silanes (Si_nH_{2n}) with n values greater than 10 are rare. The lower homologs may be prepared by the acidification of magnesium silicide. Higher-molecular-weight silanes have been produced by heating silicon tetrachloride and silicon at 1000° in an inert atmosphere. These products are unstable in the presence of air or moisture. The germanes are obtained by the acidification of magnesium germanide. The stability of these catenated compounds decreases as the atomic numbers increase, i.e., as the electronegativity decreases. The alkylated polymers are more stable than the unsubstituted polymers.

That silanes, germanes, and stannanes are more vulnerable than carbon to nucleophilic attack is related to the presence of empty d orbitals which may accept unshared pairs of electrons. As the atomic number increases, the valence electrons are less strongly held by the nucleus. Thus these atoms become less electronegative and the strength of the catenated covalent bonds decreases as one goes from carbon to tin.

Fortunately, as demonstrated by the stability of the silicones, heteropolymeric chains of silicon, germanium, and tin are more stable than homopolymeric chains. For example, the strength of the silicon-carbon bond in the silicarbons is 58 kcal/mole and that of the silicon-oxygen bond in the siloxanes is 89 kcal/mole. The unusual stability of these bonds is demonstrated in carborundum, silicate minerals, such as asbestos, and the silicones discussed previously. The high degree of stability of the siloxane bond is also demonstrated by the formation of sodium silicate when silane is hydrolyzed in the presence of sodium hydroxide.

$$\text{SiH}_4 + \text{HOH} \xrightarrow{\text{2NaOH}} 4\text{H}_2 + \text{SiO}_3{}^{--} + 2\text{Na}^+ \qquad (8\text{-}1)$$

Hydrolysis of silane

The abundance of stable mineral silicates is additional evidence of the stability of the silicon-oxygen linkage.

Mineral silicates may consist of linear chains, such as spodumene, or two-dimensional sheets, such as talc, mica, and kaolinite. As shown in the following structural formulas, the noncovalently bonded oxygen atoms, which are electron-deficient, accept electrons from metal atoms to form macroanions:

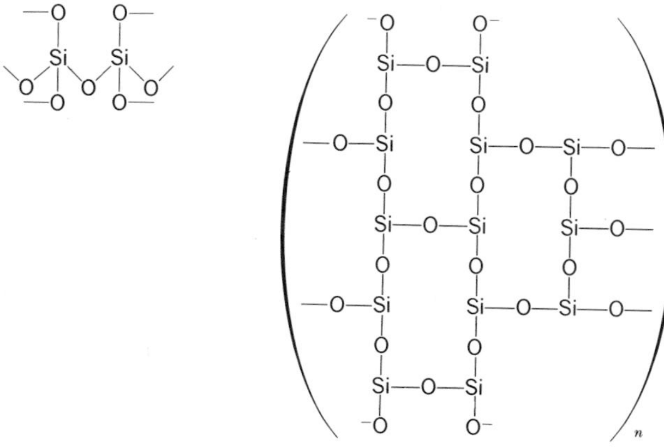

$$(8\text{-}2)$$

Chain and sheet silicates

Some of the silicon atoms may be replaced by aluminum atoms. When this replacement occurs, additional electrons are present between these two-dimensional sheets. Thus mica and some clays are readily cleaved because of the presence of anionic charges between sheets. In contrast, talc is neutral and resistant to cleavage. Kaolinitelike materials have been synthesized by adding a mixture of ashed aluminum hydroxide and ashed silicic acid to a suspension of silica gel.

Quartz is a three-dimensional neutral silicate. Portland cement is a complex silicate produced by sintering calcium carbonate and clay at high temperatures. This product and other hydraulic cements set by slow exothermic hydration. As demonstrated by the resistance of silicones to heat and moisture, alkyl or aryl substituents tend to increase stability of polymers with inorganic backbones. Thus low-molecular-weight poly(organogermanoxanes) and poly(organostannoxanes) have been produced by the hydrolysis of alkyl metal chlorides.

Glass is a polysilicate but the silicon atoms in the siloxane chains may be replaced by boron, aluminum, or lead to produce specialty glasses. As shown by the following structural formula, oligomers, containing silicon and boron atoms in the chain, may be produced by the reaction of boric acid and chlorosilanes. These products are characterized by low resistance to water.

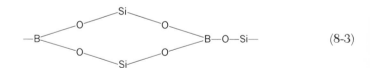

$$(8\text{-}3)$$

Suggested structural formula for oligomers with silicon, oxygen, and boron atoms

Crystalline brittle solids with aluminum and silicon atoms in the molecule have been produced by the reaction of alkyl silanols with metallic aluminum in the presence of mercury (II) chloride. Fibrous polymer crystals which are readily hydrolyzed but which sublime without melting may be produced by heating aluminum sulfide with silicon dioxide, as shown in the following equation:

$$\text{Al}_2\text{S}_3 + \text{SiO}_2 \xrightarrow{1200^\circ} \text{Al}_2\text{O}_3 + \left(\begin{array}{c} \text{S} \\ \text{Si} \quad \text{Si} \\ \text{S} \end{array} \right)_n \qquad (8\text{-}4)$$

Synthesis of polymers with silicon and sulfur atoms

Polymers with silicon and titanium atoms in the polymer backbone have been obtained by the reaction of alkyl titanates and alkyl chlorosilanes, as shown in the following equation:

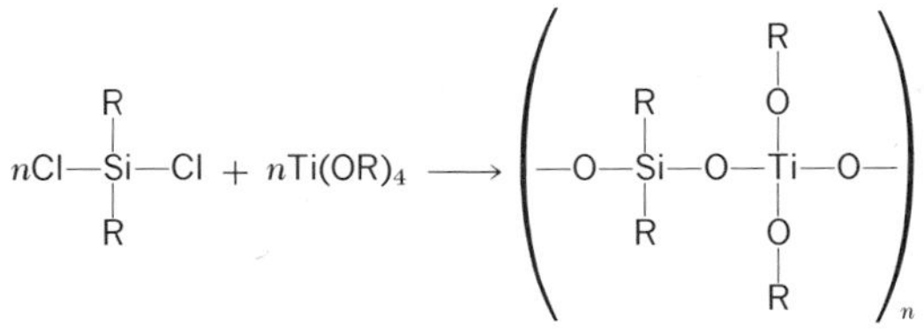

$$
n\text{Cl}-\underset{\underset{\text{R}}{|}}{\overset{\overset{\text{R}}{|}}{\text{Si}}}-\text{Cl} + n\text{Ti(OR)}_4 \longrightarrow \left(-\text{O}-\underset{\underset{\text{R}}{|}}{\overset{\overset{\text{R}}{|}}{\text{Si}}}-\text{O}-\underset{\underset{\text{O}}{\underset{|}{\text{R}}}}{\overset{\overset{\text{R}}{\overset{|}{\text{O}}}}{\text{Ti}}}-\text{O}- \right)_n \qquad (8\text{-}5)
$$

Synthesis of polymers with silicon and titanium atoms

Low-molecular-weight polysilazanes (Si—N—Si—) have also been prepared. The thermal stability and water resistance are improved and longer chain lengths are obtained when alkyl or aryl groups are present as substituents. Thus, as shown by the chain segment below, cyclolinear polysilazanes may be produced by the reaction of amines and dialkyl or diaryl chlorosilanes.

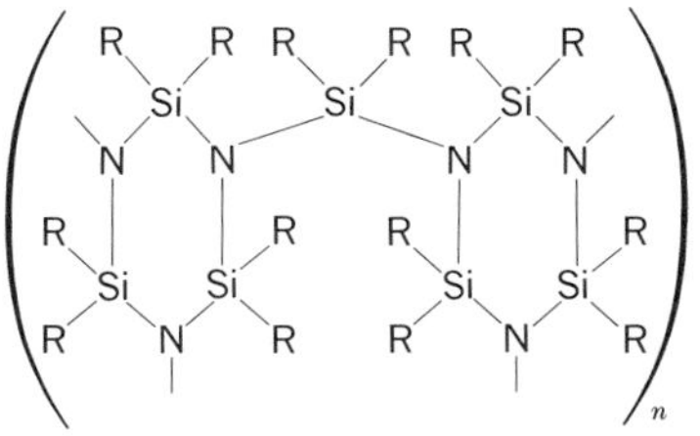

$$(8\text{-}6)$$

Segment of polysilazane molecule

Elemental boron may be amorphous, glassy, or crystalline, depending on the method of preparation. The black amorphous variety is obtained by the reduction of boric acid or boron tribromide at 600 to 800°C. A glassy product is obtained at 900 to 1000°C but the product obtained at higher temperatures is crystalline. X-ray diffraction studies show that the tetragonal form of boron is electron-deficient and thus the boron atoms are bonded together by resonance bonds. The structure of boron carbide (B_4C) is three-dimensional like the diamond and also contains resonance bonds.

Boranes (B_nH_{2n+2}) with up to 10 boron atoms have been prepared by the acidification of magnesium boride or by heating diborane (B_2H_6). The latter is produced by the reduction of boron trichloride over a copper-aluminum catalyst at 450°. Amorphous boron-oxygen polymers which are analogs of polypyroxenes (silicates) have been produced by heating boron and boron trioxide at 1000°. Cyclic poly(borazyl oxides) have been obtained by the hydrolysis of chloroorganoboranes.

Borazole is produced by heating the adduct obtained by the reaction of diborane and ammonia. This cyclic trimer, which is isoelectronic with benzene, polymerizes when heated, as shown below.

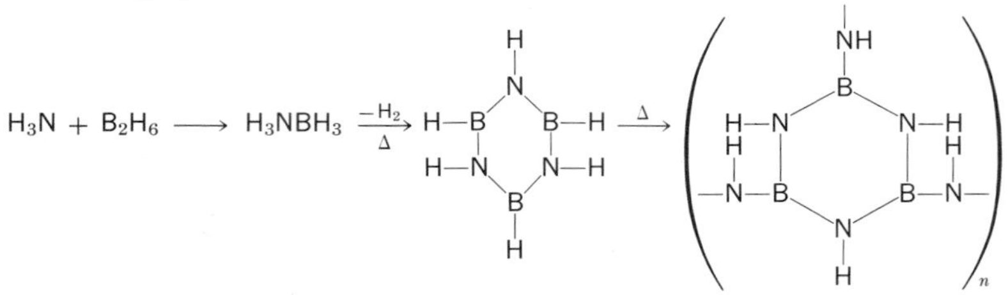

$$H_3N + B_2H_6 \longrightarrow H_3NBH_3 \xrightarrow[\Delta]{-H_2} \text{[structure]} \xrightarrow{\Delta} \text{[structure]} \quad (8\text{-}7)$$

Synthesis of a borazole

Poly(phenylbutylborimide) has been prepared, but only dimeric and trimeric organoborimides are obtained when only alkyl substituents are present. A fibrous aluminum oxide polymer (boehmite) with a composition corresponding to

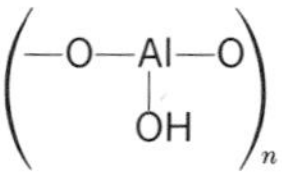

$$\left(-O-Al-O \atop OH \right)_n$$

has been produced by heating an aqueous basic aluminum chloride solution. Linear elastomeric carboranesiloxane polymers which resemble silicones have also been prepared.

There is some evidence that low-molecular-weight polymers of nitrogen exist at low temperatures but there is little tendency for catenation at ordinary temperatures because of the low strength of the nitrogen-nitrogen bond (32 kcal/mole). White phosphorus consists of tetrahedral tetramers (P_4) which are stable up to 800°. Presumably, the less reactive and less soluble red allotrope consists of chains of tetrahedra $(P_4)_n$.

Poly(metal phosphinates) which are stable at 300° may be produced by the reaction of zinc chloride and a phosphoric acid. A low-molecular-weight polymer with phosphorus-oxygen linkages in the backbone may be obtained by heating dichlorophosphoric acid. The latter is obtained by the partial hydrolysis of phosphorus pentachloride:

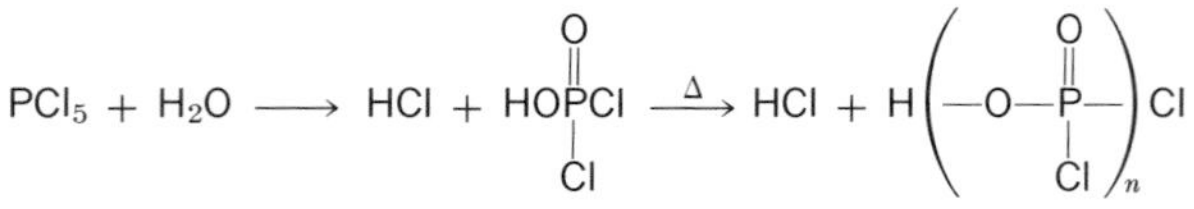

$$PCl_5 + H_2O \longrightarrow HCl + HO\overset{\displaystyle O}{\underset{\displaystyle Cl}{\overset{\|}{P}}}Cl \xrightarrow{\Delta} HCl + H\left(-O-\overset{\displaystyle O}{\underset{\displaystyle Cl}{\overset{\|}{P}}}- \right)_n Cl \quad (8\text{-}8)$$

Synthesis of polymers from dichlorophosphoric acid

Linear polyphosphates have also been produced by heating measured quantities of phosphorus pentoxide and phosphorus oxychloride or amide $[PO(NH_2)_3]$. Typical products are a gelatinlike amorphous polymer with the empirical formula $POCl_{1.1}$ and an elastomer with the empirical formula $PO(N(CH_3)_2)_{1.1}$.

The most widely investigated synthetic tractable inorganic heterochain polymer is poly(phosphonitrilic chloride) which is obtained by the reaction of phosphorus pentachloride and ammonium chloride. This polymerization is catalyzed by alcohols, acids, and active metals.

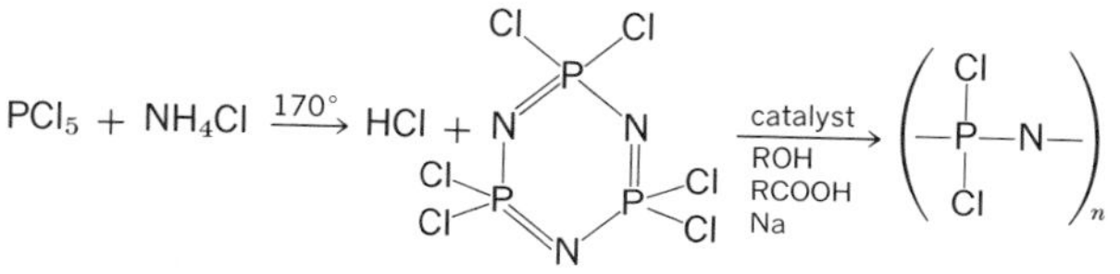

$$PCl_5 + NH_4Cl \xrightarrow{170°} HCl + \text{(ring structure)} \xrightarrow[\substack{ROH \\ RCOOH \\ Na}]{catalyst} \left(\begin{matrix} Cl \\ | \\ -P-N- \\ | \\ Cl \end{matrix} \right)_n \qquad (8\text{-}9)$$

Equation for preparation of poly(phosphonitrilic chloride)

These phosphonitrilic chloride polymers have sharp x-ray diffraction patterns and are readily hydrolyzed in moist air. Products that are more resistant to hydrolysis may be obtained by heating the polymer with alcohols or amines. Polymeric arsenous oxyfluorides and polymeric antimony pentafluorides have been prepared.

That elemental sulfur exists as a cyclic octahedron which is converted to a catenated chain when heated is well known. A metastable elastomer called *amorphous sulfur* may be obtained by quenching the molten sulfur polymer. Similar allotropic forms of selenium and tellurium have been reported. High-molecular-weight metastable polymers have also been obtained by the condensation of low-molecular-weight polysulfides, as shown in the following equation:

$$HS_nH + 2Cl\,S_mCl \longrightarrow 2HCl + Cl\,(S)_{n+2m}Cl \qquad (8\text{-}10)$$

Equation for synthesis of polysulfides

Polysulfates with two and four sulfur atoms are present in oleum. Higher-molecular-weight polysulfates which resemble asbestos have also been prepared. However, these polymers are readily hydrolyzed and depolymerize when heated at 80°.

Polysulfones may be produced by the reaction of sulfur dioxide and propylene, as shown below:

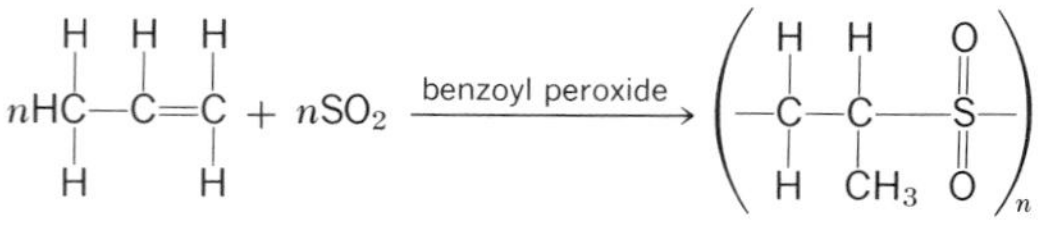

$$nH\overset{\overset{\displaystyle H}{|}}{\underset{\underset{\displaystyle H}{|}}{C}}-\overset{\overset{\displaystyle H}{|}}{C}=\overset{\overset{\displaystyle H}{|}}{\underset{\underset{\displaystyle H}{|}}{C}} + nSO_2 \xrightarrow{\text{benzoyl peroxide}} \left(-\overset{\overset{\displaystyle H}{|}}{\underset{\underset{\displaystyle H}{|}}{C}}-\overset{\overset{\displaystyle H}{|}}{\underset{\underset{\displaystyle CH_3}{|}}{C}}-\overset{\overset{\displaystyle O}{\|}}{\underset{\underset{\displaystyle O}{\|}}{S}}-\right)_n \qquad (8\text{-}11)$$

Preparation of polysulfones

Polymers with sulfur-nitrogen linkages have been obtained by heating the cyclic tetrasulfurtetranitride and by the reaction of ammonia and sulfur oxyfluoride, as shown by the following equation:

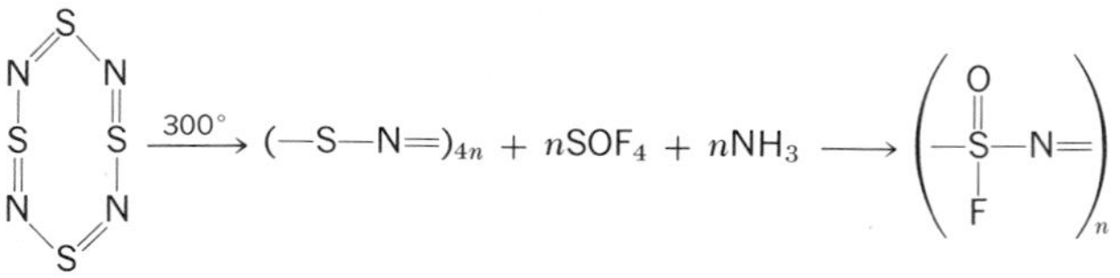

$$\xrightarrow{300°} (-S-N=)_{4n} + nSOF_4 + nNH_3 \longrightarrow \left(-\overset{\overset{\displaystyle O}{\|}}{\underset{\underset{\displaystyle F}{|}}{S}}-N=\right)_n \qquad (8\text{-}12)$$

Synthesis of polymers with sulfur and nitrogen atoms

REFERENCES

Andrianov, K. A.: "Metalorganic Polymers," Interscience Publishers, a division of John Wiley & Sons, Inc., New York, 1965.

Block, B. P.: Inorganic High Polymers, in A. Standen (ed.), "Encyclopedia of Chemical Technology," Interscience Publishers, a division of John Wiley & Sons, Inc., New York, 1966.

————, S. H. Rose, et al.: Polymetalphosphinates, *ACS Div. Polymer Chem., Polymer Preprints*, **6**(2):1106 (1965).

Burg, A. B.: Polymers of Nonmetallic Elements, in Inorganic Polymers, *Chem. Soc.*, (*London*), *Spec. Publ.*, 1961.

Carmichael, J. B.: Ring Chain Equilibrium in Inorganic Polymers, *ACS Div. Polymer Chem., Polymer Preprints*, **6**(2):1157 (1965).

Davies, A. G., P. G. Harrison, and P. R. Palan: Stannoxanes, *J. Organomet. Chem.*, **10**(3):33 (1967).

Gee, G.: Rings and Chains in Inorganic Polymers, *Chem. Soc.* (*London*), *Spec. Publ.*, 1961.

Gerrard, W.: "The Organic Chemistry of Boron," Academic Press, Inc., New York, 1961.

Gimblett, F. G. R.: "Inorganic Polymer Chemistry," Butterworth & Co. (Publishers), Ltd., London, 1963.

————: "Inorganic Polymers," Blackwell Scientific Publications, Oxford, 1963.

Haber, C. P.: Phosphonitriles, *Chem. Soc. (London), Spec. Publ.*, 1961.

Hunter, D. V.: "Inorganic Polymers," John Wiley & Sons, Inc., New York, 1963.

Lappert, M. F., and G. J. Leigh: "Developments in Inorganic Polymer Chemistry," American Elsevier Publishing Company, Inc., New York, 1962.

Laubengayer, A. W.: Boron-Nitrogen, Aluminum-Nitrogen Polymers, *Chem. Soc. (London), Spec. Publ.*, 1961.

Meyer, K. H.: "Natural and Synthetic Polymers," chap. 3, Interscience Publishers, a division of John Wiley & Sons, Inc., New York, 1962.

Miles, D. C., and J. H. Briston: "Polymer Technology," chap. 20, Chemical Publishing Company, Inc., New York, 1965.

Moedritzer, K., and J. R. Van Wazer: Germanium Compounds, *ACS Div. Polymer Chem., Polymer Preprints,* **6**(2):1140 (1965).

O'Driscoll, K. R.: "The Nature and Chemistry of High Polymers," chap. 3, Reinhold Publishing Corporation, New York, 1964.

Parker, G. M.: Inorganic Polymers, *ACS Div. Polymer Chem., Polymer Preprints,* **6**(2):1165 (1965).

Petrov, A. D., F. Mitonov, et al.: "Synthesis of Organosilicon Monomers," Plenum Press, New York, 1968.

Schmulbach, O. D.: Phosphonitrile Polymers, in F. A. Cotton (ed.), "Progress in Inorganic Chemistry," vol. 4, p. 75, John Wiley & Sons, Inc., New York, 1962.

Stone, F. G. A., and W. A. G. Graham: "Inorganic Polymers," Academic Press, Inc., New York, 1962.

Van Wazer, J. R.: Inorganic Polymer Chemistry, *ACS Div. Org. Coatings and Plastics, Preprints,* **25**(2):275 (1965).

————: Inorganic Polymer Chemistry, *ACS Div. Polymer Chem., Polymer Preprints,* **6**(2):1887 (1965).

————: in C. L. Segal (ed.), "High Temperature Polymers," chap. 3, Marcel Dekker, Inc., New York, 1967.

West, R. (ed.): "Organosilicon Chemistry," Plenum Press, New York, 1968.

9

Reactions of Organic Polymers

Polymers are synthesized by specific chemical reactions which may be accompanied by other accidental or controlled competing reactions. Subsequent reactions with active pendant groups on the polymer chain are often essential for the production of useful end products. Thus, thermosetting polymers are crosslinked in molds or in other useful shapes, such as films or coatings. The physical form of polymers such as cellulose and proteins may be changed by forming a more readily processible reaction product and regenerating the original polymer after it has been processed, as in the production of films or filaments. The physical properties of polymers may be modified by graft copolymerization, by block copolymerization, and by capping the end groups. These reactions have been discussed in preceding chapters.

Degradative reactions such as oxidation, ozonolysis, and environmental stress cracking are undesirable and are usually avoided. However, surface oxidation may be advantageous in the printing of films, such as polyethylene, and for the continuous renewal of outdoor painted surfaces by rain washing of the oxidized surface. Those reactions are dependent on the availability of reactive sites and are usually confined to surfaces and amorphous areas. When reactive sites are available, the reactions that occur are similar to those observed for smaller molecules with comparable structures (model compounds).

The simplest reactions are *isomerization reactions* such as the cyclization of natural rubber, which occurs in the presence of Lewis acids. Thus, cyclized rubber (Pliolite) may be produced by a carbonium-ion mechanism in the presence of chlorostannic acid. The end product is denser and more soluble than natural rubber and contains cyclohexene rings in its polymer structure.

Staudinger prepared cyclized polymers by heating rubber hydrochloride with zinc dust. Thermoprenes used for rubber-metal adhesives in the Vulcalock process are obtained by heating rubber and *p*-phenol sulfonic acid. Cyclized products obtained from natural and synthetic rubbers are used in adhesives, coatings, and printing-ink formulations.

Double-chained (ladder) polymers are obtained when polyacrylonitrile or polymethacrylonitrile is heated. As shown in the following equation, these dark cyclized polymers are readily oxidized to cyclic polyenes.

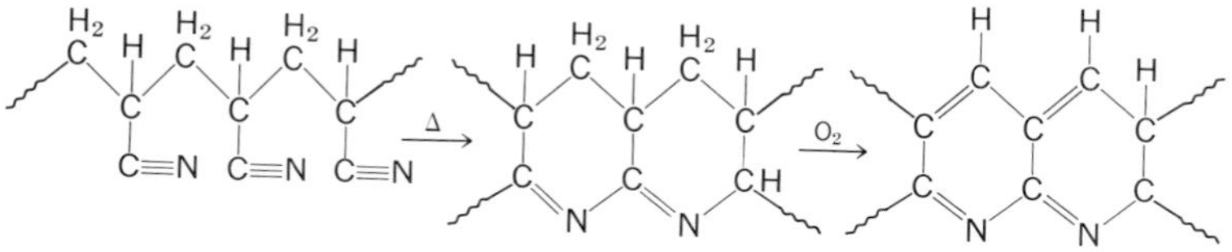

$$(9\text{-}1)$$

Thermal cyclization of polyacrylonitrile

Double-bond shifts may occur when polymers are heated or exposed to irradiation. Thus *cis*-polyisoprene (from *Hevea braziliensis*) may be converted to the trans isomer (gutta-percha) when nitrogen dioxide is added to a benzene solution of natural rubber.

The hydrogenation of polyisoprene, which was investigated originally by Berthelot in 1869, was used subsequently by Harries and Staudinger to prove the structure of natural rubber. The rate of this reaction may be followed by observing the increase in glass transition temperature and the degree of crystallinity. Similar products are obtained when rubber, gutta-percha, or balata are completely hydrogenated. The product obtained by the partial hydrogenation of polybutadiene (Hydropol) has been used as a wire coating and as a fiber. Poly(vinyl cyclohexane) has been produced by the catalytic hydrogenation of polystyrene.

Chlorinated rubber (Parlon), which was produced by Traun in 1859, has been available commercially for many years. Halogenation of polydienes involves a series of complex reactions including substitution, addition, cyclization, and crosslinking. Chlorination may take place in carbon tetrachloride or benzene solutions. The natural-rubber derivative is soluble in both solvents. Chlorinated SBR copolymer is insoluble in carbon tetrachloride but is soluble in benzene and chloroform.

The natural-rubber derivative containing 66 to 68 percent chlorine may be plasticized by alkyl phosphates, alkyl phthalates, or alkylnaphthalene. The plasticized product is used in adhesive, printing-ink, and coating formulations. The latter are characterized by excellent adhesion to portland cement surfaces and are used as swimming-pool coatings.

Chlorinated polyethylene (Tyrin) is produced commercially by the addition of chlorine to a hot solution of the polymer in carbon tetrachloride. Degradation, which also occurs during the chlorination of polyolefins, takes place preferentially at the branch points. Thus highly branched polyethylene or polypropylene should be chlorinated in the dark in the presence of large quantities of salt in order to minimize the degradative reaction.

Poly(vinyl dichloride) is obtained when an aqueous suspension of poly(vinyl chloride) is chlorinated in the presence of chloroform at 55°C. This product may be used in place of poly(vinyl chloride) when superior heat resistance is required, such as in hot-water piping systems.

Sulfochlorinated polyethylene (Hypalon) is obtained when a suspension of polyethylene in carbon tetrachloride is reacted with sulfuryl chloride or a mixture of sulfur dioxide and chlorine in the presence of pyridine. The commercial product, which contains 27.5 percent chlorine and 1.5 percent sulfur, is soluble in solvents such as tetralin. Sulfochlorinated polyethylene may be vulcanized when mixed with sulfur and diphenyl guanidine. These polymers are used as protective coatings in the chemical process industry.

Ion-exchange resins are produced by amination of chloromethylated polystyrene. The latter is obtained by the reaction of polystyrene with chloromethyl ether or a mixture of formaldehyde and methanol, in the presence of aluminum chloride. Chlorinated polystyrene is obtained by the addition of chlorine to a solution of polystyrene. Bachman prepared 3,4-dichlorostyrene by the pyrolysis of chlorinated polystyrene.

Rubber hydrochloride (Pliofilm) is produced when gaseous hydrogen chloride is added to a solution of rubber in chloroform at low temperatures. The commercial product, which contains 28 to 30 percent chlorine, is obtained by casting the film on a continuous belt or by precipitation of the product in a miscible liquid such as ethanol. The principal use of rubber hydrochloride is as a packaging film.

Epoxidized polymers, such as epoxidized polybutadiene (Oxiron), are produced by the reaction of hydrogen peroxide or peracetic acid with a solution of a polyene at room temperature. These derivatives may be used as coatings or films or cured with polyamines or anhydrides. Derivatives of polyenes are also obtained by reactions of these unsaturated polymers and maleic anhydride, formaldehyde, glyoxal, or chloral. The properties of these derivatives depend on the reactants and the extent of the reaction. Polybutadiene may be carboxylated by carbon dioxide to produce carboxylated polymers.

Block copolymers are produced when alkylene oxides or diisocyanates are reacted with polymers having terminal hydroxyl or amine groups. Graft copolymers are obtained when alkylene oxides react with polyamides.

The manufacture of leather is dependent on the reaction of proteins with polyfunctional reactants such as tannic acid or formaldehyde. Comparable reactions are used to stabilize protein filaments which are regenerated from alkaline solutions of proteins from casein, soybeans, feathers, and peanuts. Casein plastics (Galalith) are also stabilized by crosslinking with formaldehyde.

Alkylated polystyrenes may be obtained by the reaction of olefins, such as propylene, with polystyrene in the presence of aluminum chloride. These products, which have lower solubility-parameter values than polystyrene, may be used as lubricating-oil additives. Polystyrene may be readily sulfonated and nitrated. Poly(dinitrostyrene) is soluble in dimethyl formamide and may be reduced to poly(diaminostyrene). The crosslinked polymers have been used as ion-exchange resins.

Rosin (abietic acid) and its esters with glycerol (ester gum), ethylene glycol, or pentaerythritol may be hydrogenated to produce proprietary derivatives (Abalyn, Hercolyn, Pentalyn) which are used as constituents of varnishes. Rosin may also be reacted with phenol-formaldehyde condensates to produce soluble resins for the coatings industry.

Cellulose nitrate was obtained by Schönbein, in 1846, by the reaction of cellulose with a mixture of sulfuric and nitric acids at room temperature. The extent of nitration (DS) is controlled by the water content of the nitrating acid mixture. The degree of polymerization ($\overline{DP}$) is reduced when solutions of cellulose nitrate are heated in the presence of air.

The highest-molecular products ($\overline{DP} = 2{,}000$) with the highest nitrate content (cellulose trinitrate) (DS = 2.8) are used for the production of explosives (guncotton). Cellulose dinitrate (DS = 2.0 to 2.3) with a lower molecular weight is used as film ($\overline{DP} = 500$) and lacquers ($\overline{DP} = 200$). These lacquers (Pyroxylin) are used as coatings for metals, paper, and textiles.

A polymer with a slightly lower nitrate content (DS = 1.9 to 2.0) may be plasticized by camphor to produce a plastic (Celluloid). This polymer may be pressed into sheets (Pyralin) or extruded in the presence of solvents. Cellulose nitrate is usually stabilized by the addition of amines or substituted ureas.

Cellulose triacetate (DS = 2.8 to 2.9) was prepared by Schutzenberger and Naudine in 1865 by the reaction of cellulose with acetic anhydride and acetic acid in the presence of sulfuric acid. Cellulose diacetate (DS = 2.3 to 2.4) was prepared by Miles in 1905 by the partial hydrolysis of the triacetate by dilute acetic acid. Additional hydrolysis results in the production of water-soluble cellulose acetate and regenerated cellulose (Fortisan).

The solubility of cellulose acetate is related to the extent of acetylation.

Polymers with DS values greater than 2.6 are insoluble in acetone but soluble in chloroform or in a mixture of methylene chloride and ethanol. The so-called triacetate may be plasticized by ethyl phthaloyl ethyl glycollate. Moldings and extrusions of the plasticized cellulose triacetate are characterized by good clarity and toughness. Rayon-grade cellulose diacetate (DS = 2.3 to 2.4) may be dry-spun from an acetone solution (dope). Both cellulose triacetate and diacetate may be used for the production of film, tubing, fibers, and moldings.

Cellulose propionate (Forticel) and cellulose acetate butyrate (Tenite I) require less plasticizer and are more resistant to moisture than cellulose acetate. Malm showed that the resistance to moisture increases and the melting point decreases as the size of the ester group increases from the acetate to cellulose caprylate. However, the melting point increases, as a result of side-chain crystallization, when the pendant group contains 10 or more carbon atoms.

These cellulose esters of higher-molecular-weight acids and other polyesters may also be hydrolyzed. Thus, poly(acrylic acid) is readily obtained by the saponification of poly(methyl acrylate). Polymethacrylates and polyphthalates are more resistant to hydrolysis than the polyacrylates. Poly(acrylic acid) and its sodium or ammonium salts are soluble in water. These polymers have been used as thickeners, components of drilling muds, and soil conditioners.

As shown in the following equation, poly(vinyl alcohol) (Elvanol, Gelvatol, Lemol, Vinol) may be produced by the alkaline hydrolysis of poly(vinyl acetate);

$$\left(\begin{array}{c} \overset{\underset{\displaystyle H}{|}}{C}\overset{\underset{\displaystyle H}{|}}{C}\overset{\underset{\displaystyle H}{|}}{C}\overset{\underset{\displaystyle H}{|}}{C} \\ \underset{\displaystyle CH_3}{\overset{\displaystyle }{C}=O} \ \underset{\displaystyle CH_3}{\overset{\displaystyle }{C}=O} \end{array}\right)_n \xrightarrow[OH^-]{H_2O} \left(\begin{array}{c} \overset{\underset{\displaystyle H}{|}}{C}\overset{\underset{\displaystyle H}{|}}{C}\overset{\underset{\displaystyle H}{|}}{C}\overset{\underset{\displaystyle H}{|}}{C} \\ H \quad H \end{array}\right)_n + 2nH_3C-\underset{\displaystyle O}{\overset{\displaystyle \|}{C}}-OH \quad (9\text{-}2)$$

Saponification of poly(vinyl acetate)

The solubility of the hydrolytic product depends on the extent of hydrolysis. The polymer, which has 45 percent residual acetyl groups, is soluble in cresols. The completely hydrolyzed polymer is insoluble in organic solvents but is soluble in water. Commercial products with 12 percent residual acetyl groups are available in several different molecular-weight ranges.

When heated above 250°C, poly(vinyl alcohol) produces a dark-colored insoluble polyethene. The hydroxyl groups in poly(vinyl alcohol) react with acyl chlorides, sulfur trioxide, boric acid, isocyanates, thiourea, acrylonitrile, alkylene oxides, and aliphatic aldehydes.

Poly(vinyl alcohol) has been used as an adhesive, emulsifier, sizing, film, and fiber. A major end use is for the production of poly(vinyl acetals). Approximately 50 million pounds of poly(vinyl butyral) (Butvar) is produced annually. Poly(vinyl formal) (Formvar) has been used in adhesives and in electrical-magnetic-wire coating formulations. The principal use of poly(vinyl butyral) is as the interlayer in automotive windshield glass.

Poly(vinyl acetals) are produced by the acetalization of poly(vinyl alcohol) with excess aldehyde in the presence of an acid, such as phosphoric acid. The solubility of these derivatives is dependent on the aldehyde used and the extent of acetalization. It is customary to retain residual acetyl and hydroxyl groups in commercial poly(vinyl acetals).

Poly(vinyl formal) and poly(vinyl butyral) are soluble in ethyl cellosolve, acetic acid, and a mixture of ethanol and toluene. An alcoholic solution of poly(vinyl butyral) is obtained when a suspension of poly(vinyl alcohol) is reacted with a solution of butyraldehyde in ethanol. This reaction is illustrated in the following equation:

$$\sim\left(\begin{array}{c} H\ H\ H\ H \\ -C-C-C-C- \\ H\ O\ H\ O \\ H\quad\ H \end{array}\right)_n \sim + \ nH_3C(CH_2)_2\overset{H}{C}=O \longrightarrow \sim\left(\begin{array}{c} H\ H\ H\ H \\ -C-C-C-C- \\ H\ O\ H\ O \\ H-C \\ (CH_2)_2CH_3 \end{array}\right)_n \sim \quad (9\text{-}3)$$

Preparation of poly(vinyl butyral)

Acetals and ethers may also be produced from alkali cellulose. The principal commercial products are methyl cellulose (Methocel), ethyl cellulose (Ethocel), benzyl cellulose, carboxymethyl cellulose (CMC, Carbose), hydroxyethyl cellulose (Cellosize), and cyanoethyl cellulose. Most of the commercial products have DS values of 2 to 2.5. Trialkyl celluloses may be produced by etherification of cellulose triacetate.

Methyl cellulose, which was first produced by Suida in 1905, may be obtained by the reaction of alkali cellulose with methyl sulfate or methyl chloride. Derivatives containing 25 to 30 percent free hydroxyl groups (DS = 2.1 to 2.3) are soluble in cold water. Methyl cellulose is used as an adhesive, paper sizing, and an edible emulsifier.

Ethyl cellulose is obtained by the reaction of alkali cellulose and ethyl chloride. When this derivative has 50 to 55 percent residual hydroxyl groups (DS = 1.5 to 1.7), it is soluble in an 80 percent toluene–20 percent ethanol mixture. When plasticized with alkyl phthalates, ethyl cellulose may be used as a lacquer, hot applied coatings, or for the production of extruded- and injection-molded articles. Benzyl cellulose is produced by the reaction of alkali-cellulose and benzyl chloride.

The sodium salt of carboxymethyl cellulose is obtained from the reaction of alkali cellulose and sodium chloroacetate. The degree of substitution (DS) may be varied from 0.5 to 0.8 for sizes and detergent additives to 0.8 to 1.2 for thickening agents. Carboxymethyl cellulose with a DS value greater than 1.3 is soluble in water. The sodium salt is soluble when the DS value is greater than 0.3. Carboxymethyl cellulose has been used as a viscosity control agent, in pharmaceuticals, in drilling-mud formulations, and as an ingredient of proprietary detergents.

Hydroxyethyl cellulose is obtained by the reaction of alkali-cellulose and ethylene oxide. These water-soluble products have been used as sizes and finishes for textiles. Mixed ethers (carboxymethyl hydroxyethyl cellulose) are more compatible with salt solutions and may be used in place of the simple ethers.

Cyanoethyl cellulose is obtained by the reaction of alkali-cellulose and acrylonitrile. This reaction has been used to produce cyanoethylated derivatives of paper and cotton which have improved resistance to abrasion and to biological degradation. The solubility of these derivatives in organic solvents is related to the degree of substitution. These cyanoethyl ethers may be hydrolyzed to produce carboxyethyl cellulose. Polyacrylonitrile may also be hydrolyzed to produce poly(acrylic acid). Polymethacrylonitrile is more resistant to hydrolysis than polyacrylonitrile. Woven cellulose textiles may be made water-repellent by a surface reaction with stearoxymethyl pyridinium chloride (Zelan).

One of the most important reactions of organic polymers is the reaction of fibers with reactive dyes. Many dyes actually react with wool, silk, and modified cellulose fibers. This interesting subject has been reviewed by Taber, Renfrew, and Tiefenthal.

REFERENCES

Bachman, G. B., H. Hellman, et al.: Chlorinated Polystyrene, *J. Org. Chem.*, **12**:108 (1947).

Berthelot, P. E. M.: Hydrogenation of Rubber, *Bull. Soc. Chem. France*, **11**:33 (1869).

Burlant, W. J., and A. S. Hoffman: "Block and Graft Copolymers," chap. 5, Reinhold Publishing Corporation, New York, 1960.

Canterino, P. J.: Halogenation, in E. M. Fettes (ed.), "Chemical Reactions of Polymers," chap. 20, Interscience Publishers, a division of John Wiley & Sons, Inc., New York, 1964.

Dannis, M. L., and F. L. Ramp: Poly(vinyl dichloride), U.S. Patent 2,996,486, 1961.

De Bell, J. M.: Cellulose Nitrate, *Mod. Plastics,* **17**(2):40 (1939).

Dickstein, J., and R. Bouchard: Poly(vinyl alcohol), in W. M. Smith (ed.), "Manufacture of Plastics," vol. I, chap. 5, Reinhold Publishing Corporation, New York, 1964.

Engelhard, G. A., and H. H. Day: Chlorinated Rubber, British Patent 2,734, 1859.

Fettes, E. M. (ed.): "Chemical Reactions of Polymers," Interscience Publishers, a division of John Wiley & Sons, Inc., New York, 1964.

Golub, M. A.: Isomerization of Polymers, in E. M. Fettes (ed.), "Chemical Reactions of Polymers," chap. 2a, Interscience Publishers, a division of John Wiley & Sons, Inc., New York, 1964.

Grassie, N., and I. C. McNeill; Cyclization of Polyacrylonitrile, *J. Polymer Sci.,* **27**:207 (1958).

Haviland, H. K.: Cellulose Acetate, *Mod. Plastics,* **17**(2):34 (1939).

Hill, R. O.: Cellulosics, in "Modern Plastics Encyclopedia," p. 145, McGraw-Hill Book Company, New York, 1967.

Keeley, F. W.: Hypalon, in M. Morton (ed.), "Introduction to Rubber Technology," chap. 14, Reinhold Publishing Corporation, New York, 1959.

Langton, H. M.: Ester Gums, in R. S. Morrell (ed.), "Synthetic Resins and Allied Plastics," chap. 8, Oxford University Press, London, 1951.

Le Bras, J., and A. Delalande: "Les Derives chemique du caoutchooc naturel," Dunod, Paris, 1950.

Lenz, R. W.: Polymer Reactions, in "Organic Chemistry of Synthetic High Polymers," sec. 5, Interscience Publishers, a division of John Wiley & Sons, Inc., New York, 1967.

Malm, C. J., J. W. Mench, D. L. Kendall, and G. D. Hiatt: Cellulose Esters, *Ind. Eng. Chem.,* **43**:684, 688 (1951).

Mark, H. F.: Cellulose Esters, *Ann. N.Y. Acad. Sci.,* **57**(4):445 (1953).

Martins, J. G., and A. F. Price: Poly(vinyl acetal), W. M. Smith (ed.), "Manufacture of Plastics," vol. I, chap. 6, Reinhold Publishing Corporation, New York, 1964.

McQueen, D. M.: Hypalon, U.S. Patent 2,212,786, Aug. 27, 1946.

Miles, R. D.: "Cellulose Nitrate," Oliver & Boyd, Ltd., London, 1955.

Penning, C. H.: Cellulose Acetate Butyrate, *Mod. Plastics,* **17**(2):38 (1939).

Pinner, S. H. (ed.): "Weathering and Degradation of Plastics," Gordon and Breach, Science Publishers, Inc., New York, 1966.

Powers, P. O.: "Synthetic Resins and Rubber," Pt. 5, John Wiley & Sons, Inc. New York, 1943.

Pummerer, R., and P. A. Burkhard: Hydrogenated Rubber, *Ber.,* **55**:3458 (1922).

Ranby, B. G., and S. A. Rydholm: Cellulose Derivatives, in C. E. Schildknecht (ed.), "Polymer Processes," Interscience Publishers, Inc., New York, 1956.

Rathman, D. M.: Zein, *Mod. Plastics,* **38**(1A):269 (1961).

Ravve, A.: Reactions of Polymers, in "Organic Chemistry of Macromolecules," Pt. 6, Marcel Dekker, Inc., New York, 1967.

Seymour, R. B., I. Branum, and F. W. Hayward: Surface Reactions of Polymers, *Ind. Eng. Chem.,* **41**(7):1479, 1482 (1949).

Suen, T. J.: Chemical Modification of Phenolic and Amino Resins, in C. E. Schildknecht (ed.), "Polymer Processes," chap. 8, Interscience Publishers, Inc., New York, 1956.

Staudinger, H., and E. Geiger: Cyclized Rubber, *Helv. Chim. Acta,* **9**:549 (1926).

Swern, D.: Epoxidation, *Chem. Rev.*, **45**:1 (1949).

Taber, D., E. E. Renfrew, and H. E. Tiefenthal: Fiber-reactive Dyes, in E. M. Fettes (ed.), "Chemical Reactions of Polymers," chap. 15, Interscience Publishers, a division of John Wiley & Sons, Inc., New York, 1964.

Thies, H. R., and A. M. Clifford: Isomerized Rubber, *Ind. Eng. Chem.*, **26**:123 (1934).

Ward, K., and A. J. Morak: Reactions of Cellulose, in E. M. Fettes (ed.), "Chemical Reactions of Polymers," chap. 5, Interscience Publishers, a division of John Wiley & Sons, Inc., New York, 1964.

Wentz, C. A., and E. E. Hooper: Telechelic Polymers, *Ind. Eng. Chem., Prod. Res. Develop.*, **6**(4):209 (1967).

Whitfield, R. E., and W. L. Wasley: Reactions of Proteins, in E. M. Fettes (ed.), "Chemical Reactions of Polymers," chap. 6, Interscience Publishers, a division of John Wiley & Sons, Inc., New York, 1964.

Wicklatz, J.: Hydrogenations of Polyenes, in E. M. Fettes (ed.), "Chemical Reaction of Polymers," chap. 2F, Interscience Publishers, a division of John Wiley & Sons, Inc., New York, 1964.

Wiggam, D. R.: Ethyl Cellulose, *Mod. Plastics*, **17**(2):48 (1939).

10
Processing
of Polymers

The process in which polymeric products are converted to useful shapes is termed *polymer processing.* This procedure may be part of the polymerization process if the end product is usable without additional shaping or processing. Thus the forming of thermosetting polymers in molds or as laminates, adhesives, or polymer coatings represents a combination of the polymerization and processing steps. Comparable techniques may be used for the chain-reaction polymerization of vinyl monomers to produce sheets, rods, or specific shapes by the bulk-polymerization technique. Coating or adhesive compositions may be obtained directly by solution or emulsion techniques. Compounding may be accomplished readily by use of solutions or emulsions of polymeric products.

The advantage of compounding emulsions or solutions is evident when attempts are made to admix solid polymer and additives to solid polymers or to blend different polymers. Provided the comminuted resins and additives are uniformly mixed, a homogeneous composition may be obtained during the extrusion process. Thus an extruder may be used for intensive mixing (compounding) of polymers. Otherwise, this processing is accomplished on two-roll mills or in a heavy-duty mixer, such as a Banbury mixer.

The casting process was used by Baekeland in the early 1900s to convert liquid *A*-stage phenolic resins to infusible *C*-stage resinous products. This casting process is also used to a limited extent for casting articles from epoxy and polyester resins and from poly(methyl methacrylate). This process may be used to cast molten thermoplastics such as ethyl cellulose,

Poly(ethylene-co-vinyl acetate), and petroleum resins. Vinyl plastisols are cast in a similar manner at elevated temperatures. These products will be discussed in Sec. 11-2. Many polymers used for coatings, such as poly(vinyl acetate), are prepared directly by dispersion polymerization.

The application of many room-temperature-curing polymer systems such as resinous cements, adhesives, caulking compositions, and fibrous-glass-reinforced polyester and epoxy resins is based in part on casting resin technology. Resinous cements consist of acid-curing phenolic or furan cements with carbon or silica filler, filled amine-curing epoxy cements, or filled peroxide-catalyzed polyester compositions. The latter usually contain amine activators and silica or asbestos filler. Comparable compositions are used for the construction of chemical processing equipment.

These readily cured resins may also be used as coatings and adhesives. Filled room-temperature-curing Thiokol and Neoprene compositions are used as caulking materials and sealants. Competitive filled bituminous compositions are applied as hot melts or solvent-containing cements. The latter, like lacquers, harden by evaporation of the solvent. Curing or crosslinking may occur if epoxy resins and amines are added to these thermoplastic materials.

Complex structures may be constructed by impregnating fibrous glass with epoxy or polyester resins. These systems may be cured at room temperature when appropriate curing agents are present. Superior physical properties are attained when these compositions are postcured at elevated temperatures.

10-1 COMPRESSION MOLDING

Many useful plastic articles are produced by the molding and extrusion processes. The simplest and oldest process (cold compression molding) is essentially a refinement of the ceramic and hydraulic cement arts. The hydraulic press developed by Pascal in the seventeenth century was used in the early 1900s for compressing mixtures of resinous binders, such as bitumens, and fillers, such as clay and asbestos. Pressures of 2,000 to 10,000 psi are used in this rapid molding process. The cold-molded articles produced are stabilized by a subsequent heating process in which residual solvents are volatilized and the resin is adsorbed on the filler.

Cold-molded articles are characterized by dull surfaces and lack of precise dimensions of the molded parts. Filled phenolic A-stage resins may be used in the cold-molding process to produce infusible products. This process is used to form battery cases and some nonprecision electrical parts. The hot-compression-molding process yields a superior molded article

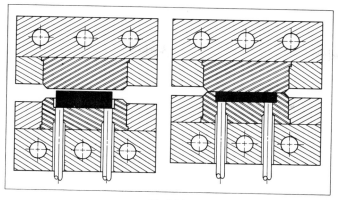

Fig. 10-1

in a one-step process in which the compression and heating steps are combined. The temperature range is 280 to 380°F. The heat is supplied by steam or electricity. The pressure range is 2,000 to 10,000 psi. In contrast to casting and cold-molding processes in which the weight of the product and the charge are similar, excess material may be used and expelled as *flash* in this hot compression process. In both the hot and cold compression processes, the plastic material is forced into a two-piece mold which provides a cavity with interior boundaries similar to the external shape of the molded article.

Cross sections of an open and closed flash mold are shown in Fig. 10-1. A positive mold assures greater pressure on the molded part and allows for very little flash. The thin flash produced is removed by tumbling the molded parts end over end in a drum. Typical positive and semipositive molds are shown in Fig. 10-2.

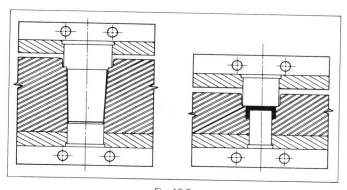

Fig. 10-2

The molding charge may be controlled by using a measured volume, corresponding to a slight excess of the molding powder. Thermosetting molding materials consist of coarse granules called *molding compounds,* which cure when heat is applied to the closed mold. The molding cycle varies with the formulation and the thickness of the molded part. Preheating shortens the cycle but it is essential that sufficient time be provided to obtain a structurally stable molding. When thermoplastic materials are compression-molded, it is necessary to cool the mold before removing the molded part. However, the compression-molding process is seldom used for molding thermoplastics.

The molded parts may vary in size from buttons to equipment weighing 50 lb or more. This process is widely used for molding objects from phenolic, alkyd, urea, melamine, and epoxy resins.

The transfer or plunger molding process developed in the 1920s reduces the time required for compression molding. It is customary to cold-mold preforms with a slight excess of the amount of material required to fill the mold cavity and to preheat the preforms by high-frequency current (to 225 to 275°F) before placing the molding compound in the press. The preheated polymer is forced by a ram through a main artery (sprue), then through tubes (runners) to constrictions at the mold entrance (gates), and finally to multicavity molds.

These frictional processes heat the resin so that it is essentially fluid when it enters the mold cavity. The molded parts are ejected by ejector pins, sleeves, or stripper plates. Excess molded materials, such as that in the sprue and runners, must be discarded but the cost of this additional material is less than the savings resulting from this process. A typical transfer mold is illustrated in Fig. 10-3.

The rate of compression molding may be increased to a greater extent by a modified process called *jet flow* or *offset injection molding.* In this process, the temperature of the molding powder is held just below the curing temperature until it enters the mold cavity through a heated nozzle. Higher

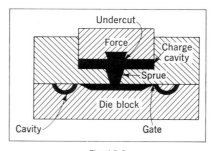

Fig. 10-3

pressures are required for jet flow molding, and the entrance nozzle must be alternately heated and chilled. The design of the injection molding press shown on page 238 is similar to that of a jet molding press.

The plastics molding industry consists of custom molders and captive molders. Since the latter are located in large industry, little statistical information is available on this proprietary phase of the molding business. The custom molders employ about 70,000 people and have invested almost ½ billion dollars in plant and equipment. Their annual production of molded parts is valued at approximately 1 billion dollars. Automation has aided the growth of the compression-molding segment of this business but injection molding of thermoplastics is by far the more important segment of the plastic molding industry.

REFERENCES

Bainbridge, R. W.: Molding of Phenolics, in "Modern Plastics Encyclopedia," p. 873, McGraw-Hill Book Company, New York, 1967.

Bikerman, J. J.: "The Science of Adhesive Joints," Academic Press, Inc., New York, 1960.

Butler, J. A.: "Compression and Transfer Molding," Iliffe Books, Ltd., London, 1964.

DuBois, J. H.: Fundamentals of Plastics Molding, in J. H. DuBois and W. I. Pribble (eds.), "Plastics Mold Engineering," chap. 1, Reinhold Publishing Corporation, New York, 1967.

Ducca, F. W., and T. S. Stoughton: Thermoset Molding, *Plastic Technol.*, **13**(10):119 (1967).

Evans, V.: "Plastics as Corrosion Resistant Materials," Pergamon Press, New York, 1966.

Freund, M.: "Plastics Moulding Engineering," Sir Isaac Pitman & Sons, Ltd., London, 1950.

Greniger, E. G.: Design of Compression and Transfer Molds, *Plastics World*, **23**(1):30 (1965).

Golding, B.: "Polymers and Resins," chap. 11, D. Van Nostrand Company, Inc., Princeton, N.J., 1959.

Kinney, G. G.: "Engineering Properties and Applications of Plastics," chap. 13, John Wiley & Sons, Inc., New York, 1956.

Miles, D. C., and J. H. Briston: "Polymer Technology," chap. 13, Chemical Publishing Company, Inc., New York, 1965.

Morita, Y.: Thermoset Injections Molding, *Mod. Plastics*, **42**(4):135 (1965).

Perry, H. A. G.: "Adhesives for Reinforced Plastics," McGraw-Hill Book Company, New York, 1959.

Randolph, A. F. (ed.): "Plastics Engineering Handbook," 3d ed., chap. 3, Reinhold Publishing Corporation, New York, 1959.

Seymour, R. B.: Recent Advances in Plastics Engineering, in "Modern Plastics Encyclopedia," McGraw-Hill Book Company, New York, 1968.

————: Plastics Technology, in A. Standen (ed.), "Encyclopedia of Chemical Technology," vol. 15, Interscience Publishers, a division of John Wiley & Sons, Inc., New York, 1968.

————, and R. H. Steiner: "Plastics for Corrosion Resistant Applications," Reinhold Publishing Corporation, New York, 1955.

————: "Hot Organic Coatings," Reinhold Publishing Corporation, New York, 1960.

Simonds, H. R., and J. M. Church: "A Concise Guide to Plastics," 2d ed., chap. 7, Reinhold Publishing Corporation, New York, 1957.

Skeist, I.: "Handbook of Adhesives," Reinhold Publishing Corporation, New York, 1962.

Vaill, E. W.: Thermoset Molding, in "Modern Plastics Encyclopedia," p. 746, McGraw-Hill Book Company, New York, 1966.

Winding, C. C., and G. D. Hiatt: "Polymeric Materials," chap. 4, McGraw-Hill Book Company, New York, 1961.

10-2 INJECTION MOLDING

The injection molding process which was developed by Hyatt in 1872 is similar to the metal-die casting process. This process was unsuitable for the molding of cellulose nitrate (Celluloid) but was used successfully in the 1920s for molding articles from the less hazardous cellulose acetate. This sophisticated automatic molding process is preferred for molding thermoplastics. The high cost of the equipment is justified by low labor costs and high production rates.

As shown in Fig. 10-4, a measured amount of the granulated plastic is fed at programmed intervals through a hopper to a cylinder where it is pushed through the heated section by a hydraulically driven plunger (ram), in the classic method. The thermoplastic polymer is softened as it moves toward the mold cavity. The transfer of heat from the cylinder wall is aided by spreaders such as the torpedo shown in Fig. 10-4.

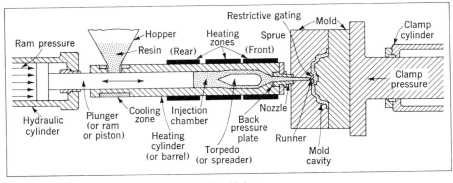

Fig. 10-4

The molten material is forced through the nozzle through runners to the cold-mold cavities during the part of the cycle in which the mold is closed. After the material has cooled, the mold is separated and is reclosed after the molded part has been ejected. The ejected material includes that from the sprue, runners, and gates. The molded parts are separated from the material from the runners and sprue at the narrow gates. Provided no contamination or degradation occurs, the material from the sprue and runners, and the rejects may be ground and remolded. This step is avoided in modern presses by using the so-called hot-runner technique in which the gate serves as a modified injection nozzle.

The softening or plasticizing of the plastic material in most modern presses is accelerated by a rotating spreader or a reciprocating screw in the cylinder. The screw design is related to that shown for extruders in Fig. 10-5.

The mold capacity of an injection molding press varies from 1 to 300 oz. Typical conditions for readily flowable polymers such as polyethylene are injection pressure, 15,000 psi; cylinder temperature, 450°F; and a minimum molding cycle of 30 sec. The mold is designed to provide for contraction during solidification. Thus the mold temperature for polyethylene is 40 to 60°F.

REFERENCES

Beyer, C. E., R. B. Dahl, and R. B. McKee: Temperature and Pressure Measurements in Injection Molding, *Mod. Plastics*, **32**(8):127; (9):110; (10):127 (1955).

Filbert, W. C.: Screw Plasticization, *Mod. Plastics*, **41**(11):123 (1964).

Griff, A. L.: "Plastics Extrusion Technology," 2d ed., Reinhold Publishing Corporation, New York, 1967.

Grundman, V. R.: Screw Injection Molding, *Mod. Plastics*, **44**(3):117 (1966).

Jones, D. A., and T. A. Mullen: "The Principles of Injection Molding," Reinhold Publishing Corporation, New York, 1962.

Levy, S.: Injection Molding, in "Modern Plastics Encyclopedia," p. 710, McGraw-Hill Book Company, New York, 1966.

Raus, J. E., and H. J. Fralish: Scrap and Regrind, *Plastics Technol.*, **12**(11):51 (1966).

Schlich, W. R., and R. S. Hagan: Molding Parameters, *SPE J.*, **22**:45 (1966).

Temesvary, L.: Mold Cooling, *Mod. Plastics*, **44**(4):125 (1966).

Thayer, G. B., et al.: Injection Molding, in E. C. Bernhardt (ed.), "Processing of Thermoplastic Materials," chap. 5, Reinhold Publishing Corporation, New York, 1959.

Vaill, E. W.: Mold Design, *SPE J.*, **21**:274 (1965).

10-3 EXTRUSION AND BLOW MOLDING

The technique of plastics extrusion is an adaptation of ceramic arts as patented by Newley in 1845. In this widely used process, a molten polymer is forced through an orifice (die) under pressure to produce a continuous extrudate. The profile of the extrudate corresponds in general to the shape of the die but may be modified by subsequent physical manipulations.

The extrusion technique may be understood by referring to Fig. 10-6. A dry granulated plastic material is fed continuously from a hopper to an electrically heated cylinder. The plastic is also heated by shear friction as it is moved forward by an archimedean screw. The cylinder consists of a feed section, a transport zone where plasticization takes place, a transition zone, and a metering zone which supplies the thermally homogeneous melt to the die at a steady rate. Thus the extruder serves as a conveyor, a screw pump, a melting device, a heat exchanger, and a mixer.

As shown in Fig. 10-5, the simplest single screw has a constant helix angle or pitch and variable channel or flight depth. Since the channel depth decreases from the feed to the metering zone, the molten plastic is compressed as it travels toward the die. Double-screw extruders are also available.

The power is supplied to the extruder by a variable-speed motor so that many different polymers may be extruded on the same piece of equipment. The ratio of output to horsepower is about 8 lb/hp-hr but may range from 5 to 15 lb/hp-hr. Screws are characterized by the ratio of the length (L) from the rear of the hopper to the breaker plate and the diameter (D) of the barrel. The inside of the cylinder ranges from $1\frac{1}{2}$ to 20 in.

The L/D ratio for a single-screw extruder is generally 20:1 to 24:1 but may range from 16:1 to 30:1. Extruders are also characterized by the ratio of the volume of each flight of the screw at the hopper and die ends. This value, called the *compression ratio,* may vary from 2:1 to 4:1.

Pressure backflow is related to the magnitude of the compression ratio. The presence of the die and breaker plate also contributes considerably to this pressure backflow. The breaker plate includes a series of screens which filter out undesirable contaminants. The main forward flow is called the *drag flow.* The net output is the difference between the drag flow and the pressure backflow.

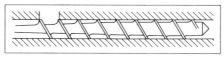

Fig. 10-5

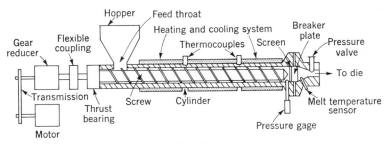

Fig. 10-6

Approximately a billion linear feet of thermoplastic pipe is extruded annually in the United States. Plastics are also extruded through slit dies to form continuous lengths of sheet. Thin film is produced by the extrusion of low-density polyethylene through a circular die and expanding this tubing by blowing with air or other gases. The tube may be used as is or slit and placed on rolls.

The extrusion process may also be used for coating textiles, paper, and wire. This process is used for coating paperboard for the production of

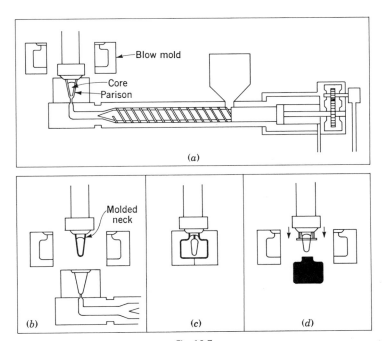

Fig. 10-7

liquid containers and of insulated metal wire. This versatile procedure provides for many variations in processing technique. For example, the plasticizing step may be omitted if the polymer is melted before entering the extrusion cylinder. This step is accomplished in the Engel process by melting the granulated polymer on a rotating hot plate and adding the molten product to the extruder.

A mixture of ammonium carbonate and polymer will produce a foamed extrudate in the Engle process. When gases or low-boiling liquids are present with the polymer in the cylinder, cellular extrudates will also be produced. Hollow containers may be obtained by blowing short molded or extruded hollow sections (parisons) in a mold, as shown in Fig. 10-7.

The tubing may be blown after extrusion or it may be cut and blown in a separate operation. The extruded tube may be modified by using a variable mandrel in order to assure a blow article of uniform thickness. Blow-molded containers in sizes ranging from small vials to 50-gal containers have been produced. Automatic blow-molding equipment will produce 20 to 30 small containers per minute.

Approximately 4 billion plastic bottles and other hollow containers are produced annually by the blow-molding process in the United States. This segment of the plastics industry consumes more than 350 million pounds of polymer annually.

REFERENCES

Beckwith, A. C.: Sheet Extrusion, in Processing Handbook, *Plastic Technol.,* **13**(10):94 (1967).

Braun, K. J.: Extruder Die Design, *Plastics,* **29**(12):50 (1964).

Carley, J. F.: Plastics Extrusion, in E. C. Bernhardt (ed.), "Processing of Thermoplastic Materials," Reinhold Publishing Corporation, New York, 1959.

Castagna, E. G.: Extrusion Equipment, in Processing Handbook, *Plastics Technol.,* **13**(10):85 (1967).

Domininghaus, H.: Dry Blend Extrusion, in "Modern Plastics Encyclopedia," p. 850, McGraw-Hill Book Company, New York, 1966.

Fear, J. V. D. (ed.): *Chem. Eng. Prog., Symp. Ser.* 49, vol. 60, p. 38, 1964.

Fisher, E. G.: "Extrusion of Plastics," Iliffe Books, Ltd., London, 1964.

Griff, A. L.: "Plastics Extrusion Technology," Reinhold Publishing Corporation, New York, 1962.

Gore, W. L.: Principles of Extrusion, *SPE J.,* **9**(3):6 (1955).

Goslin, J. P., and R. M. Bonner: Extrusion, in "Modern Plastics Encyclopedia," p. 743, McGraw-Hill Book Company, New York, 1967.

Hansen, F., and W. Utermann: Monofilaments, *Intern. Plastics Eng.,* **5**:385 (1965).

Hughes, M. J., and M. J. Cawkwell: Tubular Film, *Plastics,* **31**:274 (1966).

Jones, D. A., and T. W. Muller: "Blow Molding," Reinhold Publishing Corporation, New York, 1961.

Koch, G. J., and B. M. O'Rear: Flat Film Extrusion, *Mod. Plastics,* **41**(10):138 (1964).

McKelvey, J. M.: "Polymer Processing," John Wiley & Sons, Inc., New York, 1962.

Miller, R. L.: Single Screw Extruders, *Chem. Eng. Progr.,* **62**(11):90 (1966).

Nickerson, J. A.: Rotational Molding, *Mod. Plastics,* **44**(11):109 (1967).

Pickering, G. E.: Blow Molding, in Processing Handbook, *Plastics Technol.,* **13**(10):67 (1967).

Scheiner, L. F.: Blown Film, in Processing Handbook, *Plastics Technol.,* **13**(10):101 (1967).

Spies, H.: Blown Plastic Articles, *Plastics,* **20**:114 (1955).

Tadmor, E., D. I. Marshall, and I. Klein: Plasticating Extrusion, *Polymer Eng. Sci.,* **6**:185, 191 (1966).

Whitcut, H. M.: Extrusion Equipment, *Rubber Plastics Age,* January, 1957.

White, C. E., and A. E. Irvine: Extrusion Coating, *Plastics Technol.,* **12**(9):41 (1966).

10-4 THERMOFORMING AND WELDING

Thermoplastic sheet may be produced by the extrusion of polymers through a slit die, by calendering, or by laminating thin sheets. A calender consists of a series of metal rolls. The calender may receive softened plastic from a Banbury mixer or an extruder. The plastic material passes through successive nips and, as a result of a squeezing process through these hot rolls, is reduced to a continuous sheet of uniform thickness. The rolls are usually crowned to assure uniformity in thickness. The last two rolls may be chilled and serve as embossers of the sheet stock.

Plastic film, such as polyethylene or poly(vinyl chloride) film, may be formed to provide simple shapes such as tubes or trays at room temperature. However, these thin sheets may return to their original shape unless they are held in place by mechanical devices or adhesives or are thermally welded.

Plastic film or sheet may be shaped at room temperature, using techniques similar to those used to form shapes from paperboard. Standard metal or plastic machine screws and rivets may be used to maintain the formed sheet stock in position. Simple bends of thick plastic sheet stock may be made at room temperature by techniques used to bend sheet metal.

More complex shapes may be produced at room temperature from special formulations like ABS. However, most thermosetting sheet is shaped during the curing process, and most thermoplastic sheet is shaped at elevated temperatures (*thermoformed*) and cooled while held in the desired shape.

The thermoforming art was developed by the ancient Egyptians who used hot water to form tortoise shells into useful shapes. The modern process uses pressure or vacuum to bring heated thermoplastic sheet in contact with a mold surface. Many variations have been made in an attempt to assure uniformity in the thickness of the end product.

Thermoplastic sheets may be thermoformed by using a vacuum to draw a clamped thermoplastic sheet into a female mold. Forming cycles of 40 to 50 sec are used to obtain useful articles such as half sections of luggage made from ABS sheet.

Cast or extruded poly(methyl methacrylate) sheet may be converted to complex shapes by draping a heated sheet over a mold surface. In an alternative procedure, the mold may be forced into the warmed sheet. Uniform contact with the mold surface is assured by using vacuum to pull the draped sheet against the mold surface.

The nonuniform thinning of the thermoplastic sheet in the thermoforming process may be reduced by using spring pads to hold the heated sheet in place. In this slip ring forming process, the slip of the sheet under the pads is gradually reduced by increasing the spring tension as the forming takes place.

Better reproduction of mold shapes and surfaces may be obtained through the use of matched molds. This technique is similar to that used in compression molding but a heated sheet is used instead of granulated plastic. Inexpensive materials such as wood, plaster, or filled epoxy resin cements may be used for the construction of crude molds.

Other modifications include plug-assist, vacuum, and pressure forming. In these techniques, a loose-fitting plug is used to force the heated sheet into the mold cavity. The final contact with the mold surface is assured by the use of vacuum below or increased pressure above the warmed sheet.

Other techniques include the vacuum snap-back process in which the heated sheet is vacuum-drawn or prestretched by pressure before use of a

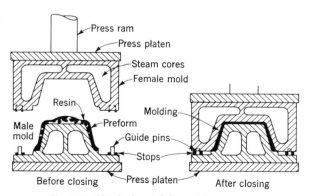

Fig. 10-8 Matched metal die molding

matched-molding procedure. Commercial equipment, such as shown in Fig. 10-8, is available for various types of thermoforming.

Laminates of thermosetting resins are produced by impregnating paper, mat, fabric, or wood with uncured resins and heating these composites in a platen press. Plywood and other laminates are widely used as materials of construction. Laminates produced from paper, mat, or fabric may be bent by postforming, using techniques similar to those discussed for thermoforming thermoplastic sheets.

Complicated shapes such as boats, car bodies, and radomes may be produced from thermosetting laminates by so-called "low-pressure molding" techniques. In this process, the fibrous-glass sheet impregnated with epoxy or polyester resin is partially cured while in contact with the mold surface. The curing process is completed in an oven in the absence of the mold. In a modification called bag molding, a flexible sheet is drawn by a vacuum so that the uncured composite makes positive contact with the mold surface.

Solvents, Neoprene-based cements, or epoxy resins may be used to adhere many different types of plastic film or sheet to the same material or to other surfaces. For example, poly(vinyl chloride) or ABS sheet or pipe may be joined by use of a liquid solvent with a similar solubility parameter. It is customary to increase the viscosity of the solvent and to provide gap-filling characteristics by dissolving a small amount of polymer in the solvent for use in the solvent welding process.

Many techniques used to adhere plastic sheet to dissimilar materials are adaptations of the older art of producing piano keys by coating wood with Celluloid sheet. This art has been extended to the production of composite sheet stock of cellular plastics and plastic film and plastic-metal laminates. These laminates, which may be based on poly(vinyl chloride) or poly(vinyl fluoride), may be plastic-coated (clad) on one or both sides. The vinyl-clad metals may be drawn or formed by using standard sheet-metal-working techniques. The end products are used for equipment housings and as building materials. The annual output of these laminates in the United States is in excess of 100 million square feet.

Adhesives are also used to adhere rubber plasticized poly(vinyl chloride) sheet to metal to produce polymer-lined metal tanks. Rubber-lined tanks are in general use for storage and reaction vessels containing nonoxidizing acids, in the absence of organic solvents, at temperatures up to 160°F. Plasticized-poly(vinyl chloride)-lined tanks are used for storage or reaction vessels containing oxidizing acids, such as nitric or chromic acids, at temperatures up to 150°F.

Poly(vinyl chloride) or polyethylene sheet or pipe may be joined by hot-gas-welding, heated-tool-welding, induction-welding, ultrasonics, or friction-welding techniques. Plastic pipe or plastic sheet with beveled edges may be

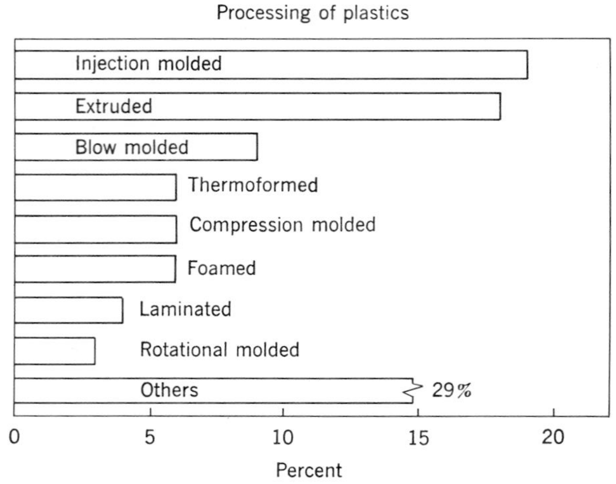

Processing of plastics

Fig. 10-9

joined by using heated plastic filler rods or splines. Heat is supplied by proprietary gas or electric torches which permit hot gases to soften both the spline and the surfaces to be joined. A properly formed joint is thicker and almost as strong as the adjacent sheet.

Plastic sheet or pipe may also be jointed by preheating the surfaces to be joined. The heat may be supplied by a heated tool or by rotational rubbing of the surfaces. Thermal sealing may be accomplished by placing the films between hot dies or hot rollers. Over 10 billion bags are made annually in the United States by heat sealing. Induction welding results from the frictional heat produced by molecular motion in the electromagnetic field between electrodes with high-frequency current.

Mechanical vibrations at 18,000 to 20,000 cps (ultrasonic vibrations) may be used to melt adjacent plastic surfaces prior to joining. Good welds have been obtained with polypropylene, polycarbonate, polystyrene, and ABS copolymer. Ultrasonic welding horns are available commercially.

The relative amounts of plastics processed by the various techniques are compared in Fig. 10-9.

REFERENCES

Alten, F. C.: Welding Thermoplastics, in "Modern Plastics Encyclopedia," p. 1004, McGraw-Hill Book Company, New York, 1966.

Black, P. B.: Heat Sealing of Plastics, in "Modern Plastics Encyclopedia," p. 984, McGraw-Hill Book Company, New York, 1966.

Brown, J.: Plastic Calendering /—/ Types of Machines and Layouts, in "Plastics Progress," Iliffe Books, Ltd., London, 1951.

Butzko, R. L.: "Plastic Sheet Forming," Reinhold Publishing Corporation, New York, 1958.

Colley, R.: High Frequency Welding, *Plastics*, **30**(9):67 (1965).

Curtis, F. W.: "High Frequency Induction Heating," McGraw-Hill Book Company, New York, 1944.

Dietz, A. G. H.: "Engineering Laminates," John Wiley & Sons, Inc., New York, 1949.

DuBois, J. H.: Cold Molding, *Plastics World*, **26**(3):26 (1968).

Duffin, D. J., and C. Nerzig: "Laminated Plastics," Reinhold Publishing Corporation, New York, 1958.

Epstein, G.: "Adhesive Bonding of Metals," Reinhold Publishing Corporation, New York, 1954.

Ford, K. C.: Solvents Cements for ABS, *Mod. Plastics*, **45**(4):119 (1967).

Gooch, K. J.: Calender Design, *Mod. Plastics*, **34**(11):167 (1957).

Gross, J.: Heat Sealing of Plastics, in "Modern Plastics Encyclopedia," p. 1001, McGraw-Hill Book Company, New York, 1967.

Haim, G., and J. A. Neumann: "Manual for Plastic Welding," vol. II, Crosby Lockwood & Son, Ltd., London, 1954.

Kaminsky, S. J.: Welding Thermoplastics, in "Modern Plastics Encyclopedia," p. 997, McGraw-Hill Book Company, New York, 1967.

Kolb, D. J.: Ultrasonic Welding, in "Modern Plastics Encyclopedia," p. 989, McGraw-Hill Book Company, New York, 1966.

———: Ultrasonic Welding, in "Modern Plastics Encyclopedia," p. 988, McGraw-Hill Book Company, New York, 1967.

Maghton, J. W.: Plug-Assist Forming, *SPE J.*, **12**(6):83 (1956).

Marshall, D. I.: Calendering, in E. C. Bernhardt (ed.), "Processing of Thermoplastic Materials," chap. 6, Reinhold Publishing Corporation, New York, 1959.

McConnell, W. K.: Thermoforming, in "Modern Plastics Encyclopedia," p. 812, McGraw-Hill Book Company, New York, 1967.

McDonald, E. J.: Vacuum Forming ABS, *Plastics Technol.*, **11**(12):35 (1965).

Morgan, P.: "Glass Reinforced Plastics," Philosophical Library, Inc., New York, 1957.

Perry, H. A.: "Adhesive Bonding of Plastics," McGraw-Hill Book Company, New York, 1959.

Platzer, N.: Sheet Forming, in E. C. Bernhardt (ed.), "Processing of Thermoplastics Materials," chap. 8, Reinhold Publishing Corporation, New York, 1959.

Randolph, A. F.: "Plastics Engineering Handbook," 3d ed., chap. 22, Reinhold Publishing Corporation, New York, 1960.

Rouse, B. P., and T. M. Hearst: Sealing and Welding of Thermoplastics, in E. C. Bernhardt (ed.), "Processing of Thermoplastic Materials," chap. 10, Reinhold Publishing Corporation, New York, 1959.

Sasso, J. (ed.): "Plastics Handbook for Product Engineers," McGraw-Hill Book Company, New York, 1946.

Scheiner, L. L.: Thermoforming, in Processing Handbook, *Plastic Technol.*, **13**(10):145 (1967).

Schmidt, A. X., and C. A. Marlies: "Principles of High-polymer Theory and Practice," McGraw-Hill Book Company, New York, 1948.

Shatton, B.: Deep-draw Vacuum Forming, *Plastics World*, **16**(1):1 (1958).

Skow, N. A., and G. A. Ebelhare: Laminated Plastics, *Mod. Plastics*, **45**(1A):614, (1967).

Sonneborn, R. H.: "Fiberglass Reinforced Plastics," Reinhold Publishing Corporation, New York, 1954.

Sorrell, S. E.: "Paper Base Laminates," Cleaver-Hume Press, Ltd., London, 1950.

Van Sickle, R. W., and V. L. Hannaford: Thermoforming, in Processing Handbook, *Plastics Technol.*, **13**(10):155 (1967).

Zelnick, D. R.: Thermoforming, in "Modern Plastics Encyclopedia," p. 736, McGraw-Hill Book Company, New York, 1966.

10-5 FABRICATIONS AND FINISHING

The processing procedures discussed in the previous section may be used to fabricate plastic structures. For example, extremely large self-supporting tanks, towers, and processing equipment may be constructed from plastic sheet, pipe, and molded parts by assembling smaller units, using mechanical, adhesive, or thermal welding techniques.

Plastic materials may be fabricated by modifications of the conventional machining operations used by the wood and metals industries. It is essential that the machining operations, such as drilling, cutting, tapping, threading, and sawing, on thermoplastics be conducted at a slow rate or that selected coolants be used to prevent excessive softening of these thermoplastic materials. Because notches lower the resistance to impact, sharp corners and notches should be avoided.

Similar precautions must be observed in the ashing and polishing of thermoplastics. Thermosetting plastics are more readily machined than thermoplastics. However, extremely close tolerances characteristic of metals are difficult to obtain when plastics are machined. Plastic parts may be readily painted. For example, epoxy-resin-based paints have been used to produce colored plastics. When plastics, such as polypropylene and ABS, are metal-plated they have the outward appearance of metals and the characteristic properties of plastics.

REFERENCES

Delmonte, J.: "Plastics in Engineering," 3d ed., Penton Publishing Company, Cleveland, 1949.

Kobayashi, A.: "Machining of Plastics," McGraw-Hill Book Company, New York, 1967.

Maranchik, J., and R. L. Williams: Machining Plastics, in "Modern Plastics Encyclopedia," p. 982, McGraw-Hill Book Company, New York, 1967.

Randolph, A. F. (ed.): Machining, Finishing, Decorating, in "Plastics Engineers Handbook," chap. 21, Reinhold Publishing Corporation, New York, 1960.

Silk, T. R.: Machining of Laminated Plastics, in D. J. Duffin and C. Nerzig (eds.), "Laminated Plastics," chap. 6, Reinhold Publishing Corporation, New York, 1958.

11

Additives for Polymers

Cast poly(methyl methacrylate), gum rubber, and many fibers may be used in the absence of additives but most nonfibrous polymer compositions are admixtures of polymers and selected ingredients. These additives, which improve the performance of many polymers, include fillers and reinforcements, plasticizers, antioxidants, pigments, ultraviolet-light stabilizers, flame retardants, antistatic agents, and miscellaneous ingredients.

11-1 FILLERS AND REINFORCEMENTS

The use of straw as a reinforcement for brick is recorded in the Bible. Other empirical developments such as the addition of hair to plaster, whiting to unsaturated oils (putty), asbestos to asphalt, graded silica to hydraulic cements, wood flour to phenolic resins, and carbon black to rubber are classic examples of the production of composites with properties that are superior to the unfilled products. Finely divided pigments are usually added to coating compositions for decorative and functional purposes. However, these pigments also function as fillers in the ultimate polymer films.

The nature of the interaction of polymer molecules and active fillers is not completely understood. However, it is known that fillers restrict chain mobility and thus increase the resistance of polymers to elevated temperatures. The improvement in performance of carbon-filled polymers is evidenced by an average life of 25,000 miles for a carbon-reinforced pneumatic tire vs. less than 2,500 miles of road service for a tire made from gum stock.

Phenolic resins are seldom used without fillers or reinforcements. However, some polymers like Neoprene are characterized by a high modulus and may be used in the absence of filler (gum stock). In contrast, the SBR elastomer has a low modulus, and the addition of carbon filler is essential for the production of serviceable rubber articles from this polymer.

Wood, which is one of the oldest and most widely used materials, is also a good example of a naturally occurring useful composite material. That the properties of this product differ from its cellulose reinforcement and its lignin binder has been recognized for many years. The symbiotic effect demonstrated by these "building blocks" is also a requirement for synthetic composites that are used as engineering plastics. Many of the characteristics of wood and synthetic composites are similar. The latter are more versatile since composition is not limited to any specific matrix or reinforcement or to the ratio of the amount of the building blocks used in the composite. In addition, as in plywood production, isotropic or anisotropic systems may be designed. Because of the relative newness of the reinforced-plastics art, the emphasis has been on the forming of intricate shapes by an in situ shaping process. However, the classic techniques used to fabricate end products from wood may also be applied to increase the versatility of these modern engineering materials.

Some fillers are inert, but there is ample evidence to suggest a high degree of interaction between active fillers and functional groups on the polymer chains. However, the International Standards Organization (ISO) recommends that all inorganic additives in composites be designated as fillers, regardless of the degree of surface interaction with the polymer chains. The Technical Standards Committee on Plastics follows this international recommendation. Admittedly, each individual interaction between active sites is small. However, these small forces are additive and become significant for long polymer chains with a multiplicity of active sites. This aggregate interaction produces a weak network which stiffens the polymer and increases the tensile strength, hardness, and glass transition temperature.

Since most of the investigations on filler-polymer interactions have been made with carbon and rubber, this system will be emphasized in the discussion of polymer-particle attractions. The reinforcing action of carbon black is decreased if it is graphitized by heating to 3200°C. Beebe showed that a monolayer of inert gas may be adsorbed on the carbon-black surface but that this surface activity is decreased by graphitization.

Rubber molecules in poor solvents may also be preferentially adsorbed on carbon black in the presence of graphitized carbon. When fillers that are less active than carbon black are used, an increase in viscosity is noted, and this increase is related to the degree of attraction of the polymer to the solvent and filler surfaces.

Strong interactions between active surfaces, like carbon black, and polymers, such as rubber, produce an insoluble composite called *bound rubber*. This phenomenon has been explained by the use of a dual tetrahedral model. The total number of tetrahedra present in a filled elastomer (N_T) may be calculated from the volume fraction of the filler (V_F), the diameter of the particles (d_F), and the distance (λ) from the origin to the vertices in the tetrahedra, as shown in the following equation:

$$N_T = \frac{9(3)^{1/2}}{8\lambda^3} \left(1 - V_F - \frac{8\lambda V_F}{3d_F} \right) \qquad (11\text{-}1)$$

Equation for calculating number of tetrahedra in dual tetrahedral model

The tetrahedral coordination number may be calculated, and the ratio of filled to unfilled crosslinks may be estimated from equilibrium swelling measurements. Guth used the Einstein equation for the viscosity of suspended spherical particles to relate the volume fraction of filler (V_F) to the stress of filled (F) and unfilled elastomers (F_0). The reduction in free volume reduces chain mobility. Since the glass transition temperature is defined as that at which all polymers have similar fractional free volume, relationships between fractional free volume, glass transition temperature, and modulus may be calculated. As shown in Eq. (11-2), the modulus (F) will be increased by 50 percent when the volume fraction of filler (V_F) is equal to 20 percent. This expression holds well for moduli less than 2.

$$F = F_0(1 + 2.5V_F + 14.1V_F{}^2) \qquad (11\text{-}2)$$

Relationship of modulus to volume of filler

The rate of wetting of filler surfaces and the heat of adsorption are readily measured and are characteristic of both the filler and resin. The viscoelastic yield of both thermosetting resins and thermoplastics is reduced by the addition of fillers. NMR spectroscopy may be used to show a decrease in spin-spin relaxation time when the chain mobility of plasticized poly(vinyl chloride) is reduced by the addition of silica gel.

Fillers, such as aluminum hydrate, reduce the flammability of polyester laminates so that they are comparable to halogenated resin–antimony oxide systems. Fillers vary widely in availability, cost, and composition, as well as in physical, electrical, and chemical properties. The filler content may vary from over 97 percent when present in the foundry shell-molding process to a few percent in carbon-filled polyethylene. The optimum amount of resin is the minimum required to produce a monomolecular layer on the filler surface.

This requirement is approached in furan resin or alkyd urethaneresin–sand mixtures used in the shell-molding process but is exceeded in most true molding compositions where emphasis is on good flow or a minimum amount of voids and discontinuities. As little as 10 percent resin is used with 90 percent wood waste for molding large articles like trays and desk tops. However, these composite mixtures do not possess the good flow properties of genuine molding compounds.

Most of the reinforcing fillers are high-molecular-weight organic or inorganic products. Particle shape, size, and distribution affect the performance of fillers. Fibrous fillers are usually more effective than nonfibrous ones. Finely divided fillers are not effective in thermoplastic composites, but their effectiveness increases when a small amount of crosslinking occurs. A linear relationship has been demonstrated when mechanical properties are plotted against the reciprocal of particle size. The principal commercial fillers are listed in Table 11-1.

Kraft paper may be impregnated with resin and compression-molded to produce laminated sheet. The impregnated paper may also be dried and chopped to yield a product that can be compression-molded to form objects of various shapes. Wood flour is obtained by attrition mill or hammer-mill grinding of fibrous softwood and, to a lesser extent, hardwood. Modern size classification and separation yield wood flour which is free from large particles. Classification results in uniform-sized particles which are readily wetted by resin.

Baekeland added wood flour to phenolic resins over a half century ago in order to reduce the brittleness of Bakelite. This inexpensive organic filler reduces mold shrinkage and provides a filled thermosetting resin with good electrical and impact-resistance properties. Wood flour is also used to reinforce urea resins when dark-colored products are acceptable. Both types of filled resins are used for molding electrical parts, such as plugs, receptacles, and toggle switches. The particle size of wood flour may be as small as 200 mesh. Fine powder yields a smooth surface finish. However, the fibrous structure is reduced by the fine-grinding process. Wood-flour-filled phenolic molding compounds have Izod impact values of about 0.3 ft-lb/in. of notch. Wood-filled plastics should not be used for extended periods of time at high temperatures since the wood flour chars when heated above 325°F.

Shell flour obtained by grinding walnut, pecan, or peanut shells contains

Table 11-1   Types of Fillers for Polymers

I. Organic Materials
  A. Cellulosic products
      1. Wood products
          a. Kraft paper
          b. Chips
          c. Coarse flour
          d. Ground flour
              (1) Softwood flour
              (2) Hardwood flour
              (3) Shell flour
      2. Comminuted cellulose products
          a. Chopped paper
          b. Diced resin board
          c. Crepe paper
          d. Pulp preforms
      3. Fibers
          a. Alpha cellulose
          b. Pulp preforms
          c. Cotton flock
          d. Textile byproducts
          e. Jute
          f. Sisal
          g. Rayon
  B. Lignin-type products
      1. Ground bark
      2. Processed lignin
  C. Synthetic fibers
      1. Polyamides (Nylon)
      2. Polyesters (Dacron)
      3. Polyacrylonitrile (Orlon, Acrilan)
  D. Carbon
      1. Carbon black
          a. Channel black
          b. Furnace black
      2. Ground petroleum coke
      3. Graphite filaments
      4. Graphite whiskers

II. Inorganic Materials
  A. Silica products
      1. Minerals
          a. Sand
          b. Quartz
          c. Tripoli
          d. Diatomaceous earth
      2. Synthetic materials
          a. Wet processed silica
          b. Pyrogenic silica
          c. Silica aerogel
  B. Silicates
      1. Minerals
          a. Asbestos

     (1) Chrysotile
     (2) Amosite
     (3) Anthophyllite
     (4) Crocidolite
     (5) Tremolite
     (6) Actinolite
    b. Kaolinite (China clay)
    c. Mica
    d. Nepheline syenite
    e. Talc
    f. Wollastonite
   2. Synthetic products
    a. Calcium silicate
    b. Aluminum silicate
 C. Glass
   1. Glass flakes
   2. Solid glass spheres
   3. Hollow glass spheres
   4. Milled fibers
   5. Fibrous glass
    a. Filament
    b. Rovings
    c. Woven roving
    d. Yarn
    e. Mat
    f. Fabric
 D. Metals
 E. Boron filaments
 F. Metallic oxides
   1. Ground material
    a. Zinc oxide
    b. Alumina
    c. Magnesia
    d. Titania
   2. Whiskers
    a. Aluminum oxide (sapphire)
    b. Beryllium oxide
    c. Magnesium oxide
    d. Thorium oxide
    e. Zirconium oxide
 G. Calcium carbonate
   1. Chalk
   2. Limestone
   3. Precipitated calcium carbonate
 H. Polyfluorocarbons
 I. Other fillers
   1. Whiskers (nonoxide)
    a. Aluminum nitride
    b. Beryllium carbide
    c. Boron carbide
    d. Silicon carbide
    e. Silicon nitride
    f. Tungsten carbide
   2. Barium ferrite
   3. Barium sulfate

lignin and furfural which contribute to good flow properties. It also contains a wax (cutin) which provides gloss, luster, and improved resistance to moisture. Since these fillers are spherical rather than fibrous, molded products which contain shell flour have low shear strength and lower resistance to impact than those with wood flour.

Light-colored moldings with fair resistance to impact are produced when α-cellulose is added to resins. This filler, which is obtained by alkaline treatment of wood pulp, yields readily processed molding powders which are characterized by low shrinkage and low resistance to moisture. The latter deficiency may be overcome by surface treatment of the filler. Cellulose-filled molding compounds are characterized by excellent arc resistance.

Molding compounds with medium resistance to impact are obtained by using processed cotton flock or caustic-purified cotton linters. Cotton-flock-filled molding powders are characterized by a high bulk factor and low moisture resistance. The former property may be modified by blending with wood flour; the latter is improved by surface treatment of the flock. These molded products have impact-resistance values as high as 0.6 ft-lbs/in. of notch. Products with still higher impact-resistance values are obtained by the resin impregnation of small pieces of cotton cloth (macerated fabrics). Chopped-cotton-cord composites have higher impact values. Moldings with impact values of 1.0, 2.0, and 4.0 ft-lb/in. of notch may be obtained from cotton-cord-filled resins.

Jute fibers, yarn, and fabric have been used for reinforcements in phenolic composites. These fabrics have low strength but this deficiency is overcome in part by using parallel jute fibers. Molding powders with moderate resistance to impact are produced by use of chopped fibers from the agave shrub. These sisal fibers have a diameter of 0.005 to 0.020 in. and are 2 to 5 ft in length. Rayon fibers are produced by the coagulation of a viscose solution after it has been extruded through spinnerets. Rayon may be used both as flock and as yarn. The impact resistance of the molded products is a function of the fiber length of the rayon used.

Nylon is also available as flock, filament, and chopped fabric. Because it is a thermoplastic, it flows at the temperatures used to mold phenolic resins. Thus considerable shrinkage takes place during molding. Gears and other products molded from nylon-filled phenolic resin are characterized by excellent resistance to abrasion and wear. Chopped fibers and filaments of polyester (Dacron) and polyacrylonitrile (Orlon, Acrilan) are used to reinforce allylic resins.

Lignin is the natural binder for cellulose in wood. A commercial product containing this type of filler may be obtained by grinding the bark of Douglas fir trees or by extending wood flour with a derivative of lignosulfonic acid. These dark-colored fillers have been admixed with resins to produce molding powders. Less resin is required in these compositions because the lignin contributes to flow. Lignin is released and hemicellulose is removed when wood chips are heated with high-pressure steam. A mixture of cellulose, lignin, and phenolic resin is heated in platen presses to produce a composition board (Masonite).

Reinforcing carbon black consists of crystallites made up of layers of carbon atoms. Channel black with particle sizes ranging from 200 to 300 Å is produced by burning gas in a limited supply of air and allowing the products to deposit on cold metal surfaces. Furnace black with particle sizes ranging from 300 to 500 Å is the most common type of carbon black. It is produced by burning gas or oil in a limited supply of air and removing the products by centrifugation or electrostatic precipitation. Thermal, acetylene, and lamp black and ground petroleum coke are coarser than the more widely used reinforcing carbon black.

Carbon black was produced by an impingement process by the Chinese in 1600 b.c. Its use was patented by Charles Goodyear but since its reinforcement qualities were not recognized, it was not used as a filler by the rubber industry until 1912. About 33 percent of modern tire tread stock is carbon black. A stress of over 2,000 psi is required for a 400 percent elongation of carbon-reinforced butyl rubber or SBR elastomer. However, gum stocks of these elastomers may be stretched more than 400 percent by a stress of less than 500 psi.

Suito showed that the carboxyl band at $1,710$ cm^{-1} disappears and a new band appears at $1,540$ cm^{-1} when carbon-filled elastomers are vulcanized. Carbon black is also used as a pigment and filler for polyethylene, polypropylene, poly(vinyl chloride), and phenolic, furan, and epoxy resins. This filler reduces the size of crystallites and improves the resistance to stress cracking and to ultraviolet degradation of polyolefins. These improvements are more readily demonstrated when carbon black is added to crosslinked polymers. Stiehler observed an increase in modulus when crystalline compounds with a β-naphthyl group are added to elastomers. He proposed that the alignment of mobile polymer backbones and these crystals is related to that which occurs with carbon reinforcement.

Carbon filaments were used by Edison in his original light bulbs. They may be produced by the pyrolysis of rayon or other organic fibers at 1400 to 1700°C. The composition and properties may be varied by the incorporation of additives before extrusion of synthetic fibers. Removal of surface water is essential for the production of high-strength composites. Graphite filaments have high tensile strengths (400,000 psi) and retain 40 percent of this strength at 4800°F. These filaments may be used directly or may be woven into fabric. Their resistance to oxidation is increased by coating with silicon carbide. Still stronger composites are obtained by use of graphite "whiskers" as reinforcements. Ground petroleum coke is used as a filler in plastic cements.

Sand, quartz, tripoli, and diatomaceous earth are naturally occurring forms of silica which differ in particle size, structure, and degree of crystallinity. Naturally occurring quartz has been used as a filler with phenolic and epoxy resins to provide ablative insulators for nose cones, space capsules, and rocket motors.

Diatomaceous earth, infusorial earth, or fossil flour is obtained from deposits of skeletons of unicellular organisms called *diatoms*. The commercial products (Celite, Dicalite, and kieselguhr) are obtained by a heat treatment which removes much of the water from the naturally occurring products. The use of this type of filler in polyurethane foams provides improved compressive strength and reduces shrinkage.

Silica fillers are also produced by both wet and pyrolytic processes. Amorphous silica (Hi-Sil) with uniform particle size (0.05 to 0.1 mμ) is obtained by precipitating silica from a solution of sodium silicate. In one commercial process, calcium chloride is added and the calcium silicate produced is treated with hydrochloric acid. In other commercial processes, the sodium silicate solution is acidified by gaseous acids, such as carbon dioxide or hydrogen chloride (Cab-O-sil).

Silica fillers contain "free water" which is reversibly removed at 100 to 200°C and "bound water" which is irreversibly removed at 900 to 1000°C. Much of the reinforcing properties of these light-colored fillers is associated with active silanol surface groups which are destroyed at elevated temperatures. Pyrogenic silica is obtained by flame or fume processing of silicon tetrachloride in the presence of hydrogen and oxygen. Pyrogenic silica has a particle-size average of 0.015 μ, low free moisture content (1 percent), and a large external surface area (200 m^2/g).

Fumed silica is a thixotropic agent and may be used as an effective thickener for liquid resin systems. Small quantities of pyrogenic silica are used to provide free-flowing properties and to prevent caking of molding powders. Silica aerogels (Santocel) are produced by the controlled acidification of sodium silicate solutions. The water present is replaced by ethanol, and the resulting organogel is heated in an autoclave to remove volatile products.

Asbestos is a naturally occurring fibrous hydrated magnesium silicate. Most of this filler is chrysotile, a fibrous serpentine type. Amosite, anthophyllite, crocidolite, tremolite, and actinolite are included in the amphibole group. Crocidolite asbestos has been used for the fabrication of filament-wound equipment, and anthophyllite asbestos has been used to reinforce thermoplastics.

Composites containing asbestos are characterized by improved dimensional stability and good resistance to corrosion, heat, rot, mildew, and weather. Asbestos in the fibrous form and as "floats" has been used as a filler with a wide variety of resins in the production of molding compositions, mastics, and troweling compounds. About $\frac{1}{2}$ billion pounds of asbestos is used annually in the production of vinyl floor tile, brake linings, and clutch facings.

Other silicate minerals are kaolinite (China clay), an aluminum silicate; mica, a potassium aluminum silicate obtained from the mineral muscovite; nepheline syenite, a sodium, potassium, aluminum silicate; talc, a magnesium silicate; and wollastonite, a calcium metasilicate. Clay is processed by dispersing in water, degritting, and classifying by centrifugation or air flotation. The electrical properties of kaolin are improved by calcination. Clay has been used as a filler for rubber, phenolics, alkyds, polyesters, epoxies, polyurethanes, polyolefins, polystyrene, and vinyl resins. Filler performance is enhanced by surface treatment with silanes or other resin formers.

Mica is compatible with and wetted by most resins. Mica-resin composites are characterized by excellent electrical properties and good heat resistance. Nepheline syenite has been used as a nearly transparent filler with epoxy and polyester resins. Many types of talc are available. Because of its fibrous structure, talc produces stronger composites than the nonfibrous silicate fillers. Acicular-shaped wollastonite particles have been used as fillers for polyesters, melamines, epoxies, polyurethanes, nylon, and vinyl resins. Its effectiveness as a filler may be increased by coating its surface with silicone coupling agents.

Calcium silicate (Silene EF) is produced by continuously mixing streams of solutions of calcium chloride and sodium silicate under conditions of high turbulence. Aluminum, calcium, magnesium, and sodium-aluminum silicates may also be produced by reacting sodium silicate solutions with appropriate solutions of metal salts. A hydrous calcium silicate (Microgel) is obtained by heating a dispersion of diatomaceous earth with lime water.

Thin glass flakes are produced by smashing thin tubes formed by blowing molten type E glass. This type of reinforcement yields strong multidirectional composites with excellent moisture resistance. Low-density syntactic foams may be obtained by mixing epoxy resins and hollow glass spheres (microballoons). Milled glass fibers may be added to fibrous-glass-reinforced polyester and epoxy resins. These short nodules are obtained by hammer-milling glass filaments. Solid glass spheres ranging in size from 10 to 340 μ have low sorptive forces; hence large proportions of this inactive filler may be tolerated in composites. A slight reinforcing effect is noted when the spheres are coated with hot silane coupling agents.

Fibrous glass is produced by melting C, E, or S glass and passing the molten mass through small orifices. The C glass has a low soda content and is resistant to most acids except hydrofluoric acid. The E glass is a lime-alumina-borosilicate glass. The S glass is characterized by a high modulus and high tensile strength at temperatures as high as 1600°F. The extruded filaments, which range from 12 to 75×10^{-5} in. in diameter, may be combined as multiple filaments or bundles (strands).

Rovings are ropelike untwisted multistrands. Reinforced plastic structures may contain as much as 80 percent by weight of continuous rovings. Chopped-strand mat may consist of resinous bonded strands or mechanically bonded strands. The latter are held together by use of a needle punching process. Continuous-strand mats consist of unchopped strands laid down in a swirl pattern. Mat-reinforced resins may contain up to 50 percent glass. The binders are usually thermosetting resins, such as polyester, epoxy, silicone, or phenolic resins.

Glass roving may be cut into 1- to 2-in. lengths and used as a reinforcement. These fibers may be used for the production of filled molding compounds. Proprietary gums are available for applying a mixture of resin and chopped strands. Fibrous glass may be woven in either plain or taffeta patterns. Reinforced plastics may contain as much as 75 percent glass fabric. Three-dimensional glass-fabric reinforcements have been made by using untwisted glass yarn.

Filament-wound structures consist of resin-impregnated filaments oriented with either helical or polar winding to provide a balanced high-strength structure. Structures such as rocket nose cones, radomes, heat shields, tanks, and even rectangular shapes may be produced by the continuous winding of resin-coated filament on a form or mandrel. Resin-impregnated glass tape may also be used in place of filament for the production of wound structures.

A size is applied to protect the glass fibers after they are extruded. Additional finishes consisting of coupling agents are applied to assure a good bond between the resin and the glass surface. Finishes such as aminopropyltriethoxysilane or chromic methacrylate complex are essential for strong resin-glass bonds. A finish provides a strong bond when the energy of its adhesion to the fibrous surface is sufficient to prevent its displacement by water. Over 500 million pounds of reinforced plastics are used annually in the United States. The principal end uses are for transportation, boats, and materials of construction.

The physical properties of thermoplastics such as polystyrene, styrene-acrylonitrile copolymers, ABS copolymers, acetals, acrylics, chlorinated polyether, polysulfones, polycarbonates, polyethylene, polypropylene, nylon, and poly(ethylene terephthalate) are improved by the addition of 30 to 40 percent glass fibers. Little reinforcement is noted with less than 10 percent glass; more than 40 percent produces moldings with inferior surface properties.

The high strength-to-weight properties of glass-reinforced thermoplastics such as nylon compare favorably with light metal alloy castings. Because of their improved resistance to flow, these composites must be molded at higher temperatures than unfilled resins. These moldings have excellent dimensional stability even in the presence of metal inserts. Although the impact values at ordinary temperatures are not noticeably improved, these values are maintained or improved when the temperature is increased.

Metal powders, such as bronze or aluminum, may be added to acetal resins or nylon to produce conductive moldings that may be plated with metals. Polymers with a high percentage of powdered zinc are useful as protective coatings. Polyolefins containing a heavy metal powder, such as lead, are useful as shields for neutron and gamma rays. Epoxy resins with large quantities of finely divided metals, such as aluminum powder, are used to cast forming tools and for the production of metal cements and coatings.

Boron filaments are strong, light in weight, and much stiffer than aluminum or glass filaments. The commercial product (Borofil), which has six times the modulus of glass fibers, is produced by the deposition of boron from a boron trichloride–hydrogen mixture on a hot tungsten filament similar to that used in incandescent lamps. The diameter of the tungsten core is 0.5 mil and that of the composite is 3 to 5 mils. The uniformity of adhesion of resins such as epoxy resins to the boron surface may be improved by etching with nitric acid.

Zinc oxide is used both as a vulcanization promotor and as a filler in rubber. Aluminum, magnesium, and titanium oxides have also been used as reinforcing agents for elastomers and plastic materials. Composites made from these fillers are characterized by increased stiffness, hardness, and resistance to creep. Alumina-coated silica filaments have been used to reinforce epoxy resins.

Whiskers are single-crystal filaments with strengths which approach the maximum theoretical strength of the material because of the absence of imperfections. Whiskers have been formed from about 30 elements and 50 compounds. Silicon carbide whiskers are produced by heating methyl trichlorosilane in an atmosphere of hydrogen at 1240°C. Single crystals of α-alumina fibers are produced by heating aluminum oxide in a refractory oxide boat at 1400°C. The strength of these whiskers is inversely proportional to size. These products are available in the form of loose fibers, mats, paper, and yarns. The high cost has limited their use to aerospace composites. However, blends of whiskers and glass fibers yield economical com-

Table 11-2   Physical Properties of Typical Reinforcements

MATERIAL	SPECIFIC GRAVITY	MELTING POINT, °C	TENSILE STRENGTH $\times 10^{-3}$, psi	MODULUS OF ELASTICITY $\times 10^{-6}$, psi
Aluminum	2.7	1220	90	11
Aluminum oxide	4.0	3780	1000	76
Aluminum nitride	3.3	3990	100	50
Asbestos	2.5	2770	200	25
Beryllium	1.8	2343	250	44
Beryllium oxide	3.0	4650	75	51
Boron	2.6	3812	500	60
Boron carbide	2.5	4400	500	65
E glass	2.6	2400	500	11
S glass	2.5	3000	700	13
Graphite	1.4	6600	250	37
Molybdenum	10.2	4370	200	52
Nylon	1.2	4880	120	0.4
Polyester	1.4	480	100	0.6
Quartz	2.2	3500	1000	10
Silicon carbide	3.2	4200	100	1000
Silicon nitride	3.2	3450	50	55
Steel	7.9	2920	600	30
Tantalum	16.6	5425	90	28
Titanium	4.7	3035	280	17
Tungsten	19.3	6170	620	58
Tungsten carbide	15.7	5200	106	104

posites with intermediate physical properties. Their physical properties are compared with other reinforcements in Table 11-2.

Calcium carbonate is available as natural chalk and limestone and as precipitated calcium carbonate. Calcite is the principal constituent of white limestone. Chalk consists essentially of deposits of skeletons of microorganisms. Paris white is obtained by allowing wet ground calcium carbonate or chalk to settle in large tanks.

Synthetic fillers are often obtained as byproducts of chemical manufacturing and are graded according to particle size. Performance of these fillers is improved by surface treatment. Surface qualities of the molded products are improved and mold shrinkage is reduced when calcium carbonate filler is added to phenolic molding compounds. This type of filler is also used with polyolefins, poly(vinyl chloride), polyester, and epoxy resins. Calcium carbonate improves the cell structure of polyurethane foams. Since the sorptive forces of calcium carbonate and resins are low, high filler concentrations may be tolerated. The surface activity of these agents may be improved by precoating the fillers with resin.

REFERENCES

Adamson, A. W.: "Physical Chemistry of Surfaces," 2d ed., Interscience Publishers, a division of John Wiley & Sons, Inc., New York, 1967.

Axelson, J. W.: Asbestos, in "Modern Plastics Encyclopedia," p. 594, McGraw-Hill Book Company, New York, 1967.

Beebe, R. A., J. Biscoe, W. R. Smith, and C. B. Wendell: Adsorption of Carbon Black, *J. Am. Chem. Soc.*, **69**:95 (1947).

Berger, H., and R. E. Oesper: "Asbestos with Plastics and Rubber," Chemical Publishing Company, Inc., New York, 1966.

Bjorksten, J.: Non-glass Reinforcement for Plastics, 12th Annual National Technical Conference SPE, vol. II, Cleveland, 1956.

Bueche, F.: "Physical Properties of Polymers," chap. 2, Interscience Publishers, a division of John Wiley & Sons, Inc., New York, 1962.

Carroll, M. N.: Composition Board, in H. F. Mark, N. G. Gaylord, and N. M. Bikales (eds.), "Encyclopedia of Polymer Science and Technology," vol. 4, Interscience Publishers, a division of John Wiley & Sons, Inc., New York, 1966.

Cook, L. E.: China Clays, *Rubber Plastics Age*, **47**(3):284 (1966).

Corten, H. T.: Reinforced Plastics, in E. Baer (ed.), "Engineering Design for Plastics," chap. 14, Reinhold Publishing Corporation, New York, 1964.

Delmonte, J.: "Metal-filled Plastics," Reinhold Publishing Corporation, New York, 1961.

Dumond, T. C.: "Shell Molding and Shell Mold Casting," Reinhold Publishing Corporation, New York, 1954.

Frissell, W. J.: Fillers, in H. F. Mark, N. G. Gaylord, and N. M. Bikales (eds.), "Encyclopedia of Polymer Science and Technology," vol. 6, Interscience Publishers, a division of John Wiley & Sons, Inc., New York, 1967.

Guth, E. J.: Filler vs. Modulus, *J. Appl. Phys.*, **16**:20 (1945).

Halpin, J. C., and F. Bueche: Polymers Reinforcement, *Rubber Chem. Technol.*, **38**(2):278 (1965).

Huke, D. W.: "Introduction to Natural and Synthetic Rubbers," chap. 5, Chemical Publishing Company, Inc., New York, 1951.

Kinna, M. A., and R. W. Warfield: Filament Winding, *Polymer Eng. Sci.*, **6**:41 (1966).

Kraus, G.: "Reinforcement of Elastomers," Interscience Publishers, a division of John Wiley & Sons, Inc., New York, 1965.

McMarlin, R. M.: Fibrous Glass, *Ind. Eng. Chem.*, **58**(3):21 (1966).

Morgan, P.: "Glass Reinforced Plastics," 2d ed., Philosophical Library, Inc., New York, 1957.

Murphy, T. P.: Filled Thermoplastics, *Ind. Eng. Chem.*, **58**(5):41 (1966).

Oberth, A.: Principles of Reinforcement in Filled Rubbers, *Rubber Chem. Technol.*, **40**(5):1337 (1967).

Oleesky, S. S., and J. J. Mohr: "Handbook of Reinforced Plastics," Reinhold Publishing Corporation, New York, 1964.

Paulus, H. J.: Fibrous Glass, in "Modern Plastics Encyclopedia," p. 590, McGraw-Hill Book Company, New York, 1967.

Raff, R. A. V., I. W. Herrick, and M. K. Adams: Post Curing by Electrical Induction, *Mod. Plastics*, **44**(2):130 (1966).

———: Fibre Reinforcements, *Wash. State Inst. Technol.*, Circ. 17, 1967.

Randolph, A. F. (ed.): Reinforced Plastics, in "Plastics Engineering Handbook," chap. 11, Reinhold Publishing Corporation, New York, 1960.

Riley, M.: "Plastics Tooling," Reinhold Publishing Corporation, New York, 1955.

Rosato, D. V.: Asbestos Reinforcements, *Mod. Plastics*, **33**:140 (1956).

———: Filament Winding, in "The Encyclopedia of Basic Materials for Plastics," Reinhold Publishing Corporation, New York, 1967.

———: Filament Winding, in "Encyclopedia of Polymer Science and Technology," vol. 6, Interscience Publishers, a division of John Wiley & Sons, Inc., New York, 1967.

——— and C. S. Grove: "Filament Winding," John Wiley & Sons, Inc., New York, 1964.

Seymour, R. B.: Fillers and Reinforcements, in "Modern Plastics Encyclopedia," McGraw-Hill Book Company, New York, 1970.

———: Fillers and Reinforcements, in H. R. Simonds and J. M. Church (eds.), "The Encyclopedia of Basic Materials for Plastics," Reinhold Publishing Corporation, New York, 1967.

Skow, N. A., and G. A. Ebelhare: Laminates, in "Modern Plastics Encyclopedia," p. 614, McGraw-Hill Book Company, New York, 1967.

Stiehler, R. D., E. J. Parks, and F. J. Linnig; Organic Fillers, *ACS Div. Org. Coatings and Plastics Chem., Preprints,* **27**(2):492 (1967).

Suito, E., and M. Arakaw: Infrared Absorption Spectra of Fillers, *Rubber Chem. Technol.,* **38**(1):219, 227 (1965).

Sutton. W. H.: Ceramic Whiskers, in H. R. Simonds and J. M. Church (eds.), "The Encyclopedia of Basic Materials for Plastics," Reinhold Publishing Corporation, New York, 1967.

Wade, W. H., and N. Hackerman: Thermodynamics of Wetting of Solid Oxides, in R. F. Gould (ed.), "Contact Angle, Wettability and Adhesion," chap. 15, American Chemical Society, Washington, D.C., 1964.

Zettlemoyer, A. C., and J. J. Chessick: Wettability by Heats of Immersion, in R. F. Gould (ed.), "Contact Angle, Wettability and Adhesion," chap. 5, American Chemical Society, Washington, D.C., 1964.

11-2 PLASTICIZERS

A plasticizer is a high-boiling solvent or low-melting solid which imparts flexibility to an amphorous polymer. The ancients plasticized pitch by the addition of oil in order to produce a useful caulking compound for water-proofing ships. Pellen patented the use of plasticizers in 1856. Hyatt and Parkes used camphor as a plasticizer for cellulose nitrate in 1868. Many developments in polymer technology since 1930 have been related to the plasticization of rigid polymers.

The gel and lubricity theories have been advanced to explain the effect of plasticizers. The gel theory considers that the van der Waals forces produce a gel-like three-dimensional structure by the formation of weak bonds at active centers. Thus the plasticization process is similar to the solution process, and, as stated in Chap. 2, this process may occur when the polymer and solvent have similar cohesive energy densities or solubility-parameter values.

The lubricity theory suggests that the plasticizer reduces the internal resistance to deformation by acting as a lubricant to promote relative intermolecular mobility. It may be reasoned that solvents or plasticizers with appropriate solubility parameters will increase chain movements of partly extended macromolecules.

Ferry suggested that each plasticizer molecule contributes a certain increment of free volume. When sufficient plasticizer is added, the percent free volume characteristic of the glass transition temperature for all polymers is reached. Thus the relaxation time a_t of polymer segments is related to the fractional free volume F_g. The logarithm of the ratio of the relaxation time a_t at any temperature T may be expressed as a modified Williams-Landel-Ferry (WLF) equation in which α_F is the expansion coefficient for free volume, and B is a constant related to the shape of the polymer:

$$\log a_t = \frac{(B/2.303F_g)(T - T_g)}{F_g/\alpha_F + T - T_g} \tag{11-3}$$

Modified WLF equation for plasticized polymers

Many flexible polymers such as poly(butyl acrylate) are *internally plasticized* because of the presence of bulky groups on the polymer backbone. Thus, as stated in Chap. 1, the glass transition temperature of these polymers decreases as the size of the bulky groups increases, provided the groups are not long enough to cause side-chain crystallization. Flexibility may also be promoted by adding a compatible polymer or by copolymerization. Graft copolymerization is a particularly effective technique for improving the flexibility.

The effect of copolymerization on the glass transition temperature may be illustrated by poly(vinyl chloride-co-vinyl acetate) in which the copolymer containing 85 percent vinyl chloride has a glass temperature of 63° in contrast to a value of 85° for poly(vinyl chloride). Other examples of internally plasticized polymers are poly(vinylidene chloride-co-vinyl chloride), poly(butadiene-co-styrene), ABS copolymers, and poly(butadiene-g-styrene).

High-boiling liquids or low-molecular-weight solids which plasticize polymers are called *external plasticizers*. Dioctyl phthalate is the most widely used high-boiling liquid plasticizer. The principal polymeric plasticizers are low-molecular-weight aliphatic polyesters. A polymer of propylene glycol and adipic acid with a $\overline{DP}$ of 12 and terminated by lauric acid is a typical example of a polymeric plasticizer.

In general, the solubility parameter δ of the polymer and the plasticizer should not differ by more than 1.5 units. Secondary plasticizers that do not meet this criterion may be tolerated in mixtures with good plasticizers if the solubility parameter of the mixture is in the required range. The solubility-parameter values of typical plasticizers are listed in Table 11-3.

The term *plasticizer efficiency* is a parameter related to the relative amounts of different plasticizers required to achieve a similar degree of plasticity. The equivalent modulus concentration, i.e., the amount of plasticizer that must be added to 100 parts of resin to produce a composition with 100 percent elongation at 1,500 psi, has been used as one measure of plasticizer efficiency. Other tests for measuring plasticizer efficiency include the time of fluxing in a Banbury mixer, the clearing temperature of a dilute solution of vinyl resin, and the fluxing temperature necessary to achieve a specific tensile strength.

Oil-extended elastomers and vinyl plastisols are good examples of externally plasticized polymers. As much as 60 parts of aromatic hydrocarbon oils may be added to a latex containing 100 parts of SBR elastomer. Oil-extended rubbers with less oil are not as expensive as the pure elastomers and are satisfactory for many applications.

A plastisol is a viscous liquid consisting of a dispersion of a finely divided

Table 11-3 Solubility Parameters of Typical Plasticizers

PLASTICIZER	SOLUBILITY PARAMETER δ
Parafinic oils	7.5
Dioctyl phthalate	7.9
Dibutoxyethyl phthalate	8.0
Tricresyl phosphate	8.4
Dioctyl sebacate	8.6
Triphenyl phosphate	8.6
Chlorinated biphenyl (Arochlor 1248)	8.8
Dihexyl phthalate	8.9
Hydrogenated terphenyl (HB-40)	9.0
Dibutyl sebacate	9.2
Dibutyl phthalate	9.3
Dipropyl phthalate	9.7
Diethyl phthalate	10.0
Dimethyl phthalate	10.7
Santicizer 8	11.9
Glycerol	16.5

polymer in a plasticizer. Modifications include organosols, plastigels, and organogels. An organosol contains both solvent and plasticizer. Plastigels and organogels are produced by the addition of a gelling agent such as bentonite to plastisols and organosols.

Commercial plastisols are produced by the addition of resin and other additives such as stabilizers, fillers, and pigments to liquid plasticizers. A typical formulation may contain equal weights of polymer and plasticizer. These products may be applied as coatings or may be used for slush or rotational molding. Flexible solids are obtained when these products are fused at 160°C.

In contrast to plasticizers which lower the elastic modulus of poly(vinyl chloride), *antiplasticizers* may be used to increase the modulus of bisphenol A polycarbonate. Typical antiplasticizers for this specific polymer are chlorinated biphenyls (Arochlors), poly(styrene glycols), and derivatives of abietic acid. For example, the modulus of bisphenol A polycarbonate may be increased from 3.3×10^5 to 4.7×10^5 psi by the additions of enough chlorinated biphenyl (Arochlor 1254) to produce a polymer having a composition of 30 percent antiplasticizer.

Rigid poly(vinyl chloride) is used to a limited extent but most of the 3 billion pounds annual production of poly(vinyl chloride) is used as a plasticized polymer. Lesser amounts of plasticizer are used with the cellulosics. The internal plasticizers and oils for oil-extended rubber are not included in plasticizer statistics. However, over 1 billion pounds of plasticizers are used annually by the American polymer industry.

REFERENCES

Bruins, P. F.: "Plasticizer Technology," vol. I, Reinhold Publishing Corporation, New York, 1965.

Burrell, H., and B. Immergut: Solubility Parameters, in J. Brandrup and E. H. Immergut (eds.), "Polymer Handbook," Interscience Publishers, a division of John Wiley & Sons, Inc., New York, 1965.

Busse, W. F.: Gel Theory, *J. Phys. Chem.*, **36**:2862 (1932).

Buttrey, D. N.: "Plasticizers," Cleaver-Hume Press, Ltd., London, 1957.

Doolittle, A. K.: "The Technology of Solvents and Plasticizers," John Wiley & Sons, Inc., New York, 1954.

Ferry, J. D.: "Viscoelastic Properties of Polymers," John Wiley & Sons, Inc., New York, 1961.

Frissell, W. J.: Polymer Plasticizers, in H. R. Simonds and J. M. Church (eds.), "The Encyclopedia of Basic Materials for Plastics," Reinhold Publishing Corporation, New York, 1967.

Gould, R. F. (ed.): "Plasticization and Plasticizers Process," American Chemical Society, Washington, D.C., 1965.

Jackson, W. J., and J. R. Caldwell: Antiplasticizers, in R. F. Gould (ed.), "Advances in Chemistry," ser. 48, chap. 17, American Chemical Society, Washington, D.C., 1965.

———— and ————: Antiplasticizers, *J. Appl. Polymer Sci.*, **11**(2):211, 227 (1967).

Manfred, O., and J. Obrist: Lubricity Theory, *Colloid Z.*, **41**:348 (1927).

McBroom, J. W.: Plasticizers, in "Modern Plastics Encyclopedia," p. 416, McGraw-Hill Book Company, New York, 1967.

Mellan, I.: "Industrial Plasticizers," The Macmillan Company, New York, 1963.

Modern Plastics, Plasticizers, **45**(1):88 (1967).

Pellen, M.: Plasticizers, British Patent 2256, 1856.

Powell, G. M., and J. E. Brister: Plastigels, U.S. Patent 2,427,507.

Semon, W. L.: Plastisol, U.S. Patent 2,188,396, 1936.

Severs, E. R.: "Rheology of Polymers," Reinhold Publishing Corporation, New York, 1962.

Seymour, R. B.: Plasticizer Identification, *Plastics World*, **21**(9):58 (1963).

————: Plasticizers, *Plastic World*, **21**(5):26; (6):16 (1963).

————: Plasticized Polystyrene, U.S. Patent 2,574,438, 1951.

————: Plasticizers, in H. R. Simonds and J. M. Church (eds.), "The Encyclopedia of Basic Materials for Plastics," Reinhold Publishing Corporation, New York, 1967.

Storey, E. B.: Oil Extended Rubbers, *Rubber Chem. Technol.*, **34**:1402 (1961).

Todd, W. D.: Plastisols, in C. E. Schildknecht (ed.), "Polymer Processes," chap. 14, Interscience Publishers, Inc., New York, 1956.

11-3 ANTIOXIDANTS AND THERMAL STABILIZERS

Most organic polymers deteriorate when processed at elevated temperatures or when used at abnormally high temperatures. These degradative reactions, which result in the cleavage of carbon-carbon bonds in the polymer backbone, are accelerated in the presence of oxygen and heavy metals and retarded in the presence of amines and hindered phenols. Chlorine-containing polymers such as poly(vinyl chloride) may lose hydrogen chloride at elevated temperatures and the residual unsaturated linkage may be readily cleaved. This type of deterioration may be retarded when heavy metal salts, such as lead stearate, are present.

Polymers may also deteriorate in the presence of ultraviolet light. As shown in Sec. 11-4, such photolytic degradation may be retarded by benzophenone derivatives and salicylates. Polyisoprene may absorb as much as 15 percent oxygen at ordinary temperatures. As little as 1 percent oxygen will destroy its elastic properties. However, natural-rubber latex contains complex phenols which retard these degradative reactions at ordinary temperatures. These naturally occurring antioxidants are not effective under tread-stock service conditions. Hence, additional stabilizers must be added to rubber used for pneumatic tires. Antioxidants are added to synthetic-rubber latex before flocculation.

The first synthetic antioxidants resulted from independent attempts by Cadwell and Winkelman and Gray to produce accelerators. The resultant products, acetaldehyde aniline (VGB) and aldol-α-naphthylamine (Agerite resin), obtained from the reaction of aromatic amines and aliphatic aldehydes are still in use. The other hundred commercial antioxidants include amines, phenols, sulfur compounds, and phosphorus derivatives.

Phenyl-β-naphthylamine (Agerite powder, Neozone D), octyl diphenyl-amine (Agerite Stabilite), N,N^1-β-naphthyl-p-phenylenediamine (Agerite white), 2,2,4-trimethyl-1,2-dihydroquinoline (Flectol A), and 6-ethoxy-1,2-dihydro-2,2,4-trimethylquinoline (Santoflex AW) are representative of the amine type. The phenolic antioxidants include hydroquinone mono-benzyl ether (Agerite Alba), 2,6-di-*tert*-butyl-*p*-cresol (Deenax), 2,2'-methylene-*bis*-(4-methyl-6-*tert*-butylphenol) (Antioxidant 2246), and styre-nated phenol (Agerite spar). Other antioxidants are nickel dithiocarbonate (NBC) and alkylaryl phosphites (Polygard). These additives are used in concentrations ranging from 0.2 to 1.0 percent based on the rubber present in the formulation.

The rate of oxidation is related to polymer structure. Linear saturated polyhydrocarbons, such as high-density polyethylene, are notably resistant to oxidation. The crystalline areas are much more resistant than the amorphous regions. Branched polyethylene (low-density polyethylene) is more readily oxidized than the linear polymer. Polypropylene, which has a pendant methyl group on every other carbon atom in the chain, is more susceptible to oxidation than polyethylene. Unsaturated polymers such as natural rubber are readily oxidized.

In the absence of antioxidants, chain branching and crosslinking may occur at the active centers (R·). When antioxidants (AH) are present, chain transfer takes place, and this hydrogen abstraction is the rate-controlling step:

$$\text{ROO}\cdot \; + \; \text{AH} \longrightarrow \text{ROOH} \; + \; \text{A}\cdot$$
$$\text{R}\cdot \; + \; \text{AH} \longrightarrow \text{RH} \; + \; \text{A}\cdot \tag{11-4}$$

Equations showing chain transfer with an antioxidant (AH)

When the antioxidant is a hindered phenol, the free radical formed (A·) is resonance-stabilized and does not propagate. Chain transfer with a hindered phenol is shown below:

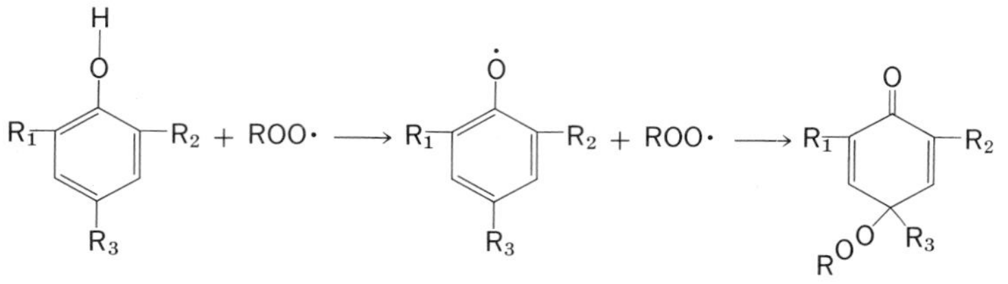

Equation showing chain transfer with a hindered phenol

In the absence of an antioxidant, the degradative reaction may be terminated by the coupling of two peroxy radicals. When an antioxidant is present, its free radical (A·) may couple with itself or with a peroxy free radical to form stable products, as shown:

$$\text{ROO·} + \text{·OOR} \longrightarrow \text{stable products}$$
$$\text{ROO·} + \text{·A} \longrightarrow \text{ROOA} \tag{11-6}$$
$$\text{A·} + \text{·A} \longrightarrow \text{AA}$$

Equations showing termination of free radical from an antioxidant

Elemental sulfur or sulfur compounds, such as disulfides or thiodipropionates, may deactivate hydroperoxides and form stable products. When two different types of antioxidants are present, the stabilization effect is generally greater than the sum of the effects of the individual stabilizers. This *synergistic effect* may also be observed in compounds having more than one active stabilizing group. The most effective synergists are those that depend on different mechanisms for their stabilizing effect.

The effect of antioxidants may be demonstrated by processing polymers in the presence or absence of these stabilizers at temperatures somewhat higher than the usual processing temperatures. Thus the average molecular weight of polypropylene was reduced from 273,000 to 112,000 when it was injection-molded at 550°F. However, the molecular weight was reduced only to 221,000 when 0.2 percent 2,6-di-*tert*-butyl-4-methylphenol was present. Over 5 million pounds of antioxidants were used by the American polymer industry in 1967.

Similar degradative reactions occur when various substituted polymeric hydrocarbons are oxidized. However, in some instances, such as the degradation of poly(vinyl chloride) or poly(vinylidene chloride), other mechanisms such as dehydrochlorination may obscure the previously discussed oxidation reaction. Poly(vinyl chloride) is a branched molecule with about 20 branches on each chain. It may also contain an unsaturated end group. Specially prepared linear polymers and chlorinated poly(vinyl chloride) are more stable than general-purpose poly(vinyl chloride).

The chlorine atoms at the branch positions and adjacent to the vinyl end group are labile and are readily removed as hydrogen chloride. The initial dehydrohalogenation is accelerated in the presence of iron or iron salts, oxygen, or hydrogen chloride. The chlorine in the allyl chloride group that results from the initial dehydrohalogenation is extremely labile. Hence, more hydrogen chloride is lost rapidly in a "zipper-type" reaction.

The residual polyene structure is chromophoric and discolors from colorless to yellow, orange, and red to black. Both ionic and free-radical reactions occur in the degradation. Hence, a synergistic stabilizing system which retards both reactions must be used. Thus the stabilized system should contain an antioxidant, such as a hindered phenol, and an acid acceptor, such as lead stearate, which will form an insoluble salt.

Lead salts may be used as scavengers of hydrogen chloride in opaque systems such as wire insulation, but they are considered too toxic for applications such as for potable-water piping. Transparent film is obtained when lead orthosilicate is used or when silica gel is added to lead soaps. Other metal salts, such as barium and calcium stearates, are generally used as mixtures. Mixtures of magnesium and calcium stearates are approved by the U.S. Food and Drug Administration for use as stabilizers in poly(vinyl chloride). This type of stabilizer is satisfactory for the blow molding of bottles from the copolymer of vinyl chloride and propylene. However, lead compounds are required for processing poly(vinyl chloride).

Epoxidized soybean oil which may react with hydrogen chloride is also used in conjunction with metal soaps. Other stabilizers are mercaptoamides, mercaptobenzothiazole, dithiocarbamates, and organotin mercaptides. The latter are free-radical chain terminators. It is customary to use as much as 2 percent of these stabilizers based on the amount of vinyl polymer present in the formulation.

The fact that antioxidants, such as phenyl-β-naphthylamine, may be extracted from rubber tubing has been the subject of many publications, and several doctoral theses suggest that nonpolymer scientists should receive some instruction in polymer chemistry. This specific antioxidant has been said to be synthesized by bacteria, to be present in the kidneys of rats, and to be present in many chemically pure (cp) solvents (siphoned through rubber tubing).

REFERENCES

Barnhart, R. R., and T. H. Newby: Antioxidants and Antiozonants, in M. Morton (ed.), "Introduction to Rubber Technology," chap. 6, Reinhold Publishing Corporation, New York, 1964.

Brown, B. S.: Antioxidants from Rubber Tubing Synthesized by Bacteria, *Chemistry in Britain*, p. 524, 1967.

Cohen, S.: Stabilizers, in "Modern Plastics Encyclopedia," McGraw-Hill Book Company, New York, 1966.

Cole, J. O.: Antioxidants, in C. S. Whitby, C. C. Davis, and R. F. Dunbrook (eds.), "Synthetic Rubber," chap. 13, John Wiley & Sons, Inc., New York, 1954.

Grassie, N.: "Chemistry of High Polymer Degradation Processes," Interscience Publishers, Inc., New York, 1956.

Hawkins, W. L.: Mechanisms of Oxidation of Hydrocarbon Polymers, *Soc. Plastics Engrs., RETEC*, Stability of Plastics Preprints, Baltimore-Washington Sec., June 4, 5, 1964.

———: Oxidative Degradation of High Polymers, in C. F. H. Tipper (ed.), "Oxidation and Combustion Reviews," vol. I, Elsevier Publishing Company, Amsterdam, 1965.

Hotten, B. W.: Benzylurea Antioxidants, *Res. Results ACS*, 1967.

Ingold, K. U.: Antioxidants, *Chem. Rev.*, **61**:563 (1961).

Kelleher, P. G.: Thermal Oxidation of Thermoplastics, *ACS Div. Polymer Chem., Polymer Preprints*, **7**(1):344 (1966).

Lally, R. E., and F. J. Ihde: Vinyl Stabilizers, in H. R. Simonds and J. M. Church (eds.), "The Encyclopedia of Basic Materials for Plastics," Reinhold Publishing Corporation, New York, 1967.

Lundberg, W. O.: "Antioxidations and Antioxidants," vol. I, Interscience Publishers, Inc., New York, 1961.

Mack, G. P.: Stabilizers, in G. L. Clark and G. G. Hawley (eds.), "Encyclopedia of Chemistry, 2d ed., Reinhold Publishing Corporation, New York, 1966.

Madorsky, S. L.: "Thermal Degradation of Organic Polymers," Interscience Publishers, a division of John Wiley & Sons, Inc., New York, 1964.

Mark, H. F.: Additives, in H. R. Simonds and J. M. Church (eds.), "The Encyclopedia of Basic Materials for Plastics," Reinhold Publishing Corporation, New York, 1967.

———: Principles of High Temperature Polymers, *Soc. Plastics Engrs., RETEC*, Stability of Plastics Preprints, Pt. A, Baltimore-Washington Section, Sept. 7, 1967.

Marshall, B. A.: Antioxidants, in "Modern Plastics Encyclopedia," p. 418, McGraw-Hill Book Company, New York, 1967.

Neiman, M. B.: "Aging and Stabilization of Polymers," Consultants Bureau, New York, 1965.

Robin, M.: Antioxidants, in H. R. Simonds and J. M. Church (eds.), "The Encyclopedia of Basic Materials for Plastics," Reinhold Publishing Corporation, New York, 1967.

Semon, W. L., and C. Dufraisse: Antioxidants, in C. C. Davis and J. T. Blake (eds.), "Chemistry and Technology of Rubber," chaps. 12, 15, Reinhold Publishing Corporation, New York, 1937.

Spacht, R. B.: Antioxidants, in G. L. Clark and G. G. Hawley (eds.), "Encyclopedia of Chemistry," 2d ed., Reinhold Publishing Corporation, New York, 1966.

Thacher, G. A.: Stabilizers, in "Modern Plastics Encyclopedia," p. 437, McGraw-Hill Book Company, New York, 1967.

11-4   ULTRAVIOLET STABILIZERS

Much of the radiation from outer space is absorbed by the atmosphere before it reaches the earth's surface.   Essentially all radiation below 280 nanometers (nm,mμ) and approximately 30 percent with longer wavelengths is absorbed. However, sufficient radiation in the 280 to 400-nm range reaches the earth's surface and affects many organic compounds.   This *ultraviolet radiation* causes yellowing and embrittlement of many organic polymers.

The energy in the 280 to 400-nm range (100 to 72 kcal) is sufficient to cleave covalent bonds.   Trace impurities present in commercial polymers may catalyze this degradation.   The rate of this deterioration may be retarded by the addition of stabilizers which absorb energy in the region of the spectrum at which the polymer is photosensitive.

Pigments have been used as ultraviolet absorbants in coatings, films, and articles made from elastomers or plastics.   Carbon black is particularly useful because, in addition to absorbing the radiation, it also supplies free radicals which form stable products by coupling with compounds produced in the degradative process.

The pioneer organic stabilizer was phenyl salicylate (salol).   This is not as effective as some of the more modern stabilizers but it meets many of the criteria for a sun screening agent and is used both in polymers and suntanning lotions.   It is now assumed that an effective ultraviolet stabilizer preferentially absorbs radiation in the 300- to 370-nm range and dissipates this energy slowly to the surroundings or remits this energy at less energetic, longer wavelengths.

These additives should be compatible, colorless, stable, nonvolatile, and nontoxic.   Since thermal degradation also occurs, antioxidants should also be present in stabilizer formulations.   This degradative process is related to the polymer structure.   Linear polymers are more resistant than branched chains, and the rate of deterioration is proportional to the surface area exposed.   Some carbonyl groups (1700 cm^{-1}) are usually detected by infrared spectrophotometry in all unexposed polymers.   The concentration of these groups increases during the ultraviolet irradiation of polymers.   The absorption by other groups at 1180 cm^{-1} (C=C) is also increased.

Volatile degradation products such as carbon monoxide, water, aldehydes, and ketones are also formed.   As shown by the following equations, decomposition of a linear polymeric hydrocarbon starts with the carbonyl group and may result in the products detected by infrared spectrophotometry, ESR, and mass spectrometry:

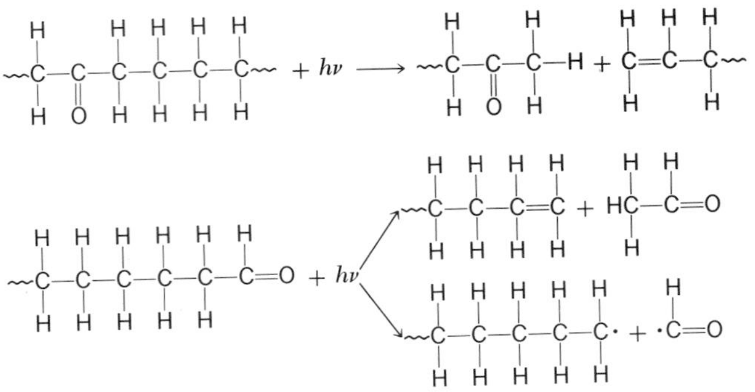

$$\sim\!\!\underset{\underset{H}{|}}{\overset{\overset{H}{|}}{C}}\!-\!\underset{\underset{O}{\parallel}}{\overset{\overset{H}{|}}{C}}\!-\!\underset{\underset{H}{|}}{\overset{\overset{H}{|}}{C}}\!-\!\underset{\underset{H}{|}}{\overset{\overset{H}{|}}{C}}\!-\!\underset{\underset{H}{|}}{\overset{\overset{H}{|}}{C}}\!-\!\underset{\underset{H}{|}}{\overset{\overset{H}{|}}{C}}\!\sim + h\nu \longrightarrow \sim\!\!\underset{\underset{H}{|}}{\overset{\overset{H}{|}}{C}}\!-\!\underset{\underset{O}{\parallel}}{C}\!-\!\underset{\underset{H}{|}}{\overset{\overset{H}{|}}{C}}\!-\!H + \underset{\underset{H}{|}}{\overset{\overset{H}{|}}{C}}\!=\!\underset{\underset{H}{|}}{C}\!-\!\underset{\underset{H}{|}}{\overset{\overset{H}{|}}{C}}\!\sim$$

$$(11\text{-}7)$$

Equations showing effect of ultraviolet irradiation
on linear polymers

Antioxidants, such as phenyl-β-naphthyl amine, may absorb radiation in the 1,700-cm^{-1} region. This magnitude of energy may produce many free radicals which may accelerate the degradation process. The proposed reactions are shown in the following equations:

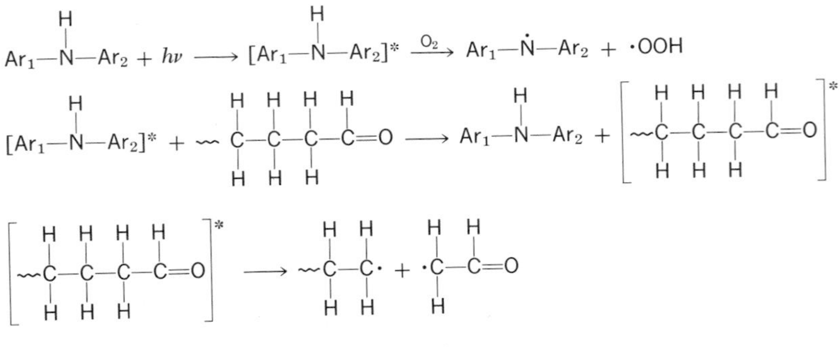

$$Ar_1\!-\!\underset{}{\overset{\overset{H}{|}}{N}}\!-\!Ar_2 + h\nu \longrightarrow [Ar_1\!-\!\overset{\overset{H}{|}}{N}\!-\!Ar_2]^* \xrightarrow{O_2} Ar_1\!-\!\overset{\overset{\cdot}{}}{N}\!-\!Ar_2 + \cdot OOH$$

$$[Ar_1\!-\!\overset{\overset{H}{|}}{N}\!-\!Ar_2]^* + \sim\!\!C\!-\!C\!-\!C\!-\!C\!=\!O \longrightarrow Ar_1\!-\!\overset{\overset{H}{|}}{N}\!-\!Ar_2 + \left[\sim\!\!C\!-\!C\!-\!C\!-\!C\!=\!O\right]^*$$

$$(11\text{-}8)$$

$$\left[\sim\!\!C\!-\!C\!-\!C\!-\!C\!=\!O\right]^* \longrightarrow \sim\!\!C\!-\!C\cdot + \cdot C\!-\!C\!=\!O$$

Proposed equations for oxidative processes in presence
of secondary amines

This intensification of photoxidation by amines is reduced when tertiary amines are used in place of secondary amines. These compounds lack labile hydrogen atoms and may undergo rearrangements in order to transfer absorbed energy.

Ultraviolet stabilizers such as 2,4-dihydroxybenzophenone (Usolvin P.S., Uvinul 400) absorb energy in the 300- to 400-nm range and form chelates in which the energy is distributed throughout the system. The transfer of energy may involve a quinoid form which results from a rearrangement as shown below.

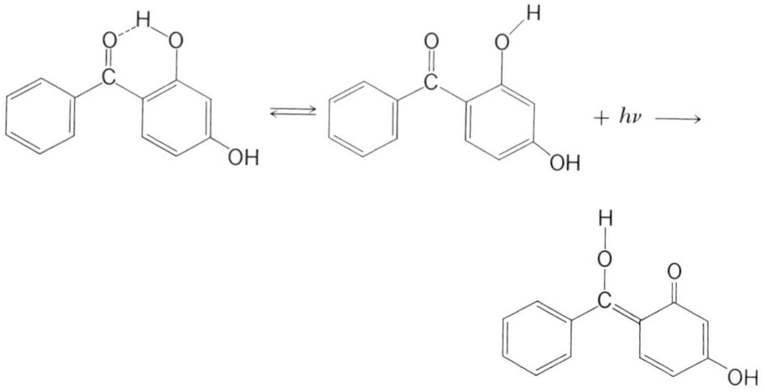

$$(11\text{-}9)$$

Proposed equation for energy transfer in 2,4-dihydroxybenzophenone

The efficiency of chelating-type stabilizers is related to the strength of the hydrogen bond between the hydroxyl hydrogen and the carbonyl oxygen atoms. This bond strength may be predicted from the magnitude of the nmr shift of the chelate proton. Although 2,4-dihydroxyacetophenone also forms a chelate, its absorbance is 30 percent less than the corresponding benzophenone derivative. The maximum absorbance is 328 nm for 2,4-dihydroxybenzophenone and 318 nm for the corresponding acetophenone derivative.

Other typical commercial benzophenone stabilizers are 2-hydroxy-4-methoxybenzophenone (Uvinul M40, Cyasorb UV9), 2-hydroxy-4-n-octoxybenzophenone (Cyasorb UV531), and 2-hydroxy-4-dodecyloxybenzophenone (DOBP). The compatibility with nonpolar polymers such as polyethylene is improved as the size of the alkoxy group increases. The trifluoromethyl derivative is less volatile than unsubstituted 2,4-dihydroxybenzophenone. 2,2'-Dihydroxy-4-methoxybenzophenone (Cyasorb UV24) may form two chelate rings, as shown below:

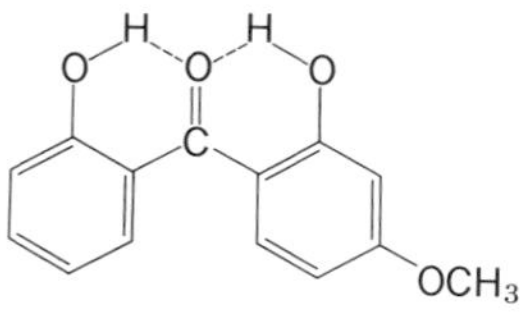

$$(11\text{-}10)$$

2,2'-Dihydroxy-4-methoxybenzophenone

The absorption of these highly conjugated compounds extends almost to the visible range. Hence some of these compounds are yellow.

4-Hydroxybenzophenone and alkylated or acylated 2-hydroxybenzo-phenone are ineffective as ultraviolet stabilizers since chelation cannot occur. It is also essential that the phenyl groups be planar to assure the formation of stable chelates. Bulky groups in the ortho position decrease the stability effect because of steric distortions of the planar rings.

Resorcinol monobenzoate (RMB) is called a pseudostabilizer. It does not absorb much radiation in the ultraviolet range initially but does rearrange to 2,4-dihydroxybenzophenone, as shown below:

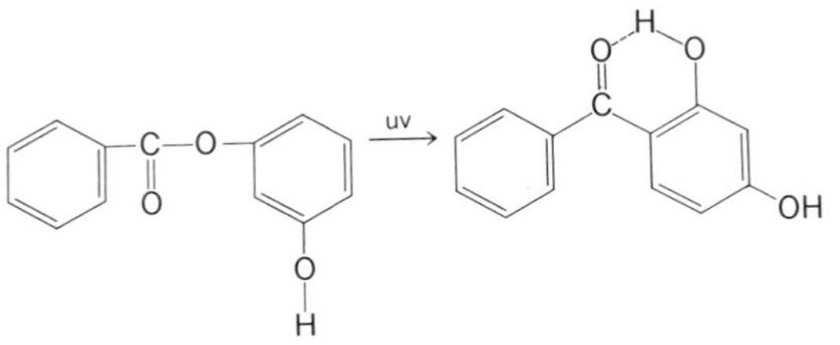

(11-11)

Rearrangement of resorcinol monobenzoate

As shown in the following equation, salicylates, such as *p*-octylphenyl salicylate (OPS), may form chelates with an initial absorbance of about 50 percent of that of 2,4-dihydroxybenzophenone and at a shorter wavelength (315 nm). However, as shown below, this ester may rearrange to form a dihydroxybenzophenone.

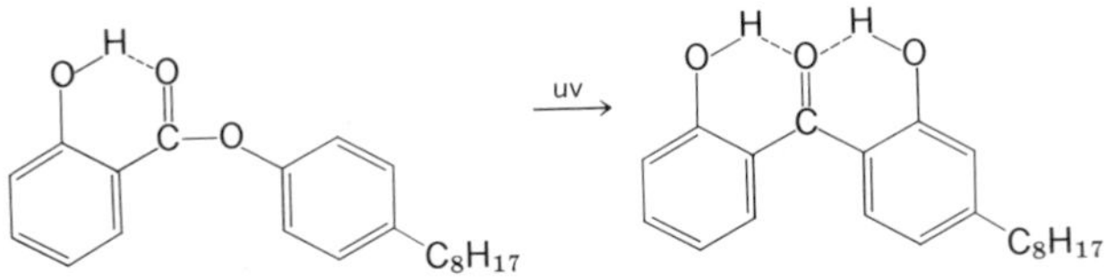

(11-12)

Rearrangement of *p*-octylphenyl salicylate

The alkyl salicylates, such as 2-ethylhexyl salicylate, may chelate but cannot rearrange to benzophenones. Hence they are less effective stabilizers than phenyl salicylates.

Benzotriazoles such as 2(2′-hydroxy-5-methyl-phenyl) benzotriazole (Tinuvin P, Usolvin VS) absorb at 300 nm. As shown by the structural formula for 2-(hydroxyphenyl) benzotriazole, this type of stabilizer forms a chelate.

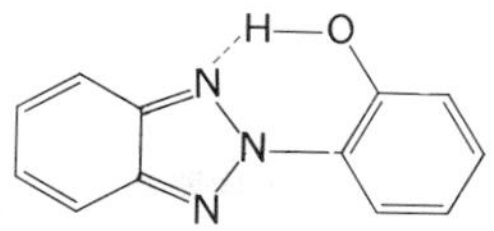

(11-13)

2-(Hydroxyphenyl) benzotriazole

The effectiveness of this additive is decreased when the hydroxyl group is in the p position or when it is alkylated since these structures cannot chelate.

Substituted acrylonitriles such as ethyl-2-cyano-3,8-diphenyl acrylate (Usolvin VSC, Uvinul N-35), hexamethyl phosphoric triamide, 2,2'-thio-bis(alkylphenol), and nickel chelates have also been used as ultraviolet stabilizers. The latter probably serve as free-radical traps. The formulas for these compounds are shown below:

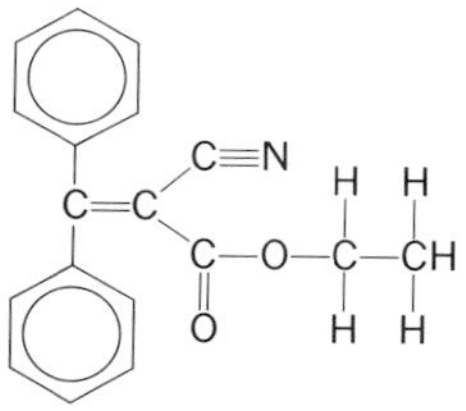

$$[(CH_3)_2N]_3 \, P{=}O$$

Hexamethyl phosphoric triamide

(11-14)

Ethyl-2-cyano-3,3-diphenyl acrylate   2,2'-Thiobis(alkylphenol)–nickel chelate

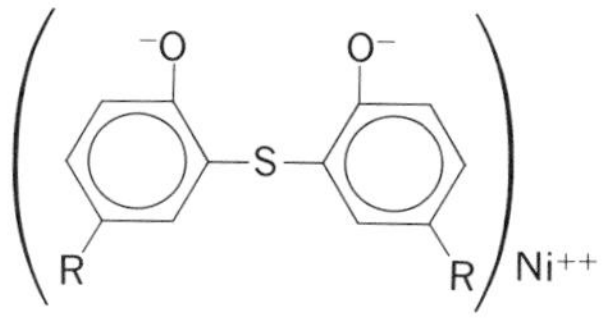

Structural formulas for some ultraviolet stabilizers

The concentration of ultraviolet-light stabilizers in stabilizer formulations ranges from 0.2 to 1.5 percent. Stabilizer efficiency may be determined by measuring the change in flexibility of films, the change in absorbance of the carbonyl bond, the rate of oxygen uptake, and the depth of color formation with N,N-dimethyl-p-phenylene diamine. Over 175 million pounds of these stabilizers are used annually by the polymer industry in the United States.

REFERENCES

Bellus, D., and P. Hrdlovic: Photochemical Rearrangements, *Chem. Rev.*, **67**(6):599 (1967).

Burgess, A. K.: Polymer Degradation Mechanisms, *Natl. Bur. St.* (U.S.), *Cir.* 525, 1953.

Calvert, J. G., and J. N. Pitts: "Photochemistry," John Wiley & Sons, Inc., New York, 1966.

Chaudet, J. H., G. C. Newland, H. W. Patton, and J. W. Tamblyn: U.V. Stabilization, *SPE Trans.*, **1**(1):26 (1961).

Cipriani, L. P., and J. F. Hosler: in "Modern Plastics Encyclopedia," p. 406, McGraw-Hill Book Company, 1967.

Gordon, D. A.: U.V. Absorbers, in H. R. Simonds and J. M. Church (eds.), "Encyclopedia of Basic Materials for Plastics," Reinhold Publishing Corporation, New York, 1967.

Gray, V. E., and J. R. Wright: Measurements of Photodegradation by Color Reactions, *ACS Div. Org. Coatings and Plastics Chem., Preprints*, **25**(2):125 (1965).

Heskins, M., and J. E. Guillet: Mechanisms for U.V. Stabilizers, *Macromolecules*, **1**(1):97 (1968).

Hill, H. E.: "Benzophenone Stabilizers," *Offic. Dig., Fed. Soc. Paint Technol.*, **36**:64 (1964).

Kan, R. O.: "Organic Photochemistry," McGraw-Hill Book Company, New York, 1966.

Koller, L. R.: "U.V. Radiation," 2d ed., John Wiley & Sons, Inc., New York, 1965.

Mack, G. P.: Stabilizers, in G. L. Clark and G. G. Hawley (eds.), "Encyclopedia of Chemistry," Reinhold Publishing Corporation, New York, 1966.

Modern Plastics, U.V. Stabilizers, **45**(1):194 (1967).

Neiman, M. B.: "Aging and Stabilization of Polymers," Consultants Bureau, New York, 1965.

Reinisch, R. F., H. R. Gloria, and D. E. Wilson: Photodegradation in Vacuum, *ACS Div. Polymer Chem., Polymer Preprints*, **7**(1):372 (1966).

Seymour, R. B.: Additives, *Plastics World*, **22**(11):60 (1964).

————: Plastics vs. Outdoor Service, *Plastics World*, **22**(6):48 (1964).

————, H. S. Tsang, and D. Warren; U.V. Stabilizers, *Polymer Eng. Sci.*, **7**(1):55 (1967).

Trozzolo, A. M., and F. H. Winslow: Mechanisms for Oxidative Photolysis, *Macromolecules*, **1**(1):98 (1968).

Weicksel, J. A.: U.V. Absorbers, in G. L. Clark and G. G. Hawley (eds.), "Encyclopedia of Chemistry," Reinhold Publishing Corporation, New York, 1966.

————: U.V. Absorbers, in H. R. Simonds and J. M. Church (eds.), "The Encyclopedia of Basic Materials for Plastics," Reinhold Publishing Corporation, New York, 1967.

Winslow, F. H., W. Matreyek, and S. M. Stills: Thermal vs. Photoxidation of Polyethylene, *ACS Div. Polymer Chem., Polymer Preprints*, **7**(1):390 (1966).

11-5 COLORANTS AND OTHER ADDITIVES

Engineering plastics are often used as working parts of various machines and are not readily observable; hence appearance is unimportant. Some transparent polymers, such as poly(methyl methacrylate), are often used without colors. However, some polymers are dark and opaque; hence it is customary to add colorants. Polar groups must be present on the polymer molecule to assure permanence of color when dyes are used.

Elastomers are usually reinforced by carbon black, and this filler serves as a pigment. Carbon black is used as the pigment for many plastics. Titanium dioxide is a white pigment which is used to a greater extent than other pigments. Its use in white-wall tires is well known. In addition to producing white-colored plastics, it also serves to opacify dark plastics. Various shades of color may be obtained when other pigments are added.

Pigments are crystalline in shape. Titanium dioxide may have an anatase or rutile form. Zinc oxide may be nodular or accicular (needle-shaped) and a few pigments, like aluminum flake, are classified as laminar (leaflike). The particle-size distribution plots of pigments show a range of 0.2 to 0.4 mμ but some particles may be as large as 25 mμ. Synthetic pigments have a more uniform size distribution than the naturally occurring materials. The surface area is important and may be measured by the Brunauer-Emmett-Teller (BET) Technique.

Pigments are insoluble, colored materials and may be inorganic or organic compounds. The former include chromates (yellow), ferrocyanides (blue), sulfides, oxides, and silicates. Aluminum silicate colors range from red to blue. Those based on iron oxide range from yellow-red-brown to black. Many color modifications are possible by coprecipitation of various metallic salts.

The organic colorants include the phthalocyanines, which range from blue to green. Another important color is 6-chloro-4-toluidine-3-sulfonic acid (Permanent Red 23). Quinacridine colors are also used alone and as blends with inorganic pigments.

Pigments may be dry-mixed with comminuted polymers for extrusion and for injection molding when a reciprocating screw is used. In other cases, a master batch (concentrate) is made by mixing the pigment and polymer in a Banbury mixer or on a two-roll mill. In all cases it is essential that the pigment be in a well-dispersed state and wet by the polymer. When wetting is complete, the contact angle is zero. However, this is an ideal case, and the degree of wetting is evaluated on the basis of the magnitude of this angle.

Organic dyes are usually more compatible with polymers than pigments. They may be used to provide transparent colors. When opaqueness is required, titanium dioxide is added to these dyes. The principal noncarbon pigment is titanium dioxide. The principal dye is Nigrosine black dye. Over 100 million pounds of colorants are used annually by the plastics industry in the United States.

The characteristic combustibility of cotton fibers and wood restricted the use of these materials even when few competitive substitutes were available. Both have been made flame-resistant by the addition of inorganic salts, such as zinc chloride, ammonium sulfate, ammonium phosphate, and borax. Some polymers, such as poly(vinyl chloride), polyacrylonitrile, and polytetrafluoroethylene, are inherently flame-resistant. However, polymers such as polyethylene, polybutadiene, and polystyrene are combustible, and flame retardants must be added when these products are used in construction, etc.

Combustion is believed to be a free-radical process; hence chain transfer agents must be present to terminate this reaction. Labile atoms are present in poly(vinyl chloride); hence free radicals are readily produced but compounds with labile atoms must be incorporated in many other polymers to achieve comparable flame resistance.

Flame retardants may be internal or external. Internal flame retardants may be incorporated in combustible polymers by using chlorine-, bromine-, or phosphorus-containing reactants. For example, polyesters produced from chlorendic anhydride (HET anhydride), tetrabromophthalic anhydride (Firemaster DHT4), or phosphate polyols (PXV-112) and epoxy resins produced from tetrabromobisphenol A (Firemaster BP4A) contain internal flame retardants.

External flame retardants such as chlorinated paraffins (Chlorowax), chlorinated biphenyls (Arochlor), zinc borate, chlorinated naphthalene (Halowax), tricresyl phosphate, or antimony oxide may be added to combustible polymers to produce flame-resistant products. Over 125 million pounds of flame retardants are used annually by the plastics industry in the United States.

Most plastics are nonconductors and may have a surface resistance as high as 10^{20} ohms/cm^2. These materials readily acquire electrostatic charges and retain these charges indefinitely. Static charges are generated in almost all phases of polymer processing and fabrication. Unless these charges are reduced below 10^{13} ohms/cm^2, dust and other fine particles will be attracted to the polymer surface.

Some reduction in surface charge occurs when static bars are held close to plastic film while it is placed on rolls. The polymer surface may also be treated with hydroscopic materials such as ethoxylated amines and amides or ethylene oxide adducts. Some antistatic agents such as N,N-bis(2-hydroxyethyl)alkyl(C_{14}—C_{18}) amines have been approved by the U.S. Food and Drug Administration.

The handling of plastics is hindered by static which may cause fire or explosions. The efficiency of antistatic agents may be determined by measuring the electrostatic charge or by using crude empirical tests such as the ash-tray and dust-chamber tests. The former measures the attraction of ashes to a plastic surface. In the latter, toluene-soaked filter paper is burned in a chamber, and the amount of soot deposited on the plastic surface is measured. Approximately 2 million pounds of antistatic agents are used annually.

Organic peroxides may also be added to polymers, such as polyethylene, in order to crosslink this thermoplastic after it is molded or extruded. As stated in Chap. 5, these compounds are used as initiators in chain-reaction polymerization. The principal products are benzoyl peroxide and lauroyl peroxide. Over 15 million pounds of organic peroxides are used annually.

Organic accelerators are added to rubber to promote the vulcanization of elastomers. The pioneer accelerator was thiocarbanilide which was discovered by Oenslager in 1912. This solid was used to replace the toxic aniline which he had introduced previously.

The structural formulas for the principal types of accelerators are shown below.

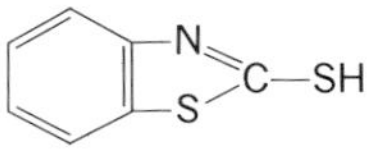

2-Mercaptobenzothiazole
(Captax)

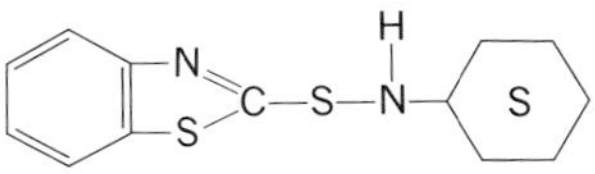

2-Mercaptobenzothiazole sulfenamide
(Santocure)

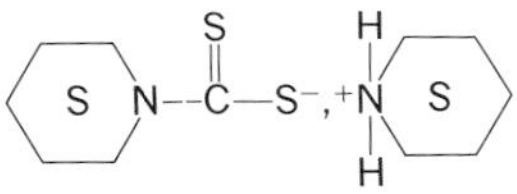

Piperidinium pentamethylene
dithiocarbamate (pip-pip)

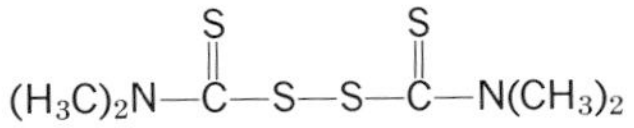

Tetramethyl thiuram disulfide
(Tuads)

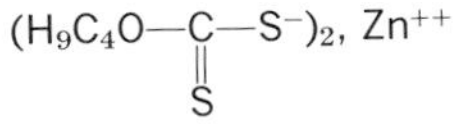

$(H_9C_4O-C-S^-)_2$, Zn^{++}

Zinc butyl xanthate

$(11\text{-}15)$

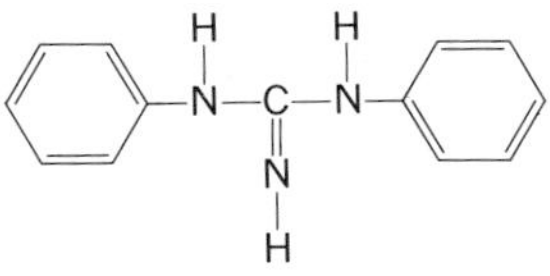

Diphenylguanidine
Structural formulas for typical commercial accelerators

Approximately 1 percent of organic accelerator is used for 100 parts of rubber. Over 50 million pounds of these products are used annually in the United States.

Polymers with inherent lubricity, like polytetrafluoroethylene, have little tendency to adhere to equipment during processing. However, lubricants or slip agents must be added to many polymers to prevent them from sticking to spinnerets, molds, etc. Thus it is customary to add surfactants such as stearic acid salts, or amides, to polymers before processing. These additives, which are used in small amounts (0.05 to 0.5 percent), usually migrate to the polymer surface and actually improve surface characteristics. When these additives are used in film production, they are called *antiblock agents*. Some special forms of fillers such as silica or calcium carbonate also act as antiblock agents.

REFERENCES

Bartoe, W. F.: Antistatic Agents, in "Modern Plastics Encyclopedia," McGraw-Hill Book Company, New York, 1966.

Baseman, A. L.: Colorants, *Plastics Technol.*, **13**(1):31 (1967).

Benzing, E. P.: Flame Retardants, in H. R. Simonds and J. M. Church (eds.), "The Encyclopedia of Basic Materials for Plastics," Reinhold Publishing Corporation, New York, 1967.

Davis, R. R.: Antistatic Ratings, *Mod. Packaging*, **37**(6):119 (1964).

DiPietro, J.: Flammability Characteristics of Plastics, *ACS Div. Org. Coatings and Plastics, Preprints*, **28**(1):185 (1968).

Doyle, D. J.: Static Buildup, *Plastics World*, **22**(10):26 (1964).

Fisher, H. L.: Accelerators, "Chemistry of Natural and Synthetic Rubber," chap. 3, Reinhold Publishing Corporation, New York, 1957.

Garvey, B. S.: Accelerators, in M. Morton (ed.), "Introduction to Rubber Technology," chap. 5, Reinhold Publishing Corporation, New York, 1959.

Gregg, S. J.: "The Surface Chemistry of Solids," 2d ed., Chapman & Hall, Ltd., London, 1961.

Hilado, C. J.: Flammability of Cellular Plastics, *Ind. Eng. Chem., Prod. Res. Develop.*, **6**(3):154 (1967).

————: Flammability Tests of Cellular Polymers, *ACS Div. Org. Coatings and Plastics, Preprints*, **28**(1):265 (1968).

Irani, R. R., and C. F. Callis: "Particle Size, Measurements, Interpretation, and Application," John Wiley & Sons, Inc., New York, 1963.

Kresser, T. O. J.: Antiblock and Slip Agents, in H. R. Simonds and J. M. Church (eds.), "The Encyclopedia of Basic Materials for Plastics," Reinhold Publishing Corporation, New York, 1967.

Kurtz, J. H.: Antistatic Agents, in H. R. Simonds and J. M. Church (eds.), "The Encyclopedia of Basic Materials for Plastics," Reinhold Publishing Corporation, New York, 1967.

Marks, M. E.: Organic Peroxides, in "Modern Plastics Encyclopedia," McGraw-Hill Book Company, New York, 1967.

Martinelli, G. A.: Dyes and Pigments, in H. R. Simonds and J. M. Church (eds.), "The Encyclopedia of Basic Materials for Plastics," Reinhold Publishing Corporation, New York, 1967.

Modern Plastics, Flame Retardants, **45**(1):92 (1967).

Orr, C., and J. M. Dallavalle: "Fine Particle Measurements," The Macmillan Company, New York, 1959.

Nametz, R. C.: Flame Retardants for Polyesters, *Ind. Eng. Chem.*, **59**(5):99 (1967).

Seymour, R. B.: Colorants, in G. L. Clark and G. G. Hawley (eds.), "Encyclopedia of Chemistry," Reinhold Publishing Corporation, New York, 1966.

———: Flame Retardants, in G. L. Clark and G. G. Hawley (eds.), "Encyclopedia of Chemistry," Reinhold Publishing Corporation, New York, 1966.

Simpson, J. E.: Colorants, in "Modern Plastics Encyclopedia," McGraw-Hill Book Company, New York, 1967.

———: Colorants for Thermosets, *Mod. Plastics*, **40**(10):89 (1963).

Spengeman, W. F.: Coloration of Plastics, in H. R. Simonds and J. M. Church (eds.), "The Encyclopedia of Basic Materials for Plastics," Reinhold Publishing Corporation, New York, 1967.

Story, W. S.: Colorants, in "Modern Plastics Encyclopedia," McGraw-Hill Book Company, New York, 1968.

Woernle, A. K: Iron Oxide Pigments, in H. R. Simonds and J. M. Church (eds.), "The Encyclopedia of Basic Materials for Plastics," Reinhold Publishing Company, New York, 1967.

12

Characterization of Polymers

Electromagnetic radiation from all regions of the spectrum may be absorbed by polymers and, in many cases, this absorption may be recorded by appropriate commercial instruments. Cosmic and gamma rays with wavelengths of less than 1 Å are highly energic and are usually considered too destructive for routine characterizations. However, x-ray (1 to 100 Å) and ultraviolet (136 to 3900 Å) radiation has been used for the structural studies of polymers.

Visible light (3900 to 7700 Å), which comprises but a very small portion of the spectrum, has limited use for characterizations. However, infrared radiation (7700 to 4×10^6 Å) is extremely useful in spectroscopy, and low-energy microwaves are used as an energy source in nuclear magnetic resonance spectroscopy. Chromatography, which depends on the selective absorption of molecules, is particularly useful in the characterization of polymers and their degradative products.

12-1 CHARACTERIZATION IN VISIBLE AND ULTRAVIOLET LIGHT

Polymers, like other materials, may be characterized subjectively by visual inspection. Certainly, neither instrumentation nor recorders are required to differentiate between the highly transparent poly(methyl methacrylate) and dark-colored phenolic resins. Similarly, observable differences in water solubility may be used to differentiate between polystyrene and poly(vinyl alcohol). However, more objective tests are essential, and many acceptable characterization techniques have been developed. More objective methods will be available as the understanding of polymer structure increases.

Since many polymers are anisotropic, *pleochromism* is characteristic and may be employed as a useful or a typical phenomenon for characterization of polymers. In some instances, the degree of crystallinity may be estimated from visual inspection of the relative transparency. For example, the *transparent point* has been defined as the temperature at which opacity develops as a clear film is cooled.

Considerable information on polymer structure may also be obtained by chemical tests. For example, pioneer investigations by Harries, Marvel, and Flory provided considerable information on diene structures and the configurations of vinyl polymers.

Harries used ozonolysis to show a 1,4 structure in *Hevea braziliensis* rubber and gutta-percha. Since the rate of reaction of perbenzoic acid with 1,4 structures is 25 times faster than with 1,2 structures, Marvel used this technique to confirm Harries' observations.

Flory showed that the amount of chlorine removed by heating poly-(vinyl chloride) with zinc corresponded to a head-to-tail structure. Marvel used reagents such as periodic acid and lead tetraacetate, which are specific for 1,2 glycols, to show a head-to-tail structure in poly(vinyl alcohol). However, Flory showed that a decrease in viscosity occurred during these reactions and hence suggested that a small amount of head-to-head arrangement was present. Those interested in other chemical tests for polymers should consult the text by Haslam and Willis.

Much information on crystalline polymers may also be obtained by electron microscopy which magnifies the specimen as viewed by the naked eye by as much as 20,000 times. For example, Holland and Lindenmeyer used electron microscopy to study the rate of growth of polymer crystals. These investigators quenched crystallizing solutions at intervals and deposited them on a carbon grid shadowed with platinum. A fine beam of electrons was then focused on these single crystals. Thicker sections were examined by observing the boundaries resulting from cleavages induced by ultrasonic irradiation or extremely low temperatures.

Information on polymer structure may also be obtained by the determination of *index of refraction*. The velocity of light varies with direction in anisotropic substances. Hence, measurements of the index of refraction (refractometry) are important in the investigation of crystalline polymers. Thus the degree of crystallinity may be estimated from the birefringence observed when polymer specimens are viewed under crossed polaroids in a polarizing microscope. The spherulites present appear as dark Maltese crosses in which the arms are parallel and perpendicular to the direction of polarization.

The general use of refractive index for the characterization of polymers is based on Snell's law which shows the relationship of the ratio of refractive indices of two substances (n_1 and n_2) and the ratio of the sines of the incident (i_1) and refracted rays (r_2):

$$\frac{n_2}{n_1} = \frac{\sin i_1}{\sin r_2} \tag{12-1}$$

Snell's law

The characteristic *molar refraction* (MR) or unit refractivity of any polymer may be calculated from the Lorentz-Lorenz equation in which the molecular weight M is that of the mer and the density d is that of the polymer. The molar refraction MR is the summation of the indices of refractions of all the constituents in the polymer molecule. The molar refraction as derived in Eq. (12-2) and other relationships of index of refraction and density have been used to characterize polymers.

$$\mathrm{MR} = \frac{n^2 - 1}{n^2 + 2} \frac{M}{d} \tag{12-2}$$

Lorentz-Lorenz equation

The index of refraction, like density, changes as the shape of the molecule changes; hence under controlled conditions it may be used to estimate the degree of branching in a polymer. As discussed in Chap. 1, the degree of crystallinity of polymers is related to density values. The indices of refraction, densities, and molar refractions of typical polymers are shown in Table 12-1.

Table 12-1 Index of Refraction and Density of Typical Polymers

POLYMER	INDEX OF REFRACTION n	DENSITY d	MOLAR REFRACTION MR
Polyacetal	1.48	1.425	8.6
Polyethylene (low density)	1.51	0.92	11
Poly(methyl methacrylate)	1.49	1.18	24
Nylon 6,6	1.53	1.14	62
Polypropylene	1.49	0.90	17
Polystyrene	1.59	1.06	33
Polytetrafluoroethylene	1.35	2.16	4.2
Poly(vinyl chloride)	1.53	1.40	14

Photometric analysis is based on the measurement of light intensities at characteristic wavelengths. The visual and ultraviolet regions are 3900 to 7700 Å and 136 to 3900 Å, respectively. Light absorbed in the visible or ultraviolet regions causes many types of energy changes but the most useful is the energy involved in electronic transitions related to the excitation of electrons. The record of the relative number of photons absorbed is called the *absorption spectrum*.

These characteristic spectra which consist of a series of maxima and minima may be characterized by the wavelength λ or the frequency v of light but it is more convenient to use *wave numbers* $\bar{v}$. As shown by the following equations, the wave number $\bar{v}$ is the frequency v divided by the wave velocity of light (c) $(3 \times 10^{10}$ cm/sec). The frequency is also equal to the energy of light (E) divided by Planck's constant $(h = 6.62 \times 10^{-27}$ erg-sec)

$$\lambda = \frac{c}{v} \tag{12-3}$$

$$\frac{1}{\lambda} = \frac{v}{c} = \bar{v} \tag{12-4}$$

$$v = \frac{E}{h} \tag{12-5}$$

Relationships of wavelength, frequency, and energy of light

A mole of photons has energy values of 71 to 36 kcal in the visible range (3900 to 7700 Å) and higher values in the ultraviolet region. Spectrophotometric measurements are usually reported quantitatively and may be interpreted by means of the Beer-Lambert law shown in Eq. (12-6). This law states that the logarithm of the ratio of the intensity of incident light (I_0) to that of transmitted light (I) is proportional to the concentration (c) and thickness (l) of the specimen. The proportionality constant is the molar absorption coefficient (ε) divided by 2.303.

$$\log \frac{I_0}{I} = \frac{\varepsilon c l}{2.303} \tag{12-6}$$

Beer-Lambert law

The π electrons in chromophores, such as C=C, C=O, and C≡N, are readily excited to higher orbitals (π^*). Hence polymers with chromophoric groups have high absorption maxima in the vacuum ultraviolet range $(<2000$ Å). Auxochromes which are electron donors, such as alkyl, hydroxyl, alkoxyl, or amino groups, shift the absorption to longer wavelengths. This *bathochromic shift* is also evident with conjugated double bonds. In contrast, electron acceptors shift the absorption of chromophores to shorter wavelengths.

The wavelengths and intensities of ultraviolet and visible spectra may be determined with a high degree of precision. The shift of polyenes from isolated to conjugated bonds may be followed by observing changes by ultraviolet spectrophotometry. These techniques are not of general interest for the characterizations of macromolecules. However, absorption in the infrared region excites the molecules to higher rotational and vibrational energy levels, and these data may be used to characterize polymer molecules and to show differences in molecular structure.

REFERENCES

Berl, W. G.: "Physical Methods in Chemical Analysis," Academic Press, Inc., New York, 1960.

Chamot, E. M., and C. W. Mason: "Handbook of Chemical Microscopy," John Wiley & Sons, Inc., New York, 1950.

Forziati, A. F.: Optical Methods, in G. M. Kline (ed.), "Analytical Chemistry of Polymers," Pt. II, chap. 111, Interscience Publishers, a division of John Wiley & Sons, Inc., New York, 1962.

Gibb, T. R. P.: "Optical Methods of Chemical Analysis," McGraw-Hill Book Company, New York, 1942.

Hall, C. E.: "Introduction to Electron Microscopy," 2d ed., McGraw-Hill Book Company, New York, 1966.

Haslam, J., and H. A. Willis: "Identification and Analysis of Plastics," D. Van Nostrand Company, Inc., Princeton, N.J., 1965.

Lawson, D. R.: "The Technique of Photomicrography," George Newnes, London, 1960.

Seymour, R. B.: Characterization of Polymers by Index of Refraction and Density Measurements, *Plastics World*, **20**(11):16 (1962).

Stein, R. S., M. B. Rhodes, et al.: Light Scattering from Fibers, *ACS Div. Polymer Chem.*, *Polymer Preprints*, **6**(1):90 (1965).

Tryon, M., and E. Horowitz: Ultraviolet Spectrophotometry, in G. M. Kline (ed.), "Analytical Chemistry of Polymers," Pt. 2, chap. 7, Interscience Publishers, Inc., 1961.

12-2 INFRARED SPECTROSCOPY

In addition to other motions, the absorption of radiation at wave numbers of 4000 to 660 cm^{-1} (2.5 to 15μ) also causes stretching and vibrations of bonds in polymer molecules. The motions for any specific functional group are essentially independent of the rest of the molecule and comparable to those observed for low-molecular-weight compounds with similar structures (model compounds). The characteristic band frequencies are related to degrees of freedom which are distributed as rotational, translational, and vibrational motions. These motions are related to the number of atoms in simple molecules and to the number of atoms in the mer or repeating unit in a polymer molecule.

Thus a polymer such as polystyrene may be considered to be similar to a molecule with 16 atoms:

$$
\begin{array}{c}
\quad \text{H} \quad \text{H} \\
\quad | \quad | \\
-\text{C}-\text{C}- \\
\quad | \quad | \\
\quad \text{H} \quad \text{C}_6\text{H}_5
\end{array}
$$

Since it has no symmetry, all vibrations are active, i.e., 3 degrees of rotational freedom, 3 degrees of translational freedom, and 42 degrees of vibrational freedom $(3n - 6)$. As in the case of simpler molecules, these motions are characteristic of the groups present, and a sufficient number of band frequencies may be readily observed to assure proper identification of this polymer.

The infrared spectrum of polystyrene shown in Fig. 12-1 is used as a standard for the calibration of infrared spectrophotometers. This spectrum shows typical C—H stretching vibrations at 3.3, 3.4, and 3.5 μ; C—C stretching vibrations are shown at 6.2 and 6.7 μ; and out-of-plane bending of the C—H bonds in the benzene rings may be observed at 11.0 and 14.3 μ. The bands at 8.7 and 9.7 μ are said to be in the "fingerprint" region. These are characteristic of polystyrene but their origin is not readily determined.

Absorption bands for typical functional groups are shown in Table 12-2. The absorption bands for carbon-chlorine, nitrile, hydroxyl, and carbonyl may be used to identify polymers containing these functional groups. The

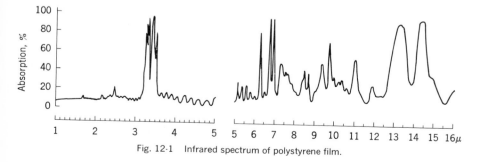

Fig. 12-1   Infrared spectrum of polystyrene film.

Table 12-2 Absorption Bands for Typical Groups in Polymers

GROUP	TYPE OF VIBRATION	WAVELENGTH λ, μ	WAVE NUMBER ν, cm^{-1}
CH_2	Stretch	3.38–3.51	2,850–2,960
	Bend	6.82	1,465
	Rock	13.00–13.80	725–890
CH_3	Stretch	3.38–3.48	2,860–2,870
	Bend	6.9	1,450
C=C (H R / H H)	C—H stretch	3.25–3.30	3,030–3,085
	C—H bend in plane	7.10–7.68	1,300–1,410
	C—H bend out of plane	10.10–11.00	910–990
	C—C stretch	6.08	1,643
C=C (H R / H R)	C—H stretch	3.24	3,080
	C—H bend in plane	7.10	1,410
	C—H bend out of plane	11.27	888
	C—C stretch	6.06	1,650
Benzene	C—H bend out of plane	14.50	690
OH	Stretch	2.7–3.2	3,150–3,700
SH	Stretch	3.9	2,550
Aliphatic acid	C=O stretch	5.85	1,710
Aromatic acid	C=O stretch	5.92	1,690
CCl	Stretch	12–16	620–830
CN	Stretch	4.8	2,200

intensity of the carbonyl absorption band at about 5.9 μ may be used to ascertain the extent of deterioration of polymers by oxidative degradation.

The extent of branching in polyethylene may be ascertained by measuring the relative absorbance of the methylene and methyl groups. The relative intensity of absorption for characteristic bands for *cis*-1,4-dienes, *trans*-1,4 dienes, and 1,2 dienes has been used to determine the relative amounts of these structures in synthetic polydienes.

The degree of crystallinity of polyethylene may be estimated from the extent of splitting of the methylene rocking band at 720 cm^{-1}. The relative intensity of this band and that typical of amorphous polyethylene at 1,303 cm^{-1} are useful measures of the degree of crystallinity.

The degree of isotacticity of samples of poly(methyl methacrylate), polypropylene, polystyrene, and poly(vinyl methyl ether) has been estimated from the ratios of characteristic absorbance bands related to tacticity. Anton determined thermal transition temperatures of polyamides, polyesters, polystyrene, and poly(vinyl acetate) by monitoring thermal-sensitive absorption bands in the 900 to 1,100-cm^{-1} region.

Infrared spectrophotometers may be modified to obtain internal reflection spectra which are similar but not identical to absorption spectra and characteristic of the polymer examined. *Internal reflectance spectroscopy,* also called *attenuated total reflectance* (ATR) by Wendlandt, may be used to analyze polymer surfaces in situ. In contrast to classic transmission spectroscopy, which requires transparent films, solutions, or pellets, transparency is not required for ATR measurements.

In this method, the polymer selectively absorbs radiation at characteristic wavelengths, because of an interaction of the polymer and the penetrating beam. The ATR spectra may be used advantageously to study the surface of fibers or composite materials. It should be used as a supplement and not as a replacement for classic infrared spectroscopy.

When the reflectance is determined as a function of temperature, the technique has been called *dynamic reflectance spectroscopy* (DRS) by Wendlandt. This technique may be used to measure thermal transitions of polymers.

REFERENCES

Allinger, N. L., and J. Allinger: "Structure of Organic Molecules," Prentice-Hall, Inc., Englewood Cliffs, N.J., 1965.

Anton, A.: Polymer Transition Temperatures, *ACS Div. Polymer Chem., Polymer Preprints,* **8**(2):873 (1967).

Ault, A.: "Problems in Organic Determination," chap. 1, McGraw-Hill Book Company, New York, 1967.

Bellamy, L. J.: "The Infrared Spectra of Complex Molecules," 2d ed., John Wiley & Sons, Inc., New York, 1958.

Clark, R. J. H.: Diffuse Reflectance Spectroscopy, in G. L. Clark and G. G. Hawley (eds.), "Encyclopedia of Chemistry," Reinhold Publishing Corporation, New York, 1966.

Conley, R. T.: "Infrared Spectroscopy," Allyn and Bacon, Inc., Boston, 1966.

Cram, D. J., and G. S. Hammond: "Organic Chemistry," 2d ed., chap. 31, McGraw-Hill Book Company, New York, 1964.

Cross, A. D.: "Introduction to Practical Infrared Spectroscopy," 2d ed., Butterworth Scientific Publications, London, 1964.

Dyer, J. R.: "Applications of Absorption Spectroscopy of Organic Compounds," Prentice-Hall, Inc., Englewood Cliffs, N.J., 1965.

Hearst, P. J.: Thermal Reflectance Spectroscopy, *ACS Div. Org. Coatings and Plastics Chem., Preprints,* **28**(1):672 (1968).

Henniker, C. J.: "IR Spectrometry of Industrial Polymers," Academic Press, Inc., New York, 1967.

Mandelkern, L.: "Crystallization of Polymers," chap. 1, McGraw-Hill Book Company, New York, 1964.

Nakanishi, K.: "Infrared Absorption Spectroscopy," Holden-Day, Inc., Publisher, San Francisco, 1962.

Potts, W. J.: ATR Spectroscopy, *ACS Div. Org. Coatings and Plastics Chem., Preprints,* **25**(2):364 (1965).

Rao, C. V. R.: "Infrared Spectroscopy," Academic Press, Inc., New York, 1963.

Rothschild, W. G.: Far Infrared Spectroscopy, *Macromolecules,* **1**(1):43 (1968).

Silverstein, R. M., and G. C. Bassler: "Spectrometric Identification of Organic Compounds," chap. 3, John Wiley & Sons, Inc., New York, 1963.

Tanford, C.: "Physical Chemistry of Macromolecules," chap. 2, John Wiley & Sons, Inc., New York, 1965.

Wendlandt, W. W.: Dynamic Reflectance Spectroscopy, in G. L. Clark and G. G. Hawley (eds.), "Encyclopedia of Chemistry," Reinhold Publishing Corporation, New York, 1966.

Wilks, P. A.: ATR Instrument, *ACS Div. Org. Coatings and Plastics Chem., Preprints,* **25**(2):357 (1965).

Zbinden, R.: "Infrared Spectroscopy of High Polymers," Academic Press, Inc., New York, 1964.

12-3 NUCLEAR MAGNETIC RESONANCE (NMR) AND ELECTRON PARAMAGNETIC RESONANCE (EPR)

In contrast to visual and ultraviolet spectroscopy, which are concerned with the excitation of electrons, and infrared spectroscopy which also measures molecular motions, *nuclear magnetic resonance* (nmr) is related to the spin of the nuclei. Under normal circumstances the nuclear spin moments are randomly oriented but these moments may become oriented when placed in a strong magnetic field.

Unlike the previously discussed techniques which require high energy, small amounts of energy, such as those available in microwave or radio-frequency radiation, may also be absorbed by specimens under appropriate conditions. Radio-frequency (RF) radiation may be absorbed by nuclei with nonzero spins such as H^1, C^{13}, F^{19}, P^{31} in which the spin number $I = \frac{1}{2}$.

The interaction of an external magnetic field (H) and the spin of hydrogen nuclei will cause these nuclei to "flip" their spin orientations from $I = -\frac{1}{2}$ to $I = +\frac{1}{2}$. Thus, absorption of energy, which is detected by a small coil around the sample, is amplified and translated into a spectrum characteristic of this hyperfine structure.

The principles of nmr were established by Rabi and coworkers in the 1930s. The first successful experiments in this field were conducted by Purcell and Block in 1946. These investigators showed that the nuclear spin I is quantized; i.e., it may be aligned (parallel) or antiparallel with the magnetic field H. The magnitude of the generated dipole is expressed in terms of the magnetic moment μ.

The energy E of the interaction of an external magnetic field H and the spin of a nucleus with nonzero spin, I, like H^1, may assume $2I + 1$ values in accordance with the selection rule for quantum numbers (M); i.e., $\Delta M = 1$.

The change in energy ΔE is equal to the product of Planck's constant h and the frequency ν of the resonance absorption; that is, $\Delta E = h\nu$. As shown in Eq. (12-7), this resonance absorption is related to the strength of the applied magnetic field H and the magnetogyric ratio γ which is characteristic for each nucleus:

$$\Delta E = h\nu = \frac{\gamma h H}{2\pi} = \frac{M\mu H}{I} \tag{12-7}$$

Relationship of energy to nuclear magnetic moment μ and magnetic field H

In the standard procedure, the radio-frequency signal (γ) is kept constant and the strength of the external field H is varied, as shown in the following equation:

$$\nu = \frac{\gamma H}{2\pi} = \frac{HM\mu}{hI} \tag{12-8}$$

Relationship of frequency γ to strength of magnetic field H

The nmr signal is dependent on the molecular environment of the nucleus to a small degree. Thus, as shown in Fig. 12-2, characteristic spectra may be obtained for polymeric hydrocarbons such as polyisobutylene, poly(3-methyl-1-butene), poly(4-methyl-1-pentene), polypropylene, and poly(4-methyl-1-pentene) since, as shown by Chamberlain, the H^1 atoms in each of these mers are in a different environment. These peaks (δ), called *chemical shifts*, are located relative to a peak for an internal standard (tetramethylsilane).

The ratio of the peaks shown in Fig. 12-2 may be understood by referring to the ratio of methyl and methylene groups in the structural formulas of the mers, using the formulas and ratios shown in Table 12-3.

In spite of the unique usefulness of this technique in identifying molecular structure, high-resolution nmr has proved to be of even greater value in the determination of the degree of crystallinity and tacticity in polymers. Because crystalline areas are immobile, an averaging of absorbed energy does not take place during the lifetime of the observed nuclear spin. However, as might be anticipated, amorphous areas behave more like liquids, and sharp absorption lines are obtained as a result of a rapid averaging of absorbed energy.

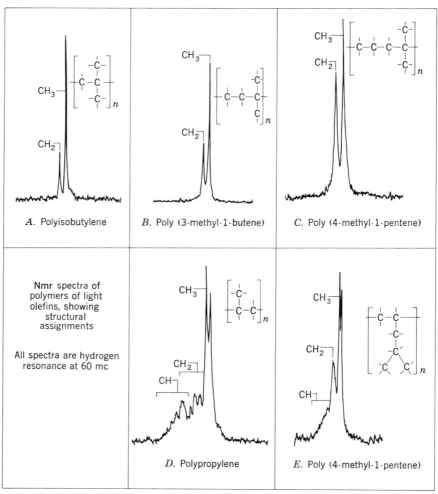

Fig. 12-2   Nmr peaks for hydrocarbon polymers (*Chamberlain*).

Thus, the relative width (broad-line studies) and the *second moment*, i.e., the mean-square deviation of the field from the center of the line H_0, may be used as a measure of the degree of crystallinity.   The second moment is a function of the sum of the inverse sixth powers of internuclear distances.

The nmr line widths for polymers decrease as the temperature is raised, i.e., as the groups rotate more freely about their axes.   Thus, nmr has been used to measure thermal transitions in polymers such as polyisobutylene and poly(vinyl chloride).

Bovey, Tiers, and Ferguson showed that high-resolution nmr may be used to determine the degree of tacticity and branching and to identify end groups in polystyrene, poly(methyl methacrylate), polypropylene, and propylene copolymers. Close-packed isotactic structures have higher second moments than atactic polymers. In many cases, the relative number of isotactic, syndiotactic, and heterotactic triads, tetrads, etc., is proportional to the areas under the appropriate peaks.

The methylene and ethylene resonances have been used to show the relative amount of head-to-tail and cis and trans structures in polydienes. Most investigations have been with H^1. However, F^{19} resonance has been used to show atacticity in polymonochlorotrifluoroethylene. NMR peaks in fluorine spectra are located relative to the internal standard fluorotrichloromethane.

Electron paramagnetic resonance (EPR), also called electron spin resonance (ESR), has been used to study irradiated polymers, trapped radicals, and the rate of decay of initiators. Some qualitative experiments have

---

Table 12-3   Relationships of Methyl and Methylene Groups in Polymers in Fig. 12-2

POLYMER	STRUCTURE	CH_3/CH_2
Polyisobutylene	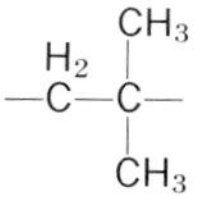 $-\overset{H_2}{\underset{}{C}}-\overset{CH_3}{\underset{CH_3}{C}}-$	2/1
Poly(3-methyl-1-butene)[1]	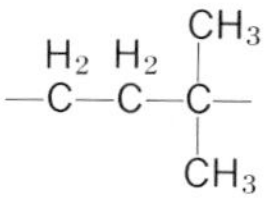 $-\overset{H_2}{C}-\overset{H_2}{C}-\overset{CH_3}{\underset{CH_3}{C}}-$	1/1
Poly(4-methyl-1-pentene)	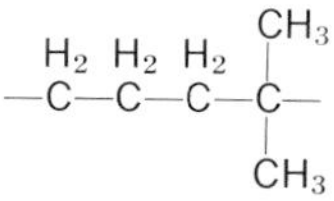 $-\overset{H_2}{C}-\overset{H_2}{C}-\overset{H_2}{C}-\overset{CH_3}{\underset{CH_3}{C}}-$	2/3
Polypropylene	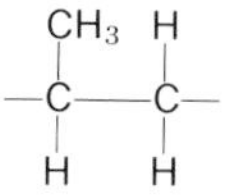 $-\overset{CH_3}{\underset{H}{C}}-\overset{H}{\underset{H}{C}}-$	1/1
Poly(4-methyl-1-pentene)[1]	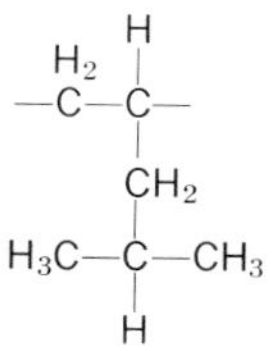 $-\overset{H_2}{C}-\overset{H}{\underset{CH_2}{C}}-$ $\quad H_3C-\overset{}{\underset{H}{C}}-CH_3$	2/2

---

[1] According to Mr. Chamberlain, the nmr measurements were used to show an unexpected structure for poly(3-methyl-1-butene) and two different structures for poly(4-methyl-1-pentene).

been conducted with polymer degradation and cleavage processes. This technique differs from wide-line nmr in that microwave radiation is used to "flip" the electron in ESR whereas radio frequency (RF) is used to flip the nucleus in nmr. Greater sensitivity for ESR is noted at extremely low temperatures. This technique has been used to study the radiolysis of polyethylene, polytetrachloroethylene, polyacrylates, and cellulose. ESR data are of considerable value in the investigation of free-radical block and graft copolymerizations.

REFERENCES

Bacskai R., L. P. Linderman, D. L. Ransley, and W. A. Sweeney: Proton Magnetic Resonance, *ACS Div. Polymer Chem., Polymer Preprints,* **9**(1):25 (1968).

Bersohn, R.: NMR and EPR, *Ann. Rev. Phys. Chem.,* **11:** (1960).

Bovey, F. A., and G. V. D. Tiers: Estimations of Tacticity, *J. Polymer Sci.,* **44:**173 (1960); *Advan. Polymer Sci.,* **3:**139 (1963); *J. Polymer Sci.,* **A1:**833 (1963).

Braude, E. A., and F. C. Nachod: "Determination of Organic Structures by Physical Methods," Academic Press, Inc., New York, 1955.

Bueche, F.: "Physical Properties of Polymers," chap. 12, Interscience Publishers, a division of John Wiley & Sons, Inc., New York, 1962.

Chamberlain, N. F., F. C. Stehling, K. W. Bartz, and J. J. R. Reed: "NMR Data for H^1," Esso Research and Engineering Company, Baytown, Texas, 1965.

Corio, P. L.: The Analysis of NMR Spectra, *Chem. Rev.,* **60:**363 (1960).

Ferguson, R. C.: High Frequency NMR Spectra of Polymers, *ACS Div. Polymer Chem., Polymer Preprints,* **8**(2):1026, (1967).

Ingram, D. J. E.: "Free Radicals as Studied by EPR," Academic Press, Inc., New York, 1958.

Jackman, L. M.: "Applications of NMR Spectroscopy in Organic Chemistry," Pergamon Press, New York, 1959.

Jen, C. K.: EPR Studies of Trapped Radicals, in "Formation and Trapping of Free Radicals," in A. M. Bass and H. P. Broida (eds.), Academic Press, Inc., New York, 1960.

Kullnig, R. K., C. M. Martini, and F. C. Nachod: NMR Spectroscopy, *Chemistry,* **38:**6, 17 (1965).

McCall, D. W., and W. P. Slichter: High Resolution NMR, in B. Ke (ed.), "Newer Methods of Polymer Characterization," chap. 8, Interscience Publishers, a division of John Wiley & Sons, Inc., New York, 1964.

Mochel, V. D.: NMR Analysis of Copolymers, *Rubber Chem. Technol.,* **40**(4):1200 (1967).

Pople, J. A., W. G. Schneider, and H. J. Bernstein: "High-resolution Nuclear Magnetic Resonance," McGraw-Hill Book Company, New York, 1959.

Ramey, K. C.: NMR Studies of Poly(methyl methacrylate), *ACS Div. Polymer Chem., Polymer Preprints,* **8**(2):1017 (1967).

Roberts, J. D.: "Nuclear Magnetic Resonance," McGraw-Hill Book Company, New York, 1959.

Schaefer, J., R. L. Kern, and R. J. Katnik: NMR Studies of Propylene Oxide Copolymers, *ACS Div. Polymer Chem., Polymer Preprints,* **8**(2):1037 (1967).

Silverstein, R. M., and G. C. Bassler: "Spectrometric Identification of Organic Compounds," chap. 4, John Wiley & Sons, Inc., New York, 1963.

Slichter, C. P.: "Principles of Magnetic Resonance," Harper & Row, Publishers, Incorporated, New York, 1963.

Slichter, W. P., and D. D. Davis: NMR Studies of Polymer Solutions, *Macromolecules,* **1**(1):47 (1968).

Smith, W. B.: NMR, in G. L. Clark and G. G. Hawley (eds.), "Encyclopedia of Chemistry," Reinhold Publishing Corporation, New York, 1966.

Wall, L. A., and R. E. Florin: NMR Spectroscopy, in G. M. Kline (ed.), "Analytical Chemistry of Polymers," Pt. II, chap. 12, Interscience Publishers, a division of John Wiley & Sons, Inc., New York, 1962.

Wiberg, K. B., and B. J. Nist: "Interpretation of NMR Spectra," W. A. Benjamin, Inc., New York, 1962.

12-4   X-RAY AND ELECTRON DIFFRACTION

Polymers with oriented crystallites yield sharp x-ray and electron diffraction patterns. Since the dimensions of the crystallites are proportional to the wavelength of the radiation, electron diffraction techniques are more applicable to these dimensions than x-rays. As shown in Fig. 12-3, these diffraction patterns are sharpened as the size of the crystallites increases and are broadened for amorphous polymers.

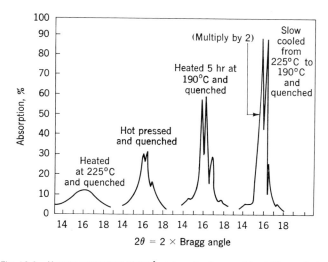

Fig. 12-3   X-ray spectrogram of 5.5Å region of polymonochlorotrifluoroethylene.

Polymers, such as polystyrene and poly(vinyl acetate), which are essentially amorphous, yield diffuse diffraction patterns that may be used for identification. The size of microcrystallites may be estimated from scattered radiation by using low-angle x-ray techniques.

The width of the layer lines in the diffraction patterns obtained from drawn fibers may be used to estimate dimensions of the unit cell along the fiber axis. Since the hydrogen and the hydroxyl groups are similar in size, polyethylene and poly(vinyl alcohol) produce similar fiber diagrams with layer lines of 2.53 Å. The repeat distance for fiber diagrams of stretched polyisobutylene (18.6 Å) corresponds to 8 mers per turn in the helix. The identity period may also be used to estimate tacticity.

REFERENCES

Fischer, E. W.: Electron Diffraction, in B. Ke (ed.), "Newer Methods of Polymer Characterization," chap. 7, Interscience Publishers, a division of John Wiley & Sons, Inc., New York, 1964.

Geil, P. H.: "Polymer Single Crystals," Interscience Publishers, a division of John Wiley & Sons, Inc., New York, 1963.

Guinier, A.: "X-ray Crystallographic Technology," Helger and Watts, London, 1952.
——— and G. Fournet: Small Angle Scatterings of X-rays, John Wiley & Sons, Inc., New York, 1955.

Klug, H. P., and L. E. Alexander: "X-ray Diffraction Procedures," John Wiley & Sons, Inc., New York, 1954.

Posner, A. S.: X-ray Diffraction, in G. M. Kline (ed.), "Analytical Chemistry of Polymers," vol. 2, chap. 2, Interscience Publishers, a division of John Wiley & Sons, Inc., New York, 1962.

Stokes A. R.: The Theory of X-ray Diagrams, *Prog. Biophys. Biophys. Chem.*, **5**:140 (1955).

Statton, W. O.: Small Angle X-ray Studies of Polymers, in B. Ke (ed.), "Newer Methods of Polymer Characterization," chap. 6, Interscience Publishers, a division of John Wiley & Sons, Inc., New York, 1964.

12-5   THERMAL ANALYSIS OF POLYMERS

The physical and chemical changes of polymers may be investigated by *differential thermal analysis* (DTA), *electrothermal analysis* (ETA), and *thermal gravimetric analysis* (TGA). DTA, which has been called *thermal spectrometry*, is based on investigations conducted by Le Châtelier in the nineteenth century. This technique, which has been instrumented, was applied to the study of polymers in the 1950s.

Endothermic   Exothermic   Thermal transition

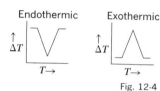

Fig. 12-4

This type of analysis is based on the difference in temperature (ΔT) of a polymer sample and an inert control when both are heated at a programmed rate in an inert atmosphere. This difference in temperature, ΔT, as measured by two opposed thermocouples, is plotted against temperature T to obtain characteristic *thermograms*. Since polymers are poor conductors of heat, the rate of heating for polymer samples is much slower than that for inorganic materials (0.5 to 5°/min).

As shown in Fig. 12-4, typical thermograms are observed for endothermic and exothermic reactions and for thermal transitions. The area under the peaks is proportional to the size of the sample used; it is customary to use a small sample (0.2 g).

DTA has been used to study both the synthesis and degradation of polymers. The peak in a DTA thermogram is the optimum reaction temperature. This technique has been used to study the optimum ratio of reactants, heats of reaction, and mechanisms for step-reaction polymerizations, such as the production of phenolic and saturated polyester resins.

DTA techniques have been used to study the rate of cure of polymers, such as rubber, epoxy resins, and unsaturated polyester resins. This technique has also been used to follow degradative reactions, such as radiolysis, photolysis, hydrolysis, and oxidation of polymers. Many of these thermograms are characteristic for the polymer under the specific conditions used.

DTA has also been used to determine melting points and glass transition temperatures of polymers. Barrell used DTA to analyze physical mixtures of polyethylene and polypropylene. Ke showed that poly(ethylene-*b*-propylene) has a characteristic melting point for each block present in the copolymer.

Useful modifications of DTA include the determination of changes in pressure, weight, and electrical properties of polymers. Thermogravimetric analysis (TGA) was developed by Honda in 1915. This technique uses the change in weight with temperature increase to characterize polymers. TGA may be used to study polymerization but has been used primarily for the investigation of oxidative and thermal degradation of polymers. Electrothermal analysis (ETA) is based on the change in volume resistivity with increasing temperature. The change in pressure with temperature has been used to characterize poly(ethylene-co-methacrylic acid).

REFERENCES

Anderson, H. C.: TGA, in P. E. Slade and L. T. Jenkins (eds.), "Techniques and Methods of Polymer Evaluation," vol. I, Marcel Dekker, Inc., New York, 1966.

Barrell, E. M., R. S. Porter, and J. F. Johnson: DTA—Poly(ethylene-co-propylene), *ACS Div. Polymer Chem., Polymer Preprints*, **5**(2):816 (1964).

Chiu, J.: DTA and ETA, *ACS Div. Polymer Chem., Polymer Preprints*, **5**(2):1033 (1964).

Clampitt, B. A.: DTA of Polymer Mixtures, *Anal. Chem.*, **35**:577 (1963).

Findeis, A. F.: Instruments for Thermal Analysis, *ACS Div. Polymer Chem., Polymer Preprints*, **9**(1):981 (1968).

Garn, P. D.: DTA, in G. L. Clark and G. G. Hawley (eds.), "Encyclopedia of Chemistry," Reinhold Book Corporation, New York, 1969.

Hearst, P. J.: Thermal Reflectance Spectroscopy, *ACS Div. Org. Coatings and Plastics Chem., Preprints*, **28**(1):185 (1968).

Honda, K.: TGA *Sci. Rept. Tohoku Univ.*, **4**:97 (1951).

Ke, B.: DTA, "Newer Methods of Polymer Characterization," chap. 9, Interscience Publishers, a division of John Wiley & Sons, Inc., New York, 1964.

————: "Thermal Analysis of High Polymers," Interscience Publishers, a division of John Wiley & Sons, Inc., New York, 1964.

Kissinger, H. E., and S. B. Newman: DTA, in G. M. Kline (eds.), "Analytical Chemistry of Polymers," Pt. II, chap. 4, Interscience Publishers, a division of John Wiley & Sons, Inc., New York, 1962.

Le Châtelier, H.: DTA, *Bull. Soc. Franc. Mineral.*, **10**:204 (1877).

Mackenzie, R. C.: "DTA Data," Cleaver-Hume Press, Ltd., London, 1962.

Manley, T. R.: DTA, "Techniques of Polymer Science," SCI Monograph 17, Gordon and Breach, Science Publishers, Inc., New York, 1963.

Murphy, C. B.: DTA, *Anal. Chem.*, **30**:867 (1958); *Mod. Plastics*, **37**(12):125 (1960).

Slade, P. E., and L. T. Jenkins: Thermal Analysis, in "Techniques and Methods of Polymer Evaluation," vol. I, Marcel Dekker, Inc., New York, 1966.

Smothers, W. J., and J. Chiang: "DTA," Chemical Publishing Company, Inc., New York, 1959.

Warfield, R. W.: TGA, *SPE J.*, **14**:39 (1958); **17**:364 (1961).

Wendlandt, W. W.: Thermogravimetry, in G. L. Clark and G. G. Hawley (eds.), "Encyclopedia of Chemistry," Reinhold Publishing Corporation, New York, 1966.

12-6 CHROMATOGRAPHY

Tswett coined the term *chromatography* in 1906 to describe the extraction of pigments from green leaves in a column packed with limestone. However, chromatography is limited neither to colored substances nor to packed columns. The general technique includes all separations and identifications based on the transport of a substance by a mobile gaseous or liquid phase through a stationary phase. The separations are related to selective sorption forces and are recorded on *chromatograms*.

Gas chromatography (GC) may be used to separate and identify the products evolved in the pyrolysis of polymers. As discussed in Chap. 4, paper chromatography and thin-layer chromatography have been used to separate and identify amino acids in proteins. However, elution chromatography in appropriate columns is much more versatile for the characterization of polymers.

Polymers such as cellulose diacetate were fractionated in the 1930s by passing solutions of these polymers through packed columns. Baker and Williams used an elution method with a temperature gradient to fractionate solutions of polystyrene. They used glass beads and silica gel as column packings in most of their investigations. They called this method *crystallization chromatography* but the term *precipitation chromatography* is more appropriate and is preferred. The most widely used technique of this type is gel permeation chromatography (GPC).

Deuel used a form of GPC to separate naturally occurring polysaccharides in 1950. Many other naturally occurring polymers were separated in columns containing gels such as dextran (Sephadex) in the 1950s. These materials are still employed for the characterization of water-soluble polymers. However, the fractionation of synthetic polydisperse macromolecules is based, to a large extent, on packings and detectors developed by Moore and Waters.

These investigators prepared highly porous crosslinked polystyrene gels for use as a column packing and also designed a detector consisting of an analytical instrument utilizing differential refractometry. The commercial instruments are available for both analytical and preparative work.

Resolution by GPC is based on relationships between the size of the pores in the gel-type packings and the size and shape of the macromolecules. The largest-sized molecules can enter only the largest holes and are eluted first. Crosslinked polystyrene meets the requirements for a preferential fractionator. Beads with large pore size do not have the optimum mechanical properties required for a stable column packing but have given trouble-free service for several years.

GPC techniques have been used to fractionate asphalt, polybutadiene, polyisobutylene, cellulose derivatives, epoxy resins, poly(methyl methacrylate), polypropylene, poly(propylene glycol), polystyrene, poly(butadiene-co-styrene), and silicon resins. When bulkiness, branching, and hydrogen bonding as well as size are considered, GPC may be applied to a wide variety of natural and synthetic polymers. Although the use of gel permeation chromatography as a tool for fractionation of homopolymers of different molecular-weight ranges has been emphasized, it should be noted that this technique may also be used to separate different low-molecular-weight compounds and its use is not restricted to the characterization of polymers.

Fig. 12-5   Gel permeation chromatograph.

REFERENCES

Altgelt, K. H., and J. C. Moore: GPC, in M. J. R. Cantow (ed.), "Polymer Fractionation," chap. 4, Academic Press, Inc., New York, 1967.

Baker, C. A., and R. J. P. Williams: Precipitation Chromatography, *J. Chem. Soc.*, p. 2352, 1956.

Bobbitt, J. M.: "Thin Layer Chromatography," Reinhold Publishing Corporation, New York, 1963.

Caplan, S. R.: Precipitation Chromatography, *J. Polymer Sci.*, **35**:409 (1959).

Cassel, J. M.: Chromatography, in G. M. Kline (ed.), "Analytical Chemistry of Polymers," chap. 10, Interscience Publishers, a division of John Wiley & Sons, Inc., New York, 1962.

Cazes, C.: G. P. C., *J. Chem. Educ.*, **43**(7):A 567 (1966).

Deuel, H., J. Solms, and L. Anyas-Weisz: GPC (Pactins, Algins), *Helv. Chem. Acta*, **33**:2171 (1950).

Hall, R. W.: in P. W. Allen (ed.), "Techniques of Polymer Characterization," chap. 2, Butterworth & Co. (Publishers), Ltd., London, 1959.

Haller, W. J.: Porous Glass Packing, *J. Chem. Phys.*, **42**:686 (1965).

Heftmann, E.: "Chromatography," Reinhold Publishing Corporation, New York, 1961.

Johnson, J. F., R. S. Porter, and M. J. R. Cantow: GPC, *Rev. Macromol. Chem.*, **1**(2):393 (1966).

——— and ———: "Analytical Gel Permeation Chromatography," John Wiley & Sons, Inc., New York, 1968.

LePage, M., R. Bean, and A. J. de Vries: "GPC," *ACS Div. Polymer Chem., Polymer Preprints*, **8**(2):1211 (1967).

Lewin, S. Z.: GPC, *J. Chem. Educ.*, **38**:A515 (1961).

Moore, J. C.: "GPC," *J. Polymer Sci.*, **2A**:835 (1964).

Salovey, R., and M. Y. Hellman: GPC of Branched Polyethylene, *J. Polymer Sci.*, Pt. A-2, **5**(2):333 (1967).

Screaton, R. M.: Column Fractionation of Polymers, in B. Ke (ed.), "Newer Methods of Polymer Characterization," chap. 11, Interscience Publishers, a division of John Wiley & Sons, Inc., New York, 1964.

Vaughn, M. F.: GPC, *Nature*, **188**:55 (1960); **195**:801 (1962).

———: Silica Gel Packing, British Patent 1,000,185, 1965.

——— and J. H. S. Green: "Techniques of Polymer Science," Gordon and Breach, Science Publishers, Inc., New York, 1963.

Waters, J. L.: GPC, *ACS Div. Polymer Chem., Polymer Preprints*, **6**(2):1061 (1965).

Williams, T. I.: "An Introduction to Chromatography," Chemical Publishing Company, Inc., New York, 1950.

13

Testing of Polymers

Many classic applications of polymers depended on actual use since successful performance was not predictable. Successful performance may sometimes have been the result of overdesign, and failure may often have been due to a lack of knowledge of the engineering properties of these viscoelastic materials.

As stated in Chap. 2, polymers are neither perfect solids nor perfect liquids, but Hooke's and Newton's laws may be used to approximate the relationships of external forces to stresses and strains in these materials. Much information may be obtained from a study of stress-strain relationships. A knowledge of molecular structure also aids in the interpretation of these relationships. However, significant tests are essential for the final selection of appropriate polymers for specific applications.

As shown in Fig. 13-1, Carswell and Nason proposed five typical classifications of polymers based on stress-strain relationships. The designations shown for the *hard and tough class* (*e*) may be applied to all other classes. These hard-tough polymers such as plasticized cellulose acetate show moderate elongation prior to the break, i.e., *yield point*. These high-modulus products are essentially Hookean before this yield point; hence this deformation is recoverable. This elastic deformation results from the instantaneous bending and stretching of covalent bonds in the polymer backbone. Some recoverable uncoiling of polymer chains also occurs before the yield point which is the upper limit of usefulness of a polymeric material. The range before the yield point is called the elastic range.

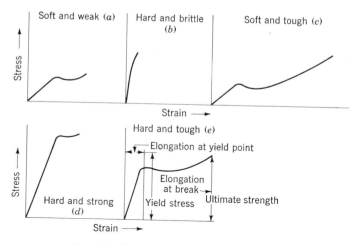

Fig. 13-1 Typical stress-strain curves for plastics.

In contrast, the deformation that occurs after the yield point is related to a very slow nonrecoverable slippage of polymer chains. The area under the stress-strain curves is a measure of toughness. Thus it may be concluded that the polymer class represented by curves (c) and (e) are tough. The energy absorbed after the yield point, i.e., in the *plastic range,* is also indicative of toughness but this energy is not completely recoverable. In spite of these relationships of area and toughness, impact tests rather than tensile tests are preferred as a measure of this important property because of the relative ease of measurement.

Since the toughness, as measured by the area under these curves or by impact test, is also time- and temperature-dependent, it is essential that both these variables be controlled in all polymer tests. The embrittlement resulting from lowering the temperature may be observed when tough plasticized poly(vinyl chloride) becomes brittle as it is cooled below 0°C. Thus the area under the stress-strain curves for plasticized poly(vinyl chloride) decreases as the temperature is decreased and as the slippage of polymer chains is reduced.

The effect of time on toughness may be demonstrated by observing the effect of loading rates on the elastic vs. the plastic properties of silicone putty. This interesting product exhibits elastic properties when the stress is applied at a rate that does not allow for slippage of chains. Thus the product will bounce when dropped. However, when the rate of loading is slow, slippage between chains occurs as indicated by considerable nonrecoverable deformation, i.e., the large area under the stress-strain curve after the yield point.

Hard and brittle polymers, such as polystyrene, are characterized by a high slope and a small area under the stress-strain curve, as indicated by curve *b* in Fig. 13-1. These polymers have a high modulus of elasticity, a poorly defined yield point, and little elongation before failure.

Polymers that are *hard and strong,* such as rigid poly(vinyl chloride), as indicated by curve *d,* are characterized by a high modulus and high yield strength. Unlike brittle polymers, such as polystyrene, these polymers stretch after the observable yield point. Hence the area under the curve is greater than that for curve *b* but much less than that for curve *e.*

These stress-strain properties of plasticized poly(vinyl chloride) are similar to those shown for curve *c.* These *soft and tough* polymers are characterized by a low modulus of elasticity and high elongation both before and after the well-defined yield point. *Soft and weak* polymers, such as polyisobutylene, have stress-strain properties similar to curve *a.* They are characterized by a low modulus of elasticity, low yield point, and moderate time-dependent elongation.

The cross section of a polymer decreases as the product is stretched. The ratio of this contraction (transverse strain) to elongation (longitudinal strain) is called *Poisson's ratio* and is characteristic of the molecular changes taking place during the elongation of polymers. The Poisson's ratio of an ideal liquid is 0.5. That for highly crosslinked polymers, such as ebonite and brittle thermoplastics, is approximately 0.3. The magnitude of this ratio may be increased by the addition of plasticizers which increase chain mobility. Thus Poisson's ratio for plasticized cellulose acetate is approxmatiely 0.45. The value for vulcanized rubber is slightly less than 0.50 but is decreased as the amount of sulfur is increased.

As shown in Fig. 13-2, the properties of polymers are temperature dependent. In addition to being affected by the temperature and rate of testing, polymer properties are also affected by humidity. Conditioning of polymers prior to testing includes storage under standard conditions for sufficient time to assure that the test specimens are in equilibrium with the environment. Standard conditions are usually 50 percent humidity at 23°C. Tests should be conducted under standard conditions at loading rates prescribed in test procedures.

The American Society for Testing Materials (ASTM) is the leading organization for the development and improvement of tests and specifications for polymers in the United States. Other technical organizations, such as the Society of the Plastics Industry (SPI), the Society of Plastics Engineers (SPE), the Rubber Division of the American Chemical Society, and the Technical Association of the Pulp and Paper Industry (TAPPI), usually cooperate with ASTM and the American National Standards Institute (ANSI; formerly the American Standards Association) in the development of tests. These organizations have their counterparts in other nations, and there is

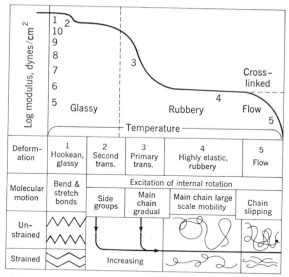

Fig. 13-2 Characteristic effects of temperature on the properties of a typical polymer.

considerable exchange of information and cooperation among these associations. The International Standards Organization (ISO) consists of representatives from most of the industrial countries' standards organizations, including ASTM, British Standards Institute (BSI), and those of U.S.S.R., France, West Germany, Italy, etc. ISO is subdivided into technical committees

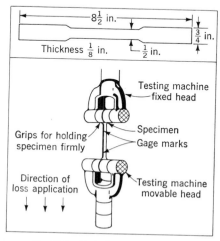

Fig. 13-3 Typical tensile test.

which meet periodically in attempting to set up worldwide standards. Committee ISO/TC 61 is concerned with plastics, and ISO/TC 45 covers rubber. ASTM and ANSI publish monthly periodicals, viz., *Materials Research and Standards* and *Magazine of Standards*.

Stress is commonly measured as tensile strength, i.e., the maximum load based on the original cross section of the test specimen. A typical specimen being tested for tensile strength is shown in Fig. 13-3. Tensile testing machines are usually equipped with variable-speed motors so that an appropriate testing speed may be used for the material under test.

The tensile strength of fibrous materials may be determined on a Scott tester using a single filament, yarn, or fabric as the test specimen. In this test, the specimen is clamped in a vertical position and strained by a uniform pull. Both the stress and the elongation (strain) are recorded automatically. The strength of yarns is reported as *tenacity*, i.e., the breaking strength in grams per denier. The common denier is the weight in grams of a skein measuring 9,000 m in length. Because of confusion of terms, such as hanks (840 yd), etc., for different fibers, the ASTM has proposed the typp as a unit of measurement in which the hank is 1,000 yd.

The bursting strength of woven textiles may be determined by the Mullen tester or the ball burst tester. In the Mullen tester, hydraulic pressure is applied to a cloth sample by forcing oil or glycerol against a thin rubber diaphragm. In the ball burst test, the fabric is pulled down against a steel ball until failure occurs.

The Mullen hydrostatic test is also used to measure the bursting strength of paper. The tensile strength of dry and wet paper may be determined by a Thwing-Albert tester which measures both stress and strain; hence the modulus of elasticity may be calculated from these test results.

The tensile strength of elastomers is measured on a Scott tester using a dumbbell specimen pulled at a rate of 20 in./min. Resilience may be calculated from the differences in area under stress-strain curves during extension and relaxation, i.e., the energy lost between test cycles (hysteresis). The tensile strength of plastics may be determined by pulling a molded dumbbell specimen at specified speeds in accordance with the type of plastic being tested. Complete details of this test are given in ASTM tentative method ASTM D638-67T. Subsequent designations relate to ASTM unless specified otherwise. The letter T indicates that the test is tentative.

The tensile strength of an adhesive bond may be determined by measuring the maximum load per unit area required to break the bond when the force is applied perpendicularly to the plane of the adhesive film. The peel strength of an adhesive bond is the force required to strip off a flexible member from the bonded assembly. The shear stress, i.e., the force acting parallel to the adhesive film, is determined by measuring the tensile strength of lapped joints.

The common method of using a penknife to determine the adhesion of coatings to metal or wood surfaces has been replaced to some extent by more precise instruments such as the Arco microknife. The cutting tool makes parallel cuts at controlled distances. The relative adhesion is determined from the width of the cut at which the coating remains adhered to the surface.

The elongation of coatings may be determined by bonding a coated metal panel around cylindrical mandrels of varying diameter or around a conical mandrel. The smallest diameter of the mandrel on which the film does not crack is a measure of elongation and the resistance to deformation. This property may also be measured by pressing a steel ball or rod against the uncoated side of the test specimen and noting the depth of the bump at which cracks appear in the coating.

The flexural strength (cross breaking strength or modulus of rupture) is a measure of the bending strength or stiffness of test specimens. In the ASTM test D790-66, as shown in Fig. 13-4, a force is applied midway on a simple beam. The ends of the specimen are unrestrained, and failure is recorded at rupture or at a maximum deflection of 5 percent when rupture does not occur before this deflection is reached. This test may be modified so that the load is applied at more than one point, such as at one-quarter points. Cantilever beams loaded at the free end may also be used.

An Elmendorf paper tear tester is used to measure the tearing strength of paper, films, and coated fabrics. This is the force required to complete the tear in a single sheet of paper. This test is also applicable to elastomers in which a standard crescent cut is made in the test specimen (ASTM D624-54).

In spite of many controversies associated with impact tests, these tests continue to be used because of the lack of more significant standardized test procedures. The impact strength is a measure of the work done in breaking a test specimen and is indicative of the resistance to stress concentration at the standard rate of loading. This test is related to deformation and breaking strength, i.e., toughness. Impact resistance of test specimens may be measured by using falling weights, projectiles, rotating hammers, tumbling tests, and pendulum tests.

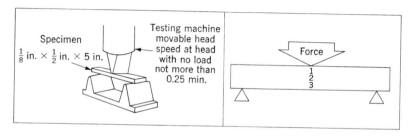

Fig. 13-4   Typical flexural strength test.

In the falling-weight test, the minimum height from which a metal ball cracks a specimen on impact is a measure of impact resistance. Tups with both blunt and pointed ends are used to measure the impact resistance of plastic pipe (D2444-67). Modifications include falling darts (D1709-67) or dropping of the polymer specimen itself. For example, the impact resistance of blown plastic bottles may be measured by dropping a bottle filled with liquid (D2463-65T).

The impact resistance of plastic sheet may be determined by using the Myers varying-speed rotary flywheel impactometer. The projectile test uses the high velocities obtained from a pressurized gun to test the impact resistance of flat objects such as films. The impact resistance of coatings may be determined by the use of falling weights or rotating hammers. In the tumbling test, the frequency of breakage of finished articles is compared with that of similar articles having known impact resistance. These articles are tumbled together in a barrel, and the percent breakage of these samples vs. standard samples is recorded.

The impact resistance of a bonded assembly is determined by striking a member of a bond assembly with a pendulum hammer in a direction parallel to the adhesive layer. In another test, one end of the specimen is attached to the pendulum and the other is attached to a traveling cross head which is stopped at the instant of maximum pendulum energy (D1822-61T).

The most widely used impact tests also make use of a swinging pendulum to break test bars of polymer. These tests are based on the assumption that all energy lost by the swinging pendulum is consumed in rupturing the specimen. The velocity at impact is designed to correspond to that of a 2-ft fall of a working part, such as a tool handle.

In the Charpy test, a standard test piece is freely suspended at both ends as a simple beam and struck in the center by a weighted pendulum. The test piece is notched on the side opposite to the side struck by the pendulum. The Izod test, which is the most popular impact test, also uses a notched specimen as the cantilever beam but, as shown in Fig. 13-5, the notch is on the same side as that struck by the pendulum [D256-56 (1961)].

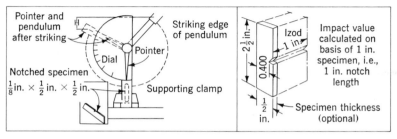

Fig. 13-5   Izod impact test.

Among the objections to the Izod test is that all the energy lost by the swinging pendulum is not used for rupturing the specimen. The total energy is the summation of the energy expended in producing the first crack, that required to shear off the remainder of the test specimen, and that used to toss off the broken end. In addition, variations may result from changes in gripping pressure and from losses from friction, vibration, and jarring. The results are reported as energy (foot-pounds) per unit width (length of notch).

Since many static tests were designed for testing isotropic materials, they may be unreliable for predicting the performance of anisotropic materials under actual use conditions. In some cases, polymers which meet static test specifications may fail under conditions of repeated stress associated with vibration or continuously variable loads. Fatigue failure, which is a common type of service failure, may result from either a small number of cycles with stresses approaching the ultimate static strength or a large number of cycles at lower stress levels.

The fatigue limit has been arbitrarily defined as the time for complete failure or when the values of a specific property are less than that of a specified critical value. The ratio of the fatigue test limit and the static strength is called the *endurance ratio*. Fatigue tests have been based on oscillating compressive stresses (D623-62) or repeated flexural stresses (D671-63T).

Since polymers are notch-sensitive, parts must be designed to eliminate sudden changes in cross section. Irreversible deformation of polymers may result from stresses beyond the yield point or from the repeated applications of smaller stresses. Small stresses beyond the yield point produce considerable strain in tough polymers. A similar effect may be noted when stress below the yield point is maintained for long periods of time. The time-dependent portion of this strain is called *creep*. Stress-relaxation tests may be made under tension or compression loads at various temperatures [D674-56 (1961)].

It is customary to make frequent observations during the early stages of the test and to decrease the frequency of observations as the stress-relaxation experiment continues over weeks or months. It is advantageous to plot creep as a function of time on log-log coordinates. These plots are usually straight lines and may be extrapolated to predict long-term results. Creep is related to slippage of polymer chains and is greatest in polymers with high elongation. This slippage may be reduced by the addition of fillers or by crosslinking of polymer chains.

Hardness is a general term which describes a combination of properties such as the resistance to penetration, abrasion, and scratching. Hardness is correlated with mechanical strength and rigidity. Indentation hardness may be measured by a Barcol Impressor (D2583-67), a Shore durometer (D1706-

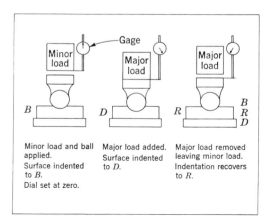

Fig. 13-6   Rockwell hardness test.

61, D2240-64T), a Rockwell indentor (D785-65), or a Brinell tester (D2240-64T). The latter uses steel balls with different weights. The various Rockwell scales correspond to variations in the size of the indentor, the load, and the time interval before a reading is recorded. In Fig. 13-6, the hardness shown on the dial is the indentation from B to R.

The Barcol Impressor is a portable spring-loaded instrument providing arbitrary measurements which correlate well with Rockwell hardness numbers. The durometer is a pocket instrument consisting of a needlelike indentor which penetrates the surface of the polymer. Type A has a truncated cone with a blunt point and is used for elastomers or soft polymers. Type D has a spherical point and is used for hard plastics. The Rex hardness gauge is a modification of the durometer.

The hardness of film is estimated from the number of swings of a Sward Hardness Rocker on the film vs. the amount of rocking on polished plate glass. Scratch hardness may be determined by using sharpened pencils with hardnesses ranging from 9H to 6B. These values are less critical than the Mohs values which are made by scratching the polymer surface with graded minerals.

Abrasion resistance is defined as the ability of a material to withstand erosion or scraping. The abrasion-resistance tests for rubber or plastics are based on the rate of loss in weight when a mechanical abraser is rubbed on the surface of these polymers [D394-59 (1965), D1242-56 (1961)]. The test pieces may also be revolved against the rubber wheels of a Taber abraser. Other methods use finely divided abrasives which impinge on the polymer surface [D968-51 (1965)]. The change in surface gloss may also be used as a measurement of abrasion [D658-44 (1965)].

Cavitation erosion may be determined by measuring the loss in weight and change in appearance of a test specimen placed in the venturi throat of a water tunnel, in a tube with a magnetostrictive transducer with vibrations of 6,500 Hz (cycles per second) or in a beaker with a barium titanate ring oscillator (piezoelectric vibrator) with vibrations of 18,000 or 24,000 Hz.

Prior to the twentieth century, the production of electrical equipment depended on the application of naturally occurring polymers, such as amber, asphalt, cotton glass, mica, paper, rubber, and sulfur. However, since most synthetic polymers are nonconductors of electricity, a wide choice of insulating materials is now available.

The volume resistivity is the reciprocal of the conductivity and may be defined as the electrical resistance between opposite faces of a cube of unit dimensions (D257-66). The arc resistance or resistance to tracking is considered the minimum time required for a high-voltage discharge to find a conducting path across the polymer surface as evidenced by the arc disappearing into the test specimen (D495-61).

The dielectric constant (permittivity) is the ratio of the capacitance of a capacitor with the test polymer as a dielectric and that when air or a vacuum is used as the dielectric (D150-65T). The maximum applied voltage that a polymer can withstand for one minute divided by the sample thickness (1×10^{-3} in.) is called the *dielectric strength* or dielectric breakdown voltage (D149-64).

The temperature increases when alternating current is applied to a capacitor, i.e., a dielectric between two conductors. The amount of heat generated is inversely related to the insulating value of the material used to produce the capacitor and may be used in dielectric heating processes. The energy released is associated with the alternate rotation of the dipoles which is opposed by internal viscosity and molecular kinetic energy. The energy required for rotation of the dipoles (the power factor) increases as the frequency of the electrostatic field is increased. However, at extremely high frequencies the molecular oscillations are reduced because there is insufficient time available for alignment of molecules.

Power-factor values may range from 1.5×10^{-4} for polystyrene to about 5×10^{-2} for plasticized cellulose acetate. These values increase at the glass transition temperature because of the increase in chain mobility that occurs. Thus these techniques may be used to determine second-order transition values and other thermal properties.

The other important thermal properties of polymers are softening and melting points, cold flex temperature, coefficient of thermal expansion, specific heat, and conductivity. Appropriate tests are available for determining these characteristic properties.

The softening point of low-melting thermoplastics such as asphalt may

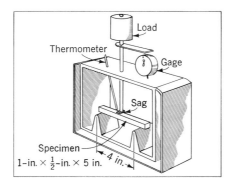

Fig. 13-7   Deflection temperature test.

be determined by the ball and ring test in which the temperature is observed when a small steel ball falls through a horizontal ring filled with the thermoplastic. A Vicat softening point (D1525-65T) is the temperature at which a flattened needle penetrates a thermoplastic surface to a depth of 1 mm under a specified load (usually 1 kg).

The deflection softening points may be determined by the Marten method or by the ASTM method D648-56 (1961). In the former, the test specimen is used as a cantilever beam, and the temperature is observed when the beam deflects 30 and 60° under a constant load. As shown in Fig. 13-7, a simple beam with a load of 66 or 264 psi is used in the ASTM test. The temperature at which the beam deflects 0.01 in. is called the *heat-deflection temperature*. The melting point of semicrystalline polymers may be determined by DTA techniques or by observing the point at which double refraction or birefringence disappears as the temperature is increased (D2117-64).

As stated previously, the glass transition temperature (T_g) may be determined by observing the abrupt change that occurs in specific volume or power factor at this temperature. Since polymers behave much like liquids above these temperatures, glass transition values may also be determined by noting the temperature at which Poisson's ratio approaches a maximum.

The low-temperature properties of polymers may be determined by the Gehman low-temperature flexibility test, the Clash and Berg torsion stiffness test, or the impact brittle failure test (D746-64T, D1790-62). The cold bend or cold flex temperature is defined as the lowest temperature at which the test sample meets the minimum requirements for flexibility or deflection when subjected to standard torque.

The specific heat of polymers, i.e., the energy required to raise the temperature of one gram of polymer one degree Celsius, may be determined experimentally or calculated from the atomic values for the monomer. Specific-heat values for polymers range from 0.2 to 0.4 cal/°C and are much higher than those for metals.

The thermal conductivity of polymers may be determined by means of a guarded hot plate (C177-63) in which the temperature differential across the specimen is determined after it has reached a steady state. The thermal conductivity of cellular plastics may be determined by using a galvanometer to measure the temperature differential between a probe thermocouple and a reference junction (D2326-64T).

The coefficient of linear thermal expansion may be determined by mounting a test specimen in a dilatometer and noting the increase in length on a dial gauge (D696-44-61) when the temperature is increased. The coefficient of linear expansion is the change in length per unit length per degree. The coefficient of cubical thermal expansion is determined by placing a sample with known volume in a tube containing mercury and noting the change in height of the mercury in a connecting capillary tube as the temperature is increased [D864-52 (1961)].

Tests of flammability are concerned with ignition temperatures and combustion rates. The tests for the lowest ignition temperature are based on procedures developed by Setchkin. Commercial equipment is available for measuring the lowest ambient air temperature at which ignition of the specimen takes place (D1929-62T).

Burning tests (D635-63) assess the combustion rate of rigid plastics after removal of the ignition source. The rate of burning of self-extinguishing polymers may be compared by the Globar test (D957-65) or various tunnel tests (E162-62T). The Underwriters Laboratories (UL Standard 723) use a 25-ft ventilated tunnel. The Forest Products Laboratories use an 8-ft tunnel.

There are specific tests for thin polymer sheets (D668-61), foam (169-59T), and flexible film [D569-059 (1961)]. These tests are empirical and controversial, but significant test procedures for flammability and smoke production are essential when materials are to be used for construction or clothing. Underwriter Laboratories (UL) approval is required for electrical equipment ranging from lamp sockets to power tools.

When some polymers are subjected to extremely high temperatures (5000°C) they undergo ablation; i.e., the surface is charred, and the energy which is absorbed restricts the flow of heat into the material below the carbonized surface. The performance characteristics of ablative materials may be determined by measuring the temperature drop and the rate of loss in weight and by optical examination during and after exposure to gaseous oxygen-hydrogen rocket motor exhaust or an electric-arc air heater.

Polymers may crosslink or degrade when exposed to high-energy radiation. Thus films and coating of polyethylene may be cured by radiolysis. Likewise, appropriately selected polymers may be used to reduce radiation

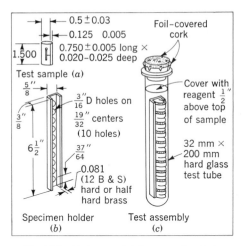

Fig. 13-8   Environmental stress cracking test.

damage to animals.   ASTM has a defined list of exposure conditions to high-energy radiation (1672-66) and specific conditions for adhesives and electronic components.

Tests for resistance to less hazardous environments are also available. Considerable progress has been made in exposure tests ranging from the effect of detergents on polyethylene (stress cracking) to the ozonolysis of rubber.   Many of the tests for environmental stress cracking of low-density polyethylene (type I) were developed by the Bell Telephone Laboratories (D1693-66).   As shown in Fig. 13-8, a scored strip of polymer is bent 180° and held in this position in a tube of a solution of a standard detergent (Antarox A400, alkyl aryl polyethylene glycol) until failure occurs because of rupture at the point where the sample was scored.

Stress cracking may also be observed with other polymers, such as polystyrene, and other environments, such as polar solvents.   Stress-cracking testing procedures have also been developed for high-density polyethylene (type III) (D255-66T), for polyethylene pipe (D2239-67, D2447-66), and for blow-molded containers (D2561-67T).

The moisture vapor permeability of organic films may be determined by use of a permeability cup in which 25 cm^2 of film is exposed to high humidity on one side and low humidity on the other.   The amount of moisture permeating the film is determined by measuring the change in weight after a 24-hr interval.   Electrohygrometry and hydrophotography have been used to measure the permeation of water vapor through films.   Standards have also been established for measuring gas transmission (D1434-63) and vapor transmission (E96-63T) of polymer films.

The effect of aging is important in determining the useful life of fibers, plastics, polymer coatings, and elastomers. Detailed procedures have been established for the preparation of panels [D609-61, D823-53 (1965)] for natural and accelerated exposures. Outdoor durability is usually determined by exposing coated panels or polymer specimens at an angle of 45°, usually facing south (D1014-66). Photographic standards are available for comparing the effect of panel exposure on the degree of rusting [610-43 (1961)], chalking [D659-44 (1965)], checking (D660-44), cracking [D661-44 (1965)], erosion (D662-44), blistering (D714-56), and flaking or scaling [D772-47 (1965)].

Attempts have been made to simulate accelerated natural weathering and aging. Accelerated weathering devices (Weatherometer) (D822-60) are available but correlations with natural weathering processes are questionable. The amount of natural sunshine striking test samples has been increased by using machines to keep these panels at right angles to the incident sunlight throughout the day (EEK) and by equatorial mounting of samples with mirrors for the acceleration of weathering (EMMA).

Aging tests of elastomers have been made by measuring stress-strain relationships before and after aging of dumbbell test pieces in a Geer oven at 70° [D1573-53 (1965)], in hot air under pressure [D454-53 (1965)], or in an oxygen bomb (D572-67). The effect of ozone on elastomers may be determined by observing the time required for rupture of cut test specimens placed under tension in an ozone atmosphere (D518-61, D1149-64).

Coated panels to be tested in corrosive environments are usually scribed with an appropriate tool with an included angle of 60 ± 15° (D1654-66). The scribe penetrates the full depth of the coating but is discontinued before reaching the panel edge. Scribed test panels may be exposed to standard salt-spray atmospheres (D117-64, B287-62, B368-65) or they may be used as end closures for specially designed glass tee test cells containing corrosive liquids.

The effect of corrosive liquids on polymers has been determined by measuring the change in weight of the test specimens (D543-65, D1203-67). Van Delinder showed that a weight change of 5 percent correlated well with other significant data and may be used to measure the deterioration of rigid plastics.

Degradation by corrosive liquids may also affect other measurable physical and electrical properties of polymers. Changes in hardness are useful indices if progressive softening occurs. In the absence of significant softening, changes in flexural strength or flexural modulus may be used to measure the corrosive degradation of polymers. Flexural-strength tests are included in modified ASTM testing procedures (C581-67T, D543-65, procedure 2, note 8).

The results of even the most sophisticated laboratory tests seldom supply all the answers necessary to assure successful end-use performance. Even the best test data must be interpreted judiciously. Simulated tests are advantageous but are no substitute for actual case histories of successful performance in corrosive environments.

REFERENCES

Alfrey, T.: "Mechanical Behavior of Polymers," Interscience Publishers, Inc., New York, 1948.

Allen, L. B., and L. N. Chellis: Flammability Tests, in J. V. Schmitz (ed.), "Testing of Plastics," vol. 2, chap. 11, Interscience Publishers, a division of John Wiley & Sons, Inc., New York, 1966.

Baer, E. (ed.): "Engineering Design for Plastics," Reinhold Publishing Corporation, New York, 1964.

Bergen, R. L.: Stress Relaxation Tests, in J. V. Schmitz (ed.), "Testing of Polymers," vol. 2, chap. 1, Interscience Publishers, a division of John Wiley & Sons, Inc., New York, 1966.

Britt, K. W.: Testing of Paper, in K. W. Britt (ed.), "Handbook of Pulp and Paper Technology," chap. 14, Reinhold Publishing Corporation, New York, 1964.

Brown, W. E., F. C. Frost, and P. E. Willard: Standards and Sources of Tests for Polymers, in J. V. Schmitz (ed.), "Testing of Plastics," vol. 1, chap. 1, Interscience Publishers, a division of John Wiley & Sons, Inc., New York, 1965.

Brunton, J. H.: Cavitation Erosion Tests, in J. V. Schmitz (ed.), "Testing of Polymers," vol. 1, chap. 10, Interscience Publishers, a division of John Wiley & Sons, Inc., New York, 1965.

Burton, W. E.: "Engineering with Rubber," chap. 2, McGraw-Hill Book Company, New York, 1949.

Carey, R. H. (ed.): Simulated Service Testing in the Plastics Industry, *ASTM Spec. Tech. Publ.* 375, 1964.

Carswell, T. S., and H. K. Nason: Classification of Polymers, *Mod. Plastics,* **21**(10):121 (1944).

Conant, F. S., and G. L. Hall: Rubber and Elastomers, in C. L. Mantell (ed.), "Engineering Materials Handbook," sec. 32, McGraw-Hill Book Company, New York, 1958.

Dillon, J. H.: Fatigue Phenomena in High Polymers, in H. F. Mark and E. J. W. Verwey (eds.), "Advances in Colloid Science," vol. III, Interscience Publishers, Inc., New York, 1950.

Ehlers, G. F. L.: Thermal Properties, in E. Baer (ed.), "Engineering Design for Plastics," chap. 6, Reinhold Publishing Corporation, New York, 1964.

Ferry, J. D.: "Viscoelastic Properties of Polymers," John Wiley & Sons, Inc., New York, 1961.

Feuer, S. S.: Tee Test Cells, *Plastics World,* **19**(6):38 (1962).

Gardner, H., and G. Sward: "Physical and Chemical Examination of Paints, Varnishes, Lacquers and Colors," 12th ed., Henry A. Gardner Laboratory, Bethesda, Md., 1962.

Gavan, F. M., and F. A. Joy: Conditioning, in J. V. Schmitz (ed.), "Testing of Polymers," vol. 1, chap. 2, Interscience Publishers, a division of John Wiley & Sons, Inc., New York, 1965.

——— and J. T. Wein: Indentation Tests, in J. V. Schmitz (ed.), "Testing of Polymers," vol. 1, chap. 12, Interscience Publishers, a division of John Wiley & Sons, Inc., New York, 1966.

Gordon, P. L., and R. Gordon: "Paint and Varnish Manual, Formulation and Testing," Interscience Publishers, a division of John Wiley & Sons, Inc., New York, 1965.

Hess, M., W. A. Edwards, W. A. Wilkinson, and N. A. Bennett: "Paint Film Defects —Their Causes and Cure," 2d ed., Chapman & Hall, Ltd., London, 1965.

Hilado, C. J.: Flammability Tests for Cellular Plastics, *ACS Div. Org. Coatings and Plastics Chem.*, **28**(1):265 (1968).

Howard, J. B.: Stress Cracking, in E. Baer (ed.), "Engineering Design for Plastics," chap. 11, Reinhold Publishing Corporation, New York, 1964.

Juve, A. E.: Physical Testing, in A. M. Morton (ed.), "Introduction to Rubber Technology," chap. 19, Reinhold Publishing Corporation, New York, 1959.

Kinney, G. F.: "Engineering Properties and Applications of Plastics," chap. 14, John Wiley & Sons, Inc., New York, 1956.

Kline, G. M.: "Analytical Chemistry of Polymers," Interscience Publishers, a division of John Wiley & Sons, Inc., New York, 1962.

Lever, A. E., and J. Rhys: "The Properties and Testing of Plastics Materials," 3d ed., Temple Press Ltd., London, 1968.

Lieb, J. H., and R. E. Mowers: Tests at Cryogenic Temperatures, in J. V. Schmitz (ed.), "Testing of Polymers," vol. 2, chap. 3, Interscience Publishers, a division of John Wiley & Sons, Inc., New York, 1966.

Loveless, H. S.: Flexural Tests, in J. V. Schmitz (ed.), "Testing of Plastics," vol. 2, chap. 10, Interscience Publishers, a division of John Wiley & Sons, Inc., New York, 1966.

Mathes, K.: Electrical Properties, in E. Baer (ed.), "Engineering Design for Plastics," chap. 7, Reinhold Publishing Corporation, New York, 1965.

Matiellio, J. J.: "Protective and Decorative Coatings," vols. 4 and 5, John Wiley & Sons, Inc., New York, 1944, 1946.

Metz, D. J.: Radiation Resistance Tests, in J. V. Schmitz (ed.), "Testing of Polymers," vol. 2, chap. 5, Interscience Publishers, a division of John Wiley & Sons, Inc., New York, 1966.

Miles, D. C., and J. H. Briston: "Polymer Technology," Pt. 4, Chemical Publishing Company, Inc., New York, 1965.

"Modern Plastics Encyclopedia," ASTM Tests, p. 24, McGraw-Hill Book Company, New York, 1967.

Neilsen, L. E.: "Mechanical Properties of Polymers," Reinhold Publishing Corporation, New York, 1966.

Nylen, P., and E. Sunderland: "Modern Surface Coatings," chap. 15, Interscience Publishers, a division of John Wiley & Sons, Inc., New York, 1965.

Parker, R. S., and P. Taylor: "Adhesion and Adhesives," chap. 4, Pergamon Press, New York, 1966.

Payne, H. F.: "Organic Coating Technology," chap. 15, John Wiley & Sons, Inc., New York, 1954.

Petronio, M.: Testing of Adhesives, in I. Skeist (ed.), "Handbook of Adhesives," chap. 5, Reinhold Publishing Corporation, New York, 1962.

Randolph, A. F. (ed.): "SPI Plastics Engineering Handbook," chap. 24, Reinhold Publishing Corporation, New York, 1960.

Rogers, C. E.: Permeability vs. Chemical Resistance, in E. Baer (ed.), "Engineering Design for Plastics," chap. 9, Reinhold Publishing Corporation, New York, 1964.

Schmidt, D. L.: Ablation, in E. Baer (ed.), "Engineering Design for Plastics," chap. 13, Reinhold Publishing Corporation, New York, 1964.

Schmitz, J. V. (ed.): "Testing of Polymers," vols. 1–3, Interscience Publishers, a division of John Wiley & Sons, Inc., New York, 1965–1967.

Setchin, N. P.: *ASTM Bull.*, **15:**66 (1948).

Seymour, R. B.: Tests for Chemical Resistance, in I. M. Kolthoff and P. J. Elving (eds.), "Treatise on Analytical Chemistry," Pt. 3, Interscience Publishers, a division of John Wiley & Sons, Inc., New York, 1970.

———— and R. B. Steiner: "Plastics for Corrosion Resistance Applications," Reinhold Publishing Corporation, New York, 1955.

Sharbaugh, A. H.: Electrical Property Tests, in J. V. Schmitz (ed.), "Testing of Polymers," vol. 1, chap. 5, Interscience Publishers, a division of John Wiley & Sons, Inc., New York, 1965.

Skinkle, J. H.: "Textile Testing," chap. 10, Chemical Publishing Corporation, Inc., New York, 1949.

Stannett, V., and H. Yasuda: Gas and Vapor Permeation, in J. V. Schmitz (ed.), "Testing of Polymers," vol. 1, chap. 13, Interscience Publishers, a division of John Wiley & Sons, Inc., New York, 1965.

Strella, S.: Impact Behavior, in E. Baer (ed.), "Engineering Design for Plastics," chap. 12, Reinhold Publishing Corporation, New York, 1964.

Teeple, J. H.: Methods of Testing, in R. Houwink (ed.), "Elastomers and Polymers," vol. 3, chap. 2, American Elsevier Publishing Company, Inc., New York, 1948.

Thorkildsen, R. L.: Mechanical Behavior of Polymers, in E. Baer (ed.), "Engineering Design for Plastics," chap. 5, Reinhold Publishing Corporation, New York, 1948.

Tobolsky, A. V.: "Properties and Structures of Polymers," John Wiley & Sons, Inc., New York, 1960.

Van Delinder, L. S.: Weight and Loss Tests, *Mater. Protection*, **2**(5):30 (1963).

Weiss, E.: Ozone Resistance, in J. V. Schmitz (ed.), "Testing of Polymers," vol. 2, chap. 9, Interscience Publishers, a division of John Wiley & Sons, Inc., New York, 1966.

14

Polymer Technology

Much of the present polymer technology has benefited from both empirical and theoretical contributions. The modern polymer scientist must recognize the importance of both approaches. Major contributions, such as those of Ziegler and Natta, have been representative of both theoretical and empirical advances in polymer science. Typical applications of polymers as fibers, elastomers, organic coatings, and plastics will be discussed in this chapter.

14-1 FIBERS

By the ASTM definition of a fiber, the ratio of length to diameter is at least 100 : 1. The properties of all fibers are related to macromolecular structure and production techniques. The processing of natural fibers is dependent on their inherent properties and the fiber lengths of these materials. Synthetic fibers are much more versatile, and the processing techniques are usually an adaptation of the natural-fiber art. Fibers may be of natural origin, such as cotton or wool, or they may be obtained by an extrusion process using a spinneret. This process may use a molten polymer, such as nylon (melt spinning), or a solution of polymer. After the polymer solution passes through the small orifices in the spinnerets, it may be coagulated in a non-solvent (*wet spinning*), or the solvent may be evaporated (*dry spinning*). Rayon is produced by passsing a xanthate solution into an acid bath. Poly-acrylonitrile fiber is produced by evaporation of the solvent used to form the solution. It is customary to draw (stretch) these filaments in order to align the molecular chains and thus improve the physical properties of the fibers.

The term *rayon* was coined in 1924 to replace the less desirable term artificial silk. These continuous cellulosic filaments were originally produced by Chardonnet by the extrusion of collodion through spinnerets and the denitrification of the cellulose nitrate filaments produced. Cellulose may also be dissolved in Schweitzer's reagent (cuprammonia process). The regenerated cellulose obtained by the extrusion of this solution has excellent properties but is not competitive with fibers obtained by other techniques used for rayon production.

Most rayon is produced by the viscose process in which α-cellulose is converted to alkali cellulose which in turn is reacted with carbon disulfide to produce cellulose xanthate. The degree of polymerization $(\overline{DP})$ of the extrudate is controlled by aging the alkali cellulose and/or cellulose xanthate solution (ripening). A high-molecular-weight cellulose fiber (polynosic rayon) is obtained when the aging steps are omitted.

Cellulose acetate fibers are obtained by the dry spinning of an acetone solution of cellulose diacetate (secondary acetate). The triacetate (Tricel) which is obtained by the acetic acid–acetic anhydride acetylation of cellulose in the presence of sulfuric acid is insoluble in acetone. It is converted to the more soluble product by saponification. Complete saponification of extruded cellulose acetate filaments yields regenerated cellulose (Fortisan).

The processing of rayon or cellulose acetate fiber is similar to that of cotton or other natural fibers. However, the staple length of synthetic fibers is not dependent on nature but is controlled by cutting the continuous filament into appropriate lengths. Likewise, artificial proteinaceous fibers (Azlon) may be processed like wool. These fibers are obtained by passing an alkaline solution of natural proteins through spinnerets into an acid solution. Casein, peanuts (Ardil), soybean (Aralac), and zein (Vicara) have been used as a source of protein. The properties of the filaments are improved by subsequent treatment with formaldehyde.

The principal totally synthetic fibers are nylon, polyesters, polyurethanes, polyacrylonitrile, and polypropylene. Nylon 6,6 or 6 is produced by melt-spinning the molten polymers in an inert atmosphere. The coarse filaments may be used for the production of brush bristles. The finer filaments are processed to form yarn.

Melt-spinning techniques are also used to produce polyester filaments (Dacron, Terylene, Kodel, Vycron). Polyacrylonitrile (Acrilan, Orlon) is dry-spun from solutions such as dimethyl formamide. Polyurethane filaments (Perlon, Spandex) are obtained by melt-spinning polyurethane resins in an inert atmosphere.

Filaments of polypropylene, polyethylene, Saran, or other thermally stable thermoplastic polymers may be obtained by melt-spinning or by film slitting. In the latter process, a film strip or tape may be twisted to form a twine. This twine may be used as such, or it may be heated and stretched to form fibrils which may be spun to form textile yarns. These yarns may be used for carpets or other textile products.

Fibers, such as cellulose or glass, may be bonded together by thermoplastic resins. These resins may be added in the form of solution, latex, or fiber, and the composite may be converted to a bonded product (nonwoven textile) by heating. These products are sometimes referred to erroneously as paper. The production of wool felt and paper are classic examples of bonding processes which do not require additional polymers as binder.

Paper is produced by forming a wet web of fibers on a screen from an aqueous suspension. Additives such as fillers, starch, dyes, etc., may be added to the fibers in a beater before the admixture is placed on the screen. Water is then removed from the cellulosic web in a series of steps on a Foudrinier machine. Wool felt is produced by steam heating and pressing a thick layer of webs of wool. The resulting dense sheet is hammered while wet to obtain a strong entanglement of fibers (felt).

The physical properties of typical fibers are listed in Table 14-1.

Table 14-1   Physical Properties of Typical Fibers

POLYMER	TENACITY, g/denier	TENSILE STRENGTH, psi	ELONGATION, %
CELLULOSE			
Cotton	2.1–6.3	42–125,000	3–10
Rayon	1.5–2.4	29– 47,000	15–30
High-tenacity rayon	3.0–5.0	66– 88,000	9–20
Cellulose diacetate	1.1–1.4	18– 23,000	25–45
Cellulose triacetate	1.2–1.4	20– 23,000	25–40
PROTEINS			
Silk	2.8–5.2	45– 83,000	13–31
Wool	1.0–1.7	17– 28,000	20–50
Vicara	1.1–1.2	18– 20,000	30–35
Nylon 6,6	4.5–6.0	66– 88,000	26
Polyester	4.4–5.0	77– 88,000	19–23
Polyacrylonitrile	2.3–2.6	33– 38,000	20–28
Saran	1.1–2.9	25– 60,000	20–35
Polyurethane (Spandex)	0.7	9,000	575
Polypropylene	7.0	80,000	25
Asbestos	1.3	300,000	25
Glass	7.7	300,000	3.0

REFERENCES

American Viscose Co.: "Rayon Technology," McGraw-Hill Book Company, New York, 1953.

Britt, K. W.: "Pulp and Paper Technology," Reinhold Publishing Corporation, New York, 1964.

Buresh, F. M.: Nonwoven Materials, in H. R. Simonds and J. M. Church (eds.), "The Encyclopedia of Basic Materials for Plastics," Reinhold Publishing Corporation, New York, 1967.

Cook, J. G.: "Handbook of Textile Fibers," Morrow Publishing Company, Wolford, England, 1964.

Frados, J. E.: Slit-Split Film, *Mod. Plastics,* **44**(12):82 (1967).

Galanti, A. V., and C. L. Mantell: "Polypropylene Fibers and Films," Plenum Press, New York, 1968.

Goldman, J. H.: Bonded Textiles, U.S. Patent 2,039,312, May 5, 1936.

Harris, M.: "Handbook of Textile Fibers," Harris Research Laboratories, Washington, D.C., 1957.

Hill, R.: "Fibers from Synthetic Polymers," American Elsevier Publishing Company, Inc., New York, 1953.

Kornreich, E.: "Introduction to Fibers and Fabrics," American Elsevier Publishing Company, Inc., New York, 1966.

Lewis, F. D.: "Chemistry and Technology of Rayon," Reigate Publishing Ltd., London, 1961.

Lynn, J. E., and J. J. Press: "Advances in Textile Processing," Interscience Publishers, Inc., New York, 1961.

Mark, H. F. (ed.): "Man-made Fibers," vol. I, John Wiley & Sons, Inc., New York, 1967.

Meyer, K. H.: "Natural and Synthetic High Polymers," 2d ed., Interscience Publishers, Inc., New York, 1950.

Moncrief, R. W.: "Artificial Fibers," John Wiley & Sons, Inc., New York, 1954.

Press, J. J.: "Man-made Textiles Encyclopedia," Interscience Publisher, Inc., New York, 1959.

Riley, J. L.: Spinning and Drawing of Fibers, in C. E. Schildknecht (ed.), "Polymer Processes," chap. 18, Interscience Publishers, Inc., New York, 1956.

Rosato, D. V.: "Revolution in Textiles," *Plastics World,* **25**(12):34 (1967).

Seymour, R. B., and G. M. Schroeder: Nonwoven Textiles, *Paper Trade J.,* p. 15, Mar. 31, 1949.

14-2 ELASTOMERS

Rubber latex which is obtained by tapping *Hevea braziliensis* trees may be concentrated by centrifugation or creaming and stabilized by the addition of ammonia. Dispersions of curing agents and pigments are usually added before removal of the water when the latex is used for the production of dipped articles, such as gloves, or of foam rubber.

Pale crepe is produced by coagulating latex, washing the coagulum, and then passing the coagulated rubber through corrugated rolls. Smoked sheet is obtained when the coagulated rubber sheet is dried with smoke and hot air. Decomposition of nonrubber organic materials occurs when the coagulated rubber is aged before drying. A dark-colored rubber blanket is produced in this aging process. Compounding ingredients are usually added to the dried coagulated rubber in a Banbury mixer or on a rubber mill.

The principal synthetic elastomers are poly(butadiene-co-styrene) (GRS, SBR, Buna S), butyl rubber (IIR), Neoprene (CR), poly(butadiene-co-acrylonitrile) (NBR, Buna N), *cis*-polybutadiene (BR), poly(ethylene-co-propylene) (EPM), poly(epichlorohydrin) (CO), polyurethane (AU, EU), polyacrylates (AR), silicones (SI), and poly(fluorinated hydrocarbon) (FPM).

Over 4 billion pounds of synthetic elastomers are produced annually in the United States. The principal product, poly(butadiene-co-styrene), which contains 75 percent butadiene and 25 percent styrene, accounts for about two-thirds of the total synthetic-rubber production. Some of the trade names for this elastomer are Ameripol, ASRC, COPO, Duradene, Flosbrene, Gentro SBR, Goodrite, Kraton, Naugopol, Philprene, Plioflex, Solprene, and Synpol.

This elastomer is produced by the emulsion polymerization of butadiene (75) and styrene (25) in the presence of soap (2); a buffer (2), dodecyl; mercaptan (1); potassium persulfate (1); and water (400) at 40°F. The propagation is discontinued after about 60 percent conversion by the addition of a "short stop" (hydroquinone) and an antioxidant (phenyl-β-naphthylamine). The residual monomers are removed by distillation (stripping). Dispersions of carbon black and oil may be added to the latex before flocculation or they may be added with sulfur accelerators and zinc oxide on a rubber mill or in Banbury mixer. The principal use of this copolymer (SBR) is for tire-tread stocks.

Poly(butadiene-co-acrylonitrile) (Buna N) is also produced by emulsion polymerization. The percent of acrylonitrile may be varied from 10 to 40 percent of the total monomers. These copolymers are characterized by good low-temperature flexibility and solvent resistance. The products are sold under the trade names Butaprene-N, Chemigum N, FRN, Hycar, Krynar, Krylene, Paracril, and Perbunan. These copolymers may be blended with poly(styrene-co-acrylonitrile) to increase the impact resistance of these plastics. The oil-resistant polyacrylates are also produced by emulsion-polymerization techniques. They are sold under the names Lactoprene, Cyanacryl, and Thiacril and are used principally as gaskets.

Poly(ethylene sulfide) (Thiokol), which is characterized by good resistance to solvents, is used for the production of mechanical goods, such as gasoline hose. Neoprene, which is produced by the emulsion polymerization of chloroprene, is characterized by excellent tensile strength and good resistance to oils and flame.

Butyl rubber is produced by the cationic copolymerization of isobutylene (97) and isoprene (3). These elastomers, which are sold under the trade names Enjay Butyl and Polysar, are characterized by excellent resistance to ozonolysis and low permeability to gases. The principal uses for this copolymer are for inner tubes and liners for pneumatic tires.

Polybutadiene and polyisoprene are produced by the polymerization of the appropriate dienes in the presence of coordination catalysts, such as Ziegler-Natta catalysts. These products are sold under the trade names Ameripol SN, Budene, Cisdene, cis-4, Coral rubber, Diene, Duragen, Natsyn, and Synpol.

Copolymers of ethylene (75) and propylene (25) may be cured in the presence of benzoyl peroxide. Diene-containing terpolymers produced from ethylene and propylene may be cured with sulfur. Since these elastomers have high molecular weights, they may be oil-extended and reinforced with large proportions of carbon black. Poly(epichlorohydrin) (Hydrin 100) and the copolymer of epichlorohydrin and ethylene oxide (Hydrin 200) are

Table 14-2   Physical Properties of Typical Elastomers

POLYMER	PURE-GUM VULCANIZATES		CARBON-BLACK-REINFORCED VULCANIZATES	
	TENSILE STRENGTH, psi	ELONGATION, %	TENSILE STRENGTH, psi	ELONGATION, %
Natural rubber (NR)	3,000	700	4,500	600
Styrene-butadiene rubber (SBR)	400	800	3,800	550
Acrylonitrile-butadiene rubber (NBR)	600	600	3,000	550
Polyacrylates (ABR)			2,500	400
Thiokol (ET)	300	300	1,200	400
Neoprene (CR)	3,500	800	3,500	700
Butyl rubber (IIR)	3,000	1,000	3,000	400
Polyisoprene (IR)	3,000	700	4,500	600
Ethylene-propylene rubber (EPM)				
Poly(epichlorohydrin) (CO)				
Poly(fluorinated hydrocarbons) (FPM)				
Silicone elastomers (SI)				
Polyurethane elastomers (AU)	5,000	600	6,000	500

characterized by excellent resistance to flame, oxygen, and ozone and by low-temperature flexibility.

Poly(fluorinated hydrocarbons) (Viton, Fluorel), which are characterized by excellent resistance to solvents and corrosive liquids at elevated temperatures, are used as gaskets. Silicone elastomers (Silastic) are characterized by the retention of physical properties over a wide range of temperature. They are used for steam hose and gaskets. The poly(fluorosilicones) have excellent solvent resistance.

Polyurethane elastomers are characterized by excellent resistance to abrasion and solvents. These products are sold under the trade names Adiprene, Elastothene, Estane, Genthane, Scotchcast, Texin, and Vibrathene. These polymers may be cast to produce gaskets, seals, and printing rolls. The physical properties of typical elastomers are listed in Table 14-2.

REFERENCES

Barron, H.: "Modern Rubber Chemistry," D. Van Nostrand Company, Inc., Princeton, N.J., 1948.

Burton, G. M.: "Engineering with Rubber," McGraw-Hill Book Company, New York, 1949.

Davis, C. C., and J. T. Blake: "The Chemistry and Technology of Rubber," Reinhold Publishing Corporation, New York, 1957.

D'Ianni, J. D.: Butadiene-Styrene Rubbers, in M. Morton (ed.), "Introduction to Rubber Technology," chap. 10, Reinhold Publishing Corporation, New York, 1964.

Fisher, H. L.: "Chemistry of Natural and Synthetic Rubber," chap. 9, Reinhold Publishing Corporation, New York, 1957.

Huke, D. W.: "Introduction to Natural and Synthetic Rubber," chap. 6, Chemical Publishing Company, Inc., New York, 1961.

McGregor, R. R.: "Silicones and Their Uses," McGraw-Hill Book Company, New York, 1954.

Mienes, K.: "Plastics in Europe," chap. 9, Chemical Publishing Company, Inc., New York, 1964.

Morton, M.: Elastomers, in G. L. Clark and G. G. Hawley (eds.), "Encyclopedia of Chemistry," 2d ed., Reinhold Publishing Corporation, New York, 1966.

———: Latex, Rubber, in G. L. Clark and G. G. Hawley (eds.), "Encyclopedia of Chemistry," 2d ed., Reinhold Publishing Corporation, New York, 1966.

Naunton, W. J. S.: "The Applied Science of Rubber," St. Martin's Press, Inc., New York, 1961.

Rochow, E. G.: "An Introduction to the Chemistry of the Silicones," John Wiley & Sons, Inc., New York, 1951.

Rosato, D. V.: Elastomers, *Plastics World,* **25**(4):30 (1967); **25**(5):50 (1967).

Stern, H. J.: "Rubber: Natural and Synthetic," MacLaren and Sons Ltd. London, 1954.

Whitby, G. S.: "Synthetic Rubber," John Wiley & Sons, Inc., New York, 1953.

———, C. C. Davis, and R. F. Dunbrook: "Synthetic Rubber," John Wiley & Sons, Inc., New York, 1954.

14-3 FILMS, COATINGS, ADHESIVES, AND LAMINATES

A film is a continuous, homogeneous, dimensionally stable form of a polymer having a small thickness in relation to area. Films which may be used for either decoration or protection may be produced by the calendering or extrusion of polymers or by casting films from hot melts or solutions. Films with controlled thickness may be produced by bulk polymerization in situ. ASTM recommends that film and sheet be differentiated on the basis of thickness. Thus, a film is a polymeric sheet having a thickness of less than 0.010 in.

In spite of its wide use, the term *film* is not applied to paper or other fibrous sheets. However, the term is applied when the fibers are dissolved and passed through a slit die as in the production of cellophane from cellulose xanthate solutions. As might be anticipated from its polarity, cellophane film has a high moisture-vapor-transmission rate (MVT) and good resistance to organic vapors. About 500 million pounds of cellophane is produced annually in the United States but it is being replaced by less expensive films, such as polyethylene.

Low-density polyethylene film (type I) is more permeable to gases and has a higher folding endurance than cellophane. Polyethylene film is less transparent than cellophane but the transparency can be improved by passing warm film over chilled rolls. Polyethylene film is produced by blowing an extruded tube of the polymer prior to slitting. Approximately 1 billion pounds of polyethylene film is produced annually in the United States. In contrast to cellophane, this film may be readily heat-sealed.

Polyethylene film may be used for packaging; as a moisture barrier in construction; for temporary shelters, such as greenhouses; as tape; and for lining reservoirs. Because of its increased rigidity, high-density polyethylene (type II) is preferred when heavy polyethylene sheet is used.

Cellulose acetate, cellulose acetate butyrate, and ethyl cellulose films have high moisture-vapor-transmission rates. These films are used for transparent packaging, photographic film, and blister or skin packaging applications in which the warm film is drawn around the article to be protected. Rubber hydrochloride (Pliofilm) is used to a limited extent for packaging.

Films of plasticized poly(vinyl chloride) may be produced by extrusion, calendering, or casting. They are widely used for packaging and for water-resistant sheeting, such as shower curtains and clothing. Almost 500 million pounds of this type of film is produced annually in the United States. Both plasticized and rigid poly(vinyl chloride) sheets are used as tank linings in the chemical processing industry. Poly(vinylidene chloride) (Saran) film may be oriented to produce high-strength wrapping material (Saran Wrap).

Poly(vinyl alcohol) films are characterized by high moisture-vapor-transmission rates and moderate solubility in hot water. Thus, these strong films may be used for water-soluble packaging.

Poly(ethylene terephthalate) films (Mylar, Videne, Celanar) may be oriented after melt extrusion to produce uniformly strong films. These films are characterized by excellent resistance to moisture, solvents, and folding. However, they may be solvent-sealed with benzyl alcohol. These strong films have been used to wrap prepared foods since the foods may be cooked in this type of packaging.

Because of its inherent brittleness, most polystyrene film is modified through copolymerization with other monomers or by blending with more flexible polymers. The film is usually oriented to produce a strong transparent product suitable for packaging. The modified sheet is used for thermoforming articles ranging from luggage to automobile bodies.

Both poly(methyl methacrylate) and polycarbonate sheets have been used for glazing and display signs. Polyurethane film, which is characterized by unusual toughness, has been used as a transparent container for oil and other liquid fuels. Nylon film has been used as a food packaging material which may remain intact during the cooking process. Chlorinated polyether sheet (Penton) has been used as a lining for tanks containing corrosive liquids. Polytetrafluoroethylene film is used for electrical applications and as a coating to provide nonstick surfaces. Poly(vinyl fluoride) (Tedlar) film is used as a protective coating for building panels.

Properly selected films have been used as membranes for the dialysis of aqueous salts, alkalies, and acids. The rate of this spontaneous irreversible process may be accelerated by electrodialysis. In addition to their use in many well-known biological processes, polymeric membranes have been used for the dialysis of brackish water and industrial metallic salt solutions. The properties of typical films are listed in Table 14-3.

Polyethylene, poly(ethylene terephthalate), cellulose acetate, nylon, poly(vinyl chloride), and poly(vinylidene chloride) films have been used as membranes in industrial dialysis processes. In a typical installation in South Africa, the salinity of brackish water is reduced by 300 to 500 ppm at a daily rate of 3 million gallons. Commercial dialyzers are used to recover nickel salts in copper refineries.

Since the permeability of films is related to the molecular structure, properly selected films may be used to separate gaseous mixtures. It is assumed that in the diffusion process the gas condenses and dissolves in the surface layer and then migrates through the film in accordance with the mobility of the gaseous molecules and their solubility in the film. Thus a mixture of methane and nitrogen may be separated by use of a natural-rubber membrane in which methane is preferentially soluble.

Table 14-3 Properties of Polymer Films

PERMEABILITY TO GASES, cm³/day/100 in.²/mil @ 25°C

POLYMER	MVT	CO₂	H₂	N₂	O₂	INITIAL TEARING STRENGTH, g/mil
Cellophane	0.4–134	0.4–0.6	1.2–2.2	0.5–1.6	0.2–5.0	2–20
Polyethylene (I)	1.0–1.5	2,700	...	180	500	100–500
Polyethylene (III)	0.3	580	...	42	185	15–300
Rubber hydrochloride	...	288–13,500	...	...	38–2,250	60–1,600
Cellulose acetate	30–40	860–1,000	835	30–40	117–150	1–2
Cellulose acetate butyrate	30–40	6,000	...	250	950	5–10
Ethyl cellulose	4.8–14.2	5,000	...	600	2,000	215–395
Plasticized poly(vinyl chloride)	4	100–3,000	...	...	30–2,000	60–1,400
Saran	...	12	...	...	2.4	10–100
Poly(vinyl alcohol)	...	200	...	...	120	785–890
Poly(ethylene terephthalate)	1.7–1.8	15–25	100	017–1.0	6.0–8.0	12–27
Polystyrene (oriented)	7.0–10.0	900	...	...	350	5.0
Polycarbonate	11.0	1,075	1,600	50	300	20–25
Polyurethane	45–75	465–1,650	...	41–119	75–327	220–710
Nylon 6,6	3–6	9.1	...	0.35	5.0	50–90
Nylon 6	5.4–20	10–12	110	0.9	2.6	
Poly(vinyl fluoride)	3.24	11.1	58	0.25	3	12–100

The principal synthetic polymers used as coatings are alkyd resins, styrene copolymers, poly(vinyl acetate), urea, melamine, phenolic and epoxy resins, polyurethane, and poly(methyl methacrylate). All polymer coatings consist of a resin or resin-forming component (binder) and may contain other components such as pigments, fillers, and solvents. However, the properties of the coating are dependent primarily on the binder. In many instances, the type of coating is indicated by the descriptive name of varnish, lacquer, paint, etc.

Thus, a spirit varnish is a solution of natural resin, such as shellac, in ethanol. Oleoresinous varnishes consist of resins and drying oils dissolved in solvents (thinners). A lacquer, which is a solution of a resin such as cellulose nitrate in a solvent, may be an enamel if pigments are present. A paint is a dispersion of a pigment in a resinous solution which cures (dries) by polymerization. Printing inks are essentially viscous paints.

Drying oils may be linseed, oiticica, tung, or dehydrated castor oil or appropriate modifications of these oils. Driers such as organic salts of heavy metals catalyze the formation of resins from these oils. The annual production of alkyd resins is greater than 500 million pounds in the United States. These resins are used in coating formulations for automobile bodies, household appliances, and exterior paints.

Many coatings are deposited on a substrate by brushing or spraying solutions of thermoplastic or thermosetting resins. The latter may be cured by heating with or without appropriate catalysts. Viscous coating formulations with high proportions of fillers (mastics) may be applied by troweling. Pigmented aqueous dispersions of resins may also be used as coatings. Rubber latex was the pioneer aqueous-dispersion type of coating. This art has been extended to include aqueous dispersions of poly(vinyl acetate), poly(methyl methacrylate), and poly(styrene-co-butadiene). These pigmented aqueous dispersions are widely used as wall coatings. They may also be electrodeposited on metals such as automobile frames. The glass transition temperature (T_g) of resins in latex blends may be estimated from the Fox equation when the relative weights (W) of the polymers are known:

$$\frac{1}{T_g} \text{ blend} = \frac{W_A}{T_{gA}} + \frac{W_B}{T_{gB}} \tag{14-1}$$

Fox equation for estimation of glass transition temperature of latex blends

The hot-melt process, formerly used for the application of asphalt and coal-tar pitch to roofs, walls, and pipelines, has been extended to many other thermoplastic resins. Petroleum resins and polyethylene may be applied in the molten form and spread with a knife to control thickness. Uniform coatings of thermoplastic polymers, such as polyethylene, may also be applied by extrusion.

Finely divided particles of polyethylene or other thermoplastic polymers may be applied by the fluidized bed or swirl sintering technique. In this process, finely divided polymer particles impinge on a preheated surface at a temperature above the melting point of the polymer, and the composite is postheated to provide a uniform protective film. When a polymer film does not adhere, this process may be used to produce intricately shaped articles. Thermoplastic resins may also be flame-sprayed in a process adapted from the metal arts.

Adhesives are actually coatings between two surfaces. The classic adhesives were water-susceptible animal and vegetable glues such as those obtained from hides and blood or from starch. It is of interest to note that some plywood is still bonded with blood glues and that starch and dextrin are widely used as adhesives for paper.

Boyd and Harkins defined *adhesion* as that process that occurs when (1) a solid and a liquid are brought together to form an interface and (2) the surface energies of the two substances are transformed into the energy of the interface and heat is involved. Thus, in contrast to the attraction of like materials as in the welding process (cohesion), adhesion involves the attraction of unlike materials at an interface. Secondary valence forces are involved in adhesion, and the bond strength cannot be greater than the sum of the molecular forces present.

The forces between the adhesive and the adherend may be small but, as in other intermolecular attractions related to macromolecules, these forces are additive. Adhesives must be fluid at some stage during the application and must wet the surfaces of the adherend while in the fluid state. Adhesion is favored when the solubility parameter of the adhesive has a high numerical value. The adhesion is enhanced by the presence of polar groups. Thus, poly(cyanoacrylates) are superior to poly(fluorinated hydrocarbons) as adhesives. Adhesives may be applied as melts, solutions, or aqueous dispersions. These adhesive films must be stabilized by setting or curing so that they are not readily displaced.

The combination of an adhesive and adherend is a *laminate*. Commercial laminates are produced on a large scale, with a substance such as wood as the adherend and phenolic, resorcinol, urea, epoxy, or polyester resins as the adhesives. Wood laminates are called *plywood*. Laminates of paper or textile are known under the trade names of Formica and Micarta. Strong structural members are produced by laminating wood with thermosetting resins such as phenol-formaldehyde condensates at high pressures.

Laminates of phenolic, silicone, or nylon resins with paper, cotton, asbestos, or glass textile are used as mechanical, electrical, and general-purpose structural materials. Composites of fibrous glass, mat, or sheet and epoxy or polyester resins are used widely as reinforced plastic structures.

REFERENCES

Bobalek, E. G.: Coatings, in H. F. Mark, N. G. Gaylord, and N. M. Bikales (eds.), "Encyclopedia of Polymer Science and Technology," Interscience Publishers, a division of John Wiley & Sons, Inc., New York, 1965.

Boyd, G. E., and W. D. Harkins: *J. Am. Chem. Soc.*, **64**:1190 (1942).

Chatfield, H. W.: "The Science of Surface Coatings," D. Van Nostrand Company, Inc., Princeton, N.J., 1962.

Damusis, A. (ed.): "Sealants," Reinhold Publishing Corporation, New York, 1967.

DeBruyne, N. A., and R. Houwink: "Adhesion and Adhesives," Elsevier Publishing Company, Amsterdam, 1951.

Delmonte, J.: "The Technology of Adhesives," Reinhold Publishing Corporation, New York, 1967.

Dietz, A. G. H.: "Engineering Laminates," John Wiley & Sons, Inc., New York, 1949.

Duffin, D. J., and C. Nerzig: "Laminated Plastics," Reinhold Publishing Corporation, New York, 1958.

Frados, J.: "Modern Plastics Encyclopedia," 45 (1A), p. 528, McGraw-Hill Book Company, New York, 1967.

Fuller, E. D., W. E. Henderson, and P. H. Lindenmeyer: Film Applications, in A. Renfrew and P. Morgan (eds.), "Polythene," chap. 26, Iliffe Books, Ltd., London, 1957.

Kumins, C. A., et al.: Transport in Polymeric Films, *ACS Div. Polymer Chem., Polymer Preprints,* **6**(1):396 (1965).

Leeson, E. J.: Properties of Latex Blends, *Rubber World,* **157**(3):62 (1967).

Martens, C. R.: "Emulsion and Water Soluble Paints and Coatings," Reinhold Publishing Corporation, New York, 1964.

Morgan, P.: "Glass Reinforced Plastics," 2d ed., Iliffe Books, Ltd., London, 1957.

Myers, C. S. (ed.): Adhesives and Sealants in Building, *Bldg. Res. Inst., Publ.* 577, 1958.

Nylen, P., and E. Sunderland: "Modern Surface Coatings," Interscience Publishers, Inc., a division of John Wiley & Sons, Inc., New York, 1965.

Parker, D. H.: "Principles of Surface Coating Technology," Interscience Publishers, a division of John Wiley & Sons, Inc., New York, 1965.

Parker, R. S., and R. P. Taylor: "Adhesion and Adhesives," Pergamon Press, New York, 1966.

Payne, H. F.: "Organic Coating Technology," John Wiley & Sons, Inc., New York, 1954, 1961.

Perry, H. A.: "Adhesive Bonding of Reinforced Plastics," McGraw-Hill Book Company, New York, 1959.

Powers, W. J.: Adhesives, in C. E. Schildknecht (ed.), "Polymer Processes," chap. 12, Interscience Publishers, Inc., New York, 1956.

Rampelberg, V. H.: Paint Materials, in H. R. Simonds and J. M. Church (eds.), "The

Encyclopedia of Basic Materials for Plastics," Reinhold Publishing Corporation, New York, 1967.

Rosato, D. V.: Cable Coatings, *Plastics World*, **25**(6):38 (1967).

————: Coatings, *Plastics World*, **24**(6):42 (1966).

————: Film and Sheet, *Plastics World*, **24**(11):30 (1966).

————: Polyethylene, *Plastics World*, **25**(1):26 (1967).

————: Reinforced Plastics, *Plastics World*, **24**(2):30 (1966).

Scofield, F., J. Bigos, and R. B. Seymour: Organic Coatings, in C. L. Mantell (ed.), "Materials Engineering Handbook," sec. 34, McGraw-Hill Book Company, New York, 1958.

Seymour, R. B.: "Hot Organic Coatings," Reinhold Publishing Corporation, New York, 1960.

———— and M. Gallagher: Polyester Laminates, *Mod. Plastics*, **27**(7):111 (1950).

————: Polymer Coatings, *Org. Finishing*, **14**(3):9 (1953).

Skeist, I.: Adhesives, in G. L. Clark and G. G. Hawley (eds.), "Encyclopedia of Chemistry," Reinhold Publishing Corporation, New York, 1966.

————: "Handbook of Adhesives," Reinhold Publishing Corporation, New York, 1962.

Solomon, D. H.: "The Chemistry of Organic Film Formers," John Wiley & Sons, Inc., New York, 1967.

Sonnenborn, R. A.: "Fiberglass Reinforced Plastics," Reinhold Publishing Corporation, New York, 1964.

Toropov, N. A. (ed.): "Heat Resistant Coatings," Plenum Publishing Corporation, New York, 1967.

Tuwiner, S. B., L. P. Miller, and W. E. Brown: "Diffusion and Membrane Technology," Reinhold Publishing Corporation, New York, 1962.

Von Fischer, W. V., and E. G. Bobalek: Paints, in G. L. Clark and G. G. Hawley (eds.), "Encyclopedia of Chemistry," Reinhold Publishing Corporation, New York, 1966.

14-4 CELLULAR POLYMERS

Natural sponges have been used for centuries, but the first useful synthetic sponge was not produced until the 1920s. Cellular products from both hard and soft rubber were marketed in the early 1920s, and a product obtained by whipping or frothing rubber latex was introduced in 1929.

Polymer foams may consist of discrete unit cells (unicellular, closed cells) or they may be made up of interconnecting cells (multicellular, open cells). The type of structure obtained is controlled to a large extent by the time at which the blowing agent expands the polymer. If the polymer film formed is weak, as evidenced by low viscosity, the cell walls will be ruptured when blown and an open-cell foam will result. However, if the introduction of gas is delayed until the polymer film is stronger, the gas will be retained and the foam will be unicellular. Unicellular foams are useful for insulation, buoyancy, and flotation applications. Multicellular foams are used advantageously for upholstery and laminated clothing. The density of the product can be controlled by the amount of gas introduced. Products with densities ranging from 0.1 to 60 lb/ft^3 may be produced. The thermal conductivity (K factor) is usually less than 0.30 Btu-in./°F ft hr. The K factor is related to the area A, thickness X, time t, temperature differential ΔT, and the quantity of heat Q that flows across the specimen. These relationships are shown in the following equation:

$$K = \frac{QX}{A\,\Delta Tt} \tag{14-2}$$

Relationship of thermal conductivity to variables in cellular products

Sponge rubber is produced by mixing a blowing agent such as sodium bicarbonate or p,p'-oxy-bis(benzenesulfonyl hydrazide) (Celogen O.T., Genitron OB)

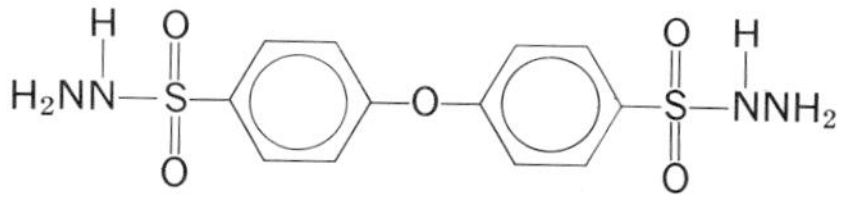

with rubber and other compounding ingredients. If curing starts before the gas is released, unicellular sponge will be produced. If the gas is released before vulcanization, the product will be multicellular.

Foamed rubber is produced from soap-stabilized rubber latex by modifications of the Dunlop or Talalay process. In the former, a delayed-action gelling agent, such as sodium fluosilicate, is added to the compounded latex and the mixture is whipped like cream or egg whites. The expanded matrix is cured and dried in the form of molded cushions or slabs. In the Talalay process, catalases in the form of yeast and hydrogen peroxide are added to produce oxygen which serves as the foaming agent. The resultant foam is frozen, and carbon dioxide is added to deactivate the soap before curing. Mold filling may be assured by the application of a vacuum to the closed mold before curing.

Foamed rubber is multicellular. The principal type of latex used is SBR but these techniques have also been used with natural rubber, Neoprene, polyisoprene, and poly(butadiene-co-acrylonitrile). Foamed rubber is used for mattresses, automotive pads, cushions, and a host of other applications.

Cellular polymers may also be produced by the volatilization of a low-boiling liquid, such as pentane; by the addition of a propellant, such as dichlorodifluoromethane (Freon 12); by the production of a gaseous product, such as carbon dioxide; or by leaching out of soluble components from a mixture of polymer and additives.

Cellulose sponges are produced by dispersing a soluble salt, such as sodium sulfate, in viscose syrup. The cellulose xanthate is then decomposed by heating, and the salt is leached from the regenerated cellulose by water. Starch may be leached from mixtures of this water-soluble product and polyethylene or poly(vinyl chloride).

Cellular cellulose acetate (CCA, Strux) is a colorless rigid unicellular product produced by the flash evaporation of a solvent when a dough of cellulose acetate and acetone and ethanol is extruded. Cellular polyethylene is produced by extruding a mixture of the polymer and a blowing agent. Since this uncellular product has a low dielectric constant (1.5), it is used advantageously as a wire coating for high-frequency applications.

Shoe soles, inner soles, foamed wine corks, and paint-brush handles may be produced by the Engelit process. In this process plastic pellets are softened on a hot turntable and then scraped off. The warm pellets and ammonium carbonate are extruded to yield a corklike material with controlled density.

Preformed logs or boards of cellular polystyrene (Styrofoam) are produced by the extrusion of a mixture of polystyrene and a gaseous blowing agent. The latter vaporizes from the hot extrudate as it is transported and cooled on a moving belt. Molded articles, such as disposable insulated coffee cups, may be produced by heating expandable polystyrene beads (Dylite). These beads, which contain an integral blowing agent, may be preexpanded by heating with hot air or steam before molding.

A wide variety of unicellular and multicellular products may be obtained from poly(vinyl chloride). The principal cellular product is a plasticized polymer used to a large extent as an embossed foam-cloth laminate. This material is produced by heating a plastisol and azodicarbonamide. The cellular product is also used as a laminated floor covering. Poly(vinyl chloride) foams may also be produced by whipping air into surfactant- stabilized plastisols (Vanderbilt process) or by adding a gas under high pressure to plastisols (elastomer process).

Cellular plastics are produced by adding hydrazide blowing agents to liquid epoxy resin formulations, by dispersing air into solutions of catalyzed urea resins, and by adding isopropyl ether to liquid phenolic resin, in the presence of phosphoric acid. Syntactic foams have been produced by mixing hollow spheres (0.0013-in. diameter) of glass, urea, or phenolic resins (microballoons) with resin-forming prepolymers. Syntactic foams have been produced from crosslinked polystyrene, and phenolic, epoxy, and silicone resins. The density of these cellular products is controlled by the proportions of resin and microballoons. Silicone sponges produced by curing silicone rubber in the presence of a blowing agent are used in plastic surgery.

When water reacts with a diisocyanate, such as 2,4-tolylene diisocyanate

(TDI), an unstable carbamic acid is formed which decomposes into an amine and carbon dioxide. The amine and polyhydric compounds present react with the diisocyanate to produce polymers. Since carbon dioxide acts as a blowing agent, cellular polyurethanes are produced. Thus the density of these foams may be controlled to some extent by the amount of water added and by the addition of other propellants, such as dichlorodifluoromethane. The resiliency of these cellular products may be varied by the choice of reactants.

Products with superior resistance to elevated temperatures may be obtained by using high-molecular-weight diisocyanates, such as dianisidine diisocyanate (DADI), in place of the tolylene diisocyanate. Rigid cellular products may be obtained from the reaction of the diisocyanate and castor oil. The principal constituent of castor oil is the triglyceride of ricinoleic acid which contains three reactive hydroxyl groups, as shown below:

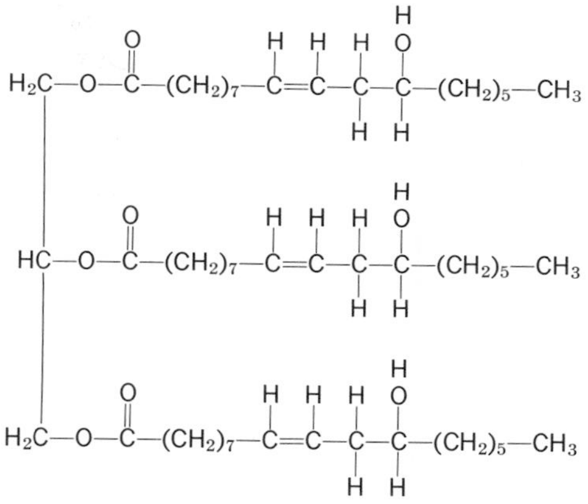

$$H_2C-O-\overset{\overset{O}{\|}}{C}-(CH_2)_7-\overset{H}{\underset{H}{C}}=\overset{H}{C}-\overset{H}{\underset{H}{C}}-\overset{\overset{H}{|}}{\underset{|}{C}}-(CH_2)_5-CH_3$$

$$HC-O-\overset{\overset{O}{\|}}{C}-(CH_2)_7-\overset{H}{\underset{H}{C}}=\overset{H}{C}-\overset{H}{\underset{H}{C}}-\overset{\overset{H}{|}}{\underset{|}{C}}-(CH_2)_5-CH_3 \qquad (14\text{-}3)$$

$$H_2C-O-\overset{\overset{O}{\|}}{C}-(CH_2)_7-\overset{H}{\underset{H}{C}}=\overset{H}{C}-\overset{H}{\underset{H}{C}}-\overset{\overset{H}{|}}{\underset{|}{C}}-(CH_2)_5-CH_3$$

Glyceryl ricinoleate (castor oil)

More flexible foams are produced when diisocyanates are reacted with polyesters having terminal end groups, i.e., low acid numbers. Products having resilience equivalent to foamed rubber are obtained by reactions of long-chain glycols containing flexibilizing groups in the polymer backbone, such as polyethers with terminal end groups. Most of the polyethers used are derivatives of propylene oxide, such as the reaction products of glycerol and propylene oxide.

The formation of cellular polyurethanes takes place at ordinary temperatures. The reaction is catalyzed by tertiary amines, such as triethylene diamine (Dabco), and tin compounds such as stannous octoate. It is cus-

Table 14-4 Properties of Cellular Polymers

POLYMER	COMPRESSIVE STRENGTH, psi	THERMAL CONDUCTIVITY (K factor), Btu-in./°F/ft²/hr	DENSITY, lb/ft³	MAXIMUM SERVICE TEMPERATURE, °F
Ebonite	40	0.21	4.0	122
Polystyrene	35	0.26	1.9	175
Poly(vinyl chloride)	40	0.19	2.2	125
Cellulose acetate	125	0.30	6–7	200
Phenolic resin	25	0.20	2.0	250
Urea resin	8	0.23	1.8	120
Silicone resin	6.2	0.28	3.5	650
Epoxy resin	25	0.11	2.3	200
Polyurethane (board form)	50	0.11	2.3	250

tomary to add silicones to stabilize the cellular structures. These products may be sprayed or poured in place. Proprietary spray guns are available for mixing the reactants either before or after the materials pass through the spray nozzle.

Polyurethane, like other cellular polymers, may be cast as slabs or foamed in place. These products are widely used for mattresses, carpet underlays, crash pads, insulation, buoyancy, and packaging. The properties of typical cellular polymers are shown in Table 14-4.

REFERENCES

Allen, H.: Vinyl Foam, *12th Ann. SPE Natl. Tech. Conf., Tech. Papers*, vol. II, p. 390, 1956.

Arnold, H. E.: Cellular PVC, *12th Ann. SPE Natl. Tech. Conf., Tech. Papers*, vol. II, p. 364, 1956.

Britain, J. W.: Polyurethanes, in W. M. Smith (ed.), "Manufacture of Plastics," vol. I, chap. 12, Reinhold Publishing Corporation, New York, 1964.

Carr, J. A., and B. B. Williams: Flexible Foams, *Mod. Plastics*, **33**(1):114 (1953).

Dombrow, B. A.: "Polyurethanes," Reinhold Publishing Corporation, New York, 1957.

Ferrigno, T. H.: "Rigid Foams," Reinhold Publishing Corporation, New York, 1967.

Franson, G. R.: Polystyrene Foam, *12th Ann. SPE Natl. Tech. Conf., Tech. Papers*, vol. II, p. 407, 1956.

Frisch, K. C., and H. C. Vogt: Foam Ingredients, in H. R. Simonds and J. M. Church (eds.), "The Encyclopedia of Basic Materials for Plastics," Reinhold Publishing Corporation, New York, 1967.

Gort, W. J.: Polystyrene Foam, in "Modern Plastics Encyclopedia," McGraw-Hill Book Company, New York, 1966.

Griffin, J. D., and R. E. Skochdopole: Plastic Foams, in E. Baer (ed.), "Engineering Design for Plastics," Reinhold Publishing Corporation, New York, 1964.

Harrington, C. J.: Polyurethane Foams, *12th Ann. SPE Natl. Tech. Conf., Tech. Papers,* vol. II, p. 380, 1956.

Laing, J. S., and H. J. Pavlansky: Polyethylene Foams, in "Modern Plastics Encyclopedia," McGraw-Hill Book Company, New York, 1969.

Lasman, H. R.: Foaming Agents, in "Modern Plastics Encyclopedia," McGraw-Hill Book Company, New York, 1969.

Lyman, D. J.: Polyurethanes, *Rev. Macromol. Chem.,* **1**(1):191 (1966).

Mark, H. F., N. G. Gaylord, and N. M. Bikales (eds.): "Encyclopedia of Polymer Science and Technology," Interscience Publishers, a division of John Wiley & Sons, Inc., New York, 1965.

Mason, C. P., and R. A. Steward: Poly(butadiene-co-methacrylonitrile) Foam, *Rubber World,* **757**(12):71 (1967).

Moiseyev, A. A., V. V. Pavlov, and M. Ya Borodin: "Expanded Plastics," The Macmillan Company, New York, 1963.

Randolf, A. R. (ed.): "Plastics Engineering Handbook," chap. 12, Reinhold Publishing Corporation, New York, 1960.

Rogers, T. H.: Plastics Foams, *Palisades Sec. SPE, Reg. Tech. Conf., New York,* 1964.

Saunders, J. M., and K. C. Frisch: "Polyurethanes: Chemistry and Technology," vols. I, II, Interscience Publishers, a division of John Wiley & Sons, Inc., New York, 1962, 1964.

Seymour, R. B.: Cellular Polymers, *Corrosion,* **12**(1):94 (1956).

Sieling, D. H. (ed.): Cellular Plastics, *Natl. Acad. Sci., Publ.* 1962, 1967.

Skochdopole, R. E.: Foamed Plastics, in A. Standen (ed.), "Encyclopedia of Chemical Technology," 2d ed., Interscience Publishers, a division of John Wiley & Sons, Inc., New York, 1966.

Werner, A. C., and A. D. Varenelli: Foamed Vinyls, in "Modern Plastics Encyclopedia," McGraw-Hill Book Company, New York, 1967.

Winspear, G. G., and R. R. Waterman: Latex Sponge and Foam, in M. Morton (ed.), "Introduction to Rubber Technology," chap. 18, Reinhold Publishing Corporation, New York, 1959.

14-5   POLYELECTROLYTES

Macromolecules with ionized groups on the chain, known as polyelectrolytes, possess the properties of both polymers and electrolytes. This class includes inorganic polymers, such as aluminum silicates (bentonite, kaolinite, zeolites); polyamides with free carboxyl or amine groups, such as proteins; polyphosphates such as nucleic acids; polyesters with free carboxyl groups; poly(carboxylic acids), such as poly(acrylic acid); polyamines such as poly(ethyleneamine) and poly(vinyl pyridinium chloride); and ion-exchange resins, such as crosslinked poly(styrene sulfonic acid).

Many of the structural properties of clay minerals are characteristic of polyelectrolytes. Thus water solutions of salts of bentonite clay are thixotropic and may be used in applications such as drilling muds.   Green sands and zeolites have been used commercially as water softeners.   Presumably, the available hydroxyl groups are sites for reversible anion and cation exchange, as illustrated below:

$$Z - OH + A^- \xrightleftharpoons{H_2O} Z - A + OH^-$$

$$Z - OH + M^+ \xrightleftharpoons{H_2O} Z - OM + H_3O^+$$

(14-4)

Reversible anion- and cation-exchange reactions
of zeolites

The naturally occurring ion-exchange materials have been replaced to a large extent by synthetic zeolites (molecular sieves) and ion-exchange resins. The synthetic products have greater structural stability and selectivity.   The rate of ion exchange is determined by particle diffusion (the exchange of counterions within the polyelectrolyte) and film diffusion (the exchange of counterions across a thin film, i.e., the Nernst layer).

As might be anticipated from the size of the hydrated ionic radii, the order of preference for replacement of ions depends on the number of charges on the cations and the atomic number of these cations.   Thus, sodium ions on crosslinked sodium poly(styrene sulfonate) may be replaced by magnesium ions and these in turn may be replaced by aluminum ions. Likewise, the sodium ions may be replaced by potassium ions, as illustrated by the following series for group IA;

$$Cs^+ > Rb^+ > K^+ > Na^+ > Li^+ > H_3O^+$$

(14-5)

Replacement order for cations in ion exchange

The order for replacement of anions from a salt of a crosslinked aminated chloromethyl polystyrene is as follows:

$$I^- > NO_3^- > Br^- > SCN^- > Cl^- > OH^- > F^- > OAc^-$$

(14-6)

Replacement order for anions in ion exchange

The most important cationic ion-exchange resin is prepared by the sulfonation of poly(styrene-co-divinyl benzene).   Other cationic-exchange materials may be produced by the sulfonation of coal, the crosslinking of poly(acrylic acid), and the synthesis of phenolic resins with sulfonic acid groups. The degree of swelling of these resins may be controlled by the extent of crosslinking. These ion-exchange resins are available commercially under the trade names Amberlite, Chempro, Dowex, Duolite, Ionac, and Permutit.

Anionic-exchange resins may be prepared by the condensation of aniline and formaldehyde, the reduction of nitrated crosslinked polystyrene, and the amination of chloromethylated crosslinked polystyrene. Chelating ion-exchange resins may be produced by the reaction of aminocarboxylic acids with chloromethylated crosslinked polystyrene.

Ion-exchange resin particles may be packed in a buret for laboratory exchange reactions. Larger columns are used industrially. Since calcium and magnesium ions may be readily removed by cationic-exchange resins, these systems are used for water conditioning. Ion-exchange resins may also be used to remove ions from milk or sugar solutions. A higher yield of crystalline sucrose may be obtained as the result of the extra crystallizations ("strikes") that are possible when the solutions are demineralized by passing through an ion-exchange-resin column. Ion-exchange resins are conveniently used as catalysts in chemical reactions. Anion-exchange resins are also used to recover uranium as $[(UO_2)(SO_4)_3]^{-4}$ or $[(UO_2)(CO_3)_3]^{-4}$ from sulfuric acid or carbonic acid leach water. Ion-exchange resins may be used as membranes for the conversion of brackish water to potable water.

Ethylene sulfonic acid polymer is a strong acid electrolyte that has been available since the early 1900s. This macroion, which has a hydrogen-ion concentration comparable to sulfuric acid, has been used as an antistatic and antisoil agent for textiles and as an anticoagulant for blood (Pergalen).

Linear and crosslinked copolymers of maleic anhydride and vinyl monomers may be hydrolyzed to produce poly(carboxylic acids). Salts of copolymers of methyl methacrylate and methacrylic acid and ions like calcium magnesium and zinc may be produced on the surfaces of polymer sheets.

Salts of copolymers of ethylene and methacrylic acids (ionomers) are available under the trade names Surlyn A and EXQD-2137. These transparent macromolecules contain 1 to 10 percent of the carboxylic acid monomer which is partially reacted to form sodium, potassium, calcium, magnesium, and zinc salts. These copolymers are characterized by low density, good transparency, flexibility, toughness, and resistance to solvents.

Ionomers may be processed on conventional equipment by using slightly higher temperatures than those used for polyethylene. Because of strong ionic intermolecular reactions, these macromolecules resemble crosslinked copolymers at ordinary temperatures but, like thermoplastics, they are readily processed at elevated temperatures.

Unionized solutions of polyelectrolytes such as solutions of poly(acrylic acid) in dioxane resemble other polymer solutions. However, anomalies in viscosity are observed in aqueous solutions. If the macroion is flexible, the chain will uncoil as a result of intramolecular repulsions. Thus the viscosity will increase. However, the presence of low-molecular-weight electrolytes will increase the ionic strength of the solution outside the macroion. Thus the polymer chain will tend to coil, and the viscosity will be reduced. Accordingly, in the presence of acids, alkalies, or salts, the viscosity-concentration relationships of polyelectrolytes are linear.

Solutions of polyelectrolytes may be used as thickening agents, soil conditioners, flocculants for phosphate slimes, and flocculation assistants in water purification. The efficiency of alum flocculation is increased in the presence of small amounts of soluble polyelectrolytes. Presumably, the aluminum hydroxide forms lakes with the polyelectrolytes. These lakes are more effective coagulants than the smaller aluminum hydroxide gels.

REFERENCES

Adams, B. A., and E. L. Holmes: Ion Exchange Resins, *J. Soc. Chem. Ind.*, **54**:1 (1935).

Amphlett, C. B.: Ion Exchange, in G. L. Clark and G. G. Hawley (eds.), "Encyclopedia of Chemistry," Reinhold Publishing Corporation, New York, 1966.

Bodamer, G. W.: Ion Exchange Resins, in "Modern Plastics Encyclopedia," p. 122, McGraw-Hill Book Company, New York, 1956.

Calmon, C. T., and R. E. Kressman: "Ion Exchanges in Organic and Biochemistry," Interscience Publishers, Inc., New York, 1957.

Fuoss, R. M.: Polyelectrolytes, *Discussions Faraday Soc.*, **11**:125 (1951).

Helfferich, F.: "Ion Exchange," McGraw-Hill Book Company, New York, 1962.

Kichener, J. A.: "Ion Exchange Resins," Methuen & Co., Ltd., London, 1957.

Kunin, R.: "Ion Exchange Resins," John Wiley & Sons, Inc., New York, 1950.

Kutner, A., and D. S. Breslow: Ethylene Sulfonic Acid Polymers, in H. F. Mark, N. G. Gaylord, and N. M. Bikales (eds.), "Encyclopedia of Polymer Science and Technology," Interscience Publishers, a division of John Wiley & Sons, Inc., New York, 1967.

Miller, M. L.: Polyelectrolytes, "The Structure of Polymers," chap. 12, Reinhold Publishing Corporation, New York, 1966.

Nachod, F. C., and J. Schubert: "Ion Exchange Technology Press, Inc., New York, 1956.

Reichenberg, D.: Ion Exchangers, in G. L. Clark and G. G. Hawley (eds.), "Encyclopedia of Chemistry," Reinhold Publishing Corporation, New York, 1966.

Rice, S. A., and M. Nagasawa: "Polyelectrolytes Solutions," Academic Press, Inc., New York, 1961.

————: Polyelectrolytes, in J. L. Oncley et al. (eds.), "Biophysical Science," chap. 7, John Wiley & Sons, Inc., New York, 1959.

Salmon, J. E., and D. K. Hale: "Ion Exchange: Laboratory Manual," Academic Press, Inc., New York, 1959.

Scheiner, L. L.: Ionomers, *Plastics Technol.,* **11**(3):44, (4)47 (1965).

Seymour, R. B., F. Harris, and I. Branum: Maleic Anhydride Copolymers, *Ind. Eng. Chem.,* **41:** 1482 (1949).

Strauss, U. P.: Polyelectrolytes, in G. L. Clark and G. G. Hawley (eds.), "Encyclopedia of Chemistry," Reinhold Publishing Corporation, New York, 1966.

Wheaton, R. M., and A. H. Seamster: Ion Exchange, in A. N. Standen (ed.), "Encyclopedia of Chemical Technology," Interscience Publishers, a division of John Wiley & Sons, Inc., New York, 1966.

Zutty, J. J., F. A. Faucher, and S. Bonotto: Ethylene Polymers—Ionomers, in H. F. Mark, N. G. Gaylord, and N. M. Bikales (eds.), "Encyclopedia of Polymer Science and Technology," Interscience Publishers, a division of John Wiley & Sons, Inc., New York, 1967.

14-6   PLASTIC PIPE

Fabricated wood, bamboo, and lead pipes have been used to transport water for centuries. They are still used today, but they have been replaced to a large extent by concrete, iron, and plastics. Extruded natural-rubber hose and fabric-wrapped hose have also been used for many years. Garden hose is produced by wrapping an extruded rubber tube with cotton braiding and passing this through an extruder in order to add an exterior coating of rubber. This reinforced hose is inflated, coated with lead, and heat-cured.

Laminated phenolic pipe has been produced by impregnating paper or fabric which is wrapped around a cylindrical mandrel and cured. A mixture of filler, such as glass fiber, may be admixed with a resin, such as an epoxy resin, and centrifugally cast inside a circular mold and heat-cured. Similar compositions may be extruded and cured. Reinforced plastic pipe may also be produced by winding a resin-impregnated filament around a mandrel and curing the resin.

The pioneer flexible plastic tubing was plasticized poly(vinyl chloride). Rigid poly(vinylidene chloride) (Saran) tubing was also introduced in the 1930s. Large-sized Saran pipe with threaded joints was introduced in the early 1940s but this pipe has been displaced to a large extent by less expensive rigid poly(vinyl chloride), ABS (acrylonitrile-butadiene-styrene copolymer), cellulose acetate butyrate, polyethylene, and polypropylene pipe.

The pioneer polyethylene pipe was the low-density type. It has the advantage of being available in coils of long length. Some difficulties have been experienced with metal insert fittings but this flexible pipe continues to be used for jet wells, rural water lines, and conduit. The heat resistance of this pipe may be improved by irradiation with cobalt 60.

Since high-density polyethylene and polypropylene pipe is more rigid, the extrudate must be cut into convenient lengths (10 to 20 ft). This rigid pipe may be joined by compression rings or screw fittings. Pipe sections of these polymers may also be joined by thermal welding.

Pipe extruded from cellulose acetate butyrate has been used for many years for conveying potable water, natural gas, and oil and as electrical conduit. Sections of this pipe and other pipe made from plastics that are attacked by solvents may be jointed by solvent welding techniques.

Pipes extruded from rigid poly(vinyl chloride) and ABS copolymer are used for potable-water pipe and have been approved for drain, waste, and vent (DWV) applications. Poly(vinyl dichloride) pipe may be used for hot-water service.

Polyacetal (Delrin) pipe is used for oil-field installations. Pipe extruded from poly(chloroether) (Penton) has been used to convey hot aqueous acids. This and other corrosion-resistant plastics, such as polypropylene and polytetrafluoroethylene (Teflon), have been used as linings in metal pipe. Injection-molded fittings are available for joining all types of rigid thermoplastic pipe.

REFERENCES

A New Look at Plastic Pipe in "Plastics in Building," McGraw-Hill Book Company, New York, 1966.

Brogan, C. G.: Polyethylene Pipe, *12th Ann. SPE Natl. Tech. Conf., Tech. Papers,* 1956.

Diedrich, G., W. Muller, and E. Gaube: Polypropylene Pipes, *German Plastics,* **56**(4):5 (1966).

Elliot, P. M.: ABS Pipe, *12th Ann. SPE Natl. Tech. Conf., Tech. Papers,* 1956.

Henning, H. R., and G. B. Cuming: Reinforced Pipe, in P. Morgan (ed.), "Glass Reinforced Plastics," chap. 11, Iliffe Books, Ltd., London, 1957.

Huke, D. W.: Rubber Hose, "Introduction to Natural and Synthetic Rubbers," chap. 7, Chemical Publishing Company, Inc., New York, 1961.

Malone, J. F.: PVC Pipe, *12th Ann. SPE Natl. Tech. Conf., Tech. Papers,* 1956.

Meyer, L. W. A.: Cellulose Acetate Butyrate Pipe, *12th Ann. SPE Natl. Tech. Conf., Tech. Papers,* 1956.

Schaul, J. S.: Plastic Pipe, in I. Skeist (ed.), "Plastics in Building," chap. 13, Reinhold Publishing Corporation, New York, 1966.

Seymour, R. B.: Plastic Ducts and Conduits, "Plastics in Building," p. 77, Building Research Institute, Washington, D.C., 1955.

————: Plastics, in A. S. Brasunas and E. R. Stansbury (eds.), "Symposium on Corrosion Fundamentals," chap. 15, The University of Tennessee Press, Knoxville, 1956.

———— and R. H. Steiner: Plastic Pipe, "Plastics for Corrosion Resistant Applications," chap. 17, Reinhold Publishing Corporation, New York, 1955.

Thorne, W. L.: Polyethylene Pipe, in A. Renfrew and P. Morgan (eds.), "Polyethene," chap. 27, Interscience Publishers, Inc., New York, 1957.

Whitaker, J. S.: Plastic Pipe, "Plastics in Building," p. 68, Building Research Institute, Washington, D.C., 1955.

14-7 MOLDED PLASTICS

The principal end use of polymers is as molded products. As discussed previously, some elastomeric products, such as pneumatic tires and motor mountings, are obtained by compression molding. Laminated plastics are also produced by pressing multiple sheets in a heated platen press. Injection-molding techniques are used routinely for molding thermoplastics. Modifications of this rapid process are also used for molding thermosetting products. However, many thermosetting molded parts are produced by compression molding.

Phenol formaldehyde resins are the most widely used thermosetting materials. The term *resin* usually applies to the uncompounded polymers. The mixture of filler, pigment, curing agent (hexamethylenetetramine), A-stage novolac resin, and other ingredients is partially cured on two-roll mills, in intensive mixers, or in extruders. The mixture containing the partially cured resin (B stage) is called a *molding compound*. This composition is converted to an infusible product (C stage) when heated in a molding press.

As shown in Table 14-5, the physical and thermal properties of phenol formaldehyde resins are improved by the appropriate choice of fillers. Thus the heat-distortion point is increased 100°F by the addition of an equal weight of wood flour and 300°F by the addition of about 40 percent fibrous glass. Approximately 20 percent of the 1 billion pounds of phenolic resin produced annually in the United States is used for molded products. Molded phenolic plastics are used for electrical switches, flatiron handles, and other appliances where good thermal and electrical properties are required.

Much of the compounding technology used for the production of urea and melamine molding powders is similar to that used for phenolic plastics. The curing agents employed are acids such as phosphoric acid. The color possibilities and the electrical properties of these light-colored plastics are superior to those of the dark-colored phenolic resins. Less than 20 percent of the 600 million pounds of amino resins produced annually in the United States is used for the production of molded products.

Filled alkyd, allyl, and epoxy resins are used in many applications where exceptional electrical properties are required. Both silicone and urethane resins are used to some extent as compression-molded products. However, most of the production of alkyd, epoxy, and urethane resins is used in non-molded applications.

Polyolefins are widely used as thermoplastic molding resins. Low-density polyethylene (type I), high-density polyethylene (type III), polypropylene, ionomers, polyallomers, poly(ethylene-co-vinyl acetate), poly(methyl pentene), and polybutylene resins are produced at an annual

Table 14-5 Properties of Molded Plastics

POLYMER	TENSILE STRENGTH, psi	FLEXURAL STRENGTH, psi	HEAT DEFLECTION POINT @ 264 psi, °F	DIELECTRIC CONSTANT (at 60 cycles)	POWER FACTOR (at 60 cycles)
Phenol formaldehyde resin	4,000	13,500	135		
Wood-flour filled	7,500	10,000	250	6.0	0.08
Glass-fiber filled	12,000	30,000	450	7.1	0.05
Urea-formaldehyde α-cellulose filled	9,000	14,000	275	8.0	0.04
Melamine-formaldehyde α-cellulose filled	10,000	13,000	266	8.7	0.05
Alkyd resin glass filled	7,000	15,000	450	5.7	0.010
Allyl resin glass filled	8,500	15,000	435	4.4	0.03
Epoxy resin glass filled	20,000	35,000	375	4.2	0.025
Polyethylene (type I)	1,600	. . .	100	2.3	<0.0005
Polyethylene (type III)	4,500	1,000	120	2.3	<0.0005
Polypropylene	4,900	7,000	135	2.4	<0.0005
Ionomers	4,500	. . .	100 @ 66 psi	2.4	0.002
Polystyrene	8,500	11,000	185	2.5	0.0002
Poly(styrene-co-acrylonitrile)	11,000	24,000	210	3.0	0.007
ABS copolymer	7,000	11,000	200	3.5	0.005
Polytetrafluoroethylene	3,500	. . .	140	<2.1	<0.0002
Cellulose acetate	5,500	9,000	150	5.5	0.05
Poly(methyl methacrylate)	9,500	14,500	190	4.0	0.05
Acetal resins	10,000	14,000	255	3.7	
Chlorinated polyether	6,000	5,000	200	3.1	0.01
Phenoxy resin	8,500	12,500	180	4.1	0.0012
Polycarbonate	9,000	13,500	275	3.0	0.0007
Polysulfone	10,000	15,000	345	3.1	0.008
Poly(phenylene oxide)	11,000	15,000	375	2.6	0.0003

rate in excess of 5 billion pounds. Over a billion pounds of these plastics are injection-molded annually. As shown in Table 14-5, these products are characterized by excellent electrical properties and relatively poor thermal and physical properties.

Polystyrene is characterized by low resistance to impact and low heat-distortion properties. The heat-distortion point of poly(styrene-co-acrylonitrile) is slightly higher, and the impact-resistance properties of this copolymer are superior to those of polystyrene. Approximately 1.5 billion pounds of polystyrene and its copolymers are injection-molded annually. Molded polystyrene parts are used for radio and television housing, automotive applications, appliances, and sporting goods.

Approximately 300 million pounds of poly(vinyl chloride) is molded annually as phonograph records, shoe soles and heels, and slush or rotationally molded plastisol products. However, the bulk of the 3 billion pounds annual production is processed by extrusion, calendering, and coating techniques. Molded parts of polytetrafluoroethylene are made by preforming the powder into billets which are sintered to obtain fused products. Other polyfluorohydrocarbons may be processed by conventional techniques.

Cellulose acetate, cellulose acetate butyrate, cellulose propionate, and ethyl cellulose continue to be used for molding fountain-pen barrels, radio cases, and toothbrushes. These moldings are characterized by excellent resistance to impact. Lenses, dishes, and knobs may be molded from poly(methyl methacrylate) but extrusion, casting, and coating are more widely used techniques for processing this type of plastic. Acetal moldings are characterized by unusual toughness. They are used for instrument housings and for appliance handles in place of zinc die-cast materials. Chlorinated polyether moldings (Penton) are used as valves and other articles when excellent resistance to the environment is required.

Nylon 6,6 has excellent physical properties. Injection-molded nylon products are used as gears, bearings, and pipe fittings. Phenoxy resin molded parts have superior dimensional stability and good resistance to creep. Polycarbonate moldings are characterized by unusual toughness. Moldings from polysulfone and poly(phenylene oxide) resins have excellent thermal and electrical properties.

REFERENCES

Akin, R. B.: "Acetal Resins," Reinhold Publishing Corporation, New York, 1962.

Aponyi, T. J.: High Temperature Resins, in "Modern Plastics Encyclopedia," p. 106, McGraw-Hill Book Company, New York, 1967.

Basdekas, C. H.: "ABS Plastics," Reinhold Publishing Corporation, New York, 1964.

Beacham, H. H.: Allyl Resins, in "Modern Plastics Encyclopedia," p. 129, McGraw-Hill Book Company, New York, 1967.

Becker, W. E., E. R. Wells, and C. E. B. Carlson: Polyurethanes, in "Modern Plastics Encyclopedia," p. 251, McGraw-Hill Book Company, New York, 1967.

Beers, T. W.: Alkyd Molding Compounds, in "Modern Plastics Encyclopedia," p. 128, McGraw-Hill Book Company, New York, 1967.

Billmeyer, F. W.: "Polymer Science," Pt. 4, Interscience Publishers, a division of John Wiley & Sons, Inc., New York, 1962.

Boundy, R. H., and R. F. Boyer: "Styrene, Its Polymers, Copolymers, and Derivatives," Reinhold Publishing Corporation, New York, 1952.

Brydson, J. A.: "Plastics Materials," D. Van Nostrand Company, Inc., Princeton, N.J., 1966.

Carswell, T. S.: "Phenoplasts," Interscience Publishers, Inc., New York, 1947.

Chouragui, J., P. De La Bruniere, and W. De C. Crater: Nylons, in "Modern Plastics Encyclopedia," p. 169, McGraw-Hill Book Company, New York, 1967.

Cox, A. P.: Polyfluorocarbons, *Plastics*, **38**(10):614 (1965).

Day, M. R.: Methylpentene Polymers, in "Modern Plastics Encyclopedia," p. 265, McGraw-Hill Book Company, New York, 1967.

DeBlieu, I. K.: Acrylic Resins, in "Modern Plastics Encyclopedia," p. 125, McGraw-Hill Book Company, New York, 1967.

Delmonte, J.: Furanes, in "Modern Plastics Encyclopedia," p. 182, McGraw-Hill Book Company, New York, 1967.

DuBois, J. H., and F. W. John: "Plastics," Reinhold Publishing Corporation, New York, 1967.

Elmore, R. O.: Ethylene Copolymers, in "Modern Plastics Encyclopedia," p. 210, McGraw-Hill Book Company, New York, 1967.

Floyd, D. E.: "Polyamide Resins," Reinhold Publishing Corporation, New York, 1958.

Flynn, R., and H. C. Luker: Epoxy Resins, in "Modern Plastics Encyclopedia," p. 153, McGraw-Hill Book Company, New York, 1967.

Frados, J.: Designing with Plastics, in "Modern Plastics Encyclopedia," p. 47, McGraw-Hill Book Company, New York, 1967.

Garvin, G. S.: Compounding and Processing of Polymers, in C. E. Schildknecht (ed.), "Polymer Processes," chap. 16, Interscience Publishers, Inc., New York, 1956.

Golding, B.: "Polymers and Resins," D. Van Nostrand Company, Inc., Princeton, N.J., 1959.

Gorham, W. F.: Parylene Polymers, in "Modern Plastics Encyclopedia," p. 173, McGraw-Hill Book Company, New York, 1967.

Gould, D. T.: "Phenolic Resins," Reinhold Publishing Corporation, New York, 1959.

Gowan, A. C., and R. B. MacCallum: Phenylene Oxides, in "Modern Plastics Encyclopedia," p. 241, McGraw-Hill Book Company, New York, 1967.

Hanson, T. A., and D. W. Towler: Fluoroplastics, in "Modern Plastics Encyclopedia," p. 157, McGraw-Hill Book Company, New York, 1967.

Hesselbalch, H.: Polyethylene Moldings, *Plastics*, **30**(10):72 (1965).

Hill, R. O.: Cellulose Plastics, in "Modern Plastics Encyclopedia," p. 145, McGraw-Hill Book Company, New York, 1967.

Honeycutt, E. M.: Polypropylene, in "Modern Plastics Encyclopedia," p. 232, McGraw-Hill Book Company, New York, 1967.

Horn, M. B.: "Acrylic Resins," Reinhold Publishing Corporation, New York, 1960.

Jost, H. D.: Phenolic Resins, in "Modern Plastics Encyclopedia," p. 183, McGraw-Hill Book Company, New York, 1967.

King, N. E.: Chlorinated Polyether, in "Modern Plastics Encyclopedia," p. 181, McGraw-Hill Book Company, New York, 1967.

Kincaid, J. N.: Polybutene Resins, in "Modern Plastics Encyclopedia," p. 185, McGraw-Hill Book Company, New York, 1967.

Kjellmark, E. W., and R. M. Stemmler: Acetal Resins, in "Modern Plastics Encyclopedia," p. 115, McGraw-Hill Book Company, New York, 1967.

Kline, G. M.: Annual Review, *Mod. Plastics*, **44**(6):129 (1967).

Kresser, T. O. J.: "Polyethylene," Reinhold Publishing Corporation, New York, 1967.

———: "Polypropylene," Reinhold Publishing Corporation, New York, 1960.

Lawrence, J. R.: "Polyester Resins," Reinhold Publishing Corporation, New York, 1960.

———: Vinyl Resins, *Plastics World*, **26**(3):45 (1968).

Lee, H., and K. Neville: "Handbook of Epoxy Resins," McGraw-Hill Book Company, New York, 1966.

Lorenz, J. H.: Silicones, in "Modern Plastics Encyclopedia," p. 262, McGraw-Hill Book Company, New York, 1967.

Lyman, D. C.: Polyurethanes, *Rev. Macromol. Chem.*, **1**(1):191 (1966).

Martens, C. R.: "Alkyd Resins," Reinhold Publishing Corporation, New York, 1961.

Martin, R. W.: "The Chemistry of Phenolic Resins," John Wiley & Sons, Inc., New York, 1956.

Megson, N. J. L.: "Phenolic Resin Chemistry," Academic Press, Inc., New York, 1958.

Miles, D. C., and J. H. Briston: "Polymer Technology," Pt. 2, Chemical Publishing Company, Inc., New York, 1965.

Moffitt, T. W.: Rigid PVC, *Plastics*, **30**(11):115 (1966).

Morgan, D. F., and B. C. Wendle: Polycarbonates, in "Modern Plastics Encyclopedia," p. 217, McGraw-Hill Book Company, New York, 1967.

Otting, R. G.: Polystyrenes, in "Modern Plastics Encyclopedia," p. 273, McGraw-Hill Book Company, New York, 1967.

Paist, W. D.: "Cellulosics," Reinhold Publishing Corporation, New York, 1958.

Parkyn, B., F. Lamb, and B. V. Clifton: "Polyesters," American Elsevier Publishing Company, Inc., New York, 1967.

Penn, W. S.: "PVC Technology," Maclaren & Sons, Ltd., London, 1962.

Petruccelli, F., and R. S. Krigbaum: The Amino Resins, in "Modern Plastics Encyclopedia," p. 141, McGraw-Hill Book Company, New York, 1967.

Powers, P. O.: "Synthetic Resins and Rubbers," John Wiley & Sons, Inc., New York, 1943.

Pritchard, E.: Polyethylene Resins, in "Modern Plastics Encyclopedia," p. 205, McGraw-Hill Book Company, New York, 1967.

Prout, E. O.: Rigid PVC, *SPE J.*, **22**(6):75 (1966).

Raff, R. A. V. (ed.): "Technical Progress in the Plastics Industry," Washington State University, Pullman, Wash., 1967.

——— and J. B. Allison (eds.): "Polyethylene," Interscience Publishers, Inc., New York, 1956.

Randolph, A. F. (ed.): "Plastics Engineering Handbook," Reinhold Publishing Corporation, New York, 1960.

Ravve, A.: "Organic Chemistry of Macromolecules," Marcel Dekker, Inc., New York, 1967.

Robitshek, P., and A. Lewin: "Phenolic Resins," Iliffe Books, Ltd., London, 1950.

Rosato, D. V.: Heat Resistant Plastics, *Plastics World*, **26**(3):30 (1968).

Schaefer, S. W., J. A. Rolls, et al.: Vinyl Polymers, in "Modern Plastics Encyclopedia," p. 277, McGraw-Hill Book Company, New York, 1967.

Schildknecht, C. E.: "Vinyl and Related Polymers," John Wiley & Sons, Inc., New York, 1962.

Schnell, H.: "Chemistry and Physics of Polycarbonates," Interscience Publishers, a division of John Wiley & Sons, Inc., New York, 1964.

Segal, C. L.: "High Temperature Polymers," Marcel Dekker, Inc., New York, 1967.

Siconolfi, C. A.: Polyester Resins, in "Modern Plastics Encyclopedia," p. 229, McGraw-Hill Book Company, New York, 1967.

Simonds, H. R.: "Source Book of the New Plastics," vol. 2, Reinhold Publishing Corporation, New York, 1961.

Seymour, R. B.: Review, *Ind. Eng. Chem.,* **61**(8):28 (1969).

Smith, W. M.: "Vinyl Resins," Reinhold Publishing Corporation, New York, 1958.

———— (ed.): "Manufacture of Plastics," Reinhold Publishing Corporation, New York, 1965.

Stehr, C. W., W. R. Hendricks, and G. Holden: Styrene-butadiene Copolymers, in "Modern Plastics Encyclopedia," p. 286, McGraw-Hill Book Company, New York, 1967.

Stewart, A. C.: Phenoxy Resins, in "Modern Plastics Encyclopedia," p. 214, McGraw-Hill Book Company, New York, 1967.

Stille, J. K.: "Introduction of Polymer Chemistry," John Wiley & Sons, Inc., New York, 1962.

Teach, W. C., and G. C. Kressling: "Polystyrene," Reinhold Publishing Corporation, New York, 1960.

Vale, C. P., and W. G. K. Taylor: "Aminoplastics," Iliffe Books, Ltd., London, 1964.

————: "Aminoplastics," Cleaver-Hume Press, Ltd., London, 1950.

Vermillion, J. L.: Polyallomers, in "Modern Plastics Encyclopedia," p. 187, McGraw-Hill Book Company, New York, 1967.

Vogl, O.: "Polyaldehydes," Marcel Dekker, Inc., New York, 1967.

Walton, R. K.: Polysulfones, in "Modern Plastics Encyclopedia," p. 259, McGraw-Hill Book Company, New York, 1967.

Weaver, E. P.: ABS Copolymer, in "Modern Plastics Encyclopedia," p. 111, McGraw-Hill Book Company, New York, 1967.

Whitehouse, A. A. K., and E. G. K. Pritchett: Phenolic Resins, *Plastics Inst. (London) Monograph,* 1955.

Whitley, M. R., and D. L. Valentine: Vinyl Plastics, *Mod. Plastics,* **41**(5):159 (1964).

Winding, C. C., and G. D. Hiatt: "Polymeric Materials," chaps. 7, 8, McGraw-Hill Book Company, New York, 1961.

15

Synthesis
of Reactants
and Intermediates

Pertinent information on the synthesis of reactants and monomers for polymer production is given in this chapter. The order of presentation is related to that used in Chaps. 5 to 7. However, structural relationships rather than polymerization mechanisms are emphasized in this chapter. These compounds are also listed alphabetically in Tables 15-1 and 15-2.

15-1 NONETHYLENIC FUNCTIONAL REACTANTS

Adipic acid (mp 151°C) may be produced by the nitric acid oxidation of cyclohexanol or cyclohexanone in the presence of a copper–ammonium vanadate catalyst at 75°C. These reactants or a mixture of cyclohexanol and cyclohexanone is obtained by the air oxidation of cyclohexane at 140 to 180°C in the presence of cobalt acetate. Cyclohexane is produced by the continuous liquid-phase hydrogenation of benzene at 210°C in the presence of Raney nickel catalyst. The principal reactions are shown below:

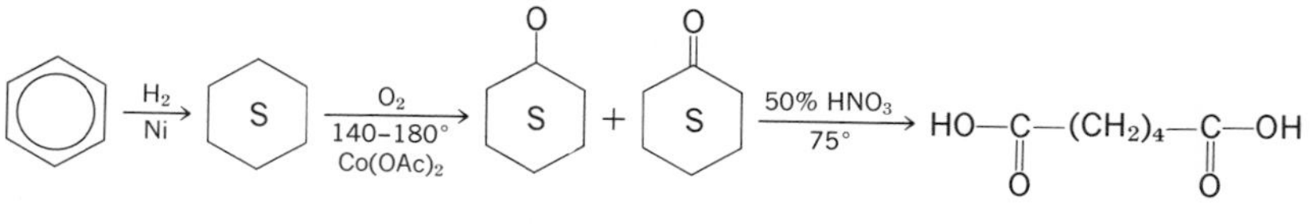

$$\underset{\underset{Co(OAc)_2}{140-180°}}{\xrightarrow{O_2}}$$

Conversion of cyclohexane to adipic acid   (15-1)

As shown by the following equation, adipic acid may also be produced by the high-pressure (2,000-atm) carbonylation of tetrahydrofuran in the presence of nickel carbonyl-nickel iodide at 270°C.

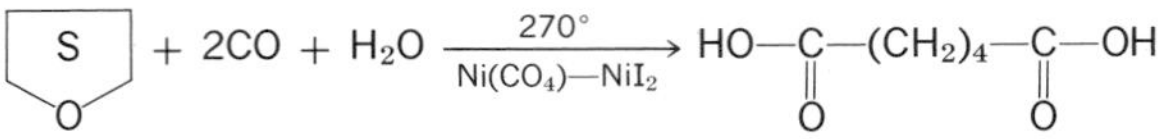

$$\boxed{\overset{\displaystyle S}{\underset{\displaystyle O}{}} + 2CO + H_2O \xrightarrow[\text{Ni(CO}_4)\text{—NiI}_2]{270°} HO-\overset{O}{\underset{\|}{C}}-(CH_2)_4-\overset{O}{\underset{\|}{C}}-OH} \qquad (15\text{-}2)$$

Conversion of tetrahydrofuran to adipic acid

Adiponitrile has been produced by the hydrodimerization of acryloni-trile.

Sebacic acid (mp 134°C) and capryl alcohol are obtained by the alkaline hydrolysis of castor oil (glyceryl ricinoleate) in an autoclave at 250°C.

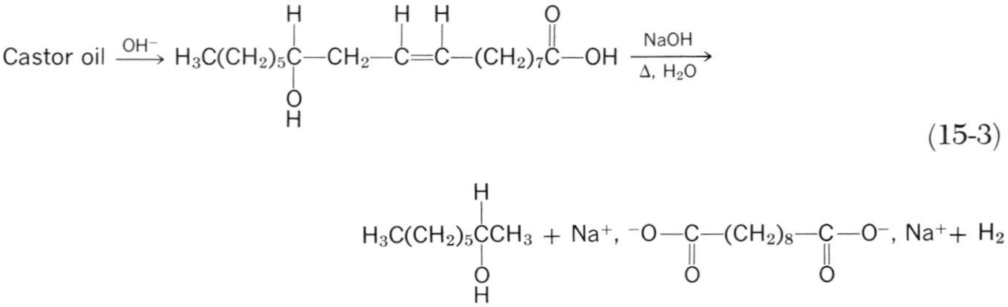

$$\text{Castor oil} \xrightarrow{\text{OH}^-} H_3C(CH_2)_5\overset{H}{\underset{\underset{H}{\overset{|}{O}}}{\overset{|}{C}}}-CH_2-\overset{H}{\overset{|}{C}}=\overset{H}{\overset{|}{C}}-(CH_2)_7\overset{O}{\overset{\|}{C}}-OH \xrightarrow[\Delta,\ H_2O]{\text{NaOH}}$$

$$(15\text{-}3)$$

$$H_3C(CH_2)_5\overset{H}{\underset{\underset{H}{\overset{|}{O}}}{\overset{|}{C}}}CH_3 + Na^+,\ {}^-O-\overset{O}{\overset{\|}{C}}-(CH_2)_8-\overset{O}{\overset{\|}{C}}-O^-,\ Na^+ + H_2$$

Preparation of sebacic acid from castor oil (glyceryl ricinoleate)

Terephthalic acid is produced by the catalytic air oxidation of *p*-xylene. Isophthalic acid (mp 347°C) is produced by the oxidation of *m*-xylene. Phthalic acid or its anhydride (mp 131°C) is produced by the oxidation of either *o*-xylene or naphthalene. The original mercury catalyst, which was discovered accidentally by Gibbs as the result of a broken thermometer, has been replaced by vanadium pentoxide.

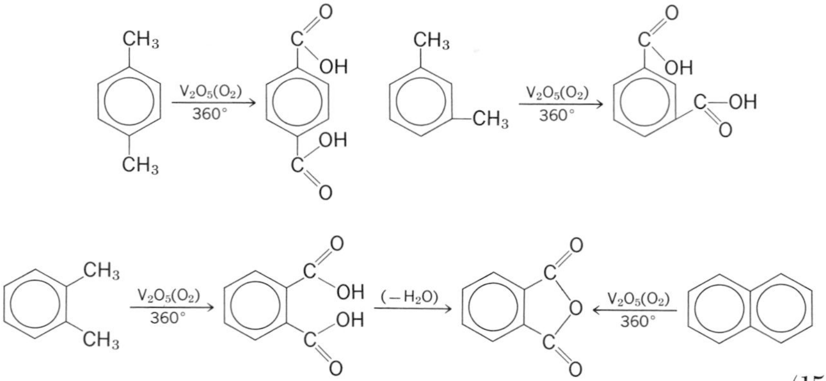

$$(15\text{-}4)$$

Production of various phthalic acids by oxidation reactions

Phthalic acid or isophthalic acid may be isomerized to terephthalic acid by heating the potassium salts at 400°C in the presence of cadmium iodide. Over 750 million pounds of phthalic anhydride is produced annually in the United States.

Pyromellitic dianhydride (1,2,4,5-benzene tetracarboxylic dianhydride) (PMDA) may be produced by the nitric acid or vapor-phase oxidation of durene at 500°.

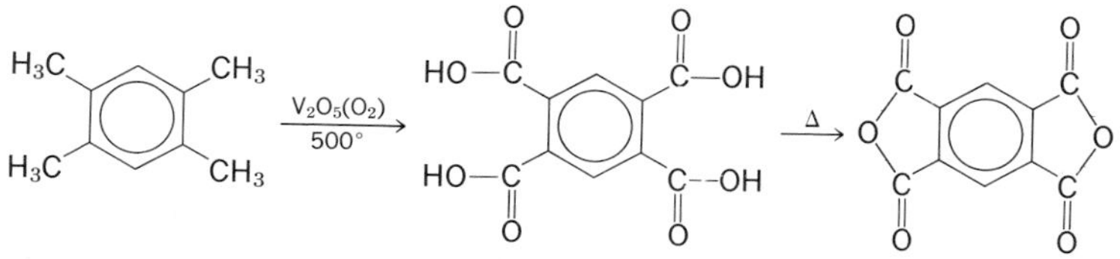

Production of pyromellitic dianhydride by oxidation of durene

Maleic anhydride (mp 53°C) is obtained as a byproduct (5 to 8 percent) in the production of phthalic anhydride. Maleic anhydride is also produced by the dehydration of malic acid (mp 130°C) and by the vanadium oxide catalytic oxidation of benzene at 450°C. Maleic anhydride may also be produced by the vapor-phase oxidation of butylene or crotonaldehyde.

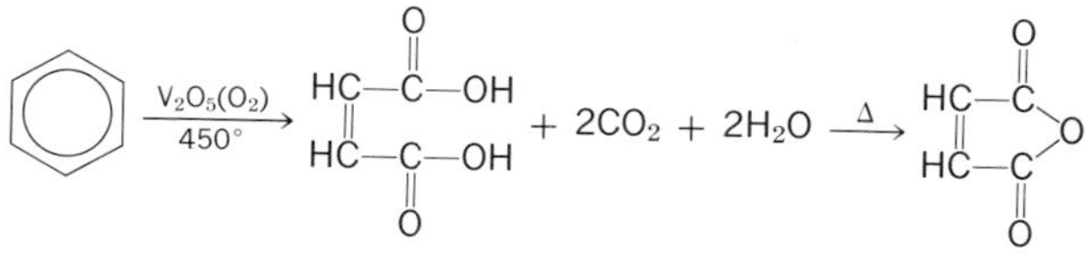

Production of maleic anhydride by oxidation of benzene

Hexamethylenediamine (b 90 to 92°, mp 30°C) is obtained by the liquid phase hydrogenation of adipamide or adiponitrile at 125°C in the presence of ammonia and a cobalt-copper catalyst. The adipamide is obtained by the ammonation of adipic acid at 350°C. These reactions are shown below:

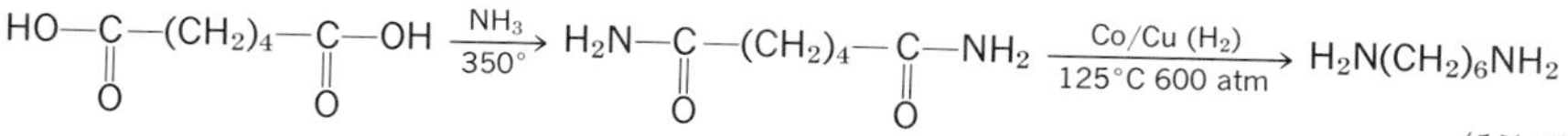

Production of hexamethylenediamine by hydrogenation of adipamide

Adiponitrile may be produced by the acid hydrolysis of tetrahydrofuran, by the hydrodimerization of acrylonitrile, and by the copper-catalyzed hydrocyanation of 1,4-dichlorobutane. The latter is obtained by the hydrogenation of the dichloro derivative obtained by chlorination of butadiene.

ε-Caprolactam may be obtained by the Beckmann rearrangement of cyclohexanone oxime, i.e., heating this oxime with 85 percent sulfuric acid, as shown in the following equation:

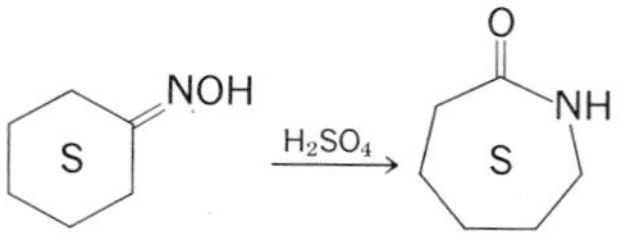

$$\text{cyclohexanone oxime} \xrightarrow{H_2SO_4} \text{ε-caprolactam} \tag{15-8}$$

Production of ε-caprolactam by Beckmann rearrangement
of cyclohexanone oxime

Cyclohexanone oxime may be produced by the addition of hydroxylamine monosulfonate to cyclohexanone, by the photonitrosation of cyclohexane, or by the hydrogenation of nitrocyclohexane. ε-Caprolactam may also be produced by the reaction of nitrosylsulfuric acid and hexahydrobenzoic acid, and by the ammonation of caprolactone.

Ethylene glycol may be produced by the catalytic hydrogenation of methyl glycolate. The glycolic acid may be obtained by the catalytic carbonylation of formaldehyde at high pressure. These reactions are shown in the following equations:

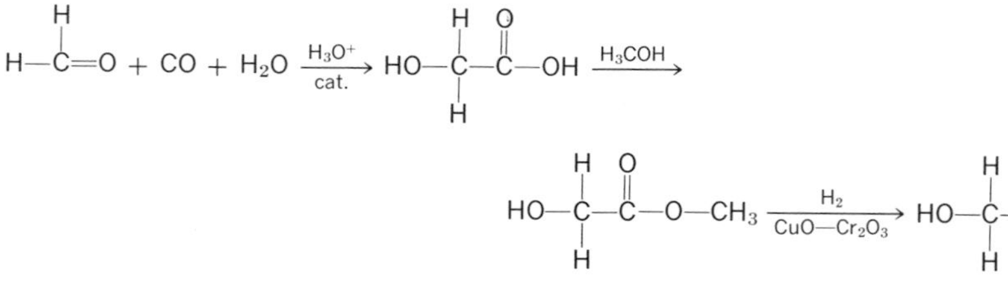

$$H\text{—}CH\text{=}O + CO + H_2O \xrightarrow[\text{cat.}]{H_3O^+} HO\text{—}CH_2\text{—}CO\text{—}OH \xrightarrow{H_3COH} \tag{15-9}$$

$$HO\text{—}CH_2\text{—}CO\text{—}O\text{—}CH_3 \xrightarrow[CuO\text{—}Cr_2O_3]{H_2} HO\text{—}CH_2\text{—}CH_2\text{—}OH$$

Synthesis of ethylene glycol from formaldehyde and carbon monoxide

Most of the ethylene glycol produced commercially is obtained by the hydrolysis of ethylene oxide at 200°C. Ethylene oxide may be produced by the chlorohydrination of ethylene followed by dehydrochlorination in the presence of lime at 100°. However, most of the ethylene oxide produced is obtained by the air oxidation of ethylene in the presence of a silver catalyst. Over 2.5 billion pounds of ethylene oxide is produced annually in the

United States. These reactions are shown in the following equations:

$$
\underset{\substack{\text{H H}\\ \text{C}=\text{C}\\ \text{H H}}}{} \xrightarrow[\text{H}_2\text{O.}]{\text{Cl}_2} \underset{\substack{\text{H H}\\ \text{HO}-\text{C}-\text{C}-\text{Cl}\\ \text{H H}}}{} \xrightarrow{\text{Ca(OH)}_2} \underset{\substack{\\ \text{H}_2\text{C}-\text{CH}_2\\ \text{O}}}{} \xrightarrow{\text{H}_2\text{O}} \underset{\substack{\text{H H}\\ \text{HO}-\text{C}-\text{C}-\text{OH}\\ \text{H H}}}{}
$$

(15-10)

$$
\underset{\substack{\text{H H}\\ \text{C}=\text{C}\\ \text{H H}}}{} \xrightarrow[250°]{\text{(O}_2\text{)Ag}} \underset{\substack{\\ \text{H}_2\text{C}-\text{CH}_2\\ \text{O}}}{}
$$

Synthesis of ethylene oxide and ethylene glycol

Ethylene imine may be prepared by the ammonation of ethylene dichloride at 75°. The β-chloroethyl amine produced cyclizes to yield ethylene imine which precipitates from a toluene solution, as shown in the following equation:

$$
\underset{\substack{\text{H H}\\ \text{Cl}-\text{C}-\text{C}-\text{Cl}\\ \text{H H}}}{} + \text{NH}_3 \xrightarrow{75°\text{C}} \underset{\substack{\text{H H H}\\ \text{Cl}-\text{C}-\text{C}-\text{N}-\text{H}\\ \text{H H}}}{} \xrightarrow{\text{NH}_3} \text{NH}_4\text{Cl} + \underset{\substack{\\ \text{H}_2\text{C}-\text{CH}_2\\ \text{N}\\ \text{H}}}{} \quad (15\text{-}11)
$$

Synthesis of ethylene imine

Glycerol has been prepared by the saponification of fats, by the catalytic hydrogenolysis of glucose, and as a byproduct of the alkaline fermentation of sugars. The principal source is the hydroxylation of allyl alcohol, using hydrogen peroxide, or the hydrolysis of the glycerol α-chlorohydrin obtained by the reaction of allyl alcohol and aqueous chlorine. As shown in the following equations, allyl alcohol is obtained by the oxidation of propylene:

$$
\underset{\substack{\text{H}\\ \text{H}_2\text{C}=\text{C}-\text{CH}_3}}{} \xrightarrow[400°]{\text{O}_2} \underset{\substack{\text{H H}\\ \text{H}_2\text{C}=\text{C}-\text{C}=\text{O}}}{} \xrightarrow[400°]{\text{Na}_2\text{ZnO}_2}
$$

$$
\underset{\substack{\text{H H}\\ \text{H}_2\text{C}=\text{C}-\text{C}-\text{OH}\\ \text{H}}}{}
$$

(15-12)

$$
\underset{\substack{\text{H H H}\\ \text{HO}-\text{C}-\text{C}-\text{C}-\text{OH}\\ \text{H O H}\\ \text{H}}}{} \xleftarrow[\text{WO}_3,\ 65°]{\text{H}_2\text{O}_2} \qquad \xrightarrow[\text{H}_2\text{O}]{\text{Cl}_2,} \underset{\substack{\text{H H H}\\ \text{Cl}-\text{C}-\text{C}-\text{C}-\text{OH}\\ \text{H O H}\\ \text{H}}}{} \xrightarrow[\text{NaOH}]{\text{Na}_2\text{CO}_3} \underset{\substack{\text{H H H}\\ \text{HO}-\text{C}-\text{C}-\text{C}-\text{OH}\\ \text{H O H}\\ \text{H}}}{}
$$

Production of glycerol from allyl alcohol

Pentaerythritol is obtained by a crossed Cannizzaro reaction of the aldehyde obtained by the aldol condensation of formaldehyde and acetaldehyde:

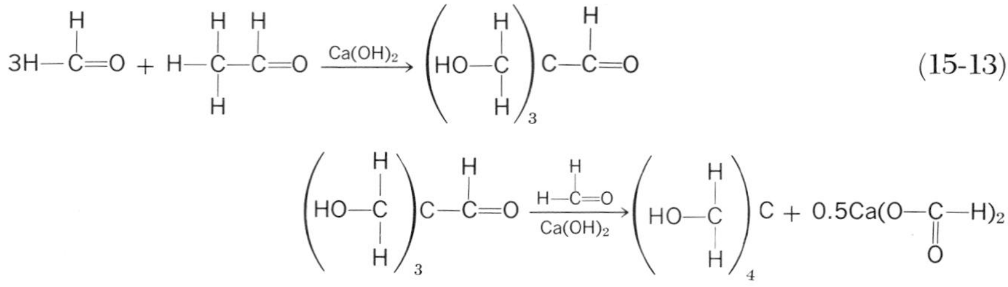

$$
3H\!-\!\overset{\displaystyle H}{\underset{\displaystyle H}{C}}\!=\!O + H\!-\!\overset{\displaystyle H}{\underset{\displaystyle H}{C}}\!-\!\overset{\displaystyle H}{C}\!=\!O \xrightarrow{Ca(OH)_2} \left(HO\!-\!\overset{\displaystyle H}{\underset{\displaystyle H}{C}}\right)_3\!\!\!C\!-\!\overset{\displaystyle H}{C}\!=\!O \tag{15-13}
$$

$$
\left(HO\!-\!\overset{\displaystyle H}{\underset{\displaystyle H}{C}}\right)_3\!\!\!C\!-\!\overset{\displaystyle H}{C}\!=\!O \xrightarrow[Ca(OH)_2]{H\!-\!C=O} \left(HO\!-\!\overset{\displaystyle H}{\underset{\displaystyle H}{C}}\right)_4\!\!\!C + 0.5Ca(O\!-\!\overset{\displaystyle}{\underset{\displaystyle O}{C}}\!-\!H)_2
$$

Synthesis of pentaerythritol

Tolylene diisocyanate (TDI) is produced by the phosgenation of tolylene diamine, as shown in the following equation. Phosgene is obtained by the reaction of carbon monoxide and chlorine in the presence of activated carbon.

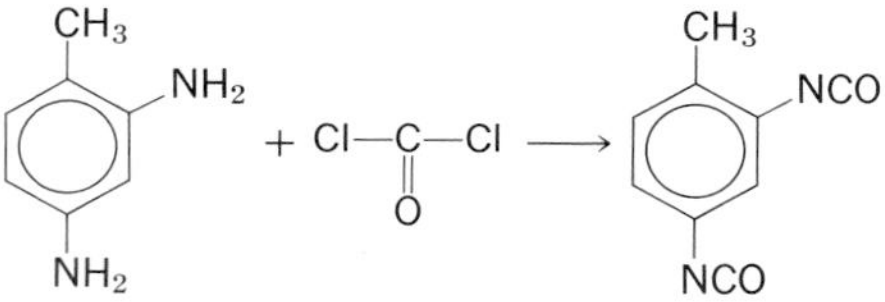

$$
\begin{array}{c} CH_3 \\ \underset{NH_2}{\bigcirc}\overset{NH_2}{} \end{array} + Cl\!-\!\overset{\displaystyle}{\underset{\displaystyle O}{C}}\!-\!Cl \longrightarrow \begin{array}{c} CH_3 \\ \underset{NCO}{\bigcirc}\overset{NCO}{} \end{array} \tag{15-14}
$$

Synthesis of tolylene diisocyanate (TDI)

Formaldehyde is produced by the hot-air oxidation of methanol using oxides of iron or molybdenum, or silver, or copper catalysts. Almost 4 billion pounds of formaldehyde is produced annually in the United States.

Hexamethylenetetramine (hexa) is produced by the reaction of 30 percent aqueous formaldehyde and ammonia.

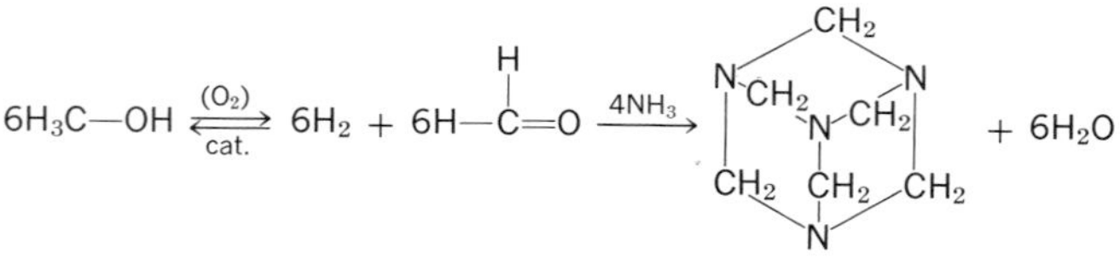

$$
6H_3C\!-\!OH \underset{cat.}{\overset{(O_2)}{\rightleftharpoons}} 6H_2 + 6H\!-\!\overset{\displaystyle H}{C}\!=\!O \xrightarrow{4NH_3} \begin{array}{c} CH_2 \\ N\!\!\diagup\!\!\overset{CH_2}{}\!\!\diagdown\!N \\ CH_2\!\!\diagdown\!\!\underset{N}{}\!\!\diagup\!CH_2 \\ CH_2\ \ CH_2\ \ CH_2 \\ N \end{array} + 6H_2O \tag{15-15}
$$

Preparation of hexamethylenetetramine

Phenol may be produced by the classic process in which benzene sulfonic acid is fused with sodium hydroxide to yield sodium phenoxide which is subsequently neutralized by sulfur dioxide.

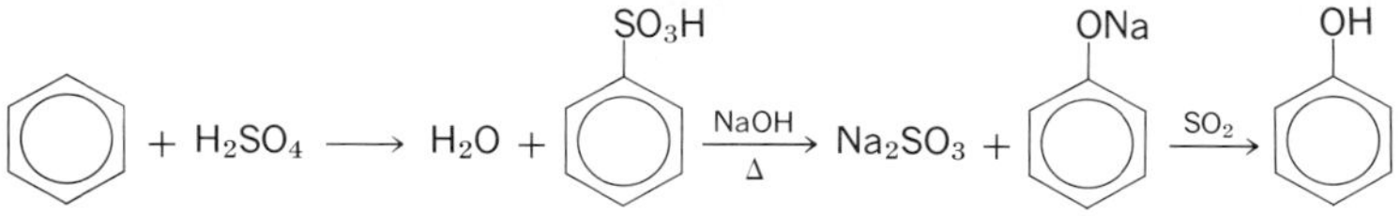

Preparation of phenol by sulfonation process

Chlorobenzene may be hydrolyzed by sodium hydroxide or high-pressure steam in the presence of catalysts to produce phenol (Raschig process):

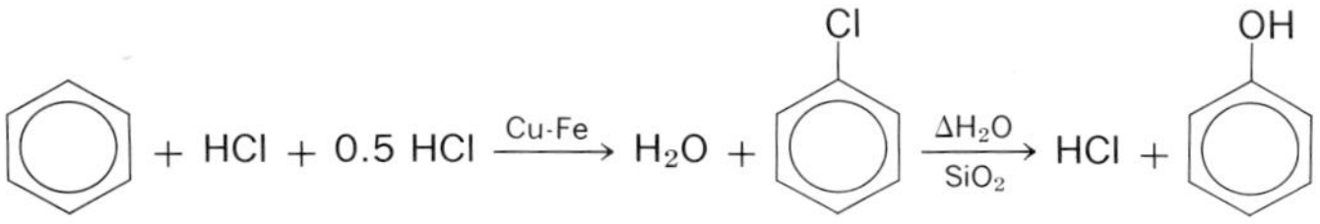

Raschig process

Phenol may be produced by the decomposition of cumene hydroperoxide in the presence of sulfuric acid. Cumene (isopropyl benzene) is readily oxidized by air to form cumene hydroperoxide.

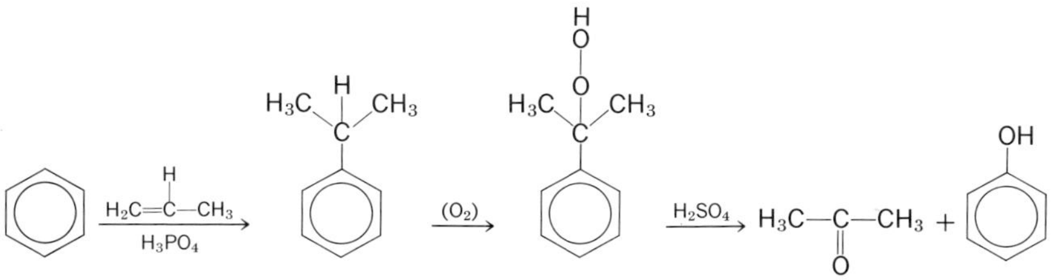

Preparation of phenol from cumene

Phenol may also be produced by the dehydrogenation of cyclohexanol and by the decarboxylation of benzoic acid. Almost 1.4 billion pounds of phenol is produced annually in the United States.

Urea (mp 133°) is produced by the reaction of carbon dioxide and ammonia in silver-lined autoclaves, as shown in the following equation:

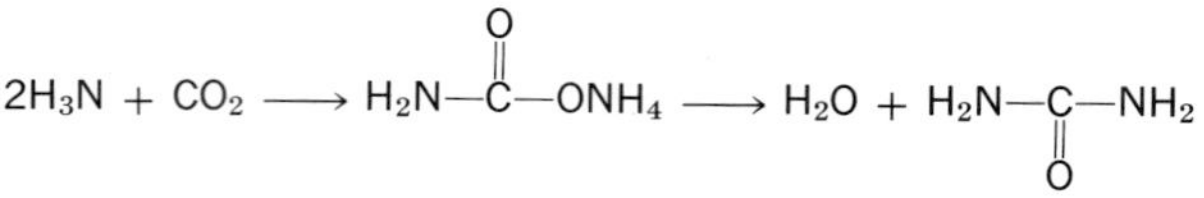

$$2H_3N + CO_2 \longrightarrow H_2N\!-\!\overset{\displaystyle O}{\underset{\displaystyle \parallel}{C}}\!-\!ONH_4 \longrightarrow H_2O + H_2N\!-\!\overset{\displaystyle}{\underset{\displaystyle \parallel}{C}}\!-\!NH_2 \quad (15\text{-}19)$$

Synthesis of urea from ammonia and carbon dioxide

Melamine (mp 354°) has been obtained by heating dicyanodiamide (dicy) at 209°C. The dicyanodiamide was obtained by heating cyanamide at 80°C.

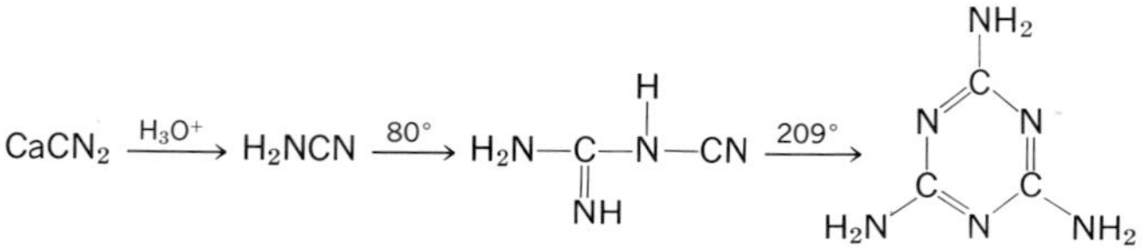

$$CaCN_2 \xrightarrow{H_3O^+} H_2NCN \xrightarrow{80°} H_2N\!-\!\overset{\displaystyle H}{\underset{\displaystyle \parallel}{\underset{NH}{C}}}\!-\!N\!-\!CN \xrightarrow{209°} \quad (15\text{-}20)$$

Production of melamine from calcium cyanamide

In the preferred method, the melamine is obtained by heating urea with appropriate catalysts, as shown below:

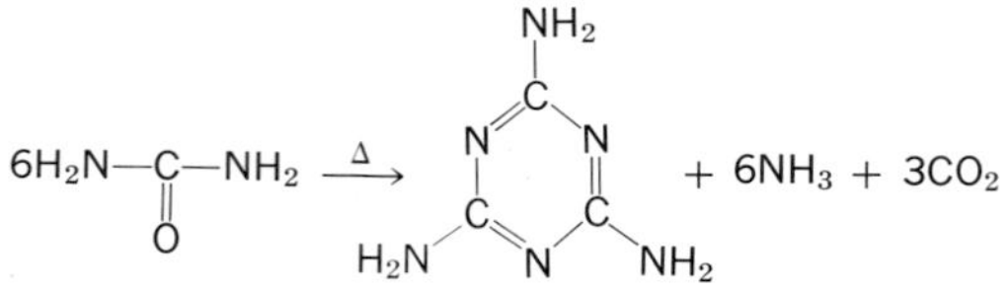

$$6H_2N\!-\!\overset{\displaystyle}{\underset{\displaystyle \parallel}{\underset{O}{C}}}\!-\!NH_2 \xrightarrow{\Delta} \quad + 6NH_3 + 3CO_2 \quad (15\text{-}21)$$

Conversion of urea to melamine

Bisphenol A (mp 153°) [bis(4-hydroxyphenyl) dimethylpropane] is obtained by the condensation of phenol and acetone, as shown below:

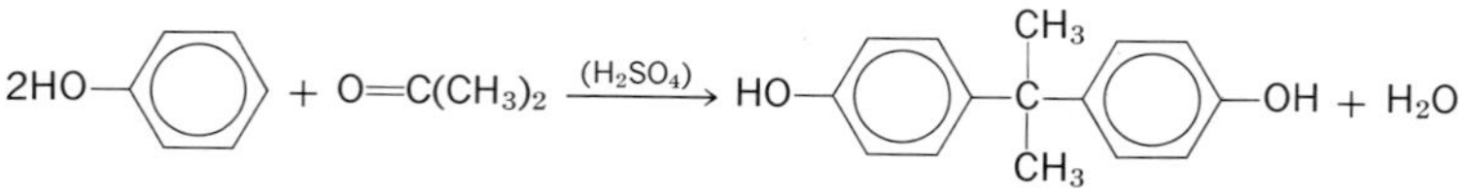

$$2HO\!-\!\!\bigcirc\!\!-\! + O\!=\!C(CH_3)_2 \xrightarrow{(H_2SO_4)} HO\!-\!\!\bigcirc\!\!-\!\overset{\displaystyle CH_3}{\underset{\displaystyle CH_3}{C}}\!-\!\!\bigcirc\!\!-\!OH + H_2O \quad (15\text{-}22)$$

Preparation of bisphenol A

Epichlorohydrin is produced by the dehydrochlorination of a chloro-dihydrin. The latter is obtained from propylene, as shown in the following equation:

$$
H_2C=\underset{\underset{H}{|}}{C}-CH_3 \xrightarrow[200°]{Cl_2} H_2C=\underset{\underset{H}{|}}{\overset{H}{\underset{|}{C}}}-\underset{\overset{H}{|}}{C}-Cl \xrightarrow{H_2O\,+\,Cl_2} H_2C-\underset{\underset{H}{\overset{|}{O}}}{\overset{H}{\underset{|}{C}}}-\underset{\overset{H}{|}}{\underset{\underset{}{Cl}}{C}}-Cl \xrightarrow{Ca(OH)_2} H_2C-\underset{O}{\overset{H}{C}}-\underset{\overset{H}{|}}{C}-Cl
$$

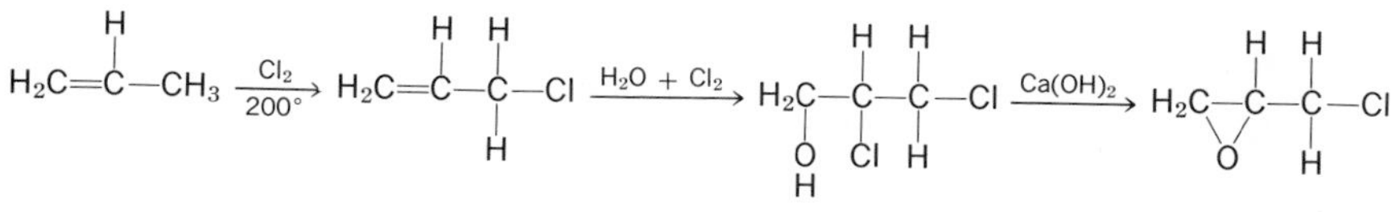

$$(15\text{-}23)$$

Preparation of epichlorohydrin

Silanes may be synthesized directly by passing methyl chloride over silicon in the presence of a copper metal catalyst, as shown below:

$$2H_3CCl + Si \xrightarrow[Cu]{250-350°} (H_3C)_2SiCl_2 \qquad (15\text{-}24)$$

Synthesis of dichlorodimethylsilane

However, the Grignard method is more versatile. As shown in the following equations, methylmagnesium chloride may react with silicon chloride or alkyl chlorosilanes to produce specific silanes.

$$H_3C\,MgCl + SiCl_4 \longrightarrow H_3C\,SiCl_3 + MgCl_2$$
$$H_3C\,MgCl + H_3C\,SiCl_3 \longrightarrow (H_3C)_2\,SiCl_2 + MgCl_2 \qquad (15\text{-}25)$$

Preparation of alkyl silanes by the Grignard reaction

Silanes will also add to ethylene or to a vinyl monomer in the presence of organic peroxides or metal catalysts, as shown below:

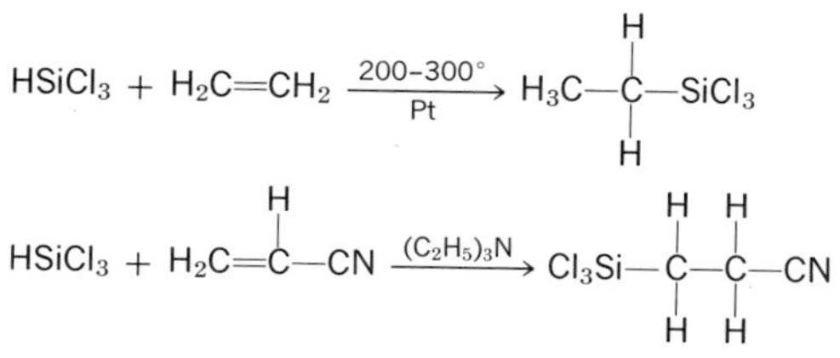

$$
HSiCl_3 + H_2C=CH_2 \xrightarrow[Pt]{200-300°} H_3C-\underset{\overset{H}{|}}{\overset{H}{\underset{|}{C}}}-SiCl_3
$$

$$
HSiCl_3 + H_2C=\underset{\overset{H}{|}}{C}-CN \xrightarrow{(C_2H_5)_3N} Cl_3Si-\underset{\overset{H}{|}}{\overset{H}{\underset{|}{C}}}-\underset{\overset{H}{|}}{\overset{H}{\underset{|}{C}}}-CN
$$

$$(15\text{-}26)$$

Addition of silanes to olefins

REFERENCES

Cram, D. J., and G. S. Hammond: "Organic Chemistry," 3d ed., McGraw-Hill Book Company, New York, 1970.

Davies, A.: Phenol, in H. R. Simonds and J. M. Church (eds.), "The Encyclopedia of Basic Materials for Plastics," Reinhold Publishing Corporation, New York, 1967.

Hardy, J. V. E.: Nylon Intermediates, in H. R. Simonds and J. M. Church (eds.), "The Encyclopedia of Basic Materials for Plastics," Reinhold Publishing Corporation, New York, 1967.

Lane, L. C.: Melamine, in H. R. Simonds and J. M. Church (eds.), "The Encyclopedia of Basic Materials for Plastics," Reinhold Publishing Corporation, New York, 1967.

Long, F. W.: Pyromellitic Dianhydride, in H. R. Simonds and J. M. Church (eds.), "The Encyclopedia of Basic Materials for Plastics," Reinhold Publishing Corporation, New York, 1967.

Noller, C. R.: "Chemistry of Organic Compounds," 3d ed., W. B. Saunders Company, Philadelphia, 1965.

Preston, R. W. G.: Alkylene Oxides and Glycols, in R. Long (ed.), "The Production of Polymers and Plastics Intermediates from Petroleum," chap. 6, Plenum Press, New York, 1967.

Smith, G. E.: ε-Caprolactam, in R. Long (ed.), "The Production of Polymers and Plastics Intermediates from Petroleum," chap. 10, Plenum Press, New York, 1967.

15-2 SYNTHESIS OF VINYL MONOMERS

Styrene (bp 145°) is produced by the vapor-phase dehydrogenation of ethylbenzene in the presence of catalysts (metallic oxides). Ethylbenzene is obtained when ethylene is condensed with benzene in the presence of aluminum chloride. The polyethylbenzenes produced as byproducts are recycled. The crude styrene is fractionated under reduced pressure in a 70-plate column in the presence of sulfur. The monomer is stored in the presence of 10 to 15-ppm *tert*-butylcatechol. Over 3.5 billion pounds of styrene is produced annually in the United States.

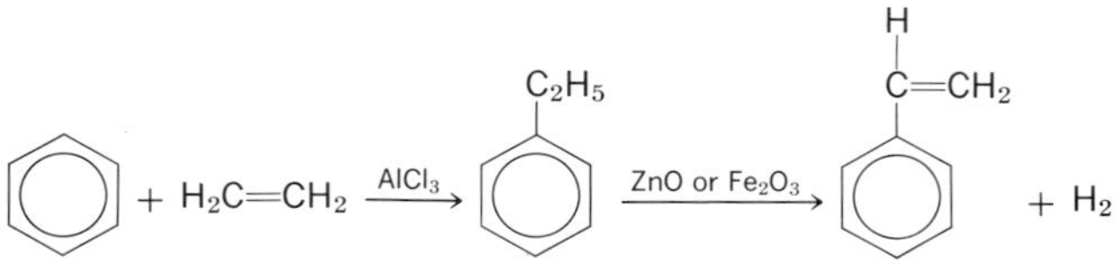

$$\text{(15-27)}$$

Preparation of styrene

Styrene has also been prepared by the dehydration of phenyl ethyl alcohol which is obtained by the oxidation of ethylbenzene. The classic method for the production of styrene was by the thermal decarboxylation of cinnamic acid. Vinyl pyridine is prepared by the condensation of pyridine and vinyl chloride in the presence of aluminum chloride.

Vinyl chloride has been prepared by the dehydrochlorination of ethylene chloride in the presence of sodium hydroxide and by thermal dehydrochlorination of this compound. Vinyl chloride has also been produced by the catalytic hydrochlorination of acetylene. Acetylene may be produced by the thermal cracking of hydrocarbons (Wulff process), partial oxidation of ethylene, and the classic hydrolysis of calcium carbide.

In the modern oxychlorination process, ethylene, hydrogen chloride, and oxygen are passed over a copper chloride–iron chloride, fluidized catalyst bed and the ethylene chloride produced is pyrolyzed. The hydrogen chloride byproduct is recycled. These reactions are shown in the following equations:

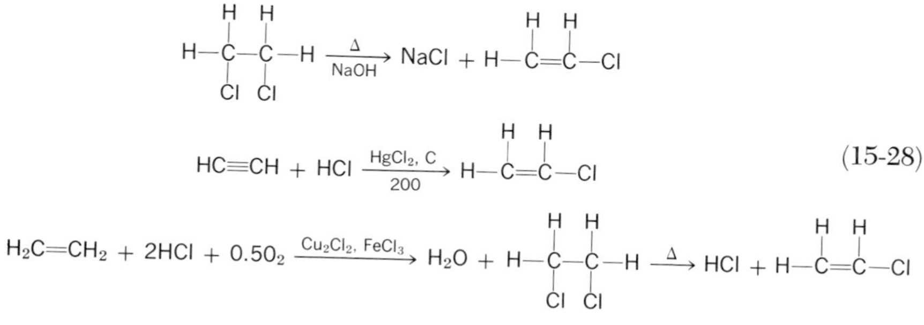

$$H-\underset{\underset{Cl}{|}}{\overset{\overset{H}{|}}{C}}-\underset{\underset{Cl}{|}}{\overset{\overset{H}{|}}{C}}-H \xrightarrow[\text{NaOH}]{\Delta} NaCl + H-\overset{\overset{H}{|}}{C}=\overset{\overset{H}{|}}{C}-Cl$$

$$HC\equiv CH + HCl \xrightarrow[200]{HgCl_2, C} H-\overset{\overset{H}{|}}{C}=\overset{\overset{H}{|}}{C}-Cl \qquad (15\text{-}28)$$

$$H_2C=CH_2 + 2HCl + 0.5O_2 \xrightarrow{Cu_2Cl_2,\ FeCl_3} H_2O + H-\underset{\underset{Cl}{|}}{\overset{\overset{H}{|}}{C}}-\underset{\underset{Cl}{|}}{\overset{\overset{H}{|}}{C}}-H \xrightarrow{\Delta} HCl + H-\overset{\overset{H}{|}}{C}=\overset{\overset{H}{|}}{C}-Cl$$

Equations for synthesis of vinyl chloride

Vinylidene chloride (bp 31.7°C) is obtained by the pyrolysis of 1,1,2-trichloroethane at 400° or by heating this *unsym*-trichloroethane with a lime slurry at 90°. The 1,1,2-trichloroethane may be produced by the chlorination of ethylene or vinyl chloride, as shown below:

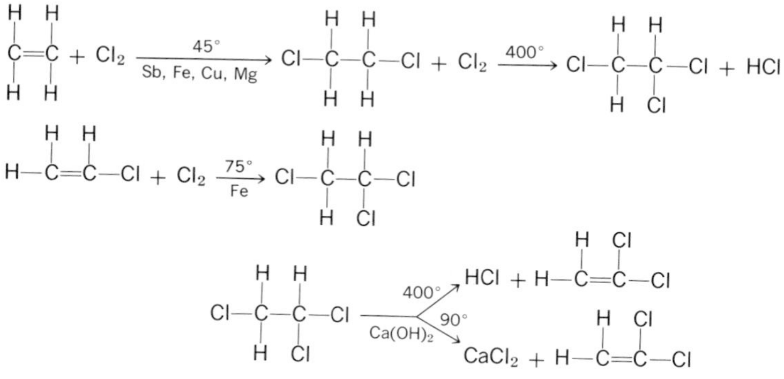

$$\overset{\overset{H}{|}}{\underset{\underset{H}{|}}{C}}=\overset{\overset{H}{|}}{\underset{\underset{H}{|}}{C}} + Cl_2 \xrightarrow[\text{Sb, Fe, Cu, Mg}]{45°} Cl-\underset{\underset{H}{|}}{\overset{\overset{H}{|}}{C}}-\underset{\underset{H}{|}}{\overset{\overset{H}{|}}{C}}-Cl + Cl_2 \xrightarrow{400°} Cl-\underset{\underset{H}{|}}{\overset{\overset{H}{|}}{C}}-\underset{\underset{Cl}{|}}{\overset{\overset{H}{|}}{C}}-Cl + HCl$$

$$H-\overset{\overset{H}{|}}{C}=\overset{\overset{H}{|}}{C}-Cl + Cl_2 \xrightarrow[\text{Fe}]{75°} Cl-\underset{\underset{H}{|}}{\overset{\overset{H}{|}}{C}}-\underset{\underset{Cl}{|}}{\overset{\overset{H}{|}}{C}}-Cl \qquad (15\text{-}29)$$

$$Cl-\underset{\underset{H}{|}}{\overset{\overset{H}{|}}{C}}-\underset{\underset{Cl}{|}}{\overset{\overset{H}{|}}{C}}-Cl \xrightarrow[\underset{Ca(OH)_2}{90°}]{400°} \begin{cases} HCl + H-\overset{\overset{H}{|}}{C}=\overset{\overset{Cl}{|}}{C}-Cl \\ CaCl_2 + H-\overset{\overset{H}{|}}{C}=\overset{\overset{Cl}{|}}{C}-Cl \end{cases}$$

Equations for synthesis of vinylidene chloride

Vinyl acetate (bp 72°) may be produced by the liquid- or vapor-phase catalytic acetylation of acetylene or the oxyacetylation of ethylene, as shown in the following equations:

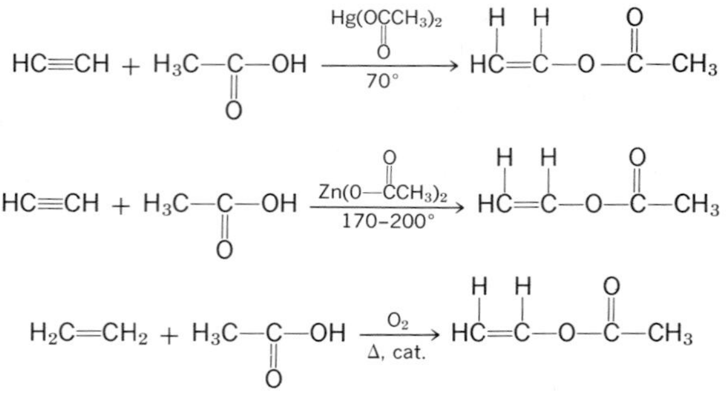

$$HC\equiv CH + H_3C-\underset{\underset{O}{\|}}{C}-OH \xrightarrow[70°]{Hg(OCCH_3)_2} HC\overset{H}{=}\overset{H}{C}-O-\underset{\underset{}{\|}}{\overset{O}{C}}-CH_3$$

$$HC\equiv CH + H_3C-\underset{\underset{O}{\|}}{C}-OH \xrightarrow[170-200°]{Zn(O-CCH_3)_2} HC\overset{H}{=}\overset{H}{C}-O-\underset{\underset{}{\|}}{\overset{O}{C}}-CH_3 \qquad (15\text{-}30)$$

$$H_2C=CH_2 + H_3C-\underset{\underset{O}{\|}}{C}-OH \xrightarrow[\Delta,\ cat.]{O_2} HC\overset{H}{=}\overset{H}{C}-O-\underset{\underset{}{\|}}{\overset{O}{C}}-CH_3$$

Equations for synthesis of vinyl acetate

Vinyl acetate may also be produced by the pyrolysis of ethylidene diacetate obtained from the reaction of acetic anhydride and acetaldehyde. This monomer is stabilized by the addition of copper salts of hydroquinone. Other vinyl esters are conveniently prepared in the laboratory by ester interchange of vinyl acetate and a carboxylic acid with a higher boiling point than acetic acid. Over 700 million pounds of vinyl acetate is produced annually in the United States.

Acrylonitrile (bp 79°) has been produced by the dehydration of the cyanohydrin obtained by the hydrocyanation of ethylene oxide or acetaldehyde. Approximately 1.5 billion pounds of acrylonitrile is produced annually in the United States.

$$H_2C\overset{}{\underset{O}{\diagdown\diagup}}CH_2 + HCN \longrightarrow H_2C-CH_2 \xrightarrow[-H_2O]{\Delta} H_2C=\overset{H}{\underset{}{C}}-CN$$
$$\qquad\qquad\qquad\qquad \underset{OH}{}\ \underset{CN}{}$$

$$H_3C-\overset{H}{\underset{}{C}}=O + HCN \longrightarrow H_3C-\overset{H}{\underset{OH}{C}}-CN \xrightarrow[-H_2O]{\Delta} H_2C=\overset{H}{\underset{}{C}}-CN$$

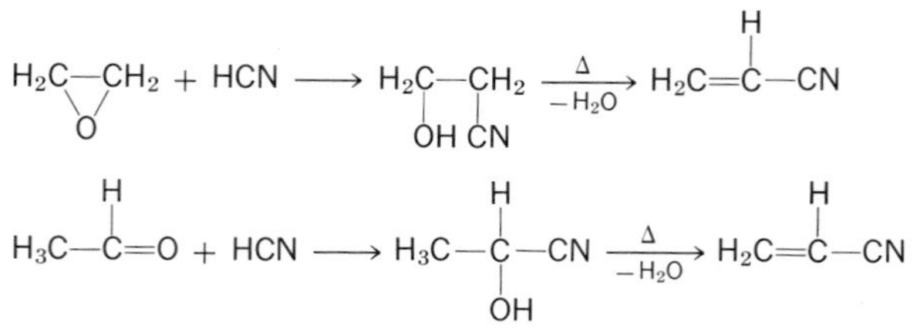

$$(15\text{-}31)$$

Preparation of acrylonitrile from ethylene oxide or acetaldehyde

This monomer may also be produced by the hydrocyanation of acetylene in the presence of copper (II) chloride, as shown below:

$$HC{\equiv}CH + HCN \xrightarrow[\text{CuCl}_2]{450°} H_2C{=}\overset{\overset{\textstyle H}{\textstyle |}}{C}{-}CN \tag{15-32}$$

Preparation of acrylonitrile from acetylene

Both acrylonitrile and methacrylonitrile have been produced by the catalytic ammoxidation of propylene or butylene in the presence of bismuth phosphomolybdate, as shown in the following equations:

$$H{-}\overset{\overset{\textstyle H}{\textstyle |}}{\underset{\underset{\textstyle H}{\textstyle |}}{C}}{-}\overset{\overset{\textstyle H}{\textstyle |}}{C}{=}\overset{\overset{\textstyle H}{\textstyle |}}{C}{-}H + NH_3 + 1.5O_2 \xrightarrow[\text{BiP(Mo}_3\text{O}_{10})_4]{300-540°} H_2C{=}\overset{\overset{\textstyle H}{\textstyle |}}{C}{-}CN + 3H_2O$$

$$\tag{15-33}$$

$$H_3C{-}\overset{\overset{\textstyle CH_3}{\textstyle |}}{C}{=}\overset{\overset{\textstyle H}{\textstyle |}}{C}{-}H + NH_3 + 1.5O_2 \xrightarrow[\text{BiP(Mo}_3\text{O}_{10})_4]{300-540°} H_2C{=}\overset{\overset{\textstyle CH_3}{\textstyle |}}{C}{-}CN + 3H_2O$$

Preparation of acrylonitrile and methacrylonitrile from olefins

Ethylene (bp $-103.7°$), propylene (bp $-47.7°$), and butylene (bp $-6.9°$) are produced by the vapor-phase cracking of naphtha (light oil fractions) of petroleum gases. The acetylenes produced as byproducts are removed by absorbants or selective solvents. The desired monomers are separated from other products by fractional distillation.

Tetrafluoroethylene (bp $-76.3°$) is obtained when chlorodifluoromethane is dehydrohalogenated, as shown in the following equations. Chlorodifluoromethane is obtained from the reaction of hydrogen fluoride and chloroform.

$$HF + HCCl_3 \longrightarrow HCl + HCClF_2$$

$$2C\overset{\overset{\textstyle H}{\textstyle |}}{C}lF_2 \xrightarrow[80°]{\Delta} 2HCl + F_2C{=}CF_2 \tag{15-34}$$

Preparation of tetrafluoroethylene

Trifluoromonochloroethylene is produced by the zinc metal dehalogenation of trichlorotrifluoroethane. The latter is obtained by the hydrofluorination of hexachloroethane. These reactions are as follows:

$$Cl_3C{-}CCl_3 \xrightarrow[\text{HF}]{\text{SbF}_3{-}\text{SbCl}_3} F_2\overset{\overset{\textstyle Cl}{\textstyle |}}{C}{-}\overset{\overset{\textstyle F}{\textstyle |}}{C}Cl_2 \xrightarrow[\Delta]{Zn} F_2C{=}\overset{\overset{\textstyle F}{\textstyle |}}{C}Cl + ZnCl_2 \tag{15-35}$$

Preparation of trifluoromonochloroethylene

Vinyl fluoride (bp $-72\,^{\circ}C$) is obtained by the hydrofluorination of acetylene in the presence of mercuric salts, as shown below:

$$HC\equiv CH + HF \xrightarrow{\text{HgCl}_2-\text{BaCl}_2} H_2C\!=\!\overset{\displaystyle H}{\underset{}{C}}F \qquad (15\text{-}36)$$

Preparation of vinyl fluoride

Vinylidene fluoride is produced by the thermal dehydrohalogenation of 1,1,1-monochlorodifluoroethane, as shown below:

$$\underset{\overset{\displaystyle |}{H}\ \ \overset{\displaystyle |}{F}}{\overset{\overset{\displaystyle H}{|}\ \ \overset{\displaystyle F}{|}}{H C\!-\!C Cl}} \xrightarrow{\Delta} H_2C\!=\!CF_2 + HCl \qquad (15\text{-}37)$$

Preparation of vinylidene fluoride

Vinyl ethyl ether (bp 35.5°) is produced by the alcoholysis of acetylene in the presence of potassium ethoxylate at 130 to 180°. The acetylene is mixed with nitrogen to reduce the hazards of explosions. Acetals are produced in the presence of mercuric ion catalysts. As shown by the following equations, these acetals are decomposed in the presence of palladium on asbestos:

$$HC\equiv CH + H\!-\!\underset{\overset{\displaystyle |}{H}\ \overset{\displaystyle |}{H}}{\overset{\overset{\displaystyle H}{|}\ \overset{\displaystyle H}{|}}{C\!-\!C}}\!-\!OH \xrightarrow[130-180^{\circ}]{\text{KOC}_2\text{H}_5} H_2C\!=\!\overset{\displaystyle H}{\underset{}{C}}\!-\!OC_2H_5$$

$$HC\equiv CH + 2H\!-\!\underset{\overset{\displaystyle |}{H}\ \overset{\displaystyle |}{H}}{\overset{\overset{\displaystyle H}{|}\ \overset{\displaystyle H}{|}}{C\!-\!C}}\!-\!OH \xrightarrow{\text{Hg}^{++}} H_3C\!-\!\overset{\displaystyle H}{\underset{}{C}}(OC_2H_5)_2 \qquad (15\text{-}38)$$

$$H_3C\!-\!\overset{\displaystyle H}{\underset{}{C}}(OC_2H_5)_2 \xrightarrow[\text{Pt-asbestos}]{200-300^{\circ}} C_2H_5OH + H_2C\!=\!\overset{\displaystyle H}{\underset{}{C}}\!-\!OC_2H_5$$

Synthesis of vinyl ethyl ether from acetylene

1,3-Butadiene is produced by the low-pressure cracking of butane or butene at 600 to $700\,^{\circ}F$ in the presence of chromia on activated alumina. The desired compound may be separated from other products by the formation of a solid sulfone with sulfur dioxide or by the selective solvent action of furfural or dimethylformamide. As shown by the following equations, butadiene may be produced by the dehydration of butanediol obtained by the hydrogenation of aldol or dihydroxybutyne. Almost 3 billion pounds of butadiene is produced annually in the United States.

$$H-\underset{\underset{H}{|}}{\overset{\overset{H}{|}}{C}}-\underset{\underset{H}{|}}{\overset{\overset{H}{|}}{C}}-\underset{\underset{H}{|}}{\overset{\overset{H}{|}}{C}}-\underset{\underset{H}{|}}{\overset{\overset{H}{|}}{C}}-H \xrightarrow[Cr_2O_3-Al_2O_3]{600-700} H_2C=\underset{\underset{H}{|}}{\overset{\overset{H}{|}}{C}}-\underset{\overset{H}{|}}{C}=CH_2 + \text{other products}$$

$$2HC\equiv CH + 2H_2O \xrightarrow{cat.} 2H_3C-\underset{\underset{H}{\overset{|}{O}}}{\overset{\overset{H}{|}}{C}}=O \longrightarrow H_3C-\underset{\underset{H}{\overset{|}{O}}}{\overset{\overset{H}{|}}{C}}-\underset{\underset{H}{|}}{\overset{\overset{H}{|}}{C}}-\underset{}{\overset{\overset{H}{|}}{C}}=O \xrightarrow{H_2} H_3C-\underset{\underset{H}{\overset{|}{O}}}{\overset{\overset{H}{|}}{C}}-\underset{\underset{H}{|}}{\overset{\overset{H}{|}}{C}}-\underset{\underset{H}{|}}{\overset{\overset{H}{|}}{C}}-OH$$

$$\text{(15-39)}$$

$$HC\equiv CH + 2H-\underset{}{\overset{\overset{H}{|}}{C}}=O \xrightarrow{cat.} HO-\underset{\underset{H}{|}}{\overset{\overset{H}{|}}{C}}-C\equiv C-\underset{\underset{H}{|}}{\overset{\overset{H}{|}}{C}}-OH \xrightarrow{2H_2} HO-\underset{\underset{H}{|}}{\overset{\overset{H}{|}}{C}}-\underset{\underset{H}{|}}{\overset{\overset{H}{|}}{C}}-\underset{\underset{H}{|}}{\overset{\overset{H}{|}}{C}}-\underset{\underset{H}{|}}{\overset{\overset{H}{|}}{C}}-OH$$

$$HO-\underset{\underset{H}{|}}{\overset{\overset{H}{|}}{C}}-\underset{\underset{H}{|}}{\overset{\overset{H}{|}}{C}}-\underset{\underset{H}{|}}{\overset{\overset{H}{|}}{C}}-\underset{\underset{H}{|}}{\overset{\overset{H}{|}}{C}}-OH \quad \text{or} \quad H_3C-\underset{\underset{H}{\overset{|}{O}}}{\overset{\overset{H}{|}}{C}}-\underset{\underset{H}{|}}{\overset{\overset{H}{|}}{C}}-\underset{\underset{H}{|}}{\overset{\overset{H}{|}}{C}}-OH \xrightarrow[cat.]{\Delta} H_2C=\underset{}{\overset{\overset{H}{|}}{C}}-\underset{}{\overset{\overset{H}{|}}{C}}=CH_2$$

Equations for production of 1,3-butadiene

Chloroprene is produced by the aqueous hydrohalogenation of vinyl acetylene at 35 to 50° in the presence of copper(I) chloride. As shown in the following equations, the original product formed by a 1,4 addition undergoes an allylic rearrangement in the presence of hydrochloric acid. Vinyl acetylene is obtained by the dimerization of acetylene at 55 to 65° in the presence of an ammonical solution of copper(I) chloride.

$$2HC\equiv CH \xrightarrow{Cu_2Cl_2}{NH_4Cl} H_2C=\underset{\overset{H}{|}}{C}-C\equiv CH \xrightarrow[Cu_2Cl_2]{HCl} \left(Cl-\underset{\underset{H}{|}}{\overset{\overset{H}{|}}{C}}-\underset{}{\overset{\overset{H}{|}}{C}}=C=CH_2\right) \longrightarrow H_2C=\underset{}{\overset{\overset{Cl}{|}}{C}}-\underset{}{\overset{\overset{H}{|}}{C}}=CH_2$$

$$\text{(15-40)}$$

Synthesis of chloroprene from acetylene

Acrylic acid may be produced by the catalytic hydrocarbonylation of acetylene in the presence of nickel carbonyl. This monomer may also be prepared by the hydrolysis of acrylonitrile or methyl acrylate. Methacrylic acid may be produced by the dehydration of α-hydroxyisobutyric acid. This acid is obtained by the nitric acid–nitrogen dioxide oxidation of isobutylene.

These reactions are shown in the following equations:

$$HC\equiv CH + CO + H_2O \xrightarrow[HCl]{Ni(CO)_4} H_2C=\overset{\overset{\displaystyle H}{|}}{C}-\underset{\underset{\displaystyle O}{\|}}{C}-OH$$

$$\underset{\underset{\displaystyle CH_3}{|}}{\overset{\overset{\displaystyle CH_3}{|}}{C}}=CH_2 \xrightarrow{HNO_3-NO_2} H_3C-\underset{\underset{\displaystyle CH_3}{|}}{\overset{\overset{\displaystyle H \;\; O}{|}}{C}}-\underset{\underset{\displaystyle O}{\|}}{C}-OH \xrightarrow[H_3O^+]{\Delta} H_2O + H_2C=\underset{\underset{\displaystyle CH_3}{|}}{C}-\underset{\underset{\displaystyle O}{\|}}{C}-OH \quad (15\text{-}41)$$

Synthesis of acrylic and methacrylic acids

Methyl acrylate (bp 80°) may be produced by the methanolysis of acrylonitrile or ethylene cyanohydrin. The latter is obtained by the hydrocyanation of ethylene oxide. The monomer may also be produced by the carbonylation of acetylene in aqueous methanol, by the dehydration of methyl lactate, and by the methanolysis of β-propiolactone or acrylic acid. These reactions are shown in the following equations:

$$H_2C=\overset{\overset{\displaystyle H}{|}}{C}-CN + H_3COH \xrightarrow{H_3O^+} H_2C=\overset{\overset{\displaystyle H}{|}}{C}-\underset{\underset{\displaystyle O}{\|}}{C}-OCH_3 + NH_4^+$$

$$H_2C\overset{\displaystyle{\diagdown O \diagup}}{-}CH_2 + HCN \xrightarrow{\Delta} H_2C-\underset{\underset{\underset{\displaystyle H}{|}}{CN}}{\overset{\overset{\displaystyle }{|}}{}}CH_2 + H_3C-OH \xrightarrow[\Delta]{H_3O^+} H_2C=\overset{\overset{\displaystyle H}{|}}{C}-\underset{\underset{\displaystyle O}{\|}}{C}-OCH_3 + NH_4^+$$

$$HC\equiv CH + CO + H_3COH \xrightarrow[HCl]{Ni(CO)_4} H_2C=\overset{\overset{\displaystyle H}{|}}{C}-\underset{\underset{\displaystyle O}{\|}}{C}-OCH_3 \quad (15\text{-}42)$$

$$H_3C-\underset{\underset{\displaystyle OH}{|}}{\overset{\overset{\displaystyle H \;\; O}{|\;\;\|}}{C}}-C-OCH_3 \xrightarrow[\Delta]{H_3O^+} H_2C=\overset{\overset{\displaystyle H}{|}}{C}-\underset{\underset{\displaystyle O}{\|}}{C}-OCH_3$$

$$\underset{\underset{\displaystyle H_2C-O}{|}}{\overset{\overset{\displaystyle H_2C-C=O}{|}}{}} \xrightarrow[H_3O^+]{H_3COH} HO-\underset{\underset{\displaystyle H}{|}}{\overset{\overset{\displaystyle H}{|}}{C}}-\underset{\underset{\displaystyle H}{|}}{\overset{\overset{\displaystyle H}{|}}{C}}-\underset{\underset{\displaystyle O}{\|}}{C}-OCH_3 \longrightarrow H_2C=\overset{\overset{\displaystyle H}{|}}{C}-\underset{\underset{\displaystyle O}{\|}}{C}OCH_3$$

Equations for synthesis of methyl acrylate

Methyl methacrylate (bp 101°) may be produced by the methanolysis of acetone cyanohydrin. The latter is obtained by the hydrocyanation of acetone. The monomer may also be produced by the oxidation and methanolysis of the product obtained by the reaction of acetone and acetylene.

$$H_3C-\underset{\underset{O}{\|}}{C}-CH_3 + HCN \longrightarrow H_3C-\underset{\underset{CN}{|}}{\overset{\overset{H}{\overset{|}{O}}}{C}}-CH_3 \xrightarrow[\Delta]{H_3O^+} H_2C=\underset{\underset{CH_3}{|}}{C}-\underset{\underset{O}{\|}}{C}NH_3^+$$

$$+ CH_3OH \xrightarrow{\Delta} H_2C=\underset{\underset{CH_3}{|}}{C}-\underset{\underset{O}{\|}}{C}-OCH_3 + NH_4^+$$

$$(15\text{-}43)$$

$$HC\equiv CH + 2H_3C-\underset{\underset{O}{\|}}{C}-CH_3 \longrightarrow H_3C-\underset{\underset{OH}{|}}{\overset{\overset{CH_3}{|}}{C}}-C\equiv C-\underset{\underset{OH}{|}}{\overset{\overset{CH_3}{|}}{C}}-CH_3 \xrightarrow{(O)} 2(H_3C)_2\underset{\underset{OH}{|}}{C}-\underset{\underset{O}{\|}}{C}-OH \xrightarrow[H_3O^+]{CH_3OH}$$

$$H_2C=\underset{\underset{O}{\|}}{\overset{\overset{CH_3}{|}}{C}}-C-O-CH_3$$

Equations for synthesis of methyl methacrylate

Esters of other alcohols and acrylic or methacrylic acid are conveniently prepared in the laboratory by ester interchange with the methyl esters.

Table 15-1   Physical Properties of Polymer Reactants

COMPOUND	MELTING POINT, °C	BOILING POINT, °C	SPECIFIC GRAVITY	INDEX OF REFRACTION
Adipic acid	152	265^{10}	$1.360\frac{25}{4}$	
Epichlorohydrin	−57	117^{756}	$1.183\frac{25}{25}$	1.4397^{16}
Ethylene glycol	−15.6	198	$1.113\frac{19}{4}$	1.4318^{20}
Ethylene oxide	−111.7	10.7	$0.887\frac{7}{4}$	$1.3599^{8.4}$
Formaldehyde	−92	−21	0.815^{20}	
Furfural	−39	162	$1.159\frac{20}{4}$	1.5261^{20}
Furfuryl alcohol	. . .	169.5^{752}	$1.129\frac{25}{4}$	1.4852^{20}
Glycerol	18.2	290	$1.261\frac{20}{4}$	1.4729^{20}
Hexamethylene diamine	42	204.5		
Maleic anhydride	53	202	1.5	
Melamine	360	. . .	1.5373^{25}	
Pentaerythritol	262	276^{30}		
Phenol	40.9	181.8^{8}	$1.071\frac{25}{4}$	1.54^{45}
Phthalic acid (*o*)	231	. . .	$1.593\frac{20}{4}$	
Isophthalic acid (*m*)	347			
Terephthalic acid (*p*)	425			
Phthalic anhydride	132	284.5	1.527^{4}	
Pyromellitic dianhydride	287	397–400	1.68	
Sebacic acid	135.5	294.5^{100}	$1.207\frac{25}{4}$	1.42^{133}
Urea	132.7	. . .	$1.335\frac{20}{4}$	

Table 15-2 Physical Properties of Monomers

COMPOUND	MELTING POINT, °C	BOILING POINT, °C	DENSITY	INDEX OF REFRACTION
Acrylamide	85	125[25]	1.122[30]	
Acrylic acid	12	141	1.0511[20]	1.4224[20]
Methyl acrylate	−75	80	0.953[20]	1.3984[20]
Acrylonitrile	−83.6	77.3	0.8060[20]	1.393[20]
1,3-Butadiene	−109	−4.4	0.6211[20]	1.4292[−25]
Chloroprene	. . .	59.4	0.9583[20]	1.4583[20]
Chlorotrifluoroethylene	−158	−28		
1-Butene	−185	−6.3	0.5951[20]	1.3962[20]
Isobutylene (2-methyl propene)	−141	−6.6	0.6266[−6.6]	1.3814[−25]
Ethylene	−169	−104	0.566[−102]	1.363[−100]
Tetrafluoroethylene	−142.5	−76.3	1.519[20]	
Isoprene	−146	34	0.6806[20]	1.4194[20]
Methacrylic acid	15.5	161	1.0153[20]	1.43143[20]
Methyl methacrylate	−48	101	0.936[20]	1.413[20]
Methacrylonitrile	−36	90.3	0.7998[20]	1.4007[20]
Methyl isopropenyl ketone	−54	98	0.8550[20]	1.4220[20]
Propylene	−185	−48	0.5139[−20]	
Styrene	−30.6	145.2	0.9090[20]	1.54682[20]
α-Methylstyrene	−23.2	163.4	0.9165[10]	1.5386[20]
Vinyl acetate	100	72.5	0.9338[20]	1.3953[20]
Vinyl chloride	−154	−13	0.99176[−15]	1.398[15]
Vinyl ethyl ether	−115	35	0.7589[20]	1.3767[20]
Vinyl fluoride	−161	−51		
Vinylidene chloride	−122	31.7	1.2129[20]	1.4249[20]
2-Vinylpyridine	. . .	80[29]	0.9985[0]	1.5494[20]

REFERENCES

Boundy, R. H., R. F. Boyer, and S. M. Stroesser: "Styrene, Its Polymer, Copolymers and Derivatives," Hafner Publishing Company, Inc., New York, 1965.

Campbell, J.: Styrene, in R. Long (ed.), "The Production of Polymers and Plastics Intermediates from Petroleum," chap. 8, Plenum Press, New York, 1967.

Castille, Y. P.: Physical Properties of Monomers, in J. Brandrup and E. H. Immergut (eds.), "Polymer Handbook," chap. 8-1, Interscience Publishers, a division of John Wiley & Sons, Inc., New York, 1966.

Cotterill, C. B.: Olefins, in R. Long (ed.), "The Production of Polymers and Plastics Intermediates from Petroleum," chap. 11, Plenum Press, New York, 1967.

Crawford, G. H., and H. A. Brown: Fluorocarbon Monomers, in H. R. Simonds and J. M. Church (eds.), "The Encyclopedia of Basic Materials for Plastics," Reinhold Publishing Corporation, New York, 1967.

Davison, J. W.: Olefin Monomers, in H. R. Simonds and J. M. Church (eds.), "The Encyclopedia of Basic Materials for Plastics," Reinhold Publishing Corporation, New York, 1967.

Duck, E. W., and D. G. Timms: Butadiene, in R. Long (ed.), "The Production of Polymers and Plastics Intermediates from Petroleum," chap. 2, Plenum Press, New York, 1967.

Hulme, P., and P. Turner: Caprolactam, *Chem. Eng.*, **75**(7):82 (1968).

Landau, R., D. Brown, A. Saffer, and J. V. Porcelli: Ethylene Oxide, *Chem. Eng. Progr.*, **64**(3):27 (1968).

Luskin, L. S.: Acrylic Esters, in H. R. Simonds and J. M. Church (eds.), "The Encyclopedia of Basic Materials for Plastics," Reinhold Publishing Corporation, New York, 1967.

Seymour, R. B.: Vinyl Monomers, in H. R. Simonds and J. M. Church (eds.) "The Encyclopedia of Basic Materials for Plastics," Reinhold Publishing Corporation, New York, 1967.

Spitz, P. H.: Vinyl Chloride, *Chem. Eng. Progr.*, **64**(3):19 (1968).

Stille, J. K.: "Industrial Organic Chemistry," Prentice-Hall, Inc., Englewood Cliffs, N.J., 1968.

Wolcock, J. W.: Olefin Production, in H. Steiner (ed.), "Introduction to Petroleum Chemicals," Pergamon Press, New York, 1961.

16

General Concepts

16-1 THE IMPORTANCE OF POLYMERS

Many laymen and even some scientists and technologists have developed erroneous notions about polymers. Laymen may visualize these important materials as shoddy substitutes, and some scientists still refer to them as goos, gunks, and messes. However, the informed scientist recognizes that there are very few important nonpolymeric organic materials. In addition, some important nonpolymeric articles of commerce, such as gasoline and glucose, are degradation products of macromolecules.

Billmeyer stated that more than a third of all American chemists and chemical engineers are employed by industries associated with polymeric materials. A survey by the U.S. National Science Foundation showed that over 40 percent of chemists work in the field of polymer science. Kline concluded that approximately half of all chemists in the United States are working in the field of polymer science and technology. He emphasized that almost 10,000 chemists are members of the Polymer, Rubber, and Organic Coatings and Plastics Chemistry Divisions of the American Chemical Society and that over 7,500 articles on high polymers are abstracted annually by *Chemical Abstracts*. No other division of chemistry has this membership or frequency of abstracts. The importance of macromolecular chemistry has also been recognized by the American Chemical Society which has published a monthly journal (*Macromolecules*) on this subject since February, 1968.

It is significant that over 100 American universities were offering courses in polymer science in 1967 in contrast to 37 institutions in 1951. In that year less than five universities offered more than 20 credits in this discipline, whereas more than 20 schools offered more than 20 credits in 1967. For example, Lowell Technological Institute offers 99 credits in polymer science. This institution and Case–Western, Cornell, Rensselaer, Stevens, Akron, and Brooklyn grant Ph.D. degrees in polymer science as a related discipline.

As might be anticipated, many polymer industries are located in areas where courses in polymer science are offered. The number of custom plastics-processing and converting plants in some of the leading polymer education areas in 1967 were New York, 208; Ohio, 170; New Jersey, 150; and Massachusetts, 95. This is far from a complete list but emphasizes the importance of polymer education.

One may obtain a better understanding of the magnitude of the polymer industry by simple observation of the immediate environment. This book consists of pigmented polymer printed on pages of a polymer of glucose (cellulose) held together by polymeric adhesives and fibers. The reader is probably sitting in a chair consisting of cellulose held together by a polymer called lignin or in a polyester chair reinforced by fibrous glass. The notepaper, the ink, and the ball-point pen used are also polymeric.

Classroom chalk is not an organic polymer, of course, but dustproof varieties depend on polymers for this desirable quality. Few modern blackboards are constructed from slate; they are sheet plastic. The "lead" in a black pencil is not an organic polymer, but cellulose or extruded thermoplastics are used to support this "lead."

The brass ferrule in many pencils has been replaced by a plastic tube, and the eraser has always been an elastomeric polymer. Actually the name *rubber* was coined by Priestley in tribute to its functionalism as an eraser. Even those who are unable to comprehend the importance of polymers are amazed to learn that its use as an eraser was one of the most important applications of natural rubber for many years prior to Goodyear's discovery of the process of vulcanization.

Visual aids used in the modern classroom are also dependent on polymers, for example, the cellulose acetate film used in transparent slides and in overhead projectors, the plastic tape or disks for recordings, and the housings and electronic circuitry used in much of the equipment.

As one evaluates the statements on the importance of polymers by examining the classroom itself or almost any modern room, he observes vinyl tile or acrylic carpet on the floor, walls of laminates of wood or plastics, and venetian blinds of rigid poly(vinyl chloride) at the windows.

If fluorescent lighting is used, the fixtures may include polystyrene louvres or light diffusers and molded melamine plastic fixtures. The copper wiring may be insulated by plasticized poly(vinyl chloride) or polyethylene.

Some classrooms have acrylic glazing and upholstered seating consisting of polyurethane foam protected by plasticized poly(vinyl chloride) sheet or nylon textile.

Further examination beyond the immediate environment reveals that polymers are and always have been the most widely used materials by man and nature. Man or any other form of life is a dynamic exhibit of a myriad variety of proteins. The variations are dependent on the kind and arrangement of the amino acids present in the polymer chain.

Plants consist primarily of cellulose or starch which are polymers of glucose. Other polymers present in plants include lignin, natural rubber, gutta-percha, zein, soya bean protein, rosin (abietic acid), copal, dammar, gum arabic, and alginic acid. Many useful polymeric materials have been produced by chemical or physical modifications of naturally occurring polymers.

Shellac, which was the pioneer constituent of Edison's gramophone records and many protective coatings, is excreted by small coccid insects (*Coccus lacca*) which feed on the twigs of trees in India, Burma, and Thailand. The term *shellac* for the refined stick lac is derived from *shel* (a Dutch word for scale) and *lac* (from the Sanskrit word *laksha*) meaning 100,000. Actually 10 lakshas or 1 million insects are required for the production of 1 lb of crude stick lac.

Silk is spun in the form of cocoons by caterpillars (*Bombyx mori*) which feed on leaves of the mulberry tree in China, Japan, India, Italy, and France. About 50 lb of this proteinaceous fiber is obtained from 1 acre of trees. Wild silks such as tussah are produced by caterpillers feeding on oak leaves.

Naturally occurring fibrous products, such as cellulose, are converted to continuous fibers or sheet by dissolving a derivative such as cellulose xanthate, extruding the solution through spinnerets, and regenerating the cellulose. Proteinaceous zein from corn, casein from milk, and soybean protein are made more durable by reacting with formaldehyde. Rosin from pine trees is upgraded by esterification with glycerol to form ester gum.

The utility of cellulose is increased by esterification with nitric acid. The cellulose nitrate is used as gunpowder (guncotton), plastics (Celluloid), protective coatings (Duco), and film. Organic esters, such as cellulose acetate and cellulose acetate butyrate, have replaced the more combustible nitrate for many applications other than explosives. Cellulose ethers, such as methyl cellulose, hydroxyethylcellulose, and carboxymethylcellulose, are used as water-soluble thickeners, coatings, and sizes.

Derivatives of natural rubber such as chorinated rubber (Parlon) and cyclized rubber (Pliolite) have been used as protective coatings. The reaction product of rubber and hydrochloric acid (Pliofilm) is used as a packaging film.

Synthetic resins such as polyethylene may be chlorinated and sulfo-chlorinated to produce useful flame-resistant materials. The properties of many polymers may be modified by the addition of plasticizers, reinforcements, and stabilizers. The utility of polymers may be increased by processing techniques such as molding, extruding, and fabrication.

Natural and synthetic polymers are widely used by the building, transportation, communication, electrical, and textile industries. Because of their versatility and unique functionalism, their use ranges from poromeric shoes to ablative nose cones in space capsules. Their properties range from the nonadhesiveness of polyfluoroethylene to the exceptional adhesiveness of cyanoacrylates. This versatility, which appears mysterious to the uninformed, is readily explained by polymer science. Such knowledge is essential for all modern scientists.

REFERENCES

Fisher, H. L.: "Chemistry of Natural and Synthetic Rubber," Reinhold Publishing Corporation, New York, 1957.

Kline, G. M.: Annual Review, *Mod. Plastics*, **44**(6):129, 1967.

Kornreich, E.: "Introduction to Fibers and Fabrics," 2d ed., chap. 2, American Elsevier Publishing Company, Inc., New York, 1966.

Mark, H. F.: "Giant Molecules," Time, Inc., New York, 1966.

Morton, M., W. V. Bailey, C. G. Overberger, R. W. Cairns, and W. V. Sparks: Polymer Science Education, *J. Chem. Educ.*, **45**:498, 500, 502, 503, 505 (1968).

Nylen, P., and E. Sunderland: "Modern Surface Coatings," chaps. 4, 6–8, Interscience Publishers, a division of John Wiley & Sons, Inc., New York, 1965.

"Plastics in Building," McGraw-Hill Book Company, New York, 1966.

Seymour, R. B.: Annual Review of Plastics, *Ind. Eng. Chem.*, **59**(8):62 (1967).

Skeist, I.: "Plastics in Building," Reinhold Publishing Corporation, New York, 1966.

Winding, C. C., and P. H. Brodsky: Polymer Education, *SPE J.*, **24**(1):31 (1968).

16-2 PRODUCTION STATISTICS

a. FIBERS

In spite of their antiquity, fibers were used only to a limited extent prior to the industrial revolution. Crude techniques for degumming silk, scouring wool, and separating cotton seeds from the fibers were used centuries ago. Likewise, weaving was an ancient art, but prior to the nineteenth century the carding, spinning, and weaving were done in the home (homespun).

The flying shuttle, spinning jenny, and spinning frame were invented by Kay, Hargreaves, and Arkwright in the eighteenth century but the textile industry was essentially nonexistent until the invention of the cotton gin by Whitney in 1793. The subsequent development of the power loom by Lowell and Moody in 1814 was also a major step in the industrialization of textile manufacture. Thus, in 1850 over one-half of all the cotton, woolen, and linen textiles was produced in mills, and home spinning continued to decline until it became a lost art.

Today, the 5 billion pounds of cotton harvested annually in the United States is valued at over 2 billion dollars. The annual production of textiles is used by the Federal Reserve System as one of its production indices.

The reign of cotton as king in the United States ended in 1968 when the production of synthetic fibers exceeded that of natural fibers. However, cotton will continue to be king on a worldwide basis for many years. Over 25 billion pounds of cotton was produced worldwide in 1968. The leading producing nations are the United States, U.S.S.R., China (Mainland), and India.

Viscose rayon has been produced in the United States since 1910 when a plant was built at Marcus Hook, Pennsylvania. Production has increased steadily from less than 400,000 pounds in 1911 to approximately 800 million pounds in 1969. Annual worldwide production is about 6 billion pounds.

The relative economic importance of all commercial cellulose fibers becomes more obvious when the production of paper and paperboard is included. As shown by the industrial production index of the Federal Reserve System, this production doubled in the period 1950 to 1966. Less than 10 million tons was produced in 1925. Almost 100 billion pounds of paper and paperboard were produced in the United States and worldwide production was greater than 225 billion pounds in 1966.

Worldwide wool production in 1968 was about 3 billion pounds. Australia produces over 50 percent of the world's supply. U.S.S.R., New Zealand, Argentina, and South Africa all produce more wool than the United States, where less than 400 million pounds of wool is used annually. The selling price is slightly less than $2.00 a pound.

In the eighteenth century, wool accounted for almost 80 percent of all fibers used but it now amounts to less than 10 percent of all fiber production. The worldwide production of silk is now less than 100 million pounds a year. Less than 4 million pounds was used in the United States in 1968. The selling price was $3.50 a pound.

Cellulose acetate (acetate rayon) fibers are produced both as the "secondary acetate," in which 20 percent of the hydroxyl groups are not esterified, and as the triacetate (Arnel). Over 400 million pounds of acetate rayon is produced annually in the United States.

No truly synthetic fiber was available commercially prior to 1930, when

Hill, an associate of Carothers, produced a crude fiber from molten poly(hexamethylene adipamide) (nylon 6,6). Nylon was patented in 1937 and produced commercially in 1939. Production has increased annually from 50,000 pounds that year to over 1 billion pounds valued at over 1 billion dollars in 1969. Considerable quantities of caprolactam are also polymerized to produce nylon 6.

The first commercial polyester fiber (Terylene) was introduced in England in 1941 by Calico Printers and made available (as Dacron) in the United States by Du Pont in 1946. Total annual production in the United States is now approximately 600 million pounds. It is produced by several firms under different trade names (Fortrel, Kodel, and Vycron).

The commercialization of fibers from polymer of acrylonitrile was delayed by their inherent resistance to solvents and dyes. Fibers containing at least 85 percent acrylonitrile are designated as *acrylic fibers*. These have been available from several firms since the 1950s (Acrilan, Creslan, Orlon, and Zefran). Those containing 35 to 85 percent acrylonitrile are called *modacrylics* by the U.S. Federal Trade Commission (Dynel and Verel). The annual production of acrylic and modacrylic fibers in the United States is about 400 million pounds.

Polyurethane fibers (Perlon U), which were developed in Germany in 1937, are now produced in sizable quantities in Europe. Polyurethane fibers with elastic properties (Spandex) are produced in the United States (Lycra).

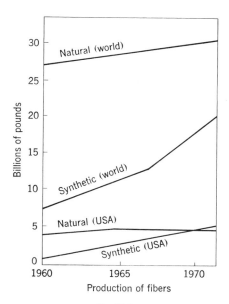

Fig. 16-1

Polypropylene fibers are used to a limited extent but this application will grow. American industry has not produced several functional fibers commercially since it maintains that an annual production of at least 10 million pounds is essential. As a result, production statistics for specific fibers vary considerably throughout the world. For example, over 50 million pounds of poly(vinyl alcohol) fibers (Kurlon) are produced annually in Japan. Blends of these and poly(vinyl chloride) fibers are used as replacements for wool in some European countries.

The worldwide production of synthetic fibers was greater than 13 billion pounds in 1967. As shown in Fig. 16-1, considerable increase in production is anticipated. However, in spite of a proliferation of new fibers, most of the growth will be restricted to the "classic" synthetic fibers.

REFERENCES

Battista, O. A.: "Fundamentals of High Polymers," Reinhold Publishing Corporation, New York, 1958.

Frazier, A. H.: "High Temperature Resistant Fibers," Interscience Publishers, a division of John Wiley & Sons, Inc., New York, 1967.

Hall, A. J.: "The Standard Handbook of Textiles," D. Van Nostrand Company, Inc., Princeton, N.J., 1946.

Hill, R.: "Fibers from Synthetic Polymers," American Elsevier Publishing Company, Inc., New York, 1958.

Mark, H. F., S. M. Atlas, and E. Cernia; "Chemistry and Technology of Man-made Fibers," vol. I, Interscience Publishers, a division of John Wiley & Sons, Inc., New York, 1967.

Mauersberger, H. R.: "Matthews Textile Fibers," 6th ed., John Wiley & Sons, Inc., New York, 1954.

McFarlane, S. B.: "Technology of Synthetic Fibers," Fairchild Publications, Inc., New York, 1953.

Moncrief, R. W.: "Man Made Fibers," 3d ed., John Wiley & Sons, Inc., New York, 1957.

Press, J. J.: "Man Made Textile Encyclopedia," Interscience Publishers, Inc., New York, 1959.

b.   ELASTOMERS

In addition to its use as an eraser of pencil marks, natural rubber was also used to produce waterproof garments many years before Goodyear's discovery of the vulcanization process. The objection to its stickiness in hot weather was overcome by Macintosh who used it as the inner layer of a cloth sandwich to produce rainwear which still bears his name.

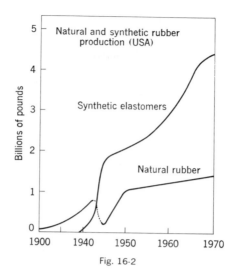

Fig. 16-2

   The use of rubber increased as a result of improvements in processing and fabrication and of new applications such as the pneumatic tire which was patented in 1880.   The annual production of rubber increased from about 5 million pounds in 1840 to almost 50 million pounds in 1900.   Increased demands resulting from the invention of the modern bicycle and the horseless carriage created problems in both the supply and selling price and fostered several improvements in rubber technology.   The use of organic accelerators and carbon black by Oenslager made curing times more realistic and increased the mileage expectations of automobile tires in the early part of the twentieth century.
   As shown in Fig. 16-2, the use of natural rubber increased rapidly and approached 1 billion pounds in 1940.   Worldwide production was almost 2 billion pounds at that time.   The original supply, which was limited to wild rubber trees (*Hevea braziliensis*), continued to decrease since no provisions were made for replanting what Vicki Baum termed "weeping wood."   The production of Brazilian rubber never exceeded 100 million pounds in any one year.   An equal poundage of wild rubber was also obtained annually from other tropical areas in America and Africa.   The price rose from 50 cents to over $2 a pound in the period of 1890 to 1912.
   Other sources of natural rubber such as guayule (*Parthenium argentatum*) were unsatisfactory.   Hence, in the absence of plantation rubber, the natural-rubber industry and dependent industries would probably have become extinct.   The plantations in Ceylon, Indo-China, Indonesia, and Malaya, which produced 90 percent of the world's supply of rubber in 1920,

resulted from seeds of *Hevea braziliensis* trees smuggled from Brazil in 1870 by Sir Henry Wickham.

The increased supply caused the price of natural rubber (NR) to decrease to 12 cents a pound in 1921. The Stephenson scheme devised by British interests to control the price of rubber had a temporary stabilizing effect. However, the price fluctuated from 3 cents a pound in 1932 to 20 cents in 1940.

Germany was able to produce only a few million pounds of synthetic elastomer (methyl rubber) during World War I but both Germany and Russia approached self-sufficiency by the production of Buna S in World War II. An olefin polysulfide elastomer (Thiokol, ET) was produced by Patrick in 1929. This was followed by the commercial production of polychloroprene (Duprene, Neoprene, CR) by Collins, Bolton, and Carothers in 1931 and the synthesis of butyl rubber (IIR) by Thomas and Sparks in 1937. These are all available commercially today but only the copolymer of butadiene and styrene (Buna S, GRS, SBR) meets the specifications for a general-purpose elastomer.

Buna S accounted for the bulk of synthetic elastomers shown for the World War II years in Fig. 16-2. Other elastomers, such as the copolymers of butadiene and acrylonitrile (Buna N, NBR) which were available before 1940, and elastomers introduced since then accounted for some of the production in subsequent years. However, almost two-thirds of the 4 billion pounds of synthetic elastomers produced in the United States in 1969 was SBR.

Worldwide production of natural rubber has exceeded that of synthetic rubber except during the early 1940s. However, the production of synthetic elastomers exceeded that of the natural product (NR) in 1962. As shown in Fig. 16-2, the use of natural rubber in the United States has continued to increase since the late 1940s but its share of the total elastomer market has continued to decrease. Both NR and SBR cost less than 25 cents a pound in 1969.

Approximately 600 million pounds of polybutadienes (IR) were produced in the United States in 1967 under the common name of "synthetic natural rubber." Other elastomers accounting for the 4 billion pounds annual production which was valued at over 1 billion dollars were 400 million pounds of Neoprene (CR) and 250 million pounds of butyl rubber (IIR). The use of poly(epichlorohydrin) elastomers (CO, ECO), ethylene-propylene copolymers (EPM, EPDM), and polyurethane elastomers (AU, EU) will increase considerably because of their potentials as general-purpose elastomers. It is anticipated that the future growth pattern of the specialty elastomers will be similar to that of natural rubber.

REFERENCES

Alliger, G., and F. C. Wissert: Elastomers, *Ind. Eng. Chem.*, **58**(8):36 (1966).

Baum, V.: "The Weeping Wood," Doubleday & Company, Inc., Garden City, N.Y., 1943.

Buttignol, V. J., R. E. Cutforth, et al.: Protective Coatings, *Ind. Eng. Chem.*, **58**(8):44 (1966).

Houwink, R.: *Mod. Plastics*, **43**(12):98 (1966).

Litchfield, P. W.: "Industrial Voyage," Doubleday & Company, Inc., Garden City, N.Y., 1954.

Morton, M.: "Introduction to Rubber Technology," chaps. 1 and 3, Reinhold Publishing Corporation, New York, 1959.

Rosato, D. V.: Elastomers, *Plastics World*, **25**(4):30; **25**(5) 1967.

Seymour, R. B.: Plastics, *Ind. Eng. Chem.*, **59**(8):62 (1967).

SPE Journal, **22**(10):17 (1966). (This includes production figures and a comprehensive list of firms in the plastics industry.)

Wolf, H., and R. Wolf: "Rubber," Covici, Friede, Inc., New York, 1936.

c. PLASTICS

The early growth of the plastics industry was much slower than that of the synthetic-fiber and synthetic-rubber industries. However, as shown in Fig. 16-3, this growth has been very rapid since about 1940. Plastics are now the world's fastest-growing industry. Over 18 billion pounds of syn-

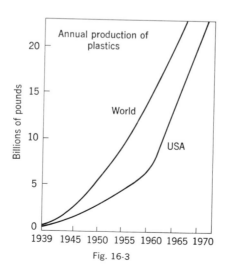

Fig. 16-3

thetic plastics were produced in the United States in 1969, and worldwide production was greater than 40 billion pounds. Less than 6 million pounds were produced in 1922.

The technology which was developed by the pioneer textile and natural-rubber industries was useful for the processing and fabrication of the synthetic fibers and elastomers when they were introduced. However, plastics had no counterpart for popular cotton textiles or rubber bicycle tires. Hence, in spite of a limited use of shellac, bitumens, and derivatives of natural polymers such as Celluloid, a plastics industry was not developed simultaneously with the textile and rubber industries.

The fiber and elastomer industries were major industries in 1940 but the total production of synthetic resins and plastics was less than 300 million pounds at that time. Unlike natural fibers and elastomers, natural resins and plastics have never been produced in large quantities.

The only synthetic plastic produced in significant amounts in the early part of the twentieth century was Bakelite. Its annual production increased

Polymer production (USA, 1969)

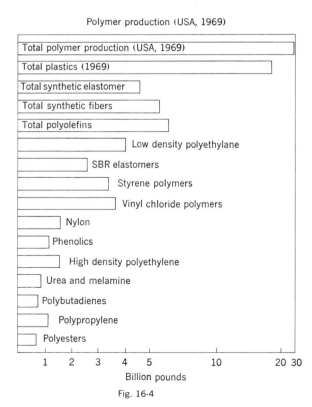

Fig. 16-4

from less than 40 million pounds in 1930 to 100 million pounds in 1935 and approximately 200 million pounds in 1940.

As shown in Fig. 16-4, over 1.1 billion pounds of phenolic resins and plastics were produced in the United States in 1969.

The annual production of cellulose nitrate (Celluloid) plastics was never greater than 20 million pounds. Cellulose acetate was introduced as a molding powder in 1929. The demand for this less hazardous plastic exceeded that for Celluloid in 1935, and this volume doubled by 1940. Approximately 90 million pounds of cellulose acetate and 10 million pounds of cellulose nitrate and ethyl cellulose plastics were produced in 1956. The total production of all cellulosic plastics in the United States in 1969 was less than 200 million pounds. It is anticipated that the production of these plastics will decrease in the future.

The annual production of hydrocarbon resins such as coumarone-indene and petroleum resins in the United States has grown from less than 10 million pounds in 1940 to over 300 million pounds in 1969. These low-cost resins are used in floor tile and in grouting compositions.

The production of urea-formaldehyde plastics (Plaskon, Beetle) increased from 2 million pounds in 1935 to more than 20 million pounds in 1940. Because of its higher price, the sales of melamine resin (Cymel, Melmac) lagged behind that of urea resins. However, as a result of a decrease in the cost of manufacture of melamine, the price differential has decreased. Production data for the two polymers are usually combined. Production for urea and melamine polymers increased from 400 million pounds in 1960 to almost 800 million pounds in 1969.

Alkyd resins (Beckosol, Duraplex, Glyptal, Rezyl) were introduced by Kienle in 1927. The annual production of these resins was less than 5 million pounds in 1935 but exceeded 125 million pounds in 1940. Their principal use is as polymer coatings but molding powders have been available since 1948. The annual production of these resins increased from 350 million pounds in 1960 to almost 600 million pounds in 1969.

The plastics which accounted for over 60 percent of all production in 1968, viz., polyethylene, polypropylene, polystyrene, and poly(vinyl chloride), were either unknown or commercially unimportant in 1940. In spite of its introduction by Ostromislensky in 1912, the use of poly(vinyl chloride) was impractical until the plasticized plastic (Koroseal) was produced by Semon in the early 1930s. Sales of this and related plastics, viz., the copolymer of vinyl chloride and vinyl acetate (Vinylite) and the copolymer of vinylidene chloride (Saran), increased annually, but less than 25 million pounds of all these related plastics were produced in 1940. The annual production increased from 100 million pounds in 1947 to over 500 million pounds in 1955. Over 1.2 billion pounds of vinyl resins were produced in 1960.

It is of interest to note that more than 10 percent of the 3.6 billion pounds of poly(vinyl chloride) produced in 1969 was rigid unplasticized poly(vinyl chloride). The difference in the modern product and that produced prior to 1940 is the result of the application of polymer science to the production and processing of this polymer. The selling price of poly(vinyl chloride) decreased from 30 cents in 1956 to about 15 cents a pound in 1969.

Polystyrene was patented by Kronstein in 1911 but was not produced commercially until 1938. The availability of large quantities of inexpensive styrene monomer produced for the synthetic-rubber program in the early 1940s promoted the production of this polymer. The selling price decreased from 75 cents a pound in 1940 to less than 16 cents a pound in 1969. The annual production of styrene plastics was 1 billion pounds in 1960.

It is also of interest that over 400 million pounds of styrene-acrylonitrile-butadiene copolymer (ABS) and over 35 million pounds of styrene-acrylonitrile copolymer were produced in the United States in 1969. The total production of styrene plastics in 1969 was over 3.3 billion pounds. This consisted of 1.5 billion pounds of molded or extruded polystyrene and over 225 million pounds of plastic foam.

Polyethylene, which was synthesized by Fawcett and Gibson in 1933, was produced by Imperial Chemical Industries (ICI) in a pilot plant in 1938. Over 200,000 pounds was produced in the United Kingdom in 1940. This polymer was introduced commercially in the United States under licenses from ICI in 1943. Over 3 million pounds of this type of polyethylene was produced by both the United Kingdom and the United States in 1945. Annual production in the United States alone exceeded 1 billion pounds in 1958 and was 4 billion pounds in 1969. The selling price of this low-density (general-purpose) polyethylene is about 12 cents a pound.

Ziegler patented a technique for producing linear (high-density) polyethylene in 1954. Its production in the United States has increased from less than 100 million pounds in 1960 to over 1.5 billion pounds in 1969. Much of the American product is made by the Phillips process. The original price of 40 cents a pound for the linear product has decreased to a price that is essentially competitive with the low-density product on a weight basis.

Polypropylene, which is produced with stereospecific catalyst systems developed by Natta in 1954, was produced at a rate of over 40 million pounds in the United States in 1960. Over 1.1 billion pounds of the polymer was produced in 1969. The selling price was reduced from 42 cents a pound in 1960 to about 20 cents a pound in 1969.

Polyester resins, which were introduced commercially in the early 1940s, are now used to a large extent in fibrous-glass-reinforced resin composites. Over 600 million pounds of this type of polyester resin was produced in 1969. Epoxy resins, which were patented by Castan in 1943, were produced at an annual rate of 66 million pounds in 1960. Over 170 million pounds of epoxy resins were produced in the United States in 1969.

The production of major plastic products in the United States in 1967 is compared in Figs. 16-4 and 16-5. As shown in the latter, the production of acrylics (Lucite, Plexiglas) exceeded that of all cellulosics. Acrylic sheet and molding powder were introduced in the late 1930s. The selling price of the molding powder, which was over 50 cents a pound in 1950, was reduced to 45 cents in 1969. Comparable reductions have been made in the selling price of extruded and cast acrylic sheet and rods. The 1969 United States production of over 300 million pounds included over 150 million pounds of cast acrylic sheet and 60 million pounds of molding and extrusion powder.

Other plastics such as the polyacetals (Delrin, Celcon), polycarbonates (Lexan, Merlon, Makrolon), silicones, polysulfones, chlorinated polyether (Penton), poly(phenylene oxide) (PPO, Noryl), phenoxy resins, polyimides (Kapton, Vespel), polyxylylenes (Parylene), polyoxyethylenes (Carbowax, Polyox), poly(ethyleneimines) (Montrek), polybutenes (Vistanex, Bu-Tuf), poly(allyl esters) (Dapon), poly(vinyl acetate), poly(vinyl alcohol) (Gelvatol, Elvanol), poly(vinyl acetals) (Formvar, Butvar, Butacite, Saflex), poly(vinyl pyrrolidone) (Kollidon), poly(fluorocarbons) (Teflon, Halon, Kel F, Kynar, Tedlar), and poly(alkyl vinyl ethers) (Acronal, Vinoflex) are all produced commercially.

Considerable quantities of plastics are produced in West Germany, Japan, the United Kingdom, Italy, and France. It is anticipated that the future growth rate of the plastics industry in these nations will be at least as great as that in the United States.

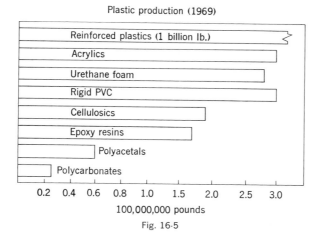

Plastic production (1969)

100,000,000 pounds

Fig. 16-5

REFERENCES

Directory of the Plastics Industry, *Plastics World,* **25**(10): (1967).
Ellis, C.: "The Chemistry of Synthetic Resins," Reinhold Publishing Corporation, New York, 1935.
Kaufman, M.: "The First Century of Plastics," The Plastics Institute, London, 1963.
Kline, G. M.: Plastics Review, *Mod. Plastics,* **45**(6):113 (1968).
Lee, H., D. Stoffey, and K. Neville: "New Linear Polymers," McGraw-Hill Book Company, New York, 1967.
Modern Plastics, The Plastics Industry in 1967, **45**(5):86 (1968).
Morrell, R. S.: "Synthetic Resins and Allied Plastics," Oxford University Press, London, 1951.
1966 Plastics Industry, *SPE J.,* **22**(10):17 (1966).
Seymour, R. B.: Plastics Review, *Ind. Eng. Chem.,* **61**(8):28 (1969).
Simonds, H. R., and J. M. Church: "A Concise Guide to Plastics," 2d ed., Reinhold Publishing Corporation, New York, 1963.

d. PROTECTIVE AND DECORATIVE POLYMER COATINGS

The surface-coating industry originated in prehistoric times. The early crude products consisted of pigments and clay suspended in water, but naturally occurring resins and beeswax were used as constituents of paints in 1000 B.C. Paint factories were established in the United States and many European nations in the last part of the nineteenth century. A U.S. patent for a paint was issued in 1865 but paint was not produced in significant quantities until the early part of the twentieth century.

The early coatings industry depended on the use of drying oils, such as linseed oil, and natural resins such as copals, rosin, and shellac. Cellulose nitrate and acetate were used in the early 1900s, and phenolic, alkyd, and urea resins were used for the formulations of polymer coatings in the 1920s. The U.S. paint industry in 1935 produced 90 million gallons of ready-mixed paints, 30 million gallons of varnish, 30 million gallons of enamels, and 20 million gallons of nitrocellulose (Pyroxylin) lacquer.

The paint, varnish, lacquer, and allied industries in the United States produced over 500 million dollars worth of products annually in the late 1930s. This volume exceeded 1 billion dollars in 1945. As shown in Fig. 16-6, the rate of growth of the paint industry was less than the average for all American industries and much less than that of other segments of the polymer industry. Nevertheless, the annual sales of coating was 2 billion dollars in 1963 and 2.5 million dollars in 1969. Over 800 million gallons of paint is sold annually in the United States.

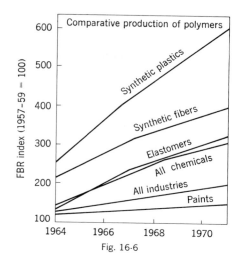

Fig. 16-6

The most primitive paints were water-based products. Casein-based paints were available in 1925 but were not competitive with oil-based paints. Interior paints based on latices of styrene-butadiene copolymer were introduced in 1948. Competitive products based on poly(vinyl acetate) and poly(methyl methacrylate) were marketed in 1950 and 1954, respectively. Latex paints for exterior use were marketed in 1957. The sales of water-based paints increased from 2 million gallons in 1948 to 11 million gallons in 1962. Over 200 million gallons of this type of coating was sold in 1969, and the demand for latex-type paints is now greater than that for solvent-based coatings.

REFERENCES

Buttignol, V. J., R. E. Cutforth, et al.: Protective Coatings Review, *Ind. Eng. Chem.,* **58**(8):44 (1966).

Heaton, N.: "Outlines of Paint Technology," 2d ed., J. B. Lippincott Company, Philadelphia, 1940.

Krumbhaar, W.: "Coating and Ink Resins," D. Van Nostrand Company, Inc., Princeton, N.J., 1932.

Martens, C. R.: "Emulsion and Water-soluble Paints and Coatings," Reinhold Publishing Corporation, New York, 1964.

Mattiello, J. J.: "Protective and Decorative Coatings, Paints, Varnishes, Lacquers and Inks," 5 vols., John Wiley & Sons, Inc., New York, 1941.

Nylen, P., and E. Sunderland: "Modern Surface Coatings," Interscience Publishers, a division of John Wiley & Sons, Inc., New York, 1965.

Payne, H. F.: "Organic Coating Technology," John Wiley & Sons, Inc., New York, 1954.

Pearce, W. T.: Synthetic Resin Coatings, *Mod. Plastics*, **16**(2):90 (1938).

Toch, M.: "The Chemistry and Technology of Paints," D. Van Nostrand Company, Inc., Princeton, N.J., 1925.

Von Fischer, W., and E. G. Bobalek: "Organic Protective Coatings," Reinhold Publishing Corporation, New York, 1953.

16-3 APPLICATIONS OF POLYMERS

a. FIBER APPLICATIONS

The major applications of fibers as woven textiles and paper are well known. The functionalism of wearing apparel, carpets, and industrial textiles has been improved by the appropriate choice of fibers from the wide variety of natural and synthetic fibers now available. Modern fibrous products vary from oxidized cellulose gauze, which is absorbed by body fluids, to poly(benzimidazole) fibers which are unaffected when heated in air at 500°C.

The demand for all noncotton natural fibers has decreased in recent years whereas the demand for rayon and synthetic fibers continues to increase. Wool, silk, and linen accounted for less than 5 percent of all textile fibers used in the United States in 1969. This industry continues to be a major employer. Approximately 2 million are employed by the American textile industry. Broad woven fabric is its principal product.

Approximately 10 billion yards of cotton fabric, 3 billion yards of synthetic fabric, and 300 million yards of woolens are produced annually in the United States. These textiles are fabricated by over 25,000 apparel-manufacturing plants. The end products have an annual selling price over 30 billion dollars.

Over 500 million pounds of rayon, nylon, and polyester fibers are consumed annually for the production of tire cord. Natural fibers such as hemp and sisal have been fabricated to produce rope, twine, and cord but continuous filaments such as nylon and polyester are preferred for many applications such as fishing lines and tow ropes. Jute has been used for the manufacture of burlap sacks, and coconut fiber (coir) has been used as floor matting.

Brooms have been produced from natural fibers, such as agave and brushwood, and from synthetic fibers such as nylon and polypropylene. Animal hair such as hog bristles has been used widely for brushes but has been displaced to a large extent by nylon staple. Pillows and mattresses have been stuffed with kapok, which is obtained from the tropical silk cotton tree.

Nylon and acrylic fibers are used as reinforcements for many resins. A mixture of cellulose fibers and thermoplastic fibers may be bonded together by heating at a temperature above the softening point of the plastic component. Other bonded fabrics may be produced by adding polymer latices to cellulose fibers. Bonded or nonwoven fabrics may be used as disposable products and draperies and for the production of inexpensive clothing.

The improvements in textile science and technology which have increased the range of applications of textiles have resulted in part from the efforts of the American Association of Textile Chemists and Colorists (AATCC) and industry-wide research such as that at the Textile Research Institute. The AATCC publishes the *American Dyestuff Reporter.*

Paper was produced from cellulose fibers by the Chinese as early as 200 B.C. but was not manufactured in Europe until the twelfth century. The first American paper mill was built at Germantown, Pennsylvania, in 1690. There were more than 200 mills in 1810; now over 1,000 pulp and paper mills are operating throughout the United States. Linen, cotton rags, and esparto grass were the principal fibers used for paper making prior to 1880 but cellulose from wood has been the principal fiber since then. However, kenaf (*Hibiscus cannabinus*) plants yield about 8 tons of cellulose fibers per acre per year and have been considered as a partial replacement for southern pine as a source of cellulose.

Paper and paperboard consumption has increased from 1 lb per capita in 1810 to 220 in 1929 and over 500 lb in 1969. Worldwide production was 218 billion pounds in 1965. About one-half of the production in the United States is paperboard. Newsprint (40 percent), wrapping paper (15 percent), book paper (6 percent), and tissue (5 percent) are the principal paper end products. Much of the technical progress in this industry may be attributed to research programs at the Institute of Paper Chemistry at Appleton, Wisconsin, and the Technical Association of the Pulp and Paper Industries (TAPPI).

REFERENCES

Buresh, F. N.: "Non-woven Fabrics," Reinhold Publishing Corporation, New York, 1961.
Brinton, R. S.: "Carpets," Sir Isaac Pitman & Sons, Ltd., London, 1947.
Casey, J. P.: "Pulp and Paper," Interscience Publishers, Inc., New York, 1952.
Coke, C. E.: "Advances in Textile Processing," Interscience Publishers, Inc., New York, 1961.

Kornreich, E.: "Introduction to Fibers and Fabrics," 2d ed., American Elsevier Publishing Company, Inc., New York, 1963.

Mauersberger, H. T.: "Matthews Textile Fibers," John Wiley & Sons, Inc., New York, 1948.

Moncrief, R. W.: "Artificial Fibers," John Wiley & Sons, Inc., New York, 1950.

Ott, E.: "Cellulose and Cellulose Derivatives," Interscience Publishers, Inc., New York, 1942.

Riegel, E. R.: "Industrial Chemistry," chaps. 21, 22, Reinhold Publishing Corporation, New York, 1949.

Seymour, R. B., and G. M. Schroeder: Bonded Fabrics, *Paper Trade J.*, **128**(13):16 (1949).

Shreve, R. N.: "Chemical Process Industries," chaps. 33, 34, McGraw-Hill Book Company, New York, 1956.

b. APPLICATIONS OF ELASTOMERS

In spite of the ready availability of plantation rubber and the economic dependence of Indonesian countries on this commodity, the worldwide demand for the synthetic product has exceeded that for natural rubber (NR) since 1962. The economy of the existing plantations is being strengthened by increasing the yield of rubber trees by grafting. New clones capable of yielding up to 2,000 lb of rubber per acre annually have been developed.

The rubber latex containing 40 percent solids, which is obtained from tapping severed capillary vessels, may be shipped as obtained or in concentrated form. It is usually coagulated, dried, and pressed into sheets. Smoked sheet is obtained when the dried sheet is exposed to smoke. Pale crepe rubber is obtained by the coagulation of latex by sodium hydrogen sulfite. Both natural and synthetic rubber is shipped as baled sheet.

Either natural or synthetic latex may be compounded by the addition of aqueous dispersions of fillers, curing agents, and oils. The principal use of the natural latex is for the production of foamed rubber. Both natural and synthetic latex is used as adhesives, coatings, and impregnants for textiles, cord, and paper.

Sheets of natural or synthetic rubber are processed by passing through a warm two-roll rubber mill or by kneading in a heavy-duty (Banbury) mixer. Since this hot mastication takes place in the presence of air, degradation occurs both by physical and oxidative chain cleavage. Chain transfer agents called peptizers are often added to prevent the chain fragments from recombining. Peptizers may be hydrazines, such as phenyl hydrazine, or mercaptans, such as β-naphthyl mercaptan.

Many synthetic polymers may be "extended" by the addition of mineral oil to the latex to produce a master batch. Other softeners, such as vegetable oils, or resins such as coumarone-indene resins may be added as processing aids. Fillers such as carbon black are added as aqueous dispersions to the latex, or they may be added to the softened rubber on the mill.

Other steps in the compounding process include the addition of accelerator activators, such as zinc oxide and stearic acid, antioxidants such as phenyl-β-naphthyl amine, and sulfur. The forming operation consists of either compression molding, extrusion, or calendering.

The major use of rubber is for the manufacture of pneumatic tires. Almost 200 million tires are produced annually in the United States. A "building" process is required in tire production, so that stocks of different composition and textile reinforcements may be joined together. The compounded formulation is cured (vulcanized) at about 300°F.

Rubber is also used for mechanical goods (industrial rubber products), such as printing rolls, conveyor belts, wire and cable insulation, gaskets, O-rings, hose, and shoe soles and heels. Over 1 billion dollars worth of mechanical goods were sold in the United States in 1969. SBR rubber has replaced *Hevea braziliensis* rubber for the production of tires and other articles where the former was satisfactory. Both elastomers sell for about 25 cents a pound. Other types of synthetic rubber are used when specific improvements are required.

GRS (butadiene 78–styrene 22 copolymer) which was polymerized at 122°F was an acceptable substitute for rubber from *Hevea braziliensis* trees during the early 1940s when the natural product was not available. GRS was displaced to a large extent by so-called "cold rubber" which was polymerized at 41°F. This elastomer (SBR) when reinforced with carbon black is more resistant to abrasion and weathering than natural rubber. However, elastomers with less unsaturation, such as polyurethanes (AU, EU), and adduct rubbers have superior resistance to weathering. The latter are produced by reacting highly unsaturated elastomers with alkyl mercaptans so that only about 10 percent of the original unsaturation remains.

Butyl rubber (IIR), a copolymer of isobutylene (95 percent) and isoprene (5 percent), is preferred for inner tubes and membranes because of its superior resistance to permeation by gases. Nitrile elastomers (butadiene-acrylonitrile copolymers), Thiokol [poly(olefin sulfide)], and Neoprene (CR) have superior resistance to oil and other solvents. Neoprene is also characterized by superior resistance to flame and elevated temperatures. Silicone rubbers are also noted for their excellent heat resistance. Synthetic *cis*-1,4-polybutadiene (IR) or polyisoprene and copolymers of ethylene and propylene (EPM, EPDM) have excellent resistance to abrasion.

The rubber industry has always been technically oriented, and it continues to be a major employer of polymer scientists and technologists. Much of the technical progress in the 1920s and 1930s may be credited to courses in rubber technology at the University of Akron. The Institute of Rubber Research at the University has been expanded to include all types of polymers. More recent progress may be attributed in part to the Division of Rubber Chemistry of the American Chemical Society, which publishes *Rubber Chemistry and Technology*.

REFERENCES

Burton, W. E.: "Engineering with Rubber," McGraw-Hill Book Company, New York, 1949.

Cook, P. G.: "Latex—Natural and Synthetic," Reinhold Publishing Corporation, New York, 1956.

Davis, C. C., and J. T. Blake: "Chemistry and Technology of Rubber," Reinhold Publishing Corporation, New York, 1937.

Houwink, R.: "Elastomers and Plastomers," Elsevier Publishing Company, Amsterdam, 1950.

Huke, D. W.: "Natural and Synthetic Rubber," Hutchinson Publishing Group, Ltd., London, 1961.

Le Bras, J.: "Rubber (Fundamentals of Its Science and Technology)," Crosby Lockwood & Son, Ltd., London, 1957.

Moakes, R. C. W., and W. C. Wake: "Rubber Technology," Butterworth Scientific Publications, London, 1951.

Naunton, W. J. S.: "The Applied Science of Rubber," Edward Arnold (Publishers) Ltd., London, 1949.

Rogers, S. S.: "The Vanderbilt Rubber Handbook," R. T. Vanderbilt Company, New York, 1948.

Shreve, R. N.: "Chemical Process Industries," chap. 36, McGraw-Hill Book Company, New York, 1956.

Winspear, G. G.: "Rubber Handbook," R. T. Vanderbilt Company, New York, 1958.

c. APPLICATIONS OF PLASTICS

Most plastic applications are relatively new. Yet more plastics are used today than all other types of synthetic organic polymers. For example, the size of the polyolefin segment of the plastics industry compares favorably with the entire elastomer or synthetic-fiber industry. The plastics industry has enjoyed an annual growth rate of about 10 percent for many years, and it is anticipated that this rate will continue. The production of synthetic polymers already exceeds that of nonferrous metals and should exceed that of all metals by 1980. Houwink predicted a coming "syntomer age" when organic polymers will be the universal material for all types of applications.

The original applications of ebonite were limited to small molded parts, those of Celluloid to billiard balls, shirt collars, and transparent buggy curtains, those of shellac to phonograph records, and those of Bakelite to smoking pipes. Modern applications are limited only by the characteristic properties of the many available plastics and the competence of the designer.

As stated by the author in the May 22, 1967, issue of *Chemical Engineering,* "Polymer properties range from the superior heat resistance of polyimides to the low-temperature flexibility of polybutenes, the adhesiveness of cyanoacrylates to the lubricity of polyfluorocarbons, the water repellency of silicones to the solubility of poly(acrylic acid), the rigidity of molded phenolics to the flexibility of *cis*-polybutadiene, the water repellency of silicones to the solubility of poly(acrylic acid), the rigidity of molded phenolics to the flexibility of *cis*-polybutadiene, the unctuosity of the poly(ethylene oxides) to the high strength of filament-wound reinforced epoxy resin composites, and the low thermal conductivity of polyurethane foams to the magnetic properties of barium ferrite-filled vinyl plastisols."

Applications of these versatile materials are increasing in areas ranging from shoe soles and uppers to space vehicles. A large percentage of boats are now constructed from reinforced polyesters. In addition to the synthetic elastomers, carbon, and fibers in the pneumatic tires, each new automobile contains over 50 lb of synthetic polymers. Each new supersonic aircraft will use over 2.5 tons of synthetic polymers.

Despite these important applications, the greatest potential use of polymers is in residential construction. Plastics are now used in most of the 400,000 mobile houses that are sold annually. Yet the use of polymers in new stationary residential construction represents less than 1 percent of the total volume of materials used in construction; as shown in Fig. 16-7, this use is increasing.

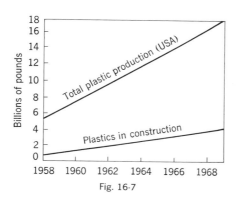

Fig. 16-7

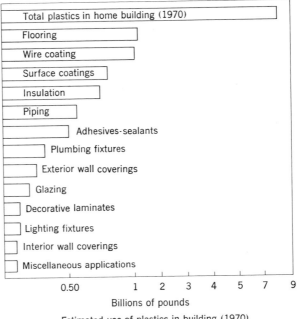

Estimated use of plastics in building (1970)

Fig. 16-8

The world's best-known plastic house was built by Monsanto at Disneyland. This six-room "house of tomorrow" designed by MIT engineering faculty members was assembled from 16 molded reinforced polyester segments. Over 55 million visitors walked through this house before it was demolished in 1967 after 10 years of service.

The modern architect is no longer restricted by the characteristics of brick and stone, as demonstrated by many successful large plastic structures in addition to the "house of tomorrow." As shown in Fig. 16-8, it was anticipated that over 7 billion pounds of plastics would be used by the building industry in 1970.

When one omits surface coatings, the principal use of plastics in construction are for flooring, such as vinyl floor tile (20 percent); wire coatings, such as polyethylene (20 percent); thermal and acoustical insulation, such as polyurethane foam (15 percent); drain, waste, vent, gas, and water pipe, such as ABS pipe (15 percent); adhesives and sealants, such as Thiokol (10 percent); plywood, such as wood laminated with phenolic, urea, or melamine resins (10 percent); and glazing, such as acrylics (5 percent).

Asphalt-type shingles and asphalt-coated paper have been used for roof construction but asphalt is not usually considered a plastic. Nevertheless, there is a definite trend toward the use of all-plastic roofs of silicone or other flexible plastics. The objection to the lack of flame resistance of some plastics has been overcome by the use of flameproof additives. In addition to their esthetic appeal, plastics also possess utility not shared by other materials of construction. Thus it is possible to prefabricate many plastic structures so that they may be assembled rapidly on the job site.

Plastics such as the polyfluorohydrocarbons, rigid PVC, ABS copolymer, and polyethylene are resistant to attack by many corrosive liquids. Thus the use of plastics as formed sheet, molded, or fabricated parts and pipe in a corrosive environment is an accepted functional application.

The aeronautics industry, which was originally dependent on collodion for waterproofing, is now a major user of plastics for multitudinous applications. The inherent low density of all polymers and the resistance of others to heat and flame made the space age possible.

Applications range from Sateloons with over 50,000 ft^2 of laminated film surface to instant reinforced helipads and composites of continuous filaments embedded in matrices of heat-resistant resins. Carbon fibers produced by the pyrolysis of polymeric filaments, boron deposited on thin tungsten wire, and metallic oxide single crystals (whiskers) have been used to fabricate strong filament-wound composites. The rigidity of boron fiber–epoxy resin composites is greater than that of any other known material.

Polyhomocyclic resins are more heat-resistant than polymers containing heterocyclic rings. Thus polyphenylenes are preferred for heat-resistant matrices but poly(phenyl ethers), polysulfones, polybenzoxazoles, benzothiazoles, polypyrrones, and polyimides have been investigated.

Future practices in agriculture will differ from present practices in much the same way that ancient land cultivation differed from present-day mechanized irrigated farming. The advantages of reduction in weed growth and evaporation by the use of large-scale sheet mulching and buried film have been demonstrated.

Polymeric film greenhouses have proved more economical than those constructed from glass. This art will be extended to provide a controlled atmosphere for fruit trees and other plants. Plastic film can be used to control insect environment, temperature, and the oxygen content in the plants' atmosphere.

In addition to universally used vinyl upholstery, the modern automobile includes polyurethane foam for safety, bundles of polymethacrylate filaments for indirect lighting, and polytetrafluoroethylene for friction-free bearings. Automobile bodies, campers, trailers, and truck cabs have been fabricated from reinforced polyesters and thermoformed ABS plastic sheet.

The uses of poly(methyl methacrylate) for dentures and of vinyl plastisols, polyurethanes, silicones, and polyolefins as implants and for the restoration of external body parts have often been the result of trial-and-error experimentation.

In contrast, many advances in biomedical technology have been the result of cooperative efforts by polymer and medical scientists. These include artificial kidneys consisting of a semipermeable cellulose dialysis membrane and the heart pump used by Dr. DeBakey. This pump consisted of woven polyester fibers, reinforced nylon tubing, silicone rubber, nylon velour lining adhered by silastic, and an acrylic housing.

From Noah's ark to modern surface and submersible vessels, the seaworthiness of such vessels depends on plastics either as caulking materials or for the entire construction. The adhesion of water to the transparent areas is reduced by the application of polydienes with carboxyl end groups. Waterproof silicone membranes permeable to oxygen may be used for oceanographic explorations.

Cellulose acetate membranes have been used successfully for the desalination of sea or brackish water. Collapsible dams for flood control and irrigation have been constructed from large Neoprene tubing. Polypropylene filaments have also been used successfully as synthetic seaweed to reduce erosion of the New Jersey coast line.

The trend toward the use of reinforced-plastic boats continues. Most modern boats up to 60 ft in length are of this type of construction. The use of this reinforced plastic has also been investigated for the construction of mine sweepers. Salvaging of sunken vessels has been accomplished by filling the hulls with polymeric foam.

Ping-Pong, tennis, billiards, golf, soccer, baseball, and football, like the ancient Aztec game of tlachtli, are played with polymeric balls. Less strenuous games like poker, bridge, Mah-Jongg, chess, checkers, and dominoes are also played with polymer pieces. The traditional golf ball made by winding rubber thread over a solid sphere has been replaced to some extent by a molded stereospecific polybutadiene. Golf greens and many other outdoor surfaces are now constructed from green polypropylene fibers.

The advantageous use of plastics for the construction of vaulting poles, fishing poles, golf clubs, and bowling balls is well known. However, the large-scale use of molded polyethylene brushlike surfaces for ski slopes is relatively new. These interlocking squares have been laid on smooth terrain to provide year-round skiing. A 7-acre slope of this type is in use in Southern California.

Plastics are also used as containers ranging from ABS copolymer luggage to polyethylene garment bags. Plasticized poly(vinyl chloride), polyethylene, and rubber hydrochloride films are used for packaging both food and industrial products.

Some plastics are used without additives but it is customary to add fillers, plasticizers, colorants, stabilizers, and processing aids. Most plastics are processed by molding or extrusion but other types of fabrication such as calendering, laminating, thermoforming, and casting are also important. Techniques such as adhesive or thermal welding increased the range of applications of plastics. The choice of material and processing technique depends to a large extent on the end use of the plastic material.

The development of plastics science and technology during the 1940s and 1950s was aided by the establishment of the Polymer Research Institute by Mark at the Polytechnic Institute of Brooklyn. More recently established institutes such as the Research Triangle Institute at Durham, North Carolina, and the Plastics Research Institute at Stevens Polytechnic Institute have assured the continued growth of plastics science and technology. The Polymer Division of the American Chemical Society publishes preprints of its semiannual meetings. In addition, many polymer science and technical journals are plastics-oriented.

REFERENCES

Baer, E.: "Engineering Design for Plastics," Reinhold Publishing Corporation, New York, 1964.

Bernhardt, E. C.: "Processing of Thermoplastics Materials," Reinhold Publishing Corporation, New York, 1954.

Beuche, F.: "Physical Properties of Polymers," John Wiley & Sons, Inc., New York, 1962.

Billmeyer, F. W.: "Textbook of Polymer Science," chap. 20, Interscience Publishers, a division of John Wiley & Sons, Inc., New York, 1962.

Brydson, J. A.: "Plastics Materials," D. Van Nostrand Company, Inc., Princeton, N.J., 1966.

Butler, J. A.: "Compression and Transfer Molding," Iliffe Books, Ltd., London, 1964.

Couzens, E. G., and V. E. Yarsley: "Plastics in the Service of Man," Penguin Books, Inc., Baltimore, 1956.

DuBois, J. H., and F. W. John: "Plastics," Reinhold Publishing Corporation, New York, 1967.

Estevez, J. M. J., and D. C. Powell: "Manipulation of Thermoplastic Sheet, Rod and Tube," Iliffe Books, Ltd., London, 1960.

Evans, V.: "Plastics as Corrosion Resistant Materials," Pergamon Press, New York, 1966.

Fisher, E. G.: "Extrusion of Plastics," Iliffe Books, Ltd., London, 1964.

Frisch, K. C., and J. H. Saunders: "Polyurethanes: II Technology," Interscience Publishers, a division of John Wiley & Sons, Inc., New York, 1964.

Golding, B.: "Polymer and Resins," D. Van Nostrand Company, Inc., Princeton, N.J., 1959.

Griff, A. L.: "Plastics, Extrusion Technology," Reinhold Publishing Corporation, New York, 1962.

Haim, G., J. A. Neumann, and H. P. Zade: "Manual for Plastics Welding," vols. I–III, Crosby Lockwood & Son, Ltd., London, 1959.

Jones, D. A., and T. A. Mullen: "Blowing Molding," Reinhold Publishing Corporation, New York, 1962.

Kinney, G. F.: "Engineering Properties and Applications of Plastics," John Wiley & Sons, Inc., New York, 1957.

Kline, G. M.: Plastics Review, *Mod. Plastics*, **44**(6):129 (1967).

Koehler, C. R.: "Plastics in Building," Building Research Institute, Washington, D.C., 1954.

Lever, A. E., and J. Rhys: "Properties and Testing of Plastics," Temple Press, Ltd., London, 1957.

Levine, S. N. (ed.): Materials in Biomedical Engineering, *Ann. N.Y. Acad. Sci.*, **146**(1):1 (1968).

MacTaggart, E. F., and H. H. Chambers: "Plastics and Building," Philosophical Library, Inc., New York, 1955.

Mark, H. F.: "Giant Molecules," Time, Inc., New York, 1966.

———, N. G. Gaylord, and N. M. Bikales (eds.): "Encyclopedia of Polymer Science and Technology," Interscience Publishers, a division of John Wiley & Sons, Inc., New York, 1964.

Miles, D. C., and J. H. Briston: "Polymer Technology," Chemical Publishing Company, Inc., New York, 1965.

"Modern Plastics Encyclopedia," McGraw-Hill Book Company, New York, 1969.

Moiseyev, A. A., V. V. Pavlov, and M. Y. Borodin: "Expanded Plastics," The Macmillan Company, New York, 1963.

Neumann, J. A., and F. J. Bockhoff: "Welding of Plastics," Reinhold Publishing Corporation, New York, 1954.

Oleesky, S., and G. Mohr: "Handbook of Reinforced Plastics of SPI," Reinhold Publishing Corporation, New York, 1963.

Palin, G. R.: "Plastics for Engineers," Pergamon Press, New York, 1967.

Penn, W. S.: "PVC Technology," Maclaren & Sons, Ltd., London, 1962.

"Plastics in Building," McGraw-Hill Book Company, New York, 1966.

Plastics Industry, *SPE J.*, **22**(10):17 (1966).

Randolph, A. F. (ed.): "Plastics Engineering Handbook," Reinhold Publishing Corporation, New York, 1960.

Renfrew, A., and P. Morgan: "Polythene, The Technology and Uses of Ethylene Polymers," Iliffe Books, Ltd., London, 1960.

Riegel, E. R.: "Industrial Chemistry," chap. 35, Reinhold Publishing Corporation, New York, 1949.

Schildknecht, C. E.: "Polymer Processes," Interscience Publishers, Inc., New York, 1956.

Seymour, R. B.: Plastics, *Ind. Eng. Chem.*, **61**(8):28 (1969).

——— and R. H. Steiner: "Plastics for Corrosion Resistant Applications," Reinhold Publishing Corporation, New York, 1955.

Shreve, R. N.: "The Chemical Process Industries," chap. 35, McGraw-Hill Book Company, New York, 1956.

Simonds, H. R., and J. M. Church: "A Concise Guide to Plastics," Reinhold Publishing Corporation, New York, 1963.

Skeist, I.: "Plastics in Building," Reinhold Publishing Corporation, New York, 1966.

Smoluk, G. R.: Engineering Advances for Plastics, *Mod. Plastics*, **44**(6):111 (1967).

Woolgar, W. J.: "Plastics in Plumbing," Hutchinson Publishing Group, Ltd., London, 1963.

d. APPLICATIONS OF POLYMERIC COATINGS

Elastomers, such as Neoprene; plastics, such as vinyl plastisols; and even fiber-forming resins such as nylon 6 are used as coatings. Also, the principles of modern polymer science are applicable to the field of coatings. However, the multitudinous applications of this multibillion-dollar industry merit separate treatment. Rule-of-thumb techniques and empirical methods, which hampered the technical development of this industry for many decades, have been replaced recently, to a large extent, by modern science and technology.

The coatings industry includes paints, varnishes, lacquers, water-base paints, and hot-applied polymers. The classic applications of interior and exterior paints are well known. Less familiar are factory-applied coatings on paper, paperboard, steel, and textiles. Some coatings are applied by techniques developed centuries ago but many coatings are applied by electrodeposition from aqueous dispersions, as plastisols, as powdered polymers, and as monomers or partially polymerized products which are polymerized in situ.

Classic paints consisted of a ground pigment which was usually inorganic, a volatile solvent such as naphtha, and a binder, such as linseed oil. The term *varnish* is often used to describe clear oleoresinous varnishes which are solutions of natural resins, such as rosin, or synthetic resins, such as oil-soluble phenolic resins, in a polymerizable oil, such as tung oil. However, spirit varnishes also contain volatile solvents. Since varnishes are usually applied at room temperature, they also contain driers such as cobalt naphthenate. When asphalt is used as the resin, the varnish is baked to obtain a lustrous black coating called *Japan*.

The original lacquers were modifications of collodion. These modifications included the replacement of the ethanol–ethyl ether solvent by methyl ethyl ketone or cellosolve and of cellulose nitrate by other resins such as alkyds. The term *enamel*, which was originally used to describe vitreous coatings, has been used to describe pigmented varnishes and lacquers such as the protective finish used on automobile bodies and appliances.

The original water-based polymer paints based on casein have been displaced by latices of styrene-butadiene copolymers, poly(vinyl acetate), and acrylic resins. Applications of aqueous dispersions of polymers range from primers for automobile frames to exterior paints. Since no volatile solvent escapes during their application, latex paints are acceptable for indoor use and for industrial finishing operations where solvent recovery systems are not available.

Approximately 3 billion pounds of synthetic resins and plastics were used for coatings in 1969. The principal resins used by this multibillion-dollar industry were alkyds (70 percent), poly(vinyl acetate) (10 percent), urea-melamine resins (7 percent), styrene polymers (6 percent), phenolic resin

(4 percent), and epoxy resins (3 percent). These data do not include resins used in many nonclassic applications such as vinyl- and Neoprene-coated fabrics, polyethylene-coated milk cartons, silicone-coated space vehicles, polyfluorohydrocarbon-coated cookware, poly(vinyl fluoride)-coated building siding, adhesives, and printing inks.

There are numerous borderline applications in which coating technology is essential for the production of specific commodities such as synthetic shoe uppers, gaskets, and carpet backings. Modern buildings ranging from the six-room "house of tomorrow" to the largest office buildings are made watertight by the use of sealants such as poly(olefin sulfide) (Thiokol). Many books, newspapers, and journals are printed with inks which are a specialized type of polymer coating.

Much of the progress in polymer technology demonstrated by the American paint industry since the 1940s may be attributed to organizations such as the Federation of Paint and Varnish Production Clubs, the Paint Research Institute, the Institute of Paint and Varnish Research, and the Division of Organic Coatings and Plastics Chemistry of the American Chemical Society.

REFERENCES

Abraham, H.: "Asphalts and Allied Substances," D. Van Nostrand Company, Inc., Princeton, N.J., 1945.

"Adhesives and Sealants in Building," Building Research Institute, Washington, D.C., 1958.

Anderson, C. C.: Adhesives, *Ind. Eng. Chem.*, **59**(8):91 (1967).

Bigos, J: "Steel Structures Manual," Steel Structures Painting Council, Pittsburgh, 1954, 1955.

Blom, A. V.: "Organic Coatings in Theory and Practice," American Elsevier Publishing Company, Inc., New York, 1949.

Chatfield, D. W.: "Science of Surface Coatings," Ernest Benn, Ltd., London, 1962.

Danziger, G. N., and F. C. Kinsler: "Formulation of Organic Coatings," D. Van Nostrand Company, Inc., Princeton, N.J., 1967.

Ellis, C.: "Printing Inks," Reinhold Publishing Corporation, New York, 1940.

Evans, V.: "Plastics as Corrosion Resistant Materials," Pergamon Press, New York, 1966.

Fisk, P. M.: "The Physical Chemistry of Paints," Chemical Publishing Company, Inc., New York, 1965.

Gardner, H. A., and G. G. Sward: "Physical and Chemical Examination of Paints, Varnishes, Lacquers and Colors," Institute of Paint and Varnish Research, Washington, D.C., 1950.

Gaylord, N. G.: An Abbreviated Coatings Textbook, *J. Polymer Sci.*, pt. C, **12**:151 (1966).

Gerhart, H. L., and E. E. Parker: Protective Coatings, *Ind. Eng. Chem.*, **59**(8):42 (1967).

Heaton, N.: "Outlines of Paint Technology," J. B. Lippincott Company, Philadelphia, 1940.

Hess, M.: "Paint and Film Defects, Their Cause and Cure," Chapman & Hall, Ltd., London, 1965.

Martens, C. R.: "Emulsion and Water-soluble Paints and Coatings," Reinhold Publishing Corporation, New York, 1964.

Matiello, J. J.: "Protective and Decorative Coatings," vols. I–V, John Wiley & Sons, Inc., New York, 1941–1946.

Mosher, R. A.: "The Technology of Coated and Processed Papers," Chemical Publishing Company, Inc., New York, 1952.

Nylen, P., and E. Sunderland: "Modern Surface Coatings," Interscience Publishers, a division of John Wiley & Sons, Inc., New York, 1965.

Payne, H. F.: "Organic Coating Technology," John Wiley & Sons, Inc., New York, 1954.

Riegel, E. R.: "Industrial Chemistry," chap. 31, Reinhold Publishing Corporation, New York, 1949.

Seymour, R. B.: "Hot Organic Coatings," Reinhold Publishing Corporation, New York, 1959.

———— and R. H. Steiner: "Plastics for Corrosion Resistant Applications," Reinhold Publishing Corporation, New York, 1956.

Shreve, R. N.: "Chemical Process Industries," chap. 24, McGraw-Hill Book Company, Inc., New York, 1956.

Skeist, I.: "Handbook of Adhesives," Reinhold Publishing Corporation, New York, 1962.

Von Fischer, W., and E. G. Bobalek: "Organic Protective Coatings," Reinhold Publishing Corporation, New York, 1953.

Weaver, P. E.: "Industrial Maintenance Painting," P. E. Weaver, Baton Rouge, La., 1958.

FINALE

Since this chapter includes production data prior to 1970, it is definitely dated and may appear to be outdated by some readers in subsequent years. It is planned to publish revisions of this book periodically. However, little

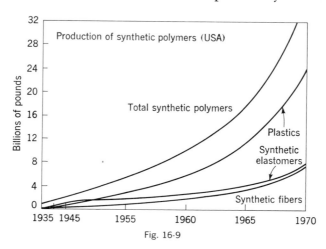

Fig. 16-9

of the fundamental information will be changed. Revisions will include new information based on research reports from current literature. Readers who have studied this book should be able to understand such reports. As shown in Fig. 16-9 the production of polymers is increasing at a rate of about 10 percent a year. The research effort in this field is increasing at a faster rate. It will be difficult for future polymer scientists to keep abreast of new developments. However, it would be foolhardy to wait for periodic revisions of this text. Hence, the polymer scientist must develop a systematic reading program and keep abreast of the many interesting developments in this most important field.

Appendix I
Symbols

Symbols	
Å	Angstrom unit (10^{-8} cm)
A	Area
A	Arrhenius constant
A	Lewis acid (cationic polymerization)
A·	Antioxidant free radical
AA	Reactant (step reactions)
ABS	Copolymer from acrylonitrile, butadiene, and styrene
Ac	Acetyl group
AH	Antioxidant
ANSI	American National Standards Institute (formerly American Standards Association)
Ar	Aryl group
AR	Polyacrylate
ASTM	American Society for Testing Materials
ATR	Attenuated total reflectance spectroscopy
AU	Polyurethane
AXF	Poly(diphenylethane)
a_t	Relaxation time
$\mathcal{A}$	Arbitrary constant
$\mathcal{A}$	Exponent in Mark-Houwink equation
$\mathcal{A}_t$	Shift factor
B	Boron atom

Symbols

B	Virial constant
BB	Reactant (step reactions)
BR	*Cis*-polybutadiene
b	Arbitrary constant
bp	Boiling point
C	Arbitrary constant
C	Carbon atom
C	Centigrade (Celsius)
C	Concentration
C	Degree of crystallinity
CA	Cellulose acetate
CAB	Cellulose acetate butyrate
CMC	Carboxymethyl cellulose
CO	Poly(epichlorohydrin)
C_p	Specific heat
CR	Neoprene
C_s	Chain transfer constant
c	Concentration
cal	Calorie
cm	Centimeter
cm^{-1}	Reciprocal centimeter
cm^3	Cubic centimeter
co	Copolymer
cp	Chemically pure
c	Velocity of light (3×10 cm/sec)
D	Debye units (dipole)
D	Density
D	Dextro
D	Diameter
D	Diffusion constant
DNA	Deoxyribonucleic acid
$\overline{DP}$	Average degree of polymerization
DRS	Dynamic reflectance spectroscopy
DS	Degree of substitution (cellulose)
DTA	Differential thermal analysis
DWV	Drain, waste, and vent pipe
d	Density
d	Dextro
d	Diameter
d	Total derivative (infinitesimal change)
d	d-Orbital (spdf)

Symbols

E	Energy of activation
E	Energy content
E	Energy of vaporization
E	Young's modulus of elasticity
ECO	Epichlorohydrin elastomer
EEK	Accelerated test with sunlight at constant right angle
EMMA	Equatorial mounting with mirrors (accelerated sunlight test)
EP	Epoxy resin
EPM	Poly(ethylene-co-propylene)
EPDM	Poly(ethylene-co-propylene)
EPR	Electron paramagnetic resonance spectroscopy
ESR	Electron spin resonance spectroscopy
ET	Thiokol
ETA	Electrothermal analysis
e	Base of natural logarithms (2.718)
e	Polarity factor (Alfrey-Price equation)
eit	Erythrodiisotactic
est	Erythrosyndiotactic
e	Exponential
F	Fahrenheit
F	Mole fraction of monomers in copolymer
F	Stress (filled elastomers)
F_g	Fractional free volume (plasticizers)
FPM	Poly(fluorinated hydrocarbon)
f	Efficiency factor (chain reactions)
f	Force
f	Segmental friction factor
f	Functionality factor (step reactions)
ft	Foot
G	Gauche conformation
G	Gibbs free energy
G	Modulus
G	Molar attraction constant (small)
GC	Gas chromatography
GPC	Gel permeation chromatography
GRS	Poly(butadiene-co-styrene)
g	Gauche conformation
g	Gram
g	Gravity
gr	Graft (copolymer)

Symbols

H	Arbitrary constant
H	Enthalpy (heat content)
H	Hydrogen atom
H	Latent heat of transition
H	Magnetic field strength
h	Height
h	Planck's constant (6.625×10^{-27} erg-sec)
hp	Horsepower
hr	Hour
I	Initiator (chain reactions)
I	Intensity
I	Spin of nucleus
IIR	Butyl rubber
IR	*Cis*-butadiene
ISO	International Standards Organization
IUPAC	International Union of Pure and Applied Chemistry
i	Incident ray
in.	Inch
it	Isotactic
K	Arbitrary constant
K	Constant in Mark-Houwink equation
K	Kelvin
K	Kinetic constant in Avrami equation
K	Thermal-conductivity factor
K	Rate constant
kg	Kilogram
kcal	Kilocalorie
L	Levo
L	Length
l	Levo
l	length
ln	Natural logarithm
log	Logarithm (base 10)
M	Chain stiffener constant
M	Molecular weight
$\overline{M}$	Average molecular weight
$\overline{M}_n$	Number average molecular weight
$\overline{M}_v$	Viscosity average molecular weight
$\overline{M}_w$	Weight average molecular weight

M	Monomer (chain reaction)
M	Quantum number
M·	Free-radical chain
Me	Methyl radical
MF	Melamine-formaldehyde resin
MR	Molar refraction
MVT	Moisture vapor transmission
m	Consistency factor (power law)
m	Meta isomer
m	Meter
m	Mole fraction of reactants (copolymers)
m	Number of mers in polymer chain
ml	Milliliter
mp	Melting point
N	Nitrogen atom
N	Number of units or items
NBR	Poly(butadiene-co-acrylonitrile)
NMR (nmr)	Nuclear magnetic resonance spectroscopy
N_n	Number average molecular weight
NR	Natural rubber
n	Index of flow (power law)
n	Index of refraction
n	Mole (step reactions) fraction
n	Normal (continuous chain, linear)
n	Number of mers in polymer chain
n	Numbers of theoretical plates
n	Ratio of mers in copolymer
nm	Nanometers (millimicrons)
O	Oxygen atom
o	Ortho isomer
oz	Ounce
P	Phosphorus atom
P	Polymer chain
P·	Polymer radical
P	Pressure
P	Resonance-stability factor (Alfrey-Price equation)
PA	Polyamide (nylon)
PC	Polycarbonate
PE	Polyethylene
PETP	Poly(ethylene terephthalate)

Symbols

PF	Phenol-formaldehyde resin
PMMA	Poly(methyl methacrylate)
POM	Poly(oxymethylene) (polyformaldehyde, acetals)
PP	Polypropylene
PS	Polystyrene
PTFE	Polytetrafluoroethylene
PUR	Polyurethane
PVAC	Poly(vinyl acetate)
PVAL	Poly(vinyl alcohol)
PVDC	Poly(vinylidene chloride) (Saran)
PVC	Poly(vinyl chloride)
p	Para isomer
p	Pressure
p	Probability, fractional yield (Carothers)
p	Propagation
psi	Pounds per square inch
Q	Quantity of heat
Q	Resonance-stability factor (Alfrey-Price equation)
q	Electronic charge
R	Alkyl radical
R·	Free radical
R	Gas constant (1.986 cal/mole °K)
R	Rate (chain reactions)
R	Run number (copolymers)
RF	Radio frequency
R_f	Rate of flow (paper chromatography)
RNA	Ribonucleic acid
$\bar{r}$	Average end-to-end distance
r	Distance between centers of charge of dipoles
r	Radius
r	Ratio of reactants (step reaction)
r	Reactivity ratio (copolymers)
r	Refracted ray
S	Entropy
S	Radius of gyration
S	Sedimentation constant
S	Solvent
S	Sulfur atom
SAM	Poly(styrene-co-acrylonitrile)
SBR	Poly(butadiene-co-styrene) elastomer
SI	Silicone

Symbols

Si	Silicon atom
S_N	Nucleophilic substitution
SPE	Society of Plastics Engineers
SPI	The Society of the Plastics Industry
s	Stress
st	Syndiotactic
T	Absolute temperature
T	Tentative (ASTM)
T	Trans
T_c	Cloud-point temperature
T_g	Glass transition temperature
T_m	Melting point
TAPPI	Technical Association of the Pulp and Paper Industry
TDI	Tolylene diisocyanate
TGA	Thermal gravimetric analysis
t	Termination (chain reaction)
t	Trans isomer
tit	Threodiisotactic
tr	Transfer
tst	Threosyndiotactic
UF	Urea-formaldehyde resin
UL	Underwriters Laboratories
uv	Ultraviolet
V	Volume
V_e	Elution volume
V_F	Fractional volume
W_n	Weight average molecular weight
WLF	Williams-Landel-Ferry equation
WS	Polyurethane
w	Width
w	Work
X	Ratio of reactants (copolymer)
X	Substituent (vinyl monomer)
X	Thickness
yd	Yard
α	Carbon atom adjacent to a functional group
α	One configuration of an isomer

	Symbols
α	First in a series
α_F	Expansion coefficient
β	One configuration of an isomer
β	Second carbon atom away from a functional group
β	Second in a series
γ	Magnetogyric ratio (nmr)
γ	Hydrogen-bonding index (Lieberman)
γ	Strain
γ	Third carbon atom away from a functional group
Δ	Change
Δ	Heat
δ	Chemical shift (nmr)
δ	Expansion factor (solution process)
δ	Fourth carbon atom away from a functional group
δ	Solubility parameter (Hildebrand)
ε	Fifth carbon atom away from a functional group
ε	Molar absorption coefficient
η	Viscosity
η_r	Reduced viscosity
η_{rel}	Relative viscosity
η_{sp}	Specific viscosity
$[\eta]$	Intrinsic viscosity (viscosity number)
Θ	Flory critical miscibility temperature at which polymer-solvent interaction is zero
θ	Angle of scattering
λ	Wavelength
λ	Distance from origin to vertices of tetrahedra in filler
μ	Dipole moment
μ	Measure of polymer-solvent interaction (Flory-Huggins)
μ	Micron (10^{-4} cm, 10^4 Å)
μ	Nuclear magnetic moment
ν	Average kinetic chain length of chain-reaction polymers
ν	Frequency (vibrations/sec)
π	A bond formed by the side-to-side overlap of two p_z orbitals which accounts for the high activity of vinyl monomers
π	Osmotic pressure
ρ	Density
Σ	Summation
σ	Sigma bonds
τ	Orientation, relaxation, or retardation time
τ	Turbidity or scattered flux
ϕ	Universal viscosity constant (Flory)

Symbols

ϕ	Fractional volume
ϕ	Jump frequency in hole filling (solution)
ϕ	Related to viscosity in Herschel-Bulkley equation
ω	Last in a series (e.g., carbon farthest away from functional group)
[ ]	Concentration

Appendix II
Trade Names

Trade Names

TRADE NAME OR BRAND NAME	PRODUCT	MANUFACTURER
Abafil	Reinforced ABS	Rexall Chemical Co.
Abalyn	Abietic acid derivative	Hercules, Inc.
Acelon	Cellulose acetate	
Aclar	Polyfluorocarbon film	Allied Chemical Corp.
Acronal	Poly(alkyl vinyl ether)	General Aniline Film Corp.
Acrylacon	Fibrous-glass-reinforced polymers	Rexall Chemical Co.
Acrylafil	Reinforced polymers	Rexall Chemical Co.
Acrilan	Polyacrylonitrile	Chemstrand Corp.
Acrylite	Poly(methyl methacrylate)	American Cyanamid Co.
Acryloid	Resin solutions	Rohm & Haas Co.
Actol	Polyethers	Allied Chemical Corp.
Adipol	Plasticizer	FMC Corp.
Adiprene	Urethane elastomers and prepolymer	E. I. du Pont de Nemours & Co., Inc.
Admex	Plasticizers	Ashland Chemical Co.
Aerodux	Resorcinol-formaldehyde resin	Ciba (A.R.L.) Ltd.
Agerite series	Antioxidants	R. T. Vanderbilt Co., Inc.
Agro	Rayon fibers	Beaunit Mills Corp.
Alathon	Polyethylene	E. I. du Pont de Nemours & Co., Inc.
Albacar	Calcium carbonate filler	Pfizer Corp.

Trade Names

TRADE NAME OR BRAND NAME	PRODUCT	MANUFACTURER
Albertols	Phenolic resins	
Aldocryl	Acetal resin	Shell Chemical Co.
Alfane	Epoxy resin cement	The Atlas Mineral Products Co.
Algil	Styrene copolymer monofilament	Shawinigan Chemicals, Ltd.; also Polymer Corp.
Alkathene	Polyethylene resins	Imperial Chemical Industries, Ltd.
Alkon	Acetal copolymer	Imperial Chemical Industries, Ltd.; Celanese Corp. of America
Alkor	Furan resin cement	Atlas Minerals Products Co.
Alsilate	Clays	Freeport Kaolin Co.
Alsynite	Reinforced plastic panels	Reichhold Chemicals, Inc.
Amberlite	Ion-exchange resins	Rohm & Haas Co.
Ameripol	Polyethylene	Goodrich-Gulf Chemicals, Inc.
Amerith	Cellulose nitrate	Celanese Corp. of America
Amilan	Nylon	Tojo Rayon Co.
Ampcoflex	Rigid poly(vinyl chloride)	Atlas Mineral Products Co.
Antron	Nylon fiber	
Aralac	Protein fiber	E. I. du Pont de Nemours & Co., Inc.
Araldite	Epoxy resins	Ciba (A.R.L.) Ltd.
Ardil	Protein fiber	
Arnel	Cellulose triacetate	Celanese Corp. of America
Aroclor	Chlorinated polyphenyls	Monsanto Chemical Co.
Aropol	Polyester resins	Ashland Chemical Co.
Arothane	Polyester resins	Ashland Chemical Co.
Atlac	Polyester cast resin	Atlas Chemical Industries, Inc.
Avron	Rayon fiber	American Viscose Corp.
Azdel	Fibrous-glass-reinforced ABS copolymer sheet	
Aztran	Poromeric sheet	B. F. Goodrich Chemical Co.
Bakelite	Phenol-formaldehyde resins	Union Carbide Chemicals Co.
Beckacite	Modified phenolic resins	Reichhold Chemicals, Inc.; Beck, Koller & Co., Ltd.
Beckamine	Urea-formaldehyde resins	Reichhold Chemicals, Inc.; Beck, Koller & Co., Ltd.
Beckosol	Alkyd resins	Reichhold Chemicals, Inc.; Beck, Koller & Co., Ltd.
Beetle	Urea-formaldehyde resins	American Cyanamid Co.
Bemberg	Rayon fiber	Beaunit Mills Corp.
Blendex	ABS resin	Borg-Warner Corp.
Boltaron	Plastic sheets	General Tire & Rubber Co.

Trade Names

TRADE NAME OR BRAND NAME	PRODUCT	MANUFACTURER
Borofil	Boron filaments	Texaco Corp.
Butacite	Poly(vinyl acetal) resins	E. I. du Pont de Nemours & Co., Inc.
Butakon	Butadiene copolymers	Imperial Chemical Industries, Ltd.
Butaprene	Styrene-butadiene elastomers	Firestone Tire & Rubber Co.
Butarez CTL	Telechelic butadiene polymer	Phillips Petroleum Co.
Buton	Butadiene-styrene resin	Enjay Chemical Co.
Bu-Tuf	Polybutene	Petrotex Chemical Corp.
Butvar	Poly(vinyl butyral) resin	Shawinigan Resins Corp.
Cab-O-Sil	Colloidal silica	Cabot Corp.
Cadon	Nylon filament	Chemstrand Corp.
Cadox	Organic peroxides	Cadet Chemical Corp.
Calwhite	Calcium carbonate	Georgia Marble Co.
Capran	Nylon 6	Allied Chemical Corp.
Captax	Accelerator (2-mercapto-benzothiazole)	
Carboloy	Cemented carbides	General Electric Co.
Carbopol	Water-soluble resins	B. F. Goodrich Chemical Co.
Carboset	Acrylic resins	B. F. Goodrich Chemical Co.
Carbowax	Poly(ethylene glycols)	Union Carbide Chemicals Co.
Castethene	Castable polyurethanes	Upjohn Co.
Catalac	Phenol-formaldehyde resin	Catalin Ltd.
Celanar	Polyester film and sheeting	Celanese Plastics Co.
Celcon	Acetal copolymers	Celanese Plastics Co.
Celite	Diatomite filler	Johns-Manville Corp.
Cellosize	Hydroxyethyl cellulose	Union Carbide Corp.
Celluloid	Plasticized cellulose nitrate	Celanese Plastics Co.
Cerex	Styrene copolymer	Monsanto Chemical Co.
Chemigum	Urethane elastomer	Goodyear Tire & Rubber Co.
Chem-o-sol	PVC Plastisol	Chemical Products Co.
Chempro	Ion-exchange resins	
Chlorowax	Chlorinated paraffins	Diamond Alkali Co.
Cibanite	Aniline-formaldehyde resin	Ciba Products Co.
Clarite	PVC stabilizers	National Lead Co.
Collodion	Solution of cellulose nitrate	
Coral rubber	*Cis*-polyisoprene	Firestone Tire & Rubber Co.

Trade Names

TRADE NAME OR BRAND NAME	PRODUCT	MANUFACTURER
Cordura	Regenerated cellulose	E. I. du Pont de Nemours & Co., Inc.
Corfam	Poromeric film	E. I. du Pont de Nemours & Co., Inc.
Corval	Rayon fiber	Courtaulds
Corvel	Plastic coating powders	The Polymer Corp.
Corvic	Vinyl polymers	Imperial Chemical Industries, Ltd.
Covol	Poly(vinyl alcohol)	Corn Products Co.
Creslan	Acrylonitrile–acrylic ester copolymers	American Cyanamid Co.
Cronar	Poly(ethylene terephthalate)	E. I. du Pont de Nemours & Co., Inc.
Cryorap	Thermoplastic sheets and films	W. R. Grace & Co.
Cryovac	Polypropylene film	W. R. Grace & Co.
Crystalex	Acrylic resin	Rohm & Haas Co.
Crystalon	Rayon fiber	American Enka Corp.
Cumar	Coumarone-indene resin	Allied Chemical Corp.
Cyasorb	Ultraviolet absorbers	American Cyanamid Co.
Cycloset	Cellulose acetate fiber	E. I. du Pont de Nemours & Co., Inc.
Cycolac	Acrylonitrile-butadiene-styrene copolymer	Borg-Warner Corp.
Cymac	Thermoplastic molding materials	American Cyanamid Co.
Cymel	Melamine molding compound	American Cyanamid Co.
Dabco	Polyurethane catalyst	Houdry Process & Chemical Co.
Dacovin	Rigid poly(vinyl chloride)	Diamond Alkali Co.
Dacron	Polyester fiber	E. I. du Pont de Nemours & Co., Inc.
DAP	Diallyl phthalate monomer	FMC Corp.
Dapon	Diallyl phthalate prepolymer	FMC Corp.
Daponite	Dapon-fabric laminates	FMC Corp.
Darex	Styrene copolymer resin	W. R. Grace & Co.
Darvan	Poly(vinylidene cyanide)	Celanese Corp. of America
Daxad	Dispersing agents	W. R. Grace & Co.
Decanox	Organic peroxides	Wallace & Tiernan, Inc.
Deenax	Antioxidants	Enjay Chemical Co.
Delrin	Acetal polymer	E. I. du Pont de Nemours & Co., Inc.
Derakane	Polyester resin	Dow Chemical Co.
Derolite	Ion-exchange resin	Diamond Alkali Co.
Devran	Epoxy resins	Devoe & Reynolds Co.

Trade Names

TRADE NAME OR BRAND NAME	PRODUCT	MANUFACTURER
Dexsil	Poly(carboranesiloxane)	Olin Mathieson Corp.
Dicalite	Diatomaceous earth	
Dimetcote	Protective coating	Americoat Corp.
Dion	Polyester resin	Diamond Alkali Co.
Doryl	Poly(diphenyl oxide)	Westinghouse Electric Corp.
Dowex	Ion-exchange resins	Dow Chemical Co.
Duco	Cellulose nitrate lacquers	E. I. du Pont de Nemours & Co., Inc.
Dulac	Lacquers	Sun Chemical Corp.
Dulux	Polymeric enamels	E. I. du Pont de Nemours & Co., Inc.
Duolite	Ion-exchange resin	Diamond Alkali Co.
Duralon	Furan molding resins	U.S. Stoneware Co.
Duramac	Alkyd resins	Commercial Solvents Corp.
Duraplex	Alkyd resins	Rohm & Haas Co.
Duraspan	Spandex fibers	Carr-Fulflex Corp.
Durethene	Polyethylene film	Sinclair-Koppers Co., Inc.
Durite	Phenolic resins	The Borden Co.
Dyal	Alkyd resins	Sherwin-Williams Co.
Dylan	Polyethylene resins	Sinclair-Koppers Co., Inc.
Dylel	ABS copolymer	Sinclair-Koppers Co., Inc.
Dylene	Polystyrene resins	Sinclair-Koppers Co., Inc.
Dylite	Expandable polystyrene	Sinclair-Koppers Co., Inc.
Dynafilm	Polypropylene film	U. S. Industrial Chemicals Co., Div., National Distillers & Chemical Corp.
Dynel	Modacrylic fiber	Union Carbide Corp.
Dyphene	Phenol-formaldehyde resins	Sherwin-Williams Co.
Dyphos	Stabilizer for poly(vinyl chloride)	National Lead Co.
Eccospheres	Hollow glass spheres	Emerson & Cummings, Inc.
Elastothene	Polyurethane elastomer	
Elf	Carbon black	Cabot Corporation
El Rexene	Polyolefin resins	Rexall Chemical Co.
El Rey	Low-density polyethylene	Rexall Chemical Co.
Elvacet	Poly(vinyl acetate) emulsion	E. I. du Pont de Nemours & Co., Inc.
Elvacite	Acrylic resins	E. I. du Pont de Nemours & Co., Inc.
Elvanol	Poly(vinyl alcohol) resins	E. I. du Pont de Nemours & Co., Inc.
Elvax	Poly(ethylene-co-vinyl acetate)	E. I. du Pont de Nemours & Co., Inc.

Trade Names

TRADE NAME OR BRAND NAME	PRODUCT	MANUFACTURER
Enkalure	Nylon fiber	American Enka Corp.
Enrad	Preirradiated poly-ethylene	Enflo Corp.
Enrup	Thermosetting resin	United States Rubber Co.
Epibond	Epoxy adhesive resin	Furane Plastics, Inc.
Epi-Rez	Epoxy cast resin	Celanese Corp.
Epocast	Epoxy resins	Furane Plastics, Inc.
Epolene	Low-melt polyethylene	Eastman Chemical Products, Inc.
Epon	Epoxy resins	Shell Chemical Co.
Epotuf	Epoxy resins	Reichhold Chemical Co., Inc.
Epoxylite	Epoxy resins	Epoxylite Corp.
Escon	Polypropylene	Enjay Chemical Co.
Estane	Polyurethane resins	B. F. Goodrich Chemical Co.
Estron	Cellulose acetate filament	Eastman Chemical Products, Inc.
Ethocel	Ethyl cellulose	Dow Chemical Co.
Evenglo	Polystyrene	Sinclair-Koppers Co., Inc.
Exon	Poly(vinyl chloride)	Firestone Plastics
Fabrifil	Chopped-rag fillers	Microfibres, Inc.
Fabrikoid	Pyroxylin-coated fabrics	E. I. du Pont de Nemours & Co., Inc.
Fibercast	Reinforced plastic pipe	Fibercast Co.
Fiberglas	Fibrous glass	Owens-Corning Fiberglas Corp.
Fiberite	Phenolic molding compounds	Fiberite Corp.
Filfrac	Cut cotton fiber	Rayon Processing Co. of Rhode Island
Firemaster	Fire retardants	Michigan Chemical Corp.
Firmex	Carbon black	Columbian Carbon Co.
Flakeglas	Glass flakes for reinforcements	Owens-Corning Fiberglas Corp.
Flectol	Amine-type antioxidants	Monsanto Co.
Flexol	Plasticizers	Union Carbide Chemical Co.
Floranier	Cellulose	Rayonier, Inc.
Fluon	Polytetrafluoroethylene	Imperial Chemical Industries, Ltd.
Fluorel	Poly(vinylidene fluoride)	Minnesota Mining and Mfg. Co.
Fluorobestos	Asbestos-Teflon composite	Raybestos Manhattan, Inc.
Fluoron	Poly(chlorotrifluoro-ethylene)	Stokes Molded Products
Fluoroplast	Polytetrafluoroethylene	U. S. Gasket Co.
Foamex	Poly(vinyl formal)	General Electric Co.
Formex	Poly(vinyl acetal)	General Electric Co.

Trade Names

TRADE NAME OR BRAND NAME	PRODUCT	MANUFACTURER
Formica	Thermosetting laminates	Formica Corp.
Formrez	Liquid resins for urethane elastomers	Witco Chemical Co.
Formvar	Poly(vinyl formal)	Shawinigan Resins Corp.
Forticel	Cellulose propionate	Celanese Corp. of America
Fortiflex	Polyethylene	Celanese Plastics Co.
Fortisan	Saponified cellulose acetate	Celanese Corp. of America
Fortrel	Polyester fiber	Fiber Industries, Inc.
Fostacryl	Poly(styrene-co-acrylonitrile)	Foster Grant Co.
Fostarene	Polystyrene	Foster Grant Co.
Freon	Blowing agents	E. I. du Pont de Nemours & Co.
Furnane	Epoxy and furan resins	Atlas Mineral Products Co.
Galalith	Casein plastics	
Gantrez	Poly(vinyl ether-co-maleic anhydride)	Dyestuff & Chemical Div., General Aniline & Film Corp.
Garan	Fibrous-glass roving	Johns-Manville Corp.
Garan Finish	Sizing for glass fibers	
Garox	Organic peroxides	Ram Chemicals, Inc.
Gelva	Poly(vinyl acetate)	Shawinigan Resins Corp.
Gelvatex	Poly(vinyl acetate) emulsions	Shawinigan Resins Corp.
Gelvatol	Poly(vinyl alcohol)	Shawinigan Resins Corp.
Genaire	Poromeric film	General Tire & Rubber Co.
Genamid	Epoxy coreactant	General Mills, Inc.
Genthane	Polyurethane elastomer	General Tire & Rubber Co.
Genetron	Fluorinated hydrocarbon monomers and polymers	Allied Chemical Co.
Gentro	Butadiene copolymer	General Tire & Rubber Co.
Geon	Poly(vinyl chloride)	B. F. Goodrich Chemical Co.
Glaskyd	Glass-reinforced alkyd resin	American Cyanamid Co.
Glufil	Shell flour	Agrashell Inc.
Glyptal	Alkyd coating	General Electric Co.
Grex	Polyethylene	W. R. Grace & Co.
Halex	Polyfluorocarbon	Allied Chemical Co.
Halon	Fluorochlorocarbon	Allied Chemical Co.
Halowax	Chlorinated naphthalene	Union Carbide Corp.

Trade Names

TRADE NAME OR BRAND NAME	PRODUCT	MANUFACTURER
Harflex	Plasticizers	Wallace & Tiernan, Inc.
HB-40	Hydrogenated terphenyl	Monsanto Co.
Hercocel	Cellulose acetate	Hercules Powder Co.
Hercoflex	Phthalate plasticizers	Hercules Powder Co.
Hercolyn	Hydrogenated methyl abietate	Hercules Powder Co.
Hercose	Cellulose acetate-propionate	Hercules Powder Co.
Herculoid	Cellulose nitrate	Hercules Powder Co.
Herculon	Polypropylene	Hercules Powder Co.
Herox	Nylon	E. I. du Pont de Nemours & Co. Inc.
Het anhydride	Chlorendic anhydride	Hooker Chemical Corp.
Heveaplus	Copolymer of methyl methacrylate and rubber	
Hexcel	Structural honeycomb	Hexcel Products, Inc.
H film	Polyimide film	E. I. du Pont de Nemours & Co., Inc.
Hi-fax	High-density polyethylene	FMC Corp.; Hercules Powder Co.
Hi-Sil	Amorphous silica	PPG Corp.
Horse Head	Zinc oxide pigments	New Jersey Zinc Co.
Hostalen	Polyethylene	Farbwerke Hoechst AG
Hyamine	Cationic surfactants	Rohm & Haas Co.
Hycar	Butadiene acrylonitrile copolymer	B. F. Goodrich Chemical Co.
Hydrocal	Gypsum	U.S. Gypsum Co.
Hydropol	Hydrogenated polybutadiene	
Hylene	Organic isocyanates	E. I. du Pont de Nemours & Co., Inc.
Hypalon	Chlorosulfonated polyethylene	E. I. du Pont de Nemours & Co., Inc.
Igepal	Wetting agents	General Aniline & Film Corp.
Igepon	Surfactants, wetting agents	General Aniline & Film Corp.
Implex	Acrylic resins	Rohm & Haas Co.
Insurok	Phenol-formaldehyde molding compounds	The Richardson Co.
Intamix	Rigid PVC	Diamond Shamrock Corp.
Ionac	Ion-exchange resins	
Ionol	Antioxidant	Shell Chemical Co.
Irganox	Antioxidants	Geigy Chemical Corp.
Irrathene	Irradiated polyethylene	General Electric Co.

Trade Names

TRADE NAME OR BRAND NAME	PRODUCT	MANUFACTURER
Isofoam	Polyurethane foam resins	Isocyanate Products, Inc.
Isomid	Polyester-polyimide film magnet wire	Schenectady Chemicals, Inc.
Isonate	Diisocyanates	Upjohn Co.
Isonol	Propoxylated amines	Upjohn Co.
Jay-Flex	Plasticizers	Enjay Chemical Co.
Jet-Kote	Furane resin coatings	Furane Plastics, Inc.
Kadox	Zinc oxide	New Jersey Zinc Co.
Kalite	Precipitated calcium carbonate	Diamond Alkali Co.
Kalmac	Calcium carbonate	Georgia Marble Co.
Kapsol	Plasticizers	Ohio-Apex Div., FMC Corp.
Kapton	Polyimide (high temperature)	E. I. du Pont de Nemours & Co., Inc.
Kardel	Polystyrene film	Union Carbide Corp.
Kaurit	Urea-formaldehyde resins	Badische Anilin & Soda-Fabrik AG
Kel-F	Trifluorochloroethylene resins	Minnesota Mining & Mfg. Co.
Keltrol	Copolymers	Textron, Inc.
Kematal	Acetal copolymers	Imperial Chemical Industries, Ltd.
Kessco	Plasticizers	Kessler Chemical Co., Inc.
Ketac	Ketone-aldehyde resin	American Cyanamid Co.
Kodacel	Cellulose acetate film	Eastman Chemical Products, Inc.
Kodaflex	Plasticizers	Eastman Chemical Products, Inc.
Kodel	Polyester fibers	Eastman Kodak Co.
Kollidon	Poly(vinyl pyrrolidone)	General Aniline & Film Corp.
Kolorbon	Rayon fiber	American Enka Corp.
Kopox	Epoxy resin	Koppers Co.
Korad	Acrylic film	Rohm & Haas Co.
Korez	Phenolic resin cement	Atlas Mineral Products Company
Koroseal	Poly(vinyl chloride)	B. F. Goodrich Chemical Co.
Kosmos	Carbon black	United Carbon Co.
Kotol	Resin solutions	Uniroyal, Inc.
Kralac	ABS resins	Uniroyal, Inc.
Kralastic	ABS	Uniroyal, Inc.
Kraton	Butadiene copolymers	Shell Chemical Co.
Krene	Plasticized vinyl film	Union Carbide Corp.
Kriston	Allyl ester casting resins	B. F. Goodrich Chemical Co.

TRADE NAME OR BRAND NAME	PRODUCT	MANUFACTURER
Kroniflex	Phosphate ester plasticizer	FMC Corp.
Kronisol	Dibutoxyethyl phthalate	FMC Corp.
Kronitex	Tricresyl phosphate	FMC Corp.
Kronox	Plasticizer	FMC Corp.
Kurlon	Poly(vinyl alcohol) fibers	
Kydex	Acrylic-poly(vinyl chloride) sheet	Rohm & Haas Co.
Kylan	Chitin	
Kynar	Poly(vinylidene fluoride)	Pennsalt Chemicals Corp.
Laminac	Polyester resins	American Cyanamid Co.
Lemac	Poly(vinyl acetate)	Borden Chemical Co.
Lemol	Poly(vinyl alcohol)	Borden Chemical Co.
Lexan	Polycarbonate resin	General Electric Co.
Lindol	Phosphate plasticizers	Stauffer Chemical Co.
Lock Foam	Polyurethane foam	Nopco Chemical Co.
Lucidol	Benzoyl peroxide	Wallace and Tiernan, Inc.
Lucite	Poly(methyl methacrylate)	E. I. du Pont de Nemours & Co., Inc.
Ludox	Colloidal silica	E. I. du Pont de Nemours & Co., Inc.
Lumarith	Cellulose acetate	Celanese Corp. of America
Lumite	Saran filaments	Chicopee Manufacturing Co.
Luperco	Organic peroxides	Wallace & Tiernan, Inc.
Luperox	Organic peroxides	Wallace & Tiernan, Inc.
Lustran	Molding and extrusion resins	Monsanto Chemical Co.
Lustrex	Polystyrene	Monsanto Chemical Co.
Lutonal	Poly(vinyl ethers)	Badische Anilin & Soda-Fabrik AG
Lutrex	Poly(vinyl acetate)	Foster Grant Co.
Luvican	Poly(vinyl carbazole)	Badische Anilin & Soda-Fabrik AG
Lycra	Spandex fibers	E. I. du Pont de Nemours & Co., Inc.
Makrofol	Polycarbonate film	Naftone, Inc.
Makrolon	Polycarbonate	Farbenfabriken Bayer AG
Maraset	Epoxy resin	The Marblette Corp.
Marbon	Polystyrene and copolymers	Borg-Warner Corp.
Marlex	Polyolefin resins	Phillips Chemical Co.

Trade Names

TRADE NAME OR BRAND NAME	PRODUCT	MANUFACTURER
Marvibond	Metal-plastics laminates	Uniroyal, Inc.
Marvinol	Poly(vinyl chloride)	Uniroyal, Inc.
Melan	Melamine resins	Hitachi Chemical Co., Ltd.
Melmac	Melamine molding materials	American Cyanamid Co.
Melurac	Melamine-urea resins	American Cyanamid Co.
Merlon	Polycarbonate	Mobay Chemical Co.
Methocel	Methyl cellulose	Dow Chemical Co.
Micarta	Thermosetting laminates	Westinghouse Electric Corp.
Micronex	Carbon black	Columbian Carbon Co.
Microthene	Powdered polyethylene	U.S. Industrial Chemicals Co.
Minex	Aluminum silicate filler	American Nepheline Corp.
Modulene	Polyethylene resin	Muehlstein & Co.
Mogul	Carbon black	Cabot Corp.
Molplen	Polypropylene	Novamont Corp.
Mondur	Organic isocyanates	Mobay Chemical Co.
Montrek	Poly(ethylene imine)	Dow Chemical Co.
Moplen	Polypropylene	Montecatini
Multron	Polyesters	Mobay Chemical Co.
Mycalex	Inorganic molded plastics	Mycalex Corp. of America
Mylar	Polyester film	E. I. du Pont de Nemours & Co., Inc.
Nacconate	Organic diisocyanate	Allied Chemical Corp.
Nadic	Maleic anhydride	Allied Chemical Corp.
Nalgon	Plasticized poly(vinyl chloride)	Nalge Co.
Natsyn	*cis*-(1,4 Polyisoprene)	Goodyear Tire & Rubber Co.
Naugahyde	Vinyl-coated fabric	U.S. Rubber Co.
Nebony	Petroleum hydrocarbon resin	Neville Chemical Co.
Neoprene	Polychloroprene	E. I. du Pont de Nemours & Co., Inc.
Neozone	Antioxidants	E. I. du Pont de Nemours & Co., Inc.
Nevindene	Coumarone-indene resin	Neville Chemical Co.
Niax	Polyol polyesters	Union Carbide Corp.
Nimbus	Polyurethane foam	General Tire & Rubber Co.
Nomex	Nylon	E. I. du Pont de Nemours & Co., Inc.
Nopcofoam	Polyurethane foams	Nopco Chemical Co.
Nordel	Ethylene-propylene copolymers	E. I. du Pont de Nemours & Co., Inc.
Noryl	Poly(phenylene oxide)	General Electric Co.
Nuba	Modified coumarone-indene resins	Neville Chemical Co.

Trade Names

TRADE NAME OR BRAND NAME	PRODUCT	MANUFACTURER
Nuclon	Polycarbonate	Pittsburgh Plate Glass Co.
Nukem	Acid-resistant resin cements	Amercoat Corp.
Numa	Spandex fibers	American Cyanamide Corp.
Nylafil	Reinforced nylon	Rexall Chemical Co.
Nylasint	Sintered nylon parts	The Polymer Corp.
Nylon	Polyamides	E. I. du Pont de Nemours & Co., Inc.
Olefane	Polypropylene film	Avisun Corp.
Olemer	Propylene copolymer	Avisun Corp.
Opalon	Poly(vinyl chloride)	Monsanto Chemical Co.
Oppanol	Polyisobutylene	Badische Anilin & Soda-Fabrik AG
Orlon	Acrylic fiber	E. I. du Pont de Nemours & Co., Inc.
Ortix	Poromeric film	Celanese Corp.
Oxiron	Epoxidized polybutadiene	
Panarez	Hydrocarbon resins	Amoco Chemicals Corp.
Panelyte	Laminates	Thiokol Chemical Co.
Papi	Polymethylene, poly-phenyl isocyanate	Upjohn Co.
Paracon	Polyester rubber	Bell Telephone Laboratories
Paracryl	Butadiene-acrylonitrile copolymer	U.S. Rubber Co.
Paradene	Coumarone-indene resins	Neville Chemical Co.
Paraplex	Plasticizers	Rohm & Haas Co.
Parfe	Rayon fiber	Beaunit Mills Corp.
Parlon	Chlorinated rubber	Hercules Corp.
Parylene	Polyxylylene	Union Carbide Corp.
Pearlon	Polyethylene film	Visking Corp.
Pee Vee Cee	Rigid poly(vinyl chloride)	ESB Corp.
Pelaspan	Expandable polystyrene	Dow Chemical Co.
Pentalyn	Abietic acid derivative	
Penton	Chlorinated polyether resins	Hercules Co., Inc.
Percadox	Organic peroxides	Cadet Chemical Corp.
Peregal	Antistatic agents	General Aniline & Film Corp.
Perlon	Polyurethane filament	
Permutit	Ion-exchange materials	
Perspex	Acrylic resins	Imperial Chemical Industries, Ltd.
Petrothene	Polyethylene	National Distillers & Chemical Corp.
Phenoxy	Poly(hydroxy ether) of bisphenol A	Union Carbide Corp.

Trade Names

TRADE NAME OR BRAND NAME	PRODUCT	MANUFACTURER
Philprene	Styrene-butadiene rubber	Phillips Petroleum Co.
Phosgard	Phosphorus compounds	Monsanto Co.
Picco	Hydrocarbon resins	Pennsylvania Industrial Chemical Corp.
Piccocumaron	Hydrocarbon resins	Pennsylvania Industrial Chemical Corp.
Piccolyte	Terpene polymer resins	Pennsylvania Industrial Chemical Corp.
Pip Pip	Rubber accelerator	
Plaskon	Alkyd resins	Allied Chemical Corp.
Plastacele	Cellulose acetate flake	E. I. du Pont de Nemours & Co., Inc.
Plastanox	Antioxidant	American Cyanamide Corp.
Plenco	Phenolic resins	Plastics Engineering Co.
Plexiglas	Acrylic sheets	Rohm & Haas Co.
Pliofilm	Rubber hydrochloride	Goodyear Tire & Rubber Co.
Plioflex	Poly(vinyl chloride)	Goodyear Tire & Rubber Co.
Pliolite	Cyclized rubber	Goodyear Tire & Rubber Co.
Pliovic	Poly(vinyl chloride)	Goodyear Tire & Rubber Co.
Pluracol	Polyethers	Wyandotte Chemicals Corp.
Plyfoam	PVC foam	
Plyophen	Phenolic resins	Reichhold Chemicals, Inc.
Pluronic	Block polyether diols	Wyandotte Corp.
Polyallomer	Ethylene block copolymers	Eastman Chemical Products
Poly-eth	Polyethylene	Gulf Oil Corp.
Poly-eze	Ethylene copolymers	Gulf Oil Corp.
Polygard	Stabilizer	Goodyear Tire & Rubber Co.
Poly-pro	Polypropylene	Gulf Oil Corp.
Polyox	Water-soluble resins	Union Carbide Corp.
Powminco	Asbestos fibers	Powhatan Mining Co.
PPO	Poly(phenylene oxide)	General Electric Co.
Pro-fax	Polypropylene resins	Hercules Powder Co.
Propathene	Polypropylene	Imperial Chemical Industries, Ltd.
Pyralin	Cellulose nitrate	E. I. du Pont de Nemours & Co., Inc.
Quadrol	Poly(hydroxy amine)	Wyandotte Chemicals, Inc.
Raybrite	Alpha-cellulose filler	Rayonier, Inc.
Resimene	Urea and melamine resins	Monsanto Co.
Resinol	Polyolefins	Allied Resinous Products, Inc.
Resinox	Phenolic resins	Monsanto Co.
Resistoflex	Poly(vinyl alcohol)	Resistoflex Corp.

TRADE NAME OR BRAND NAME	PRODUCT	MANUFACTURER
Resloom	Melamine resins	Monsanto Co.
Rezimac	Alkyds	Commercial Solvents Corp.
Rezyl	Alkyd varnish	Sinclair-Koppers Co., Inc.
Rhonite	Resins for textile finishes	Rohm & Haas Co.
Rhoplex	Acrylic emulsions	Rohm & Haas Co.
Royalite	Thermoplastic sheet material	Uniroyal Corp.
Rulon	Flame retardant	E. I. du Pont de Nemours & Co., Inc.
Ryton	Poly(phenylene sulfide)	Phillips Petroleum Co.
Saflex	Poly(vinyl butyral)	
Safom	Polyurethane foam	
Santicizer	Plasticizers	Monsanto Co.
Santocel	Silica aerogel fillers	Monsanto Co.
Santocure	Accelerator	Monsanto Co.
Santoflex	Antioxidants	Monsanto Co.
Santolite	Sulfonamide resin	Monsanto Co.
Santonox	Antioxidant	Monsanto Co.
Saran	Vinylidene chloride copolymer	Dow Chemical Co.
Scotchpak	Polyester film	Minnesota Mining & Mfg. Co.
Scotchweld	Adhesives	Minnesota Mining & Mfg. Co.
Seilon	Thermoplastic sheets	Seiberling Rubber Co.
Selectron	Polyester resins	PPG Corp.
Silastic	Silicone materials	Dow Corning Corp.
Silene	Calcium silicate	PPG Corp.
Silvacon	Lignin extenders and fillers	Weyerhauser Co.
Sir-pel	Poromeric film	Georgia Bonded Fibers
Solka-Floc	Alpha-cellulose filler	Brown Co.
Solvar	Poly(vinyl acetate)	Shawinigan Resins Corp.
Solvic	PVC	Solvay & Cie
Spandex	Polyurethane filaments	
S-polymers	Butadiene-styrene copolymer	Esso Labs
Spraythane	Urethane resin	Thiokol Chemical Corp.
Staflex	Vinyl plasticizers	Reichhold Chemicals, Inc.
Starex	Poly(vinyl acetate)	International Latex & Chem. Corp.
Statex	Carbon black	Columbian Carbon Co.
Structo-Foam	Foamed polystyrene slab	Stauffer Chemical Co.
Strux	Cellular cellulose acetate	Aircraft Specialties

Trade Names

TRADE NAME OR BRAND NAME	PRODUCT	MANUFACTURER
Stymer	Styrene copolymer	Monsanto Co.
Styraglas	Fiber-glass-reinforced polystyrene	Rexal Chemical Co.
Styrex	Resin	Dow Chemical Co.
Styrofoam	Extruded expanded polystyrene	Dow Chemical Co.
Styron	Polystyrene	Dow Chemical Co.
Sullvac	Acrylonitrile-butadiene-styrene copolymer	O'Sullivan Rubber Corp.
Super Dylan	High-density polyethylene	Plastics Div., Koppers Co.
Surlyn	Ionomer resins	E. I. du Pont de Nemours & Co., Inc.
Sylgard	Silicone casting resins	Dow Corning Corp.
Sylplast	Urea-formaldehyde resins	Sylvan Plastics, Inc.
Syntex	Alkyd resins	Celanese Corp.
Synthane	Laminated plastic products	Synthane Corp.
TDI	Tolylene diisocyanate	E. I. du Pont de Nemours & Co., Inc.
Tedlar	Poly(vinyl fluorocarbon) resins	E. I. du Pont de Nemours & Co., Inc.
Teflon	Fluorocarbon resins	E. I. du Pont de Nemours & Co., Inc.
Teflon FEP	Poly(tetrafluoroethylene-co-hexafluoropropylene)	E. I. du Pont de Nemours & Co., Inc.
Teglac	Alkyd coatings	American Cyanamid Co.
Tego	Phenolic resins	Rohm & Haas Co.
Tempra	Rayon fiber	American Enka Corp.
Tempreg	Low-pressure laminate	U.S. Plywood Corp.
Tenamene	Antioxidants	Eastman Kodak Co.
Tenite	Cellulose derivatives	Eastman Kodak Co.
Tenox	Antioxidant	Eastman Chemical Products, Inc.
Terylene	Polyester fiber	ICI
Tetran	Tetrafluoroethylene	Pennsalt Chemical Corp.
Tetronic	Polyethers	Wyandotte Chemicals Corp.
Texileather	Pyroxylin-leather cloth	General Tire & Rubber Co.
Texin	Urethane elastomer	Mobay Chemical Co.
Textolite	Laminated plastic	General Electric Co.
Thermaflow	Reinforced polyesters	Atlas Powder Co.
Thermax	Carbon black	Commercial Solvents Corp.
Thiokol	Poly(ethylene sulfide)	Thiokol Corp.
Thornel	Graphite filaments	Union Carbide Corp.
Tinuvin	Ultraviolet stabilizers	Geigy Industrial Chemicals, Div., Geigy Chemical Corp.
Titanox	Titanium dioxide pigments	Titanium Pigment Corp.

Trade Names

TRADE NAME OR BRAND NAME	PRODUCT	MANUFACTURER
Topel	Rayon fiber	Courtaulds
TPX	Poly(4-methylpentene-1)	Imperial Chemical Industries, Ltd.
Trevarno	Resin-impregnated cloth	Coast Mfg. & Supply Corp.
Trithene	Trifluorochloroethylene	Union Carbide Corp.
Tuads	Accelerator	R. T. Vanderbilt Co.
Tusson	Rayon fiber	Beaunit Mills Corp.
Tygon	Vinyl copolymer	U.S. Stoneware Co.
Tylose	Cellulose ethers	Farbwerke Hoechst AG
Tynex	Nylon bristles and filaments	E. I. du Pont de Nemours & Co., Inc.
Tyril	Styrene-acrylonitrile copolymer	Dow Chemical Co.
Tyrin	Chlorinated polyethylene	Dow Chemical Co.
Ucon	Lubricants	Union Carbide Corp.
Udel	Plastic film	Union Carbide Corp.
Uformite	Urea resins	Rohm & Haas Co.
Ultrathene	Finely divided polyolefins	National Distillers & Chemical Corp.
Ultron	Vinyl film	Monsanto Co.
Unitane	Titanium dioxide	American Cyanamide Co.
Unox	Epoxides	Union Carbide Corp.
Updown	Polychloroprene foam	
Urac	Urea-formaldehyde resins	American Cyanamid Co.
Uscolite	ABS copolymer	U.S. Rubber Co.
Uvex	Cellulose acetate butyrate	Eastman Kodak Co.
Uvinul series	Ultraviolet light absorbers	General Aniline & Film Corp.
Vanstay	Stabilizers	R. T. Vanderbilt Co.
Varcum	Phenolic resins	Reichhold Chemicals, Inc.
Vazo	Azobisisobutyronitrile	E. I. du Pont de Nemours & Co., Inc.
Velon	Poly(vinyl chloride)	Firestone Tire & Rubber Co.
Verel	Modacrylic staple fibers	Eastman Chemical Products, Inc.
Versamid	Polyamide resins	General Mills, Inc.
Vespel	Polymellitimide	E. I. du Pont de Nemours & Co., Inc.
VGB	Acetaldehyde-aniline accelerator	Uniroyal Corp.
Vibrathane	Polyurethane intermediates	Uniroyal Corp.
Vibrin	Polyester resins	Uniroyal Corp.

Trade Names

TRADE NAME OR BRAND NAME	PRODUCT	MANUFACTURER
Vicara	Protein fiber	
Viclan	Poly(vinylidene chloride)	Imperial Chemical Industries, Ltd.
Videne	Polyester film	Goodyear Tire & Rubber Co.
Vinac	Poly(vinyl acetate) emulsions	Air Reduction Co.
Vinoflex	PVC	BASF Corp.
Vinol	Poly(vinyl alcohol)	Air Reduction Co.
Vinsol	Rosin derivative	Hercules, Inc.
Vinylite	Poly(vinyl chloride co-vinyl acetate)	Union Carbide Corp.
Vinyon	Poly(vinyl chloride-co-acrylonitrile)	Union Carbide Corp.
Viscalon	Rayon fiber	American Enka Corp.
Viskon	Nonwoven fabrics	Union Carbide Corp.
Vistanex	Polyisobutylene	Enjay Chemical Co.
Vitel	Polyester resins	Goodyear Tire & Rubber Co.
Viton	Copolymer of vinylidene fluoride and hexa-fluoropropylene	E. I. du Pont de Nemours & Co., Inc.
Vulcollan	Urethane elastomer	Mobay Chemical Co.
Vycron	Polyester fiber	Beaunit Mills Corp.
Vygen	PVC	General Tire & Rubber Co.
Vynex	Rigid vinyl sheeting	Nixon-Baldwin Chemicals, Inc.
Vyram	Rigid poly(vinyl chloride)	Monsanto Co.
Vyrene	Spandex fiber	U.S. Rubber Co.
Webril	Nonwoven fabric	The Kendall Co.
Welvic	Poly(vinyl chloride)	Imperial Chemical Industries, Ltd.
Whirlclad	Plastic coatings	The Polymer Corp.
Whirlsint	Powdered polymers	The Polymer Corp.
Wing-stay	Alkylated phenol antioxidants	Goodyear Tire & Rubber Co.
Xylonite	Cellulose nitrate	B. X. Plastics, Ltd.
Zantrel	Rayon fiber	American Enka Corp.
Zee	Polyethylene wrap	Crown Zellerback Corp.
Zefran	Acrylic fiber	Dow Chemical Co.
Zelan	Water repellent	E. I. du Pont de Nemours & Co., Inc.

Trade Names

TRADE NAME OR BRAND NAME	PRODUCT	MANUFACTURER
Zendel	Polyethylene	Union Carbide Corp.
Zetafax	Poly(ethylene-co-acrylic acid)	Dow Chemical Co.
Zetafin	Poly(ethylene-co-ethyl acrylate)	Dow Chemical Co.
Zytel	Nylon	E. I. du Pont de Nemours & Co., Inc.

Index